# ADVANCED LEVEL MATHEMATICS 10

# MATHEMATICS

# PRINCIPLES & PROCESS

## Authors

FRANK EBOS, Senior Author
Faculty of Education
University of Toronto

BOB TUCK
Computer Consultant
Nipissing Board of Education

WALKER SCHOFIELD
Department Head of Mathematics
Banting Secondary School

DENNIS HAMAGUCHI
Vice Principal
West Vernon Elementary School
Vernon, British Columbia

## Consultants

Mary L. Crowley
Department of Education
Dalhousie University
Halifax, Nova Scotia

J. Harry McKnight
Mathematics Teacher
Niverville Collegiate
Niverville, Manitoba

W. Lyle Markowski
Mathematics Teacher
Bedford Road Collegiate
Saskatoon, Saskatchewan

Lyle Pagnucco
Department Head of Mathematics
Crescent Heights High School
Calgary, Alberta

**NELSON** CANADA

Published in 1987 by
Nelson Canada,
A Division of International Thomson Limited
1120 Birchmount Road
Scarborough, Ontario, MIK 5G4

**Canadian Cataloguing in Publication Data**

Ebos, Frank, 1939–
Mathematics : Principles and Process, 10

For use in grade 10.
Includes index.
ISBN 0-17-602520-0

1. Mathematics—1961–    I. Title

QA107.E26 1987    510    C87-09-3415-5

**Photo Credits**

**P. 80** Greg Lockhart, **P. 91** H. Armstrong Roberts/Miller Services, **P. 127** Rob Stocks, Athlete Information Bureau, **P. 206** D. Luria/Miller Services, **P. 217** Harold M. Lambert/Miller Services, **P. 234** Data General (Canada) Ltd., **P. 247** Ministry of Transportation & Communications, **P. 249** Winnipeg Mint, Government of Manitoba, **P. 253** Camera Press Ltd./Miller Services, **P. 262** Ken T. Marsh, **P. 283** Camerique/Miller Services, **P. 306** Province of Manitoba, Public Information Branch, **P. 337** The Globe & Mail, **P. 367** Imperial Oil Ltd., **P. 372** Rob Stocks, **P. 372** Allied Van Lines, **P. 376** S.K.F. Canada Ltd., **P. 377** Top: Saskatchewan Government, Bottom: H. Armstrong Roberts/Miller Services, **P. 385** H. Armstrong Roberts/Miller Services, The Canadian Press, **P. 386** George Haling/Miller Services, **P. 407** Camerique/Miller Services, **P. 411** H. Armstrong Roberts/Miller Services, **P. 418** Harold M. Lambert/Miller Services, **P. 437** Standard Oil Company, **P. 445** Camerique/Miller Services, **P. 462** John Deere, **P. 495** W. Whitman/Miller Services

**Project Editor**
Sheila Bassett

**Technical Art**
Frank Zsigo

The symbol for year is a. For the sake of clarity, the word year has been used, in full, in place of a.

Printed and bound in Canada by John Deyell Company
    567890   JD 89432109

The authors wish to express their thanks to Sheila Bassett, Anthony Rodrigues, Frank Zsigo, Andrew Clowes, Anna Jalandoni, Bill Allan, Maggie Cheverie, Janice Nixon, Barbara DeCarlo, Lesley Ebos, Michael Ebos.

The authors gratefully acknowledge the advice, assistance or contribution of Barbara Bernstein, RoseMary Ebos, Ron Lancaster, Paul Macallum, Tony Pontes, Ron Reid, and Walker Schofield.

# Contents

## 1 Process of Mathematics: Exponents and Real Numbers

1.1 The Language of Mathematics, 10
1.2 Nature of Mathematics: Rational Numbers, 14
Rational Numbers and Decimals, 17
1.3 Developing Mathematics: Square Roots and Radicals, 18
Applications: Space and Artificial Gravity, 21
1.4 What Are Real Numbers?, 22
1.5 Inventing Mathematics: Exponents, 26
1.6 What If . . . Any Integers?, 30
Exponents and Radicals, 34
1.7 Developing Operations: Radicals, 35

1.8 Properties of Radical Products, 38
1.9 Dividing Radicals: Calculators, 40
1.10 People and Mathematics: Pythagoras, 43
1.11 **PSP** Problem-Solving Plan, 46
1.12 **PSP** Problem-Solving: Right Triangles and Pythagoras, 48
1.13 **PSP** Problem-Solving: Strategies, 51
1.14 **PSP** Problem-Solving Strategy: Using Counter-Examples, 54
Chapter Review, Chapter Test, 56
Problem-Solving, Computer Tips, Calculator Tips, Math Tips, 13, 25, 29, 34, 53

## 2 Polynomials: Operations and Factoring

2.1 Multiplying by a Monomial, 58
2.2 Dividing by a Monomial, 62
2.3 Operations With Polynomials: Addition, Subtraction, 66
Applications: Perimeters and Areas, 69
2.4 Solving Equations, 70
2.5 Multiplying Binomials, 72
2.6 Finding Common Factors, 76
Applications: Track and Field, 80
2.7 **PSP** Strategy: Factoring Trinomials, 81

2.8 **PSP** Working Backwards: Factoring Trinomials, 84
2.9 Factoring a Difference of Squares, 87
Applications: Pipe Construction, 91
2.10 Inventory: Factoring Skills, 92
2.11 Solving Quadratic Equations, 93
Solving Problems: Quadratic Equations, 96
2.12 Problem-Solving: Strategies, 97
Chapter Review, Chapter Test, 98
Problem-Solving, Computer Tips, Calculator Tips, Math Tips, 79

## 3. Applying Skills: Rational Expressions

3.1 Essential Skills: Factoring, 100
3.2 Simplifying Rational Expressions, 101
3.3 Monomial Denominators, 103
3.4 Rational Expressions: Adding and Subtracting, 106
3.5 Combining Operations: Monomials, 109
3.6 Rational Expressions: Multiplying and Dividing, 112

3.7 Applying Skills: Solving Equations, 115
3.8 **PSP** Problem-Solving: Using Rational Expressions, 118
3.9 Solving Inequations, 121
Chapter Review, Chapter Test, 124
Problem-Solving, Computer Tips, Calculator Tips, Math Tips, 108, 120

## 4  Essential Skills: Co-ordinate Geometry

4.1  Essential Skills: Co-ordinate Plane, 126
Applications: Using Graphs, 131
4.2  Vocabulary of Relations, 132
4.3  Graphing: Equations and Inequations, 137
4.4  PSP  Problem-Solving: Strategy for Checking, 141
4.5  Inequations and Regions, 144
4.6  An Essential Skill: Calculating Distance, 147

4.7  Process of Mathematics: Distance Formula, 150
4.8  PSP  Problem-Solving: Finding the Midpoint, 153
4.9  Working With Slope, 156
4.10  Properties of Lines: Slope, 160
Chapter Review, Chapter Test, 164
Problem-Solving, Computer Tips, Calculator Tips, Math Tips, 136, 152, 155, 163

## 5  The Straight Line: Patterns and Process

5.1  Functions and Forms, 166
5.2  The Linear Function, 171
Applications: Interpreting Slope, 175
5.3  Strategy: Graphing Techniques, 176
5.4  PSP  Patterns With Slopes and Intercepts, 178
5.5  A Useful Form: $y = mx + b$, 181
Exploring Perpendicular Lines, 185
5.6  Slope: Parallel and Perpendicular Lines, 186

5.7  Writing Equations of Lines, 190
5.8  PSP  Problem-Solving: Using Given Information, 195
5.9  PSP  Strategy: Families of Lines, 197
Strategy: Slope-Point Form, 202
Chapter Review, Chapter Test, 203
Cumulative Review, 204
Problem-Solving, Computer Tips, Calculator Tips, Math Tips, 174, 177, 180, 184, 189

## 6  Using Systems of Equations: Problem-Solving

6.1  Graphing Systems of Equations, 206
6.2  Equivalent Systems of Equations, 210
PSP  Classifying Systems of Equations, 212
6.3  Method of Substitution: Solving Systems, 213
Applications: Problems Involving Systems of Equations, 217
6.4  Simplifying and Solving Systems, 218
6.5  Another Strategy: Solving a System of Equations, 221
6.6  Solving Systems of Equations: Addition-Subtraction Method, 225
Applications: Equations for Printing, 229
6.7  PSP  Strategies for Simplifying Equations, 230

Applications: Equations with Literal Coefficients, 233
6.8  Systems and Computers, 234
6.9  PSP  Translating From English to Mathematics, 236
6.10  PSP  Problem-Solving: Use a Plan, 239
6.11  PSP  Strategy for Problem-Solving: Using Charts, 242
Applications: Making More Profit, 244
6.12  PSP  Strategy: Using Diagrams, 245
6.13  PSP  Problem-Solving: Making Decisions, 248
6.14  PSP  Problem-Solving: Extraneous Information, 250
Chapter Review, Chapter Test, 252
Problem-Solving, Computer Tips, Calculator Tips, Math Tips, 209, 216, 224, 232, 235, 238

## 7  Nature of Mathematics: Inequations and Variation

7.1   Systems of Linear Inequations: Regions, 254
7.2   Applying a Linear System of Inequations, 258
7.3   Applications: Linear Programming, 262
7.4   Using Graphs: Direct Variation, 266
7.5   **PSP** Direct Variation: Problem-Solving, 270
7.6   Using Graphs: Inverse Variation, 274

7.7   Inverse Variation: Applications, 277
7.8   **PSP** Extending Strategies: Variation, 280
7.9   Using Graphs: Partial Variation, 283
7.10  **PSP** Partial Variation: Problem-Solving, 285
Chapter Review, Chapter Test, 288
Problem-Solving, Computer Tips, Calculator Tips, Math Tips, 261, 265, 273, 284

## 8  Methods of Geometry: Problem-Solving

8.1   **PSP** Thinking Strategies for Mathematics, 290
8.2   The Language of Deductive Geometry, 294
      Understanding Vocabulary, 300
8.3   **PSP** Writing Proofs, 301
      **PSP** Strategy: Proving Theorems, 305
8.4   Writing Congruences: 306
8.5   Congruence Postulate, Side-Side-Side, 310

8.6   Congruence Postulate: Side-Angle-Side, 314
8.7   Congruence Postulate: Angle-Side-Angle, 318
8.8   Congruence Postulate: Hypotenuse-Side, 324
8.9   **PSP** Proving Deductions in Geometry, 327
Chapter Review, Chapter Test, 330
Problem-Solving, Computer Tips, Calculator Tips, Math Tips, 293, 299, 304, 326

## 9  Proving Properties: Concepts and Skills

9.1   Converses in Mathematics, 332
9.2   Working with Parallel Lines: Vocabulary, 336
9.3   Parallel Lines and Their Properties, 338
      Problem-Solving: Finding Measures, 342
9.4   **PSP** Problem-Solving: Angle Sum of Triangle, 342
9.5   **PSP** Converse Statement: Parallel Lines, 347
      **PSP** Proving Deductions: Parallel Lines, 351

9.6   Proving Properties: Quadrilaterals, 352
9.7   **PSP** Proving the Pythagorean Theorem, 354
9.8   The Converse of the Pythagorean Theorem, 357
Chapter Review, Chapter Test, 359
Cumulative Review, 360
Problem-Solving, Computer Tips, Calculator Tips, Math Tips, 341, 356, 358

## 10  Applications in Three Dimensions

10.1  **PSP** Problem-Solving: Using Diagrams, 362
10.2  **PSP** Strategy: Developing a Formula, 366
10.3  Principles of Volume, 369
10.4  **PSP** Problem-Solving Strategy: Trying Formulas, 373

10.5  Applications: Cones and Spheres, 374
10.6  **PSP** Making Decisions: Using Formulas, 378
10.7  Projections: Sketching Figures, 381
Chapter Review, Chapter Test, 384

## 11 Interpreting Data: Statistics and Probability

11.1 Concepts of Statistics, 386
11.2 Types of Samples, 390
11.3 Frequency Distributions and
Histograms, 393
Applications: Stem-and-Leaf Plots, 398
11.4 Interpreting Mean, Median, Mode, 399
Applications: The Weighted Mean, 403
11.5 Statistics for Grouped Data, 404
11.6 Interpreting Data: Dispersion and
Deviation, 407
11.7 Data: Box and Whisker Diagrams, 411

11.8 Applications: Scatter Diagrams, 414
11.9 PSP Problem-Solving: Interpretation, 418
11.10 Probability: Skills and Concepts, 421
Complementary Probability, 426
11.11 Sample Spaces: Charts, Tree Diagrams, 427
11.12 Applications: Statistics and Probability, 429
11.13 Independent Events, 432
Problem-Solving: Simulating Experiments, 435
Chapter Review, Chapter Test, 436
Problem-Solving, Computer Tips, Calculator
Tips, Math Tips, 410, 425, 431

## 12 Process of Trigonometry: Applications

12.1 Similar Triangles, 438
12.2 PSP Problem-Solving: Similar
Triangles, 443
12.3 PSP Problem-Solving: What If?, 445
12.4 Process of Mathematics: Tangent of
an Angle, 448
12.5 Concepts of Trigonometry, 451

12.6 Trigonometric Values, 455
12.7 Using Trigonometry: Problem-Solving, 459
12.8 Nature of Solving Problems:
Trigonometry, 462
Chapter Review, Chapter Test, 465
Cumulative Review, 466
Problem-Solving, Computer Tips, Calculator
Tips, Math Tips, 447

## 13 Inventing Mathematics: Vectors and Matrices

13.1 Vectors as Directed Line Segments, 468
Applications: Bearing, 473
13.2 Vectors and Co-ordinates, 474
13.3 Combining Vectors, 477
Subtracting Vectors, 481
13.4 Vector and Scalar Products, 482
13.5 PSP Applications with Vectors, 485
13.6 Vectors and Polygons, 487
13.7 PSP Using Vectors: Proving
Deductions, 490

13.8 Using a Matrix, 492
Applications: Communication Networks, 495
13.9 Operations With Matrices, 497
13.10 Multiplying Matrices, 500
13.11 Inverse of a Matrix, 504
Applications: Matrices and Codes, 507
13.12 Matrices for Solving Linear Systems, 508
Chapter Review, Chapter Test, 510
Problem-Solving, Computer Tips, Calculator
Tips, Math Tips, 484, 506

## 14 Transformations: Concepts and Co-ordinates

14.1 Translations and Mappings, 512
14.2 Reflections and Properties, 515
14.3 Describing Rotations, 518
14.4 Dilatations and Properties, 522
14.5 Working With Isometries, 524
14.6 PSP Problem-Solving: What If?, 527
14.7 PSP Transformations: Proving
Properties, 531

14.8 PSP Proving Deductions:
Transformations, 534
14.9 Equations of Lines: Transformations, 536
14.10 Nature of Mathematics: Applying
Matrices to Transformations, 538
Problem-Solving, Computer Tips, Calculator,
Tips, Math Tips, 517, 521, 533
Answers, 542, Index, 559

# Using Mathematics: Principles and Process, 10

These pages explain how the text is organized. They tell you what to look for in each lesson and in every chapter.

## Lesson Features

▶ Look for the lesson number and title.

### Teaching

▶ The lesson begins with the information you need to learn. Look for photos that illustrate uses of mathematics. New words are printed in **bold type**. Look for comments about the history of mathematics.

▶ Examples and Solutions guide you step-by-step through new material.

▶ Always read the hints and learning comments printed in red type.

## Exercise Features

▶ Each lesson gives you lots of practice. Exercises are graded as A, B, and C according to their level of difficulty.

**A** These questions let you practise the skills and concepts taught in the lesson. Some of these questions can be done orally with the teacher and the class.

**B** These questions also give you practice with the skills you have learned, but they involved a combination of skills. There are also lots of problems and applications to practise with.

**C** These questions provide an extra challenge, or may involve another approach.

## Applications

These sections show how mathematics is a part of the everyday world. You will solve some problems and learn some interesting facts which apply or extend the topic.

---

6.11

**PSP** Strategy for Solving Problems: Using Charts

To solve a problem, it is important to organize or sort the information given. One strategy that will help you sort the information is to use a chart. The following examples illustrate this.

**Example** Monica invested $1400, one part of it at 7% and the other at 8%. The total interest she received amounted to $104.00. How much was invested at each rate of interest?

**Solution** Let the amounts invested be represented by $x and $y.

$$x + y = 1400 \quad ①$$
$$0.07x + 0.08y = 104 \quad ②$$

Multiply equation ② by 100.
$$7x + 8y = 10\,400 \quad ③$$
Multiply equation ① by 7.

Use a chart to record the given information.

| Money invested ($) | Interest rate | Interest received ($) |
|---|---|---|
| x | 7% | 0.07x |
| y | 8% | 0.08y |

---

8.4 Exercise

**A** Be sure you know the meaning of the symbol △ABC ≅ △DEF.

1 For each pair of congruent triangles, write corresponding pairs of equal sides and angles.
(a) △ABC ≅ △PQR
(b) △EFG ≅ △RST
(c) △XYZ ≅ △STU
(d) △BCD ≅ △QRS

2 If △PQR ≅ △ABC which of the following are true?
(a) PQ = AB (b) ∠P = ∠B (c) ∠R = ∠C (d) QR = BC
(e) RQ = BC (f) ∠Q = ∠B (g) ∠QRP = ∠BAC (h) ∠PQR = ∠ABC

3 The triangles shown in each diagram are congruent.
• write an appropriate congruence statement.
• name the pairs of equal corresponding angles ... each pair of triangles.
(a) (b)

Applications: Track and Field

Have you ever wondered why runners do not line up exactly at the start of a race, but always cross the same finish line?

The distance around the outside of the track is longer than the distance around the inside of a track. To ensure that the length of the race is the same for each runner, some runners seem to be given a head start.

A circular race track is shown. A runner on the outside track will run further than a runner on the inside track.
$$D = 2\pi R - 2\pi r$$

16 To use a calculator effectively, factor the expression.
$$2\pi R - 2\pi r = 2\pi(R - r)$$
additional distance
(a) Use $D = 2\pi R - 2\pi r$ to find $D$ to 1 decimal place for $R = 25.0$ m, $r = 20.0$ m, and $\pi = 3.14$. How many calculations did you do to find ...

## Reviews and Tests

These sections review and test skills and concepts *after* every chapter:

▶ **Practice and Problems: Review**

▶ **Chapter Test**

This section helps you review and practise skills from *earlier* chapters:

▶ **Cumulative Review**

## Problem-Solving Features

There are lots of opportunities to learn and practise problem-solving skills and strategies as part of the lessons, and also in special sections based on particular strategies for problem-solving.

▶ Lessons in many chapters give you problem-solving skills, such as, using patterns, using counter-examples, and working backwards.

▶ A **problem-solving plan** PSP , is provided to help you organize a framework for problem-solving.

▶ **Problem-Solving** in every chapter gives you a opportunity to do different types of problems and introduce you to interesting aspects of mathematics

▶ **Calculator Tips** give you suggestions for using your calculator, and for planning efficient procedures.

▶ **Computer Tips** and questions in the exercises suggest uses for the computer.

### Extension Features

▶ **Math Tips** suggest methods for doing mathematics better. They offer suggestions for helping you learn mathematics and for planning your work.

# 1 Process of Mathematics: Exponents and Real Numbers

The language of mathematics, developing mathematics, real numbers, using exponents, principles of radicals, operations with radicals, Problem-Solving Plan (PSP), right triangles and Pythagoras, strategies, applications, strategies and problem-solving

## Introduction

If you were to trace the history of mathematics, you would find that many nations have contributed to the development of mathematics.

- About 2000 B.C. the earliest known written mathematics emerged on papyri from Egypt and clay tablets from Mesopotamia. Very basic formulas were used for solving arithmetical problems.
- The Greeks made many important discoveries and were the first to appreciate the importance of proving results in mathematics. You will read about some of these Greeks on later pages in this text.
- An important contribution to mathematics was the introduction of the zero to the number system. This Indian contribution spread to Spain and then to the rest of Europe to leave its mark on the development of mathematics.
- In Renaissance Italy, as artists and architects required a knowledge of proportion and perspective in their work, so mathematics began to flourish. The French made impressive advances in algebra. Simon Stevin, a Flemish mathematician, introduced the use of decimal fractions.
- From the seventeenth century to today, great advances have been made in the study of mathematics. Some contributors to mathematics are dealt with on subsequent pages in this text. Look for them.

Mathematics has many parts. As you do mathematics on the following pages, you will see how mathematics occurs. You will experience and appreciate the many components of mathematics, some of which will include the following.

- The problem-solving process.
- The nature of mathematics.
- The use of technology.
- The applications of mathematics.
- The history of mathematics.
- The enjoyment of mathematics.
- The language of mathematics.
- The power of mathematics.
- The people of mathematics.
- The role of mathematics.
- The branches of mathematics.
- The excitement of mathematics.

# 1.1 The Language of Mathematics

Language is an essential part of the learning of mathematics. There are similarities between the everyday language you use and the language of mathematics. For example, you often use symbols to convey ideas or messages. Each of the symbols shown at the right convey a special meaning. What information or message is conveyed by each symbol?

Similarly, symbols play an important role in the study of mathematics. They are used to write mathematics precisely and concisely. The incorrect use of symbols and language can lead to the incorrect use of mathematics.

Symbols are used to represent sets of numbers.

Set of Natural Numbers
$N = \{1, 2, 3, \ldots\}$

Set of Whole Numbers
$W = \{0, 1, 2, 3, \ldots\}$

Set of Integers
$I = \{\ldots, -3, -2, -1, 0, +1, +2, +3, \ldots\}$

These are the negative integers. The negative symbol cannot be omitted.

These are the positive integers. The positive symbol is often omitted. Write 5 for $+5$.

Many words and symbols in mathematics have a special meaning. **Equations** and **inequations** are used to show relationships among numbers.

|  *Equations* | *Inequations* |
|---|---|

$$3^2 + 4^2 = 5^2 \qquad 18 \div 3 - 4 = 2 \qquad\qquad 2^3 < 3^2 \qquad 18 \div 3 - 4 > 1$$
$$x + 8 = 12 \qquad 2x + y = 3 \qquad\qquad x + 8 < 12 \qquad 2x + y \geq 3$$

The symbol $3^2$ has a unique and concise meaning in mathematics.

$3^2$ means $\underbrace{3 \times 3}_{2}$ $\qquad$ $3^3$ means $\underbrace{3 \times 3 \times 3}_{3}$ $\qquad$ $3^4$ means $\underbrace{3 \times 3 \times 3 \times 3}_{4}$

The numbers 2, 3, and 4 are called **exponents**.

Special words are introduced, in order to be able to refer to symbols in mathematics. $3^4$ is called a **power** of 3.

┌──— 4 is called the **exponent**.

$3^4$

└──3 is called the **base**.

Symbols are used to show operations with numbers. When more than one operation is used in an expression, then the operations are performed in an order that has been agreed upon, as shown in the chart.

Remember: Refer to the order of operations in evaluating expressions.

**Order of Operations**
- First, perform all operations in brackets.
- Then evaluate expressions with exponents.
- Then do the operations of multiplication and division in the order they appear from left to right.
- Then do the operations of addition and subtraction in the order they appear from left to right.

**Example 1**   Evaluate $3(8 - 3)^2 + (-9) \div (-3) - 2^2$

**Solution**   $3(8 - 3)^2 + (-9) \div (-3) - 2^2 = 3(5)^2 + (-9) \div (-3) - 2^2$
$$= 3(25) + (-9) \div (-3) - 4$$
$$= 75 + 3 - 4$$
$$= 74$$

Letter symbols are used to represent numbers and have a special meaning as shown.

$$2n + 3, \quad n \in \{-1, 0, 1, 2\} \longleftarrow \text{This set is called the } \textbf{domain} \text{ of the variable } n.$$

$n$ is a variable.     The symbol, $\in$, means "is a member of".

**Example 2**   Evaluate the expression $x^2 + 2xy + y^2$ for $x = -2$, $y = 3$.

**Solution**   $x^2 + 2xy + y^2$
$$= (-2)^2 + 2(-2)(3) + (3)^2$$
$$= 4 + 2(-2)(3) + 9$$
$$= 4 - 12 + 9$$
$$= 1$$

Remember: Record the original expression first; then substitute.

When you substitute a value for a variable, use brackets. This practice will help you avoid errors.

## 1.1   Exercise

**A 1**   Calculate.

(a) $-3 - 2 + 1$

(b) $-4 - 3 - (-6)$

(c) $-8 - (-7) - (-3)$

(d) $6 + (-12) - 6 + 3$

(e) $-2 - 3 - (-8) - 3$

(f) $-(-12) + (-3) - (-2)$

2   Simplify each of the following.

(a) $-3(-4)$     (b) $4(-3)(-2)$     (c) $(-6)(5)(-4)$     (d) $(-3)^2$

(e) $-3^2$     (f) $(-2)^3$     (g) $(-15)(-1)(0)$     (h) $-(-2)^3$

(i) $(-2)(-3)^2$     (j) $-7(-8)(-2)$     (k) $(-1)^4$     (l) $-(-2)(-3)^2$

3   Simplify.

(a) $\dfrac{-36}{4}$     (b) $\dfrac{-50}{-25}$     (c) $\dfrac{-90}{-2}$     (d) $\dfrac{75}{-3}$

(e) $(-54) \div 6$     (f) $(-27) \div (-3)$     (g) $(-60) \div 12$     (h) $-75 \div 15$

4   Simplify each of the following.

(a) $-16 \div 2 - 8$     (b) $(-8)(-3) \div (-4)$     (c) $(-3)^2 - (-4)^2$

(d) $8 - 40 \div 8$     (e) $8 \div (-4) - 3^2$     (f) $(-24) \div 2 + (-3)^2$

**B** 5   Replace ⌀ with either $<$ or $>$ to make a true statement.

(a) $-13 - (-2)^2$ ⌀ $-12 - (-2)(-3)$     (b) $9 \div 3 - 6$ ⌀ $-30 \div (-6)$

(c) $-2 - (-2)(3)$ ⌀ $-4 - (-3)$     (d) $8 \div (-2) + 6$ ⌀ $-15 \div 3$

(e) $-2(-3)^2$ ⌀ $-2(-2)^3$     (f) $(-1)^2 - (-2)^2$ ⌀ $(-4)^2 - (-5)^2$

6   Simplify.

(a) $-3(-2^3 - 3^2)$     (b) $-3 - 2[3(4 - 4)]$

(c) $(8^2 - 2^2 - 1)(-4^2 - 1)$     (d) $240 - 3[2(-3^2 + 2) - 5]$

(e) $[(-3)(-2) + (-4)(-2)] \div (-2)$     (f) $[(-1)^2 + (-2)^2 + (-3)^2] \div (-7)$

7   Simplify.

(a) $\dfrac{-24 - 6}{(-1)(-5)}$     (b) $\dfrac{(-17 + 5) \div 2}{8 \div (-8) + 4}$     (c) $\dfrac{-5 + (-3)(-6)}{(-2)^2 + (-3)^2}$

8   Find the value of each expression if $x = -2$, $y = -3$.

(a) $-x + 2y$     (b) $-3x - y$     (c) $2x^2 - y$     (d) $-3x - 2y^2$

(e) $y^2 - 3x^2$     (f) $2xy - y^2$     (g) $\dfrac{xy + y^2}{y}$     (h) $\dfrac{x^2 - y^2}{x + y}$

9   (a) Subtract the sum of $-2 + 3$ and $-4 - 3^2$ from the sum of $-3(-2)$ and $(-4)(-3)^2$.

    (b) How much less is $-3(-3)^2$ than $-4(-2)^3$?

    (c) Find the sum of $-3^2$, $-4^2 + 2$, $(-3)(-2) + 3$, and $-3(-2 + 5)$.

    (d) How much less is the sum of $-3^2 + 4$ and $2^2 - 3$ than $-4(-5)$?

10   Calculate each expression for the domain shown.

    (a) $2n + 3$, $n \in \{0, 1, 2, 3\}$          (b) $4x - 1$, $x \in \{-1, 0, 1\}$

    (c) $3 - y^2$, $y \in \{-2, -1, 0, 1, 2\}$     (d) $2x^2 - x + 1$, $x \in \{-2, -1, 0, 1, 2\}$

C 11   The numbers 3, 4, and 5 are called **consecutive numbers**. Find two consecutive numbers such that their product equals the product of three consecutive numbers.

## Calculator Tip

Throughout your work in mathematics, a calculator can be useful in helping you not only to understand concepts, but also to solve problems.

- Different calculators have different features. To know the features of your calculator, refer to the manual provided with it. Try the examples provided in the manual. They will help you learn the features of the calculator.
- In this text, calculator suggestions are provided in some of the examples, and in the features called *Calculator Tips*.
- When you use a calculator, you need to estimate the answer. The calculator will always give an answer, but, if you have used an incorrect procedure, the answer will not necessarily be the correct one. Always estimate your answer before pushing the equal sign. Are any of the following calculator keys unfamiliar to you? Refer to your manual to review the key features.

## Math Tip

In the various chapters, look for math tips that occur in solutions to examples, in exercises, and in *Math Tip* features. The *Math Tips* will include useful hints for doing mathematics, history of mathematics, suggestions to help you organize your work, etc.

## 1.2 Nature of Mathematics: Rational Numbers

To obtain a solution to the equation $x + 8 = 4$, another type of number, called an **integer**, was invented. In developing mathematics, often previous knowledge is used to gain new knowledge. For example, the set of integers and their properties are used to build a new set of numbers, namely, the set of **rational numbers**.

A rational number is written in the form $\frac{a}{b}$, $a, b \in I$, $b \neq 0$. For different values of $a$ and $b$ you obtain different rational numbers as shown at right. Thus, the set of integers can be used to generate the set of rational numbers.

**Symbols for Concepts: History**
People invent mathematical symbols in order to show important ideas in mathematics in a compact way. For example, the present-day symbols "+" and "−" first occurred in print in 1489 in a book by Johann Widman. Their purpose was to express the concept of excess and deficiency. About 25 years later, Vander Hoeche used the symbols +, − as the operation symbol for addition and subtraction.

$$a = -3, b = -5 \qquad a = 3, b = -5$$
$$\frac{a}{b} = \frac{-3}{-5} \qquad \frac{a}{b} = \frac{3}{-5}$$

The symbol $Q$ is often used to represent the set of rationals. $Q = \left\{ \frac{a}{b} \middle| a, b \in I, b \neq 0 \right\}$

**Example 1**　Simplify $\dfrac{-2}{5} + \dfrac{3}{-2} - \dfrac{3}{10}$.

To add or subtract rationals, you need to find common denominators.

**Solution**
$$\frac{-2}{5} + \frac{3}{-2} - \frac{3}{10} = \frac{-4}{10} + \frac{-15}{10} - \frac{3}{10} \longleftarrow \quad \frac{-2}{5} \text{ and } \frac{-4}{10} \text{ are equivalent rationals.}$$

$$= \frac{-4 - 15 - 3}{10}$$

$$= -\frac{11}{5} \text{ or } -2\frac{1}{5} \longleftarrow \quad \text{Remember to express your answer in lowest terms.}$$

**Example 2**　Simplify $\dfrac{3}{4} \times \dfrac{-4}{5} \div \dfrac{-3}{7}$.

To divide by a rational number, you multiply by its **multiplicative inverse** (called a **reciprocal**).

**Solution**
$$\frac{3}{4} \times \frac{-4}{5} \div \frac{-3}{7} = \frac{3}{4} \times \frac{-4}{5} \times \frac{7}{-3}$$

$$= \frac{\overset{1}{\cancel{3}}}{\cancel{4}} \times \frac{\overset{-1}{\cancel{-4}}}{5} \times \frac{7}{\underset{-1}{\cancel{-3}}} \longleftarrow \quad \text{Express rationals in lowest terms before you multiply.}$$

$$= \frac{-7}{-5} \text{ or } 1\frac{2}{5}$$

The study of one part of mathematics is often closely related to another part. You will see how rationals and their operations extend to operations in algebra.

## 1.2 Exercise

**A** Express your answers in lowest terms, and with a positive denominator.

1  Express each rational as an equivalent rational in lowest terms and with a positive denominator.

(a) $\dfrac{-15}{-30}$   (b) $\dfrac{12}{-18}$   (c) $\dfrac{-3}{-6}$   (d) $\dfrac{6}{-30}$   (e) $-\dfrac{14}{-10}$   (f) $-\dfrac{-4}{-8}$

2  Write the rational for each expression if $x = -2$, $y = 3$, $z = -1$.

(a) $\dfrac{x+y}{z}$   (b) $\dfrac{x-y}{-z}$   (c) $\dfrac{-x+2y}{x+z}$   (d) $\dfrac{y^2}{x^2+y^2}$   (e) $\dfrac{x^2+2xy+y^2}{x+y}$

3  Simplify. Express your answers in lowest terms and with a positive denominator.

(a) $\dfrac{1}{4} + \dfrac{-3}{4}$   (b) $\dfrac{1}{2} - \dfrac{-2}{3}$   (c) $\dfrac{-3}{4} - \dfrac{1}{-4}$   (d) $\dfrac{-3}{5} + \dfrac{3}{-4}$

(e) $\dfrac{-1}{4} - 1\dfrac{1}{3}$   (f) $-8\dfrac{1}{4} - \dfrac{1}{-3}$   (g) $\dfrac{2}{-3} - 1\dfrac{5}{6}$   (h) $\dfrac{5}{-6} - 2\dfrac{1}{3}$

(i) $\dfrac{-3}{5} + \dfrac{-3}{4} - \dfrac{7}{10}$   (j) $\dfrac{-1}{8} - \dfrac{1}{-4} + \dfrac{-1}{2}$   (k) $\dfrac{2}{3} - \dfrac{-1}{2} - \dfrac{1}{-6}$

4  Find the following products.

(a) $\dfrac{4}{5} \times \dfrac{-20}{25}$   (b) $\dfrac{3}{-2} \times \dfrac{6}{-5}$   (c) $\left(\dfrac{-1}{3}\right)\left(\dfrac{2}{-5}\right)$   (d) $\left(\dfrac{9}{4}\right)\left(-\dfrac{2}{-3}\right)$

(e) $\dfrac{1}{-2} \times \dfrac{-2}{5}$   (f) $\dfrac{-4}{5} \times \dfrac{10}{-4}$   (g) $\left(\dfrac{-5}{12}\right)(-24)$   (h) $\left(\dfrac{-6}{10}\right)\left(-\dfrac{1}{2}\right)$

(i) $-2\dfrac{1}{4} \times \dfrac{2}{-9}$   (j) $-1\dfrac{1}{10} \times 3\dfrac{1}{11}$   (k) $\left(1\dfrac{3}{5}\right)(-12)$   (l) $\left(-4\dfrac{1}{6}\right)\left(-7\dfrac{3}{4}\right)$

5  Simplify each of the following.

(a) $\dfrac{-4}{3} \div \dfrac{2}{-3}$   (b) $-7\dfrac{1}{8} \div \dfrac{3}{2}$   (c) $\dfrac{-2}{3} \div \dfrac{-3}{8}$

(d) $-\dfrac{3}{-2} \div \left(-\dfrac{1}{3}\right)$   (e) $-6 \div \left(-\dfrac{4}{5}\right)$   (f) $\left(-2\dfrac{1}{3}\right) \div \left(-3\dfrac{1}{2}\right)$

**B** Remember: When more than one operation occurs, refer to the order of operations.

6   Simplify.

(a) $-\dfrac{2}{5} - \left( -\dfrac{1}{10} + \dfrac{1}{-2} \right)$   (b) $-\dfrac{1}{4} - \left( \dfrac{3}{4} - \dfrac{4}{-5} \right)$   (c) $-\dfrac{3}{5} \left( \dfrac{-3}{4} - \dfrac{-1}{4} \right)$

(d) $\dfrac{1}{-8} - \dfrac{-3}{4} \div \dfrac{5}{8}$   (e) $\dfrac{1}{-3} \div \dfrac{1}{-2} - \dfrac{-2}{3}$   (f) $-\dfrac{3}{5} - \left( \dfrac{-3}{5} - \dfrac{-2}{3} \right)$

7   Use either $<$ or $>$ for ⊘ to make each of the following true.

(a) $\dfrac{-1}{8} - \dfrac{1}{-4}$ ⊘ $-\dfrac{1}{-2} - \dfrac{1}{6}$   (b) $\dfrac{5}{-8} + \dfrac{-3}{4}$ ⊘ $\dfrac{-3}{2} - 2\dfrac{1}{3}$

(c) $-\dfrac{3}{2} - \dfrac{-1}{4} + \dfrac{1}{-3}$ ⊘ $-\dfrac{2}{3} - \dfrac{3}{4} + \dfrac{-2}{3}$   (d) $\dfrac{2}{-3} \times \dfrac{6}{-8} \div \dfrac{-3}{12}$ ⊘ $\dfrac{2}{-4} \times \dfrac{-1}{2} \div \dfrac{-2}{3}$

8   Simplify. Remember: $\left( -\dfrac{1}{2} \right)^2$ means $\left( -\dfrac{1}{2} \right)\left( -\dfrac{1}{2} \right)$.

(a) $\left( \dfrac{-3}{2} \right)^2 \left( -\dfrac{1}{3} \right)^2$   (b) $\left( \dfrac{1}{2} - \dfrac{1}{3} \right)^2$   (c) $\left( -\dfrac{3}{4} - \dfrac{2}{3} \right)^2$   (d) $\left( \dfrac{-1}{2} - \dfrac{-1}{3} \right)^2$

9   Find the value of each expression for the given values.

(a) $3x - \dfrac{1}{2}$, $x \in \left\{ \dfrac{3}{4}, -\dfrac{1}{3}, \dfrac{-2}{3} \right\}$   (b) $\dfrac{1}{2}y - \dfrac{3}{4}$, $y \in \left\{ -\dfrac{1}{2}, 1, \dfrac{1}{2}, \dfrac{3}{4} \right\}$

10   If $x = -\dfrac{1}{2}$, $y = \dfrac{2}{3}$, find the value of each expression.

(a) $x + y$   (b) $x - y$   (c) $x + 2y$   (d) $3x - 2y$   (e) $\dfrac{1}{2}x - \dfrac{1}{2}y$

11   Simplify each expression if $x = \dfrac{-2}{3}$, $y = \dfrac{3}{4}$.

(a) $\dfrac{-2x + 4y}{x + y}$   (b) $\dfrac{x^2 + 2xy + y^2}{x + y}$   (c) $\dfrac{x^2 - y^2}{x - y}$

**C** 12   The expressions shown represent rational numbers

$\dfrac{1}{1 + 1}$, $\dfrac{1}{1 + \dfrac{1}{1 + 1}}$, $\dfrac{1}{1 + \dfrac{1}{1 + \dfrac{1}{1 + 1}}}$, ...

(a) Find the rational number represented by the numerical expressions.

(b) What is the 10th rational number represented by the pattern above? (Hint: Look for a simpler way of finding the answer.)

# Rational Numbers and Decimals

Each rational number has a decimal equivalent. The decimals shown are called **terminating decimals**.

$$\frac{1}{4} = 0.25 \qquad \frac{1}{8} = 0.125$$

Some rational numbers have a decimal that does not terminate. These decimals are periodic and are called **repeating decimals**. The part of the decimal shown at the right that repeats, namely, 45, is called the **period**.
The number of digits in the period is called the **length** of the period.

$$\frac{5}{11} = 0.45454545\ldots$$
$$= 0.\overline{45} \longleftarrow \begin{array}{l}\text{period is 45}\\ \text{length is 2.}\end{array}$$

Every rational number has a decimal equivalent that is either a terminating or repeating decimal. You can use algebra to find the rational number represented by a repeating decimal.

- Find the rational number represented
  by $\qquad 0.\overline{48} = 0.484848\ldots$
  Let $\qquad x = 0.484848\ldots$
  Then $\quad 100x = 48.4848\ldots$
  $$\underline{\qquad x = 0.4848\ldots}$$
  $$99x = 48$$
  $$x = \frac{48}{99} \text{ or } \frac{16}{33} \longleftarrow \begin{array}{l}\text{Check your work.}\\ \text{Use a calculator.}\end{array}$$

- Find the rational number represented
  by $\qquad 0.1\overline{5} = 0.15555\ldots$
  Let $\qquad x = 0.155555\ldots$
  Then $\quad 100x = 15.5555\ldots$
  $$\underline{\qquad 10x = 1.5555\ldots}$$
  $$90x = 14$$
  $$\longrightarrow x = \frac{14}{90} \text{ or } \frac{7}{45}$$

13 Find the period and the length of the period for each rational.

(a) $\dfrac{3}{4}$ 　　(b) $\dfrac{-9}{16}$ 　　(c) $\dfrac{11}{9}$ 　　(d) $2\dfrac{1}{4}$ 　　(e) $\dfrac{35}{99}$

(f) $-1\dfrac{3}{22}$ 　　(g) $\dfrac{-49}{54}$ 　　(h) $\dfrac{53}{100}$ 　　(i) $3\dfrac{1}{15}$ 　　(j) $\dfrac{-7}{15}$

14 Which rational is greater?

(a) $\dfrac{6}{25}, \dfrac{3}{20}$ 　　(b) $-\dfrac{11}{30}, -\dfrac{9}{26}$ 　　(c) $\dfrac{1}{6}, \dfrac{6}{29}$ 　　(d) $\dfrac{3}{-29}, -\dfrac{1}{14}$

15 Find the rational number represented by each decimal.

(a) $0.4$ 　　(b) $0.\overline{4}$ 　　(c) $0.0\overline{4}$ 　　(d) $0.3\overline{6}$ 　　(e) $0.\overline{36}$

(f) $0.3\overline{63}$ 　　(g) $3.28$ 　　(h) $-0.3\overline{15}$ 　　(i) $-2.\overline{39}$ 　　(j) $-1.0\overline{46}$

16 A periodic decimal, such as $0.\overline{4}$, may be written as a sum.
$$0.\overline{4} = 0.4 + 0.04 + 0.004 + 0.0004 + \cdots$$

Find the rational number represented by each of the following

(a) $0.3 + 0.03 + 0.003 + \cdots$ 　　(b) $0.04 + 0.004 + 0.0004 + \cdots$
(c) $0.67 + 0.0067 + 0.000067 + \cdots$ 　　(d) $0.1 + 0.02 + 0.002 + 0.0002 + \cdots$

## 1.3 Developing Mathematics: Square Roots and Radicals

In the history of mathematics, the development of much mathematics can be attributed to the Ancient Greeks. They did a lot of work in exploring the properties of numbers by using geometric figures.

triangular numbers                                square numbers

$$3 \qquad 6 \qquad 10 \qquad\qquad 4 \qquad 9 \qquad 16$$

Every positive number has only one square, but every positive number has 2 square roots.

*Square number*
36 is the square of 6

*Square root*
6 is a square root of 36 since $(6)^2 = 36$
$-6$ is a square root of 36 since $(-6)^2 = 36$

A symbol for describing square roots was invented. The symbol below is used to show the positive or **principal square root** of a number.

36 is often referred to as the **radicand**.

$\sqrt{\phantom{x}}$ is called the **radical** symbol.

$\sqrt{36} = 6$ ⟵ is called the principal square root of 36.

You can use your work with factors to find the square roots of some numbers. To find the value of the radical $\sqrt{324}$, write 324 as a product of prime factors.

$$324 = 2 \times 2 \times 3 \times 3 \times 3 \times 3$$

Choose 1 factor from each pair.

$$\sqrt{324} = \quad 2 \quad \times \quad 3 \quad \times \quad 3$$
$$= 18$$

In working with radicals, note
$$\sqrt{4} \times \sqrt{9} = 2 \times 3$$
$$= 6$$

$$\sqrt{36} = \sqrt{4 \times 9}$$
$$= \sqrt{2 \times 2 \times 3 \times 3}$$
$$= 2 \times 3$$
$$= 6$$

The above suggests that
$$\sqrt{4} \times \sqrt{9} = \sqrt{4 \times 9} = \sqrt{36}$$
and in general $\sqrt{m} \times \sqrt{n} = \sqrt{m \times n}, m \geq 0, n \geq 0$

What if the number cannot be factored? This question often leads to the development of useful mathematical skills. One method of obtaining the value of a square root of a number was contributed by Sir Isaac Newton. To find a value for $\sqrt{90}$, you know that $\sqrt{90}$ lies between two other values.

$$\sqrt{81} < \sqrt{90} < \sqrt{100}$$
$$9 < \sqrt{90} < 10$$

Newton based his method on the following important principle of mathematics.

number, $n$ = (square root of $n$)(square root of $n$)

$$n = \sqrt{n} \times \sqrt{n} \text{ or } \frac{n}{\sqrt{n}} = \sqrt{n}$$

The value of $\sqrt{90}$ is between 9 and 10. A useful first estimate of the value of $\sqrt{90}$ is thus the average of 9 and 10, as shown in the first step.

*Step 1:* A first estimate of the value of $\sqrt{90}$ is the average $\frac{9 + 10}{2} = 9.5$

*Step 2:* Divide. $\frac{90}{9.5} \doteq 9.474$

*Step 3:* Find an average again. $\frac{9.5 + 9.474}{2} = 9.487$

*Step 4:* Divide. $\frac{90}{9.487} \doteq 9.487$ ⟵ Remember the principle $\frac{n}{\sqrt{n}} = \sqrt{n}$.

The procedure is repeated until you obtain the desired accuracy. Thus, $\sqrt{90} = 9.487$ (to 3 decimal places)

Note: The importance of this method is that a computer can be programmed to follow these logical steps.

You can use the $\boxed{\sqrt{\phantom{x}}}$ key to calculate the square root of a number by the procedure shown at the right.

Output
$\boxed{C}\ 90\ \boxed{\sqrt{\phantom{x}}}\ 9.486833$

Express your answer
$\sqrt{90} = 9.487$ to 3 decimal places.

To calculate the product of radicals, first you find the product shown.

$\sqrt{3} \times \sqrt{5} = \sqrt{3 \times 5}$
$= \sqrt{15}$

From your calculator, or by Newton's Method,
$\sqrt{15} = 3.87$ (to 2 decimal places)

There are some special words that are used with radicals.

entire radical
$\sqrt{12}$

mixed radical
$2\sqrt{3}$

Multiplication is understood here.
$2\sqrt{3}$ means $2 \times \sqrt{3}$.

## 1.3 Exercise

**A** Remember: $\sqrt{a} \times \sqrt{b} = \sqrt{ab}$.

1  Use factors to find the principal square root of each number.
(a) 28 (b) 8 (c) 163 (d) 76 (e) 183
(f) 205 (g) 96 (h) 69 (i) 133 (j) 271

2  (a) Use Newton's method to find $\sqrt{32}$ to 2 decimal places.
   (b) Use a calculator to find $\sqrt{32}$ to 2 decimal places.
   (c) How do your answers in (a) and (b) compare?

3  (a) Use Newton's method to find $\sqrt{300}$ to 2 decimal places.
   (b) Use a calculator to find $\sqrt{300}$ to 2 decimal places.
   (c) How do your answers compare?

**B** A calculator is a useful tool for doing mathematics. But, you need to know the concepts and skills of mathematics.

4  Evaluate each of the following. Express your answers to 1 decimal place.
   (a) $\sqrt{124}$    (b) $\sqrt{168}$    (c) $\sqrt{1376}$    (d) $\sqrt{208}$    (e) $\sqrt{333}$
   (f) $\sqrt{544}$    (g) $\sqrt{356}$    (h) $\sqrt{603}$    (i) $\sqrt{425}$    (j) $\sqrt{162.5}$

5  Evaluate to 2 decimal places.
   (a) $\sqrt{48}$    (b) $\sqrt{980}$    (c) $\sqrt{3800}$    (d) $\sqrt{23.4}$    (e) $\sqrt{48.6}$
   (f) $\sqrt{132.2}$    (g) $\sqrt{14.9}$    (h) $\sqrt{38.9}$    (i) $\sqrt{314}$    (j) $\sqrt{285.52}$

6  Write each of the following as an entire radical.
   (a) $3\sqrt{5}$    The first one is
                      done for you

$$3\sqrt{5} = \sqrt{9} \times \sqrt{5}$$
$$= \sqrt{9 \times 5}$$
$$= \sqrt{45}$$

   (b) $3\sqrt{2}$    (c) $6\sqrt{2}$    (d) $8\sqrt{3}$    (e) $4\sqrt{5}$    (f) $9\sqrt{7}$    (g) $4\sqrt{10}$
   (h) $20\sqrt{2}$    (i) $5\sqrt{8}$    (j) $3\sqrt{14}$    (k) $6\sqrt{5}$    (l) $3\sqrt{6}$    (m) $9\sqrt{4}$

7  Express each of the following as a mixed radical in simplest form. A radical is in its simplest form when the smallest possible number is under the radical sign.
   (a) $\sqrt{75}$    The first one is
                      done for you.

$$\sqrt{75} = \sqrt{25 \times 3}$$
$$= \sqrt{25} \times \sqrt{3}$$
$$= 5\sqrt{3}$$

   (b) $\sqrt{50}$    (c) $\sqrt{20}$    (d) $\sqrt{28}$    (e) $\sqrt{32}$    (f) $\sqrt{12}$
   (g) $\sqrt{125}$    (h) $\sqrt{200}$    (i) $\sqrt{27}$    (j) $\sqrt{24}$    (k) $\sqrt{98}$
   (l) $\sqrt{72}$    (m) $\sqrt{300}$    (n) $\sqrt{208}$    (o) $\sqrt{175}$    (p) $\sqrt{240}$

8  Evaluate each of the following accurate to 2 decimal places.
   (a) $\sqrt{2} \times \sqrt{3}$    (b) $\sqrt{12} \times \sqrt{2}$    (c) $\sqrt{2} \times \sqrt{5}$
   (d) $\sqrt{3} \times \sqrt{6}$    (e) $\sqrt{5} \times \sqrt{8}$    (f) $\sqrt{7} \times \sqrt{5}$
   (g) $\sqrt{6} \times \sqrt{8}$    (h) $\sqrt{7} \times \sqrt{10}$    (i) $\sqrt{3} \times \sqrt{10}$

# Applications: Space and Artificial Gravity

If you were in a space station that did not rotate, you would float about in the interior of the space station. This would make it difficult to make accurate observations of the earth and conduct experiments. The following formula is used to calculate the number of rotations, $N$, per minute of the space station, so that its interior simulates the earth's gravity.

$$N = \frac{42}{\pi} \sqrt{\frac{5}{r}}$$ where $r$ is the radius of the space station, in metres.

$\pi \doteq 3.14$

9   For each radius, $r$, calculate the value of $N$ in the formula above to 1 decimal place.

(a) 9.2 m      (b) 16.5 m      (c) 12.38 m

10   The radius of a space station is 12.8 m. Calculate the number of rotations per minute that the space station needs to turn, in order to simulate earth's gravity.

11   The astronauts on a space station experience earth's gravity as they walk. What is the number of rotations per minute if the diameter of the space station is 35.9 m?

12   (a) Calculate the number of rotations per minute needed in a space station to simulate earth's gravity if the radius of the station is 20.5 m.

(b) If the radius is increased by 6.8 m, how many rotations per minute are needed?

13   (a) A space station has a radius of 22.9 m. Calculate the number of rotations per minute needed to simulate the earth's gravity.

(b) The space station in (a) is to be rebuilt to rotate one complete rotation more than in (a). What must the radius be?

(c) The space station in (a) is to be rebuilt again to rotate one complete rotation less than in (a). What must the radius be?

14   A space station is built with a radius of 19.6 m. Once in orbit it rotates 10 rotations per minute.

(a) Will the people inside the space station have difficulty walking? Give reasons for your answer.

(b) How could the problem in (a) be corrected?

# 1.4 What Are Real Numbers?

In a previous section, you learned that the word *rational* was invented to name numbers constructed in the following manner.

$$\frac{a}{b} \qquad a, b \text{ integers, } b \neq 0$$

Then you learned that every rational number can be described as either
- terminating   or   • non-terminating but repeating

There are numbers that have decimals that are non-terminating *and* non-repeating. One of the most fascinating numbers that mathematicians have studied is $\pi$. This remarkable number occurs throughout the study of mathematics in many mathematical formulae.

| *Area of circle* | *Volume of cone* | *Volume of sphere* |
|:---:|:---:|:---:|
| $A = \pi r^2$ | $V = \dfrac{1}{3}\pi r^2 h$ | $V = \dfrac{4}{3}\pi r^3$ |

No one has ever found its complete decimal form (and no one ever will). It is a decimal number that is non-terminating and non-repeating.

$\pi = 3.141\ 592\ 653\ 589\ 793\ 238\ 462\ 643\ 383$
$279\ 502\ 884\ 197\ 169\ 399\ 375\ 105\ 820$
$974\ 944\ 592\ 307\ 816\ 406\ 286\ 208\ 998$
$628\ 034\ 825\ 342\ 117\ 067\ 9$ (to 100 decimal places)

The rational numbers $\frac{22}{7}$ and 3.1416 are convenient approximations used for the value of $\pi$. Thus $\pi$ is not a rational number. The term **irrational number** was invented to describe numbers such as $\pi$. The decimals for $\sqrt{2}, \sqrt{3}, \sqrt{5}$ for example, are also non-terminating and non-repeating. They are also irrational numbers. Symbols have been invented to represent these numbers.

$\bar{Q}$ = set of irrational numbers
$Q$ = set of rational numbers
$R = Q \cup \bar{Q}$

⎯⎯⎯⎯ Means the union of $Q$ and $\bar{Q}$.
⎯⎯⎯⎯ $R$ stands for the set of real numbers.

Thus, the real numbers consist of all the rational numbers *and* all the irrational numbers.

When you work with the language of mathematics, you must understand clearly the meanings of the symbols used.

$I$, integers     $R$, real numbers

The symbols used to draw the graphs of sets of numbers must also be interpreted accurately.

The graph of $\{x \mid x \leq -5, x \in I\}$ is shown.

$$\xleftarrow{\hspace{1cm}} \begin{array}{ccccccc} -9 & -8 & -7 & -6 & -5 & -4 & -3 & -2 \end{array} \xrightarrow{\hspace{1cm}}$$

The graph of $\{x \mid x < -5, x \in I\}$ is shown.

$$\xleftarrow{\hspace{1cm}} \begin{array}{ccccccc} -9 & -8 & -7 & -6 & -5 & -4 & -3 & -2 \end{array} \xrightarrow{\hspace{1cm}}$$

This symbol shows the graph continues in the pattern shown.

The graph of $\{x \mid x \leq -5, x \in R\}$ is shown by

$$\xleftarrow{\hspace{1cm}} \begin{array}{ccccccc} -9 & -8 & -7 & -6 & -5 & -4 & -3 & -2 \end{array} \xrightarrow{\hspace{1cm}}$$

The graph of $\{x \mid x < -5, x \in R\}$ is shown.

$$\xleftarrow{\hspace{1cm}} \begin{array}{ccccccc} -9 & -8 & -7 & -6 & -5 & -4 & -3 & -2 \end{array} \xrightarrow{\hspace{1cm}}$$

The symbol shows the graph does not include the number $-5$.

In the process of developing mathematics, vocabulary and symbols are invented for a precise purpose. Then sometimes other mathematics is anticipated. (You know what real numbers are. What do you think non-real numbers are?)

## 1.4   Exercise

**A** The questions that follow review some properties of real numbers, as well as the vocabulary related to the work in real numbers.

1   What sets of numbers do the following symbols represent?
   (a) $N$      (b) $Q$      (c) $\bar{Q}$      (d) $R$      (e) $W$      (f) $I$

2   The diagram shows how the rational numbers and integers are related. Integers are said to be a subset of rational numbers. For each of the following sets,
  • sketch a diagram to show how the sets are related.
  • use numerical examples to illustrate your example.

   (a) $N, W$      (b) $N, I$      (c) $I, W$      (d) $R, I$
   (e) $R, Q$      (f) $R, \bar{Q}$      (g) $I, Q$      (h) $Q, \bar{Q}$

3   (a) Construct a diagram to show how all the sets $W, N, I, Q, \bar{Q}$ and $R$ are related.
   (b) Use your diagram in (a).
     (i) Is $I$ a subset of $Q$?
     (ii) Is $N$ a subset of $I$?
     (iii) Do $Q$ and $\bar{Q}$ share any numbers?

4   The average of any two rationals has the property shown. $\dfrac{1}{3} < \dfrac{\frac{1}{3} + \frac{3}{4}}{2} < \dfrac{3}{4}$

Express this property in words.

5   Simplify.

(a) $\dfrac{\frac{1}{3} - \frac{3}{4}}{2}$   (b) $\dfrac{\frac{1}{4} + \frac{1}{3}}{2}$   (c) $\dfrac{-\frac{2}{3} + \frac{1}{4}}{2}$   (d) $\dfrac{\frac{1}{8} - \frac{2}{3}}{2}$   (e) $\dfrac{\frac{1}{16} + \frac{1}{32}}{2}$

6   Find another rational number between each pair of rationals.

(a) $\dfrac{1}{4}, \dfrac{1}{5}$   (b) $-\dfrac{2}{3}, -\dfrac{1}{2}$   (c) $-1\dfrac{1}{9}, -1\dfrac{1}{10}$   (d) $-\dfrac{3}{8}, -\dfrac{3}{16}$   (e) $1\dfrac{3}{7}, 1\dfrac{4}{7}$

7   A set of numbers is said to be **dense** if, between any two numbers, you can find another number of the set.
   (a) Is the set of rationals dense?
   (b) Justify your answer in (a). Support your answer with examples of your own.

   B   Some mathematicians have spent all their lives studying the properties of irrational numbers.

8   Write the decimal for a rational number between each of the following pairs of numbers.
   (a) $0.6, 0.6\overline{7}$                      (b) $-0.3, -0.\overline{3}$
   (c) $0.\overline{45}, 0.\overline{48}$          (d) $-3.\overline{46}, -3.5\overline{6}$

9   A decimal $0.23233233323333\ldots$ is written for a number. Is the number a rational or irrational? Justify your answer.

10   Which decimals represent rational numbers? Irrational numbers? Justify your answers.
   (a) $0.45454545\ldots$        (b) $0.4545545554\ldots$        (c) $0.1234567891011\ldots$
   (d) $0.123455555\ldots$       (e) $12.3412345123456\ldots$    (f) $0.001001001001\ldots$

11   Write the decimal for an irrational number between each of the following pairs of decimals.
   (a) $0.8, 0.8\overline{3}$   The first one is      One irrational is $0.8121121112\ldots$
                                done for you.        There are other numbers.

   (b) $0.65, 0.6\overline{8}$                 (c) $-0.\overline{45}, -0.\overline{49}$            (d) $3.48\overline{2}, 3.4\overline{8}$

12  (a) How could you show that the following statement is true?

       Irrational numbers are dense.

   (b) Choose examples of your own to illustrate the fact that irrational
       numbers are dense.

   (c) What is meant by this statement? Use examples to illustrate your answer.

       $\bar{Q}$ is the set of non-periodic decimals.

13  Draw the graph of each of the following sets.

   (a) $\{x \mid x < 3,\ x \in I\}$      (b) $\{x \mid x < 3,\ x \in R\}$      (c) $\{x \mid x \geq 2,\ x \in N\}$

   (d) $\{x \mid x \geq 2,\ x \in I\}$      (e) $\{x \mid x < -3,\ x \in R\}$      (f) $\{x \mid x < -3,\ x \in I\}$

   (g) $\{x \mid x \geq 0,\ x \in I\}$      (h) $\{x \mid x \geq 0,\ x \in R\}$      (i) $\{x \mid 0 < x,\ x \in I\}$

   (j) $\{x \mid 0 < x,\ x \in R\}$      (k) $\{x \mid 9 > x,\ x \in R\}$      (l) $\{x \mid 9 > x,\ x \in N\}$

14  You may write the opposite of a symbol as shown

       = is equal to                    > is greater than

       ≠ is not equal to                ≯ is not greater than

   Draw the graph of each of the following sets.

   (a) $\{x \mid x < 5,\ x \in R\}$      (b) $\{x \mid x \not< 5,\ x \in R\}$      (c) $\{x \mid -4 \leq x,\ x \in I\}$

   (d) $\{x \mid -4 \leq x,\ x \in I\}$      (e) $\{x \mid x \geq 3,\ x \in R\}$      (f) $\{x \mid x \geq 3,\ x \in R\}$

   (g) $\{x \mid -3 \leq x,\ x \in I\}$      (h) $\{x \mid -3 \leq x,\ x \in I\}$      (i) $\{x \mid 2 \not> x,\ x \in R\}$

15  Draw the graph for each set.   The first one is
   (a) $\{x \mid -2 < x \leq 2,\ x \in R\}$   done for you.

   (b) $\{x \mid -6 < x < -3,\ x \in R\}$      (c) $\{x \mid -4 \leq x < 0,\ x \in R\}$

   (d) $\{x \mid -2 < x < 3,\ x \in R\}$      (e) $\{x \mid 5 \geq x \geq 3,\ x \in R\}$

   (f) $\{x \mid 0 \leq x < 4,\ x \in R\}$      (g) $\{x \mid -9 < x < -6,\ x \in R\}$

16  Draw the graph of each set.      The first one is
   (a) $\{x \mid x > 2$   or $x \leq -1,\ x \in R\}$   done for you.

   (b) $\{x \mid x < -3$ or $x > 0,\ x \in R\}$      (c) $\{x \mid x \geq 6$   or $x < 4,\ x \in R\}$

   (d) $\{x \mid x < 0$   or $x \geq 3,\ x \in R\}$      (e) $\{x \mid -2 < x$ or $x < -8,\ x \in R\}$

   (f) $\{x \mid -4 > x$ or $x \geq -1,\ x \in R\}$      (g) $\{x \mid x > 3$   or $x \leq -1,\ x \in R\}$

Math Tip

These symbols will occur over and over again in your study of
mathematics. Be sure you understand their meanings.

       <   >   ≤   ≥   ≮   ≯   ≰   ≱

# 1.5 Inventing Mathematics: Exponents

Exponents were invented to show a compact form of the multiplication of like factors.     $a^n$, power

$n$, exponent     $a$, base

$$a^n = \underbrace{a \times a \times a \times a \times \cdots \times a \times a}, n \in N$$

There are $n$ like factors.

Once the symbols are used, the next step is the exploration of the properties of exponents. In your earlier work in mathematics, specific numerical examples suggested the following laws of exponents.

| *Specific Examples* | *Laws of Exponents,* $m, n \in N$ | |
| --- | --- | --- |
| $x^2 \times x^3 = x^5, x^8 \times x^3 = x^{11}$ | Multiplication | $x^m \times x^n = x^{m+n}$ |
| $\dfrac{x^4}{x^2} = x^2, \dfrac{x^8}{x^3} = x^5$ | Division | $\dfrac{x^m}{x^n} = x^{m-n}, m > n, x \neq 0$ |
| $(x^2)^3 = x^6, (x^4)^2 = x^8$ | Power | $(x^m)^n = x^{mn}$ |
| $(xy)^2 = x^2y^2, (xy^2)^3 = x^3y^6$ | Power of Product | $(xy)^m = x^m y^m$ |
| $\left(\dfrac{x}{y}\right)^2 = \dfrac{x^2}{y^2}, \left(\dfrac{x}{y}\right)^5 = \dfrac{x^5}{y^5}$ | Power of Quotient | $\left(\dfrac{x}{y}\right)^m = \dfrac{x^m}{y^m}, y \neq 0$ |

These laws of exponents are then applied to the simplification of expressions containing exponents. Which laws were used in each of the following examples?

**Example 1**     Simplify. (a) $\left(\dfrac{10^5}{10^2}\right)^3\left(\dfrac{10^2 \times 10^3}{10^4}\right)^2$.       (b) $\dfrac{(x^2y)^5}{(xy^2)^2}$.

**Solution**     (a) $\left(\dfrac{10^5}{10^2}\right)^3\left(\dfrac{10^2 \times 10^3}{10^4}\right)^2 = \dfrac{10^{15}}{10^6} \times \dfrac{(10^5)^2}{10^8}$     (b) $\dfrac{(x^2y)^5}{(xy^2)^2} = \dfrac{x^{10}y^5}{x^2y^4}$

$$= 10^9 \times \dfrac{10^{10}}{10^8} \qquad\qquad = x^8y$$

$$= 10^9 \times 10^2$$

$$= 10^{11}$$

When you evaluate expressions that contain exponents, it is often more efficient to simplify before substituting.

**Example 2**     Evaluate $\dfrac{(x^3y^2)^4}{(x^2y^3)^2}$ if $x = -1, y = 3$.

**Solution**     *Step 1:* Simplify the expression.     *Step 2:* Evaluate.

$$\dfrac{(x^3y^2)^4}{(x^2y^3)^2} = \dfrac{x^{12}y^8}{x^4y^6}$$

$$(-1)^8 = 1$$
$$x^8y^2 = (-1)^8(3)^2$$

$$= x^{12-4}y^{8-6} \qquad = 9$$

$$= x^8y^2$$

Some exponents are expressed as variables. However, the same laws are used to write them with a single base.

**Example 3**  Express $\dfrac{(x^3)^n(x^2)^m}{(x^{n+3})^2}$ with a single base.

**Solution**  $\dfrac{(x^3)^n(x^2)^m}{(x^{n+3})^2} = \dfrac{x^{3n} \times x^{2m}}{x^{2(n+3)}}$

$= \dfrac{x^{3n+2m}}{x^{2n+6}}$  You may complete some of these steps mentally.

$= x^{3n+2m-(2n+6)}$

$= x^{3n+2m-2n-6}$

$= x^{n+2m-6}$

You can use a calculator to evaluate expressions containing exponents.

Evaluate           Calculator steps

           Output

$2^{12}$    $\boxed{C}\ 2\ \boxed{y^x}\ 12\ \boxed{=}$    4096

You may need to check your manual to see which key performs this step on your calculator.

## 1.5  Exercise

**A** Review the laws of exponents.

1   Use number examples to show why the following exponent laws are true. $a, b \in N$.

(a) $y^a \times y^b = y^{a+b}$     (b) $\dfrac{y^a}{y^b} = y^{a-b}, a > b$     (c) $(y^a)^b = y^{ab}$

(d) $(xy)^a = x^a y^a$     (e) $\left(\dfrac{x}{y}\right)^a = \dfrac{x^a}{y^a}, y \neq 0$

2   Write each of the following as a single power of 10.

(a) $10^6 \times 10^5$           (b) $10^8 \times 10^3 \times 10$

(c) $\dfrac{10^8 \times 10^2}{10^4}$      (d) $\dfrac{(-10)^2 \times 10^4}{10^3}$      (e) $\dfrac{(-10)^3(-10)^5}{10^4}$

(f) $\left(-\dfrac{1}{10}\right)^3 \times 10^5$      (g) $-10^3(10^5)\left(-\dfrac{1}{10}\right)^4$      (h) $\left(\dfrac{10^3 \times 10^2}{-10}\right)^3$

3 Simplify each of the following.

(a) $\dfrac{x^8}{x^5}$　　　　(b) $(k^4)(k^5)$　　　　(c) $(ab)^5$　　　　(d) $\left(\dfrac{k}{m}\right)^3$

(e) $(m^2)^5$　　　　(f) $\dfrac{a^8}{a^2}$　　　　(g) $(m^5)(m^6)$　　　　(h) $\left(\dfrac{5}{x}\right)^3$

(i) $(3a)^4$　　　　(j) $(x^3)^4$　　　　(k) $(2xy)^3$　　　　(l) $(y^7)(y^3)$

(m) $x^5 \times x^4 \times x^3$　　(n) $\left(\dfrac{3}{2}\right)^3$　　　　(o) $2^3 \times 2^4$　　　　(p) $m^2 \times m^3 \times m^4$

(q) $(x^2y)(xy^2)(xy)$　　　　(r) $(x^3y)(xy^3)(0)$　　　　(s) $(xy)(xy)(xy)$

4 Simplify each of the following.

(a) $\dfrac{(xy)^3}{xy}$　　　　(b) $\dfrac{2(ab)^5}{(-a^2)^2}$　　　　(c) $(a^2b)^3\left(\dfrac{a}{-b}\right)^2$　　　　(d) $(-y^2)^3\left(\dfrac{x}{y}\right)^2$

(e) $\left(-\dfrac{1}{x}\right)^3 (x^2y)^4$　　(f) $\dfrac{(a^3b^2)^4}{(-ab^2)^2}\left(\dfrac{-a}{b}\right)^2$　　(g) $\left(\dfrac{xy}{y}\right)^3 (x^2y)^2$　　(h) $\left(\dfrac{x}{-y}\right)^5 (-xy)^3$

5 (a) If $a = 2$, $b = -1$, evaluate　(i) $\dfrac{(a^3b^2)^3}{(a^2b^2)^2}$　　(ii) $a^5b^2$

(b) Why are the answers in (a) the same?

(c) What should be the first step before evaluating an expression?

6 (a) If $a = 2$, $b = -1$, evaluate　(i) $(-a^3b^2)^2$　　(ii) $-(a^3b^2)^2$

(b) Why are your answers in (a) different?

B Before you evaluate an expression, be sure to simplify the expression.

7 Evaluate each of the following if $a = -1$, $b = 1$, and $c = 2$.

(a) $\dfrac{(ab)^3}{b^2}$　　　　　(b) $\dfrac{(a^2bc)^2}{abc}$　　　　　(c) $(a^4b)^2 \div (ab^2)$

(d) $\left(\dfrac{a^3b^2}{ab}\right)^3$　　　　(e) $\left(\dfrac{a}{b}\right)^2\left(\dfrac{b}{c}\right)^4\left(\dfrac{c}{a}\right)^2$　　　　(f) $\left(\dfrac{a}{b}\right)^2\left(\dfrac{b}{c}\right)^2 (abc)^2$

8 (a) Write $2^2 \times 2^3 \times 4$ as a power of 2.　　(b) Write $3^2 \times 3 \times 3^4$ as a power of 3.

(c) Write $\dfrac{3^4 \times 3^2}{3^2}$ as a power of 3.　　(d) Write $\dfrac{10^4 \times 10^5}{10^2 \times 10^3}$ as a power of 10.

9 Write each of the following as a power of 2.

(a) $2^4 \times 2^3$　　(b) $2^n \times 2^3$　　(c) $(2^3)^x$　　(d) $(2^x)^4$　　(e) $4^2$

(f) $4^x$　　　　(g) $8^{x+1}$　　　(h) $4^{2x+1}$　　　(i) $16^{2x-1}$

10 Write each of the following with a single base.

(a) $a^{3m}a^m a^{m+2}$ The first one is done for you. $a^{3m}a^m a^{m+2} = a^{3m+m+m+2}$
$= a^{5m+2}$

(b) $a^{m+n}a^{m-n}$

(c) $a^{3n}a^{n-2}a^2$

(d) $\dfrac{(a^n)^2(a^{n+2})^2}{a^n}$

(e) $\dfrac{(a^{m+n})^2(a^2)^m}{(a^2)^n}$

(f) $\dfrac{a^{k+6}a^{2k+1}}{a^{3k+2}}$

(g) $\dfrac{(a^m)^2}{a^n}\left(\dfrac{a^{n+1}}{a^m}\right)^2$

11 Copy and complete.

| | | | |
|---|---|---|---|
| $(-1)^2 = ?$ | $(-1)^4 = ?$ | $(-1)^6 = ?$ | $(-1)^8 = ?$ |
| $(-1)^3 = ?$ | $(-1)^5 = ?$ | $(-1)^7 = ?$ | $(-1)^9 = ?$ |

(a) What is the value of $(-1)^n$ when $n$ is an even number?

(b) What is the value of $(-1)^n$ when $n$ is an odd number?

12 Evaluate each of the following.

(a) $(-1)^{12}$

(b) $(-1)^{15}$

(c) $(-1)^{23}$

(d) $(-1)^{21}(-1)^{24}$

(e) $(-1)^{13}(-1)^{21}$

(f) $\dfrac{(-1)^{12}(-1)^{12}}{(-1)^3}$

(g) $\dfrac{(-1)^3(-1)^8(-1)^5}{(-1)^2(-1)^3}$

C 13 Predict the last digit of the value of each of the following. Justify your answers.

(a) $7^{13}$

(b) $3^{59}$

(c) $4^{78}$

(d) $11^{100}$

## Calculator Tip

Use the $\boxed{y^x}$ key on a calculator to calculate expressions with exponents. Refer to your manual.

Output

Evaluate $2^8$.　　　　　Procedure　　$\boxed{C}\,2\,\boxed{y^x}\,8\,\boxed{=}\,256$

In the next sections you will use exponents that are integers.

Output

Evaluate $2^{-3}$.　　Procedure　　$\boxed{C}\,3\,\boxed{+/-}\,\boxed{MI}\,2\,\boxed{y^x}\,\boxed{MR}\,\boxed{=}\,0.125$

Find the value of each of the following. How would you interpret your results?

A: $2^0$　$3^0$　$5^0$　$10^0$　　B: $2^{-1}$　$2^{-2}$　$2^{-3}$　$2^{-4}$

C: $4^{\frac{1}{2}}$　$9^{\frac{1}{2}}$　$25^{\frac{1}{2}}$　$36^{\frac{1}{2}}$　　　　$8^{\frac{1}{3}}$　$27^{\frac{1}{3}}$　$64^{\frac{1}{3}}$　$125^{\frac{1}{3}}$

## Computer Tip

Look for computer tips provided in some exercises.

- Obtain a current book on computers. List ways that computers are used everyday.
- What is meant by the terms: *computer program, programmer, software, hardware*?
- List the meaning and use of the basic symbols used to write a computer program in BASIC.

## 1.6 What if ... Any Integers?

Many important developments in mathematics are the result of someone asking "What if ... ?". A lot of mathematics is dealt with in the process of answering the question. For example, you have dealt with the laws of exponents when the values of the exponents are the natural numbers. Thus, for $m, n \in N, m > n$,

$$a^m \times a^n = a^{m+n} \qquad (ab)^m = a^m b^m \qquad a^m \div a^n = a^{m-n} \qquad \left(\frac{a}{b}\right)^m = \frac{a^m}{b^m}, b \neq 0$$

What if the exponent is any integer? These next examples suggest a meaning for exponents when they are integers.

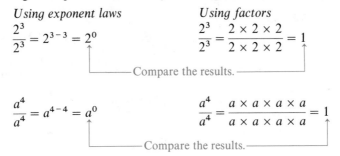

*Using exponent laws*

$$\frac{2^3}{2^3} = 2^{3-3} = 2^0$$

$$\frac{a^4}{a^4} = a^{4-4} = a^0$$

*Using factors*

$$\frac{2^3}{2^3} = \frac{2 \times 2 \times 2}{2 \times 2 \times 2} = 1$$

$$\frac{a^4}{a^4} = \frac{a \times a \times a \times a}{a \times a \times a \times a} = 1$$

—Compare the results.—

—Compare the results.—

If you compare your results, it seems reasonable to define the result when the exponent is 0.

$$2^0 = 1 \qquad\qquad a^0 = 1$$

In a similar way you can obtain some meaning for negative exponents which is consistent with your exponent laws. Compare the following.

$$(a^4)\left(\frac{1}{a^2}\right) = a^{4-2} = a^2 \qquad\qquad (a^4)(a^{-2}) = a^{4+(-2)} = a^2$$

—Compare the results.—

If you compare your results above, it seems reasonable to define

$$a^{-2} = \frac{1}{a^2}$$

In general, for all $a, a \neq 0, n \in I$,

$$a^0 = 1 \qquad\qquad a^{-n} = \frac{1}{a^n}$$

**Example 1**   Simplify $8^0 + 2^{-1} + 3^{-2} - \dfrac{1}{9}$.

**Solution**  $$8^0 + 2^{-1} + 3^{-2} - \frac{1}{9} = 1 + \frac{1}{2} + \frac{1}{3^2} - \frac{1}{9}$$

Change the numbers with negative exponents to numbers with positive exponents.

$$= 1 + \frac{1}{2} + \frac{1}{9} - \frac{1}{9}$$

$$= \frac{3}{2} \text{ or } 1\frac{1}{2}$$

When you are developing mathematics, parallel examples often suggest useful observations. For example, compare the following.

*Using exponent laws*
$$y^{\frac{1}{2}} \times y^{\frac{1}{2}} = y^{\frac{1}{2}+\frac{1}{2}} = y$$

*Using radicals*
$$\sqrt{y} \times \sqrt{y} = y$$

The process appears to be similar.

If you compare the above results, it seems that $y^{\frac{1}{2}}$ and $\sqrt{y}$ behave in a similar way. Based on these, and other examples, it seems reasonable to use  $$y^{\frac{1}{2}} = \sqrt{y}$$

Thus, with the above definition, you can use exponents to write the principal square root of numbers, as these examples show.

$$4^{\frac{1}{2}} = 2 \qquad 9^{\frac{1}{2}} = 3 \qquad 8^{\frac{1}{2}} = \sqrt{8}$$
$$= 2\sqrt{2}$$

Output

To calculate $\sqrt{8}$ on a calculator, use these steps.  $\boxed{C}$ 8 $\boxed{y^x}$ 0.5 $\boxed{=}$   2.8284271

**Example 2**  Simplify $-2^{-3} + \sqrt{9} + \frac{1}{2^2} - 4^{-\frac{1}{2}} + \left(\frac{2}{3}\right)^{-1}$.

**Solution**  $$-2^{-3} + \sqrt{9} + \frac{1}{2^2} - 4^{-\frac{1}{2}} + \left(\frac{2}{3}\right)^{-1}$$

$$= -\frac{1}{2^3} + 3 + \frac{1}{4} - \frac{1}{4^{\frac{1}{2}}} + \frac{1}{\left(\frac{2}{3}\right)}$$

$$= -\frac{1}{8} + 3 + \frac{1}{4} - \frac{1}{2} + \frac{3}{2}$$

You may complete some of these steps mentally.

$$= -\frac{1}{8} + 3 + \frac{2}{8} - \frac{4}{8} + \frac{12}{8}$$

$$= 3 + \frac{9}{8} = 4\frac{1}{8}$$

## 1.6 Exercise

**A** Review the meaning of $a^0$, $a^{-1}$, $a^{\frac{1}{2}}$, $\sqrt{a}$.

1   Find the value of each of the following.

(a) $3^3$   (b) $3^{-1}$   (c) $3^0$   (d) $4^2$   (e) $4^{-1}$   (f) $25^{\frac{1}{2}}$

(g) $16^{-\frac{1}{2}}$   (h) $3^{-2}$   (i) $\dfrac{1}{3^2}$   (j) $-4^{-2}$   (k) $\dfrac{1}{4^{-2}}$   (l) $\dfrac{4^0}{4^2}$

2   Evaluate.

(a) $\sqrt{9}$   (b) $9^{\frac{1}{2}}$   (c) $\sqrt{16}$   (d) $16^{\frac{1}{2}}$   (e) $-16^{\frac{1}{2}}$   (f) $\sqrt{4}$

(g) $-4^{\frac{1}{2}}$   (h) $-81^{\frac{1}{2}}$   (i) $-\sqrt{100}$   (j) $64^{\frac{1}{2}}$   (k) $-\sqrt{25}$   (l) $100^{\frac{1}{2}}$

3   Evaluate.

(a) $(-4)^2$   (b) $-(-4)^2$   (c) $4^{-2}$   (d) $-4^{-2}$

(e) Why do you obtain different answers in (a) to (d)?

4   (a) Simplify $(-\sqrt{9})^2$, $(\sqrt{9})^2$, $(9^{\frac{1}{2}})^2$.

(b) What do you notice about your answers in (a)?

5   Evaluate each of the following. Read carefully.

(a) $5^0$   (b) $-3^2$   (c) $\dfrac{1}{2^0}$   (d) $4^{-\frac{1}{2}}$   (e) $-3^{-2}$   (f) $-5^{-2}$

(g) $-25^{-\frac{1}{2}}$   (h) $5^{-2}$   (i) $-\dfrac{1}{3^0}$   (j) $-\dfrac{1}{3^{-2}}$   (k) $(-3^2)^2$   (l) $\left(\dfrac{1}{2^{-2}}\right)^2$

**B** 6   Evaluate each of the following.

(a) $3^{-3} \times 3^5$   (b) $2^0 + 3^0$   (c) $4^{\frac{1}{2}} \times 8^2$   (d) $4^{\frac{1}{2}} + \sqrt{16}$   (e) $(-3^{-2})^2$

(f) $4^2 \div 4^{-2}$   (g) $(-4)^0$   (h) $3^0 + \sqrt{9}$   (i) $4^{\frac{1}{2}} \div 2^{-3}$   (j) $3^3 \times 3^{-3}$

(k) $(-3^2)^2$   (l) $3^{-2} + 3^{-1}$   (m) $\dfrac{4^{-1}}{\sqrt{4}}$   (n) $\dfrac{1}{2^{-1}} + 3^{-1}$   (o) $\left(\dfrac{1}{3}\right)^{-1}$

7   Evaluate each of the following.

(a) $2^0 + 3^{-1} - 9^{\frac{1}{2}}$   (b) $3^0 - \sqrt{9} + 2 \times 3^{-1}$   (c) $\left(\dfrac{1}{2}\right)^2 - (\sqrt{4})$

(d) $\left(\dfrac{1}{2}\right)^{-2} \div 2^{-1}$   (e) $2(2^{-1} - 3^{-1})$   (f) $4^{-\frac{1}{2}} - \dfrac{3^0}{3^{-1}}$

(g) $0^2 - 9^{-\frac{1}{2}}$   (h) $\dfrac{\sqrt{16}}{3^{-1}} + \dfrac{2^0}{2^{-1}}$   (i) $\dfrac{3^0 + (\sqrt{4})^2}{3^{-1} \times 3^2}$

8  Express each of the following as a power of 10.

(a) $10^5 \div 10^3$  (b) $10^4 \times 10^3$  (c) $10^5 \times 10^{-1}$

(d) $10^{-4} \times 100^{\frac{1}{2}}$  (e) $\dfrac{10^{-8}}{10^2}$  (f) $10^{13} \div 10^1$

(g) $\dfrac{10^6 \times 100^{\frac{1}{2}}}{10}$  (h) $\dfrac{10^5 \times 10^0}{10^2 \times 10^3}$  (i) $(10^{-4})^{\frac{1}{2}}$

9  (a) Simplify $(a^{-3})^2$, $(a^{-2})^3$, $(a^2)^{-3}$, $(a^3)^{-2}$.

(b) What do you notice about your answers in (a)? Why is this so?

10  Simplify. Write your final answer without parentheses.

(a) $(a^3)^2$  (b) $(a^3b)^2$  (c) $(a^3b^3)$  (d) $(x^{-3})^3$

(e) $(b^2)^{-2}$  (f) $(a^{-1})^{-2}$  (g) $(mn^2)^{-2}$  (h) $(a^{-2}b)^2$

(i) $\left(\dfrac{b^2}{a^{-1}}\right)^{-2}$  (j) $\left(\dfrac{x^{-3}}{y^2}\right)^2$  (k) $\left(\dfrac{a^3}{b^{-2}}\right)^{-2}$  (l) $\left(\dfrac{m^{-3}}{n^3}\right)^{-1}$

11  Simplify. Write your final answer with positive exponents.

(a) $\dfrac{x^6}{x^2}$  (b) $\dfrac{x^8y^2}{x^2y^4}$  (c) $\dfrac{m^3n^2}{-m^2n^3}$  (d) $\dfrac{-(a^2)b^{-2}}{-a^{-3}b^5}$

(e) $\dfrac{s^3t^2}{-s^4(t^{-1})^2}$  (f) $\dfrac{-x^6y^{-1}}{-x^{-3}y^2}$  (g) $\dfrac{(s^2t)^2}{s^{-3}t^2}$  (h) $\dfrac{(mn^{-1})^3}{-m^4n^{-3}}$

12  Simplify. Write your final answer with denominator 1.

(a) $\dfrac{a^5b^3}{a^3b^5}$  (b) $\dfrac{x^2y^4}{-x^4(y^2)^2}$  (c) $\dfrac{m^6n^3}{-m^{-3}n^2}$  (d) $\dfrac{-x^{-1}(y^2)^2}{-x^3y^{-1}}$

(e) $\dfrac{-(ab^{-1})^2}{a^{-3}b^4}$  (f) $\dfrac{(mn)^2}{-m^2n^3}$  (g) $\dfrac{-a^3(b^{-1})^2}{(a^{-1})^2b^{-3}}$  (h) $\dfrac{(s^2)^3t^2}{-s^{-3}t^{-2}}$

13  (a) If $x = -6$, $y = -3$, find (i) $xy^{-1}$  (ii) $(xy)^{-1}$  (iii) $(-xy)^{-1}$

(b) Why are the answers in (a) different?

14  If $x = -2$, $y = -1$, $z = 2$, find the value of each of the following.

(a) $x^{-1}z$  (b) $2y^{-1}$  (c) $x^{-1} + y^{-1}$  (d) $xyz^{-1}$

(e) $\dfrac{x^{-1} + y^{-1}}{2}$  (f) $(xy)^z$  (g) $x^2 - 2y^{-1}$  (h) $x^{-2} + y^{-1} - z^{-1}$

C  15  Which of the following are true? Which are false? Justify your answers.

A: $\sqrt{9} + \sqrt{4} \stackrel{?}{=} \sqrt{13}$  B: $\sqrt{9} - \sqrt{4} \stackrel{?}{=} \sqrt{5}$

C: $\sqrt{9} \times \sqrt{4} \stackrel{?}{=} \sqrt{36}$  D: $\sqrt{9} \div \sqrt{4} \stackrel{?}{=} \sqrt{\dfrac{9}{4}}$

## Exponents and Rationals

Earlier, you learned that powers with integer exponents have a special meaning. The exponent $\frac{1}{2}$ has a special meaning related to the principal square root of a number.

$$\sqrt{2} = 2^{\frac{1}{2}} \quad \sqrt{3} = 3^{\frac{1}{2}} \quad \sqrt{5} = 5^{\frac{1}{2}}$$

principal square roots

In order to learn mathematics, it is helpful to make comparisons.
- The cube of 2 is 8, since $2 \times 2 \times 2 = 8$.
- The cube of 2 is shown by the symbol $2^3 = 8$.
- The principal cube root of 8 is 2, since $2 \times 2 \times 2 = 8$.
- The principal cube root of 8 is shown by the radical symbol $\sqrt[3]{8} = 2$.    means the principal cube root of 8.

Similarly, exponents that are rational have a special meaning.

Using exponent laws

$$8^{\frac{1}{3}} \times 8^{\frac{1}{3}} \times 8^{\frac{1}{3}} = 8^{\frac{1}{3}+\frac{1}{3}+\frac{1}{3}}$$
$$= 8 \longleftarrow \text{Compare.} \longrightarrow = 8$$

Using radicals

$$\sqrt[3]{8} \times \sqrt[3]{8} \times \sqrt[3]{8}$$

Based on the above comparison, $\sqrt[3]{8}$ and $8^{\frac{1}{3}}$ behave in a similar way.

It seems reasonable to define $\sqrt[3]{8} = 8^{\frac{1}{3}}$

In general, the $n$th principal root of a number is shown by

$$\sqrt[n]{a} = a^{\frac{1}{n}}$$

16   Simplify.
(a) $\sqrt[3]{27}$    (b) $\sqrt[4]{64}$    (c) $\sqrt[3]{64}$    (d) $\sqrt[5]{32}$    (e) $\sqrt[4]{625}$    (f) $\sqrt[5]{1024}$

17   Simplify.
(a) $8^{\frac{1}{3}}$    (b) $16^{\frac{1}{4}}$    (c) $243^{\frac{1}{5}}$    (d) $125^{\frac{1}{3}}$    (e) $256^{\frac{1}{4}}$

18   Simplify.
(a) $8^{-\frac{1}{3}}$    (b) $243^{-\frac{1}{5}}$    (c) $\dfrac{1}{16^{-\frac{1}{4}}}$    (d) $\dfrac{64^{\frac{1}{3}}}{4^{\frac{1}{2}}}$    (e) $\dfrac{32^{\frac{1}{5}}}{8^{-\frac{1}{3}}}$

## Calculator Tip

You can use the calculator key $\boxed{y^x}$ to evaluate expressions with rational exponents. Apply these calculator steps to the radical expressions above.

| Calculator Steps | Output |
|---|---|
| $2^{\frac{1}{4}}$   $\boxed{C}$ $1$ $\boxed{\div}$ $4$ $\boxed{=}$ $\boxed{MI}$ $2$ $\boxed{y^x}$ $\boxed{MR}$ $\boxed{=}$ | $1.1892071$ |
| $6^{-\frac{1}{3}}$   $\boxed{C}$ $1$ $\boxed{\div}$ $3$ $\boxed{=}$ $\boxed{+ -}$ $\boxed{MI}$ $6$ $\boxed{y^x}$ $\boxed{MR}$ $\boxed{=}$ | $0.5503212$ |

## 1.7 Developing Operations: Radicals

Many similar situations can be seen in the development of mathematics. Compare the following.

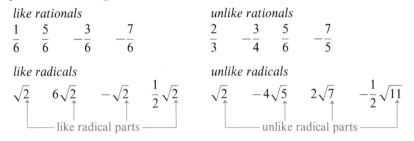

*like rationals*

$$\frac{1}{6} \quad \frac{5}{6} \quad -\frac{3}{6} \quad -\frac{7}{6}$$

*unlike rationals*

$$\frac{2}{3} \quad -\frac{3}{4} \quad \frac{5}{6} \quad -\frac{7}{5}$$

*like radicals*

$$\sqrt{2} \quad 6\sqrt{2} \quad -\sqrt{2} \quad \frac{1}{2}\sqrt{2}$$

└── like radical parts ──┘

*unlike radicals*

$$\sqrt{2} \quad -4\sqrt{5} \quad 2\sqrt{7} \quad -\frac{1}{2}\sqrt{11}$$

└── unlike radical parts ──┘

In a similar way, you can add or subtract like radicals. To do so, you base the operation on the distributive property of numbers.

$$3\sqrt{2} + 5\sqrt{2} = (3 + 5)\sqrt{2}$$
$$= 8\sqrt{2}$$

**Example 1**  Simplify $3\sqrt{2} - 2\sqrt{3} + 4\sqrt{2} + 5\sqrt{3}$.

**Solution**  
$$3\sqrt{2} - 2\sqrt{3} + 4\sqrt{2} + 5\sqrt{3} = 3\sqrt{2} + 4\sqrt{2} - 2\sqrt{3} + 5\sqrt{3}$$
$$= 7\sqrt{2} + 3\sqrt{3}$$

Since $\sqrt{2}$ and $\sqrt{3}$ are unlike radicals, you cannot simplify further.

The radicals in the next example appear as unlike radicals but you can write each of them as mixed radicals. To do so, you need to use the principle

$$\sqrt{ab} = \sqrt{a} \times \sqrt{b}$$

entire radical

$$\sqrt{18} = \sqrt{9 \times 2}$$
$$= \sqrt{9} \times \sqrt{2}$$
$$= 3\sqrt{2} \longleftarrow \text{mixed radical}$$

**Example 2**  Simplify $5\sqrt{8} - \sqrt{27} + \sqrt{50} - 2\sqrt{12}$.

**Solution**  
$$5\sqrt{8} - \sqrt{27} + \sqrt{50} - 2\sqrt{12}$$
$$= 5\sqrt{4 \times 2} - \sqrt{9 \times 3} + \sqrt{25 \times 2} - 2\sqrt{4 \times 3}$$
$$= 10\sqrt{2} - 3\sqrt{3} + 5\sqrt{2} - 4\sqrt{3}$$
$$= 10\sqrt{2} + 5\sqrt{2} - 3\sqrt{3} - 4\sqrt{3}$$
$$= 15\sqrt{2} - 7\sqrt{3}$$

You may eventually do some of these steps mentally.

## 1.7  Exercise

**A 1** (a) Which of the following radicals are equivalent to $\sqrt{32}$?

$3\sqrt{16}$    $-2\sqrt{8}$    $4\sqrt{2}$    $2\sqrt{64}$    $3\sqrt{320}$

(b) Which radicals in (a) are in simplest form? Why?

**2** (a) Which of the following radicals are equivalent to $\sqrt{800}$?

$10\sqrt{8}$    $3\sqrt{100}$    $20\sqrt{2}$    $-5\sqrt{32}$    $4\sqrt{80}$

(b) Which radicals in (a) are in simplest form? Why?

**3** Write each radical as a mixed radical in simplest form.

(a) $\sqrt{18}$     (b) $\sqrt{12}$     (c) $\sqrt{50}$     (d) $\sqrt{27}$     (e) $\sqrt{32}$     (f) $\sqrt{8}$

(g) $\sqrt{24}$     (h) $\sqrt{1000}$     (i) $\sqrt{125}$     (j) $\sqrt{28}$     (k) $\sqrt{63}$     (l) $\sqrt{20}$

**4** Write each radical as a mixed radical in simplest form.

(a) $-2\sqrt{50}$     (b) $3\sqrt{18}$     (c) $\dfrac{1}{2}\sqrt{24}$     (d) $\dfrac{3}{2}\sqrt{48}$     (e) $-\dfrac{1}{2}\sqrt{32}$

(f) $\dfrac{1}{5}\sqrt{125}$     (g) $-2\sqrt{75}$     (h) $-3\sqrt{80}$     (i) $4\sqrt{27}$     (j) $2\sqrt{40}$

**5** Simplify.

(a) $3\sqrt{2}+5\sqrt{2}$        (b) $6\sqrt{2}-3\sqrt{2}$        (c) $8\sqrt{3}-2\sqrt{3}$

(d) $3\sqrt{3}-6\sqrt{3}$        (e) $2\sqrt{5}-3\sqrt{5}$        (f) $8\sqrt{5}+2\sqrt{5}$

**6** Simplify.

(a) $3\sqrt{2}-2\sqrt{2}+5\sqrt{2}$     (b) $6\sqrt{3}-4\sqrt{3}-2\sqrt{3}$     (c) $-8\sqrt{5}-3\sqrt{5}+6\sqrt{5}$

(d) $-3\sqrt{7}-16\sqrt{7}-8\sqrt{7}$   (e) $\dfrac{1}{2}\sqrt{5}+\dfrac{2}{3}\sqrt{5}-\dfrac{1}{4}\sqrt{5}$   (f) $\dfrac{2}{3}\sqrt{8}-\dfrac{4}{6}\sqrt{8}-\dfrac{1}{2}\sqrt{8}$

**B** Express your final answer in simplest form.

**7** Simplify.

(a) $3\sqrt{2}-2\sqrt{3}+4\sqrt{2}$          (b) $2\sqrt{3}-2\sqrt{2}+\sqrt{3}$

(c) $2\sqrt{5}-3\sqrt{2}+5\sqrt{5}$          (d) $4\sqrt{7}-2\sqrt{3}-2\sqrt{7}$

(e) $3\sqrt{2}-2\sqrt{3}+4\sqrt{2}+5\sqrt{3}$      (f) $5\sqrt{3}-2\sqrt{7}+2\sqrt{7}+3\sqrt{3}-4\sqrt{3}$

**8** Simplify.

(a) $2\sqrt{2}-6\sqrt{8}$        (b) $3\sqrt{12}-2\sqrt{3}$        (c) $4\sqrt{32}-3\sqrt{2}$

(d) $7\sqrt{5}-6\sqrt{75}$       (e) $\sqrt{48}-3\sqrt{3}$        (f) $2\sqrt{6}-4\sqrt{24}$

9   Simplify.
    (a) $3\sqrt{18} - 2\sqrt{50}$         (b) $-5\sqrt{12} - 3\sqrt{48}$         (c) $-16\sqrt{20} + 12\sqrt{80}$
    (d) $-3\sqrt{75} - 2\sqrt{27}$         (e) $-3\sqrt{32} + 12\sqrt{50}$         (f) $18\sqrt{27} - 25\sqrt{75}$

10  Simplify.
    (a) $\sqrt{8} - \sqrt{18} + \sqrt{32} - \sqrt{50}$         (b) $-\sqrt{12} - \sqrt{27} + \sqrt{48} - \sqrt{75}$
    (c) $\sqrt{8} - \sqrt{12} + \sqrt{18} - \sqrt{27}$         (d) $\sqrt{32} - \sqrt{48} - \sqrt{18} + \sqrt{75}$
    (e) $3\sqrt{12} - 2\sqrt{27} - \sqrt{48}$         (f) $2\sqrt{20} - 3\sqrt{45} + \sqrt{80}$
    (g) $-\sqrt{48} + \sqrt{50} - 2\sqrt{18} + \sqrt{75}$         (h) $2\sqrt{45} - 3\sqrt{27} + \sqrt{20} - \sqrt{48}$

11  (a) Why are $\dfrac{2\sqrt{50}}{3}$ and $\dfrac{2}{3}\sqrt{50}$ equivalent?

    (b) Why are $\dfrac{-4\sqrt{27}}{3}$ and $-\dfrac{4}{3}\sqrt{27}$ equivalent?

12  Simplify.
    (a) $\dfrac{1}{2}\sqrt{8} - \dfrac{1}{3}\sqrt{27} + 4\sqrt{50}$         (b) $-\dfrac{1}{4}\sqrt{48} + \sqrt{32} - \dfrac{3}{4}\sqrt{48}$

    (c) $\dfrac{4\sqrt{50}}{5} - \dfrac{2\sqrt{27}}{3} + 3\sqrt{48} - \dfrac{2\sqrt{18}}{3}$         (d) $3\sqrt{27} - 3\sqrt{81} + 3\sqrt{75} - \dfrac{1}{2}\sqrt{36}$

13  Find each perimeter in simplest form. (Leave your answers in radical form.)
    (a)

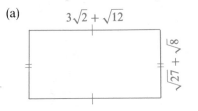

    (b)

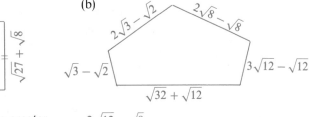

14  (a) Which rectangle has the greater
        perimeter? By how much?
    (b) Justify your answer in (a).

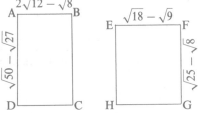

C 15  Which of the following are true? Justify your answers.
    (a) All perfect squares may be written as mixed radicals.
    (b) All mixed radicals may be written as entire radicals.
    (c) $\sqrt{2}$ may be written in the form of a rational number.
    (d) All entire radicals may be written as a mixed radical.

## 1.8 Properties of Radical Products

When you develop mathematics, often, you will find specific examples, that suggest generalizations. These generalizations are the basis for definitions. For example, a specific example suggests a product for radicals

$$\sqrt{4} \times \sqrt{25}$$
$$= 2 \times 5$$
$$= 10$$

$$\sqrt{4} \times \sqrt{25}$$
$$= \sqrt{4 \times 25}$$
$$= \sqrt{100}$$
$$= 10$$

Suggests $\sqrt{4} \times \sqrt{25} = \sqrt{4 \times 25}$

└──── Compare ────┘

Based on the example above, and on other examples, the generalization is given as

If $a, b \geq 0$, then $\sqrt{a} \times \sqrt{b} = \sqrt{a \times b}$.

There is a logical reason for *all* calculations and *all* simplifications in mathematics. Once you understand the principles underlying the steps, you can use mathematics to solve problems.

**Example**   Simplify (a) $3\sqrt{6} \times 2\sqrt{15}$   (b) $2\sqrt{3}(3\sqrt{6} - 2\sqrt{5})$
Do you understand the underlying principle of each step?

**Solution**   (a)   $3\sqrt{6} \times 2\sqrt{15}$
$= 3 \times 2 \times \sqrt{6} \times \sqrt{15}$
$= 6 \times \sqrt{90}$ ←── Simplify further.
$= 6(3\sqrt{10})$   $\sqrt{90} = \sqrt{9} \times \sqrt{10}$
$= 18\sqrt{10}$   $= 3\sqrt{10}$

(b)   $2\sqrt{3}(3\sqrt{6} - 2\sqrt{5})$
$= 2\sqrt{3}(3\sqrt{6}) - 2\sqrt{3}(2\sqrt{5})$
$= 6\sqrt{18} - 4\sqrt{15}$
$\sqrt{18} = \sqrt{9 \times 2}$
$= 3\sqrt{2}$
$= 6(3\sqrt{2}) - 4\sqrt{15}$
$= 18\sqrt{2} - 4\sqrt{15}$

## 1.8 Exercise

**A** Be sure you understand the steps for finding the products of radicals.

1   Find each product.

(a) $\sqrt{2} \times \sqrt{3}$   (b) $3\sqrt{2} \times 2\sqrt{3}$   (c) $2\sqrt{5} \times 3\sqrt{7}$

(d) $(-\sqrt{3})(-\sqrt{5})$   (e) $(-2\sqrt{3})(-3\sqrt{5})$   (f) $3\sqrt{6} \times 5\sqrt{5}$

2   Simplify. Write your answer in simplest form.

(a) $\sqrt{3} \times \sqrt{15}$   (b) $3\sqrt{2} \times 5\sqrt{6}$   (c) $(-\sqrt{10})(-\sqrt{2})$

(d) $(-2\sqrt{10})(-4\sqrt{2})$   (e) $6\sqrt{8} \times 3\sqrt{2}$   (f) $(-2\sqrt{6})(3\sqrt{27})$

3   (a) What principles were used to simplify the product in two different ways?

A $\sqrt{72} \times \sqrt{45} = \sqrt{3240}$         B $\sqrt{72} \times \sqrt{45} = 6\sqrt{2} \times 3\sqrt{5}$
$\phantom{A \sqrt{72} \times \sqrt{45}} = \sqrt{324 \times 10}$                    $\phantom{B \sqrt{72} \times \sqrt{45}} = 18\sqrt{10}$
$\phantom{A \sqrt{72} \times \sqrt{45}} = 18\sqrt{10}$

(b) Simplify each product.   (i) $\sqrt{40} \times \sqrt{12}$   (ii) $\sqrt{48} \times \sqrt{24}$   (iii) $\sqrt{400} \times \sqrt{100}$

4   Simplify.

(a) $\sqrt{20} \times \sqrt{12}$            (b) $2\sqrt{18} \times 3\sqrt{75}$          (c) $2\sqrt{64} \times 3\sqrt{100}$

(d) $(-6\sqrt{8})(-3\sqrt{27})$      (e) $\sqrt{48} \times 2\sqrt{108}$       (f) $2\sqrt{10} \times 3\sqrt{100}$

5   Simplify each of the following. Remember: $(3\sqrt{2})^2$ means $(3\sqrt{2})(3\sqrt{2})$.

(a) $(2\sqrt{2})^2$        (b) $(3\sqrt{3})^2$        (c) $(-3\sqrt{2})^2$        (d) $(4\sqrt{20})^2$

(e) $(3\sqrt{32})^2$       (f) $(-2\sqrt{50})^2$      (g) $(6\sqrt{18})^2$       (h) $(-9\sqrt{98})^2$

**B** 6   Simplify. Express your answer in simplest form.

(a) $\sqrt{3}(2\sqrt{6} - 3\sqrt{2})$       (b) $2\sqrt{5}(3\sqrt{2} - \sqrt{3})$       (c) $2\sqrt{2}(2\sqrt{5} - 3\sqrt{2})$

7   Expand. (Expand means to simplify.)

(a) $\sqrt{2}(3\sqrt{8} + .2\sqrt{18})$      (b) $2\sqrt{2}(3\sqrt{32} - 2\sqrt{50})$      (c) $4\sqrt{3}(3\sqrt{12} - 2\sqrt{48})$

8   Simplify.

(a) $-3(4\sqrt{3} - 2) + 2(8 + 2\sqrt{3})$         (b) $2(\sqrt{3} - 3\sqrt{2}) - 3(6\sqrt{3} - 2\sqrt{2})$

9   Find the value of each expression to 2 decimal places.

(a) $(5\sqrt{2})(3\sqrt{3})$          (b) $2\sqrt{2} + 3\sqrt{2}$         (c) $(2\sqrt{3})^2 - 3\sqrt{2}$

(d) $\sqrt{2}(3\sqrt{2} - 2\sqrt{3})$      (e) $-3\sqrt{2}(3\sqrt{3} - 2\sqrt{2})$     (f) $\sqrt{2}(\sqrt{12} - 3\sqrt{32})$

10   Express the value of each expression in simplest form. Use $a = 2\sqrt{3} - 3\sqrt{2}$ and $b = 3\sqrt{12} - 4\sqrt{8}$.

(a) $a + b$           (b) $a + 2b$          (c) $2b - \sqrt{3}a$         (d) $\sqrt{3}a - 2\sqrt{2}b$

11   (a) Show that $2\sqrt{8} > 3\sqrt{2}$.       (b) Show that $3\sqrt{2} > 2\sqrt{3}$.

12   Which radical expression, A or B, has the greater value?

A    $\sqrt{8} + 6\sqrt{2}$                 B    $4\sqrt{3} + 2\sqrt{12}$

**C** 13   Show that $5\sqrt{2} - 2\sqrt{3} > 4\sqrt{3} - 3\sqrt{2}$.

## 1.9 Dividing Radicals: Calculators

When you do mathematics you often follow the steps shown below. These steps are applied to the division of radical expressions.

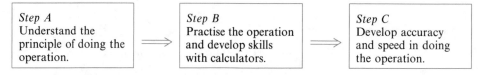

Again, numerical examples suggest a basis for dividing radicals.

*Specific Example*

$$\frac{\sqrt{100}}{\sqrt{25}} = \frac{10}{5} \qquad \sqrt{\frac{100}{25}} = \sqrt{4}$$

$$= 2 \qquad\qquad = 2$$

Compare.

*Dividing Radicals*

$$\sqrt{\frac{a}{b}} = \frac{\sqrt{a}}{\sqrt{b}}, \qquad a, b \in R, \ a, b > 0$$

To simplify a quotient involving radicals, you can do the steps shown at the right.

$$\frac{\sqrt{21}}{\sqrt{3}} = \sqrt{\frac{21}{3}}$$

$$= \sqrt{7}$$

In order to simplify radical expressions, very often it is useful to have no radicals in the denominator. You can apply the principle of multiplying the expression by 1 and obtaining the same value, as shown.

$$\frac{4\sqrt{3}}{\sqrt{2}} = \frac{4\sqrt{3}}{\sqrt{2}}\left(\frac{\sqrt{2}}{\sqrt{2}}\right)$$

$$= \frac{4\sqrt{6}}{2}$$

$$= 2\sqrt{6}$$

Multiply by an expression whose value is 1. You need to decide what form to use. Choose a radical that will result in a rational number in the denominator. $(\sqrt{2})(\sqrt{2}) = 2$    an integer in this case

The above process of obtaining a non-radical denominator is called **rationalizing the denominator**.

**Example**    Simplify this expression by rationalizing the denominator.

$$\frac{2\sqrt{2} + 3\sqrt{3}}{3\sqrt{6}}$$

**Solution**    $\dfrac{2\sqrt{2} + 3\sqrt{3}}{3\sqrt{6}} = \dfrac{2\sqrt{2} + 3\sqrt{3}}{3\sqrt{6}}\left(\dfrac{\sqrt{6}}{\sqrt{6}}\right)$

$$= \frac{2\sqrt{12} + 3\sqrt{18}}{3(6)}$$

$$= \frac{4\sqrt{3} + 9\sqrt{2}}{18}$$

Remember: Choose an appropriate form of 1 to rationalize.

You can use the following calculator steps to evaluate either expression. Can you find a more efficient procedure?

$$\frac{2\sqrt{2} + 3\sqrt{3}}{3\sqrt{6}} \doteq 1.092\ 007 \text{ (to 6 decimal places)}$$

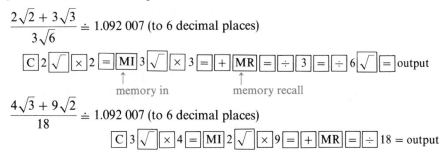

$$\frac{4\sqrt{3} + 9\sqrt{2}}{18} \doteq 1.092\ 007 \text{ (to 6 decimal places)}$$

## 1.9 Exercise

**A 1** Simplify. Rationalize the denominator.

(a) $\dfrac{5}{\sqrt{3}}$
(b) $\dfrac{-6}{\sqrt{2}}$
(c) $\dfrac{25}{\sqrt{5}}$
(d) $\dfrac{2\sqrt{6}}{\sqrt{2}}$
(e) $\dfrac{8}{\sqrt{6}}$

(f) $\dfrac{6\sqrt{5}}{-\sqrt{10}}$
(g) $\dfrac{2\sqrt{3}}{-\sqrt{5}}$
(h) $\dfrac{8\sqrt{5}}{4\sqrt{2}}$
(i) $-\dfrac{1}{2\sqrt{5}}$
(j) $-\dfrac{3}{\sqrt{18}}$

**2** Simplify. Express your answer with a non-radical denominator.

(a) $3 \div \sqrt{72}$
(b) $6 \div \sqrt{2}$
(c) $1 \div \sqrt{24}$
(d) $3 \div 2\sqrt{3}$

(e) $\dfrac{2\sqrt{75}}{\sqrt{15}}$
(f) $\dfrac{2\sqrt{84}}{-\sqrt{12}}$
(g) $\dfrac{2\sqrt{3}}{-\sqrt{8}}$
(h) $\dfrac{\sqrt{72}}{2\sqrt{8}}$

(i) $\dfrac{3\sqrt{54}}{2\sqrt{12}}$
(j) $\dfrac{5\sqrt{24}}{\sqrt{18}}$
(k) $\dfrac{-6\sqrt{75}}{5\sqrt{20}}$
(l) $\dfrac{5\sqrt{45}}{-8\sqrt{54}}$

**3** Simplify. Write your answer with a non-radical denominator.

(a) $\dfrac{\sqrt{3} - \sqrt{2}}{\sqrt{2}}$
(b) $\dfrac{2\sqrt{3} + \sqrt{2}}{\sqrt{3}}$
(c) $\dfrac{\sqrt{5} + \sqrt{2}}{2\sqrt{2}}$
(d) $\dfrac{3\sqrt{5} - 2\sqrt{2}}{-3\sqrt{2}}$

**4** Find the value of each of the following to 2 decimal places

(a) $\dfrac{3}{\sqrt{3}}$
(b) $\dfrac{-1}{\sqrt{24}}$
(c) $\dfrac{3}{2\sqrt{3}}$
(d) $\dfrac{3\sqrt{2}}{2\sqrt{3}}$
(e) $\dfrac{5\sqrt{3}}{-\sqrt{18}}$
(f) $-\dfrac{\sqrt{24}}{\sqrt{8}}$

**5** Express in simplest terms.

(a) $\dfrac{8 - \sqrt{3}}{\sqrt{3}}$
(b) $\dfrac{2\sqrt{6} + 3\sqrt{18}}{\sqrt{3}}$
(c) $\dfrac{2\sqrt{5} - 3\sqrt{2}}{3\sqrt{2}}$
(d) $\dfrac{2\sqrt{20} - 3\sqrt{10}}{2\sqrt{5}}$

**B** Remember: A radical expression in simplest form has no radicals in the denominator.

6    Find the value of each of the following to 3 decimal places.

(a) $\dfrac{3\sqrt{18} - 2\sqrt{75}}{2\sqrt{3}}$     (b) $\dfrac{2\sqrt{80} + 3\sqrt{50}}{\sqrt{5}}$     (c) $\dfrac{2\sqrt{27} - 3\sqrt{75}}{3\sqrt{2}}$

7    (a) Simplify $\dfrac{2\sqrt{12} + 3\sqrt{32} - 3\sqrt{48} + 2\sqrt{72}}{3\sqrt{2}}$.     (b) Find the value of the expression in (a) to 3 decimal places.

8    Find the value of each expression to 2 decimal places.

(a) $\dfrac{6\sqrt{20} + 2\sqrt{72} - 2\sqrt{125} - 3\sqrt{18}}{2\sqrt{5}}$     (b) $\dfrac{3\sqrt{48} - 2\sqrt{50} + 2\sqrt{75} - 3\sqrt{18}}{2\sqrt{3}}$

9    If $a = 2\sqrt{2}$ and $b = 3\sqrt{3} - 2\sqrt{2}$, then express each expression with a non-radical denominator.

(a) $\dfrac{b}{a}$     (b) $\dfrac{a+b}{2a}$     (c) $\dfrac{a-b}{a+b}$     (d) $\dfrac{2b}{a^2}$     (e) $\dfrac{a^2+b}{a}$     (f) $\dfrac{b-a}{a+b}$

10   A rectangle has an area of $(12\sqrt{3} - 12\sqrt{2})$ square units and a width of $2\sqrt{6}$ units.

(a) Find an expression for the length of the rectangle in simplest form.

(b) Express the length and width to 3 decimal places.

11   Copy and complete the chart for each rectangle. Express your answers in simplest form.

|     | Area | Length | Width |
|-----|------|--------|-------|
| (a) | ? | $3\sqrt{2}$ | $2\sqrt{3} - 3\sqrt{2}$ |
| (b) | $24 - 4\sqrt{15}$ | ? | $2\sqrt{3}$ |
| (c) | $30 + 5\sqrt{6}$ | $5\sqrt{2}$ | ? |

12   Simplify.

(a) $\dfrac{1}{\sqrt{3}} + \dfrac{1}{\sqrt{5}}$     (b) $\dfrac{2}{\sqrt{3}} - \dfrac{3}{\sqrt{2}}$     (c) $\dfrac{2}{\sqrt{5}} - \dfrac{3}{\sqrt{2}}$

(d) $\dfrac{2}{\sqrt{50}} + \dfrac{3}{\sqrt{98}}$     (e) $\dfrac{5}{2\sqrt{12}} - \dfrac{2}{\sqrt{27}}$     (f) $\dfrac{3}{2\sqrt{18}} + \dfrac{2}{3\sqrt{75}}$

13   Find the value of each expression to 2 decimal places.

(a) $\dfrac{1}{2\sqrt{2}} + \dfrac{3}{\sqrt{3}}$     (b) $\dfrac{1}{\sqrt{3}} - \dfrac{4}{2\sqrt{5}}$     (c) $\dfrac{5}{\sqrt{32}} + \dfrac{2}{2\sqrt{2}}$     (d) $\dfrac{4}{\sqrt{50}} - \dfrac{3}{\sqrt{27}}$

**C** 14   Without using decimal equivalents, prove that   $3 + \dfrac{1}{\sqrt{2}} > 2 + \dfrac{1}{\sqrt{3}}$.

## 1.10 People and Mathematics: Pythagoras

Many people have contributed to the rich development of mathematics. One such person was Pythagoras. He studied the properties of the right triangle, and noticed a very special relationship among the sides.

**Pythagorean Property**

For any right triangle, where $a$, $b$, and $c$ represent the measures of the sides,

$$a^2 + b^2 = c^2.$$

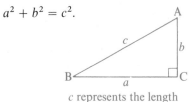

$c$ represents the length of the hypotenuse

For example, in $\triangle ABC$, use $a = 12$, $b = 5$, and $c = 13$. Then

$$a^2 + b^2 = 12^2 + 5^2 \qquad c^2 = 13^2$$
$$= 144 + 25 \qquad\qquad = 169$$
$$= 169$$

You can also interpret the Pythagorean Property visually as follows:

The square on the hypotenuse is equal to the sum of the squares on the other two sides.

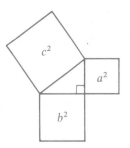

**Example 1**  Calculate the length of the hypotenuse of $\triangle ABC$ to 1 decimal place.

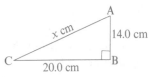

**Solution**  Let $x$ cm represent the length of the hypotenuse

Thus $x^2 = (20.0)^2 + (14.0)^2$
$= 400.0 + 196.0$
$= 596.0$
$x = \sqrt{596.0}$
$\doteq 24.4$ (to 1 decimal place)

$x^2 = 596.0$ means you want to find the number $x$ so that its square is 596.0. Thus, $x = \sqrt{596.0}$, since $x$ is positive.

Thus, the length of the hypotenuse is 24.4 cm.

In mathematics you may often need to use the same procedure more than once in the solution of a problem, as shown in the next example.

**Example 2**    Find the value of $x$ to 1 decimal place.

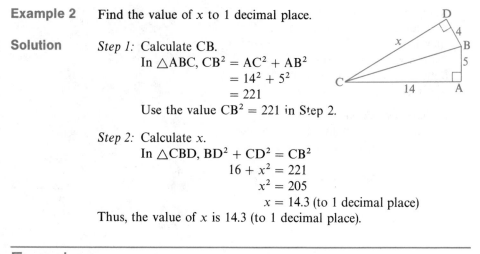

**Solution**    *Step 1:* Calculate CB.

In $\triangle ABC$, $CB^2 = AC^2 + AB^2$
$$= 14^2 + 5^2$$
$$= 221$$

Use the value $CB^2 = 221$ in Step 2.

*Step 2:* Calculate $x$.

In $\triangle CBD$, $BD^2 + CD^2 = CB^2$
$$16 + x^2 = 221$$
$$x^2 = 205$$
$$x = 14.3 \text{ (to 1 decimal place)}$$

Thus, the value of $x$ is 14.3 (to 1 decimal place).

# 1.10 Exercise

**A 1**    Solve each equation. Express your answer to 1 decimal place.

(a) $x^2 = 8^2 + 6^2$      (b) $x^2 + 4^2 = 8^2$      (c) $x^2 + 24^2 = 26^2$

(d) $x^2 = (3\sqrt{6})^2 + (\sqrt{75})^2$    (e) $x^2 + 23^2 = 31^2$      (f) $36^2 + x^2 = 89^2$

**2**    Find the distance, $d$, to 2 decimal places.

(a) $d^2 = 12^2 + 16^2$      (b) $40^2 = d^2 + 24^2$      (c) $20^2 + d^2 = 52^2$

(d) $d^2 + 24^2 = 32^2$      (e) $38^2 + d^2 = 90^2$      (f) $73^2 = 42^2 + d^2$

**3**    Find the length of the missing side.

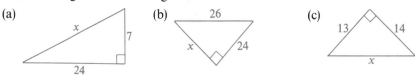

(a)            (b)            (c)

**4**    Find the length of the hypotenuse for each triangle. Express your answer in simplest form.

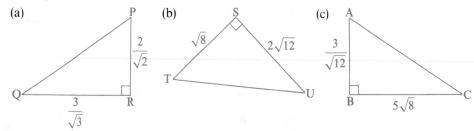

(a)            (b)            (c)

5   Each square represents 1 cm² in area. Find the length of each hypotenuse.

(a)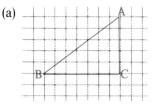

(b)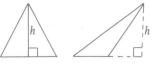

**B** 6   The altitude, *h*, is shown for an acute triangle and for an obtuse triangle. Calculate the altitude of each of the following triangles.

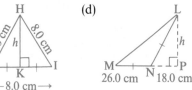

(a)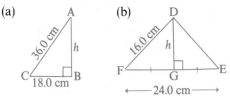

(b) 

(c) 

(d) 

7   (a) Calculate the length of AB.

(b) Use the value of AB in (a) to find the value of AD to the nearest centimetre.

8   (a) A rectangle has sides 8.0 cm and 4.0 cm. Find the length of the diagonal.

(b) Find the diagonal of a square that has sides that measure 24.0 cm

9   (a) Find the missing lengths in the diagram. Express your answers in radical form.

(b) Use the diagram to construct a line segment $\sqrt{7}$ units in length.

(c) Use only the measurements in the diagram. Construct a right triangle with hypotenuse $\sqrt{7}$ units.

**C** 10   In the diagram, $\angle BDE = 90°$, $\angle ACB = 90°$, and AC = BC = 2 units. Use the diagram to show that $\sqrt{8} = 2\sqrt{2}$.

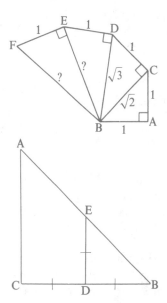

## 1.11 Problem-Solving Plan

One of the main reasons you learn mathematics is to be able to develop your skills and strategies for solving problems. Often, the process of solving a problem is not a straightforward one. Sometimes you can use a systematic approach to solve a problem. At other times you need to be creative. As you seek solutions to problems and acquire skills and strategies you will begin to develop a framework for your own particular plan for solving a problem. The *Problem-Solving Plan* **PSP**, shown on the opposite page, is provided to help you find solutions to problems.

▶ To solve a problem, you need to know the precise meaning of each word in mathematics, and you need to learn the nature of the language of mathematics. This important skill is suggested in Step A of the *Problem-Solving Plan* **PSP**.

▶ As you solve problems and practise various strategies, you will continue to acquire strategies. Record these strategies in your problem-solving plan or in the suggested chart for **PSP**.

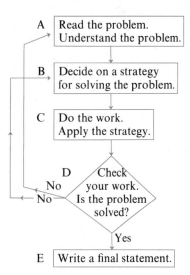

To solve any problem successfully, first you must understand the answer to these two questions which occur in Step A of the **PSP** chart.

• What information does the problem ask me to find?
• What information is given in the problem?

Once you have completed Step A of the plan, then the problem you are to solve occurs in one of these categories:

Category I: The skill or strategy required to solve the problem is immediately evident.

Category II: The skill or strategy required to solve the problem is not immediately evident.

To solve a problem occurring in Category II, you need to decide on a strategy. Then you follow some plan to test your strategy, such as the sequence of steps in the flow chart shown, or in the *Problem-Solving Plan* **PSP**.

When you are solving a problem, sometimes you need to return to the first step, as shown in the flow chart. Sometimes, you need only try another strategy (Step B).

---

1   Throughout the text, look for the symbol **PSP**. This symbol indicates skills, strategies, and suggestions to place in your own problem-solving plan. Make a copy of the chart. Leave sufficient space in each step to record additional skills, strategies and questions that you acquire.

2   During your study of mathematics, continue to record the skills and strategies for problem-solving in your problem-solving plan. Read Sections 1-12 and 1-13 that illustrate problems in Category I and Category II.

*Step A* Read the problem carefully.

- You can't solve a problem which you don't understand. You must understand the precise meaning of the words and symbols of mathematics.
- Do I know the answer to these two questions?
  I  What information am I asked to find?
  II  What information am I given?
- Do I understand the meaning of each word given in the problem?

- Continue to record other suggestion for this part of the *Problem-Solving Plan.*

*Step B* Decide on a method or strategy for solving the problem.

- What words or clues in the problem suggest a strategy for solving the problem?
- Is the strategy immediately evident?
- Do I need to draw a diagram? a chart?
- Do I need to use a formula? an equation? a variable?

- As you review and acquire skills and strategies, you will ask yourself other questions, and continue to add to this list of strategies as you decide on a method of solving a particular problem.

*Step C* Do the work. Apply or test the method or strategy you have chosen in Step B to solve the problem.

- Do I understand each step of the solution?
- Have I made any incorrect assumptions?
- Is there enough given information to solve the problem?
  Is any of the given information not needed to solve the problem?
- If my strategy isn't working, what other strategy can I use in Step B. Choose this strategy and try again.

- Continue to record other suggestion for this part of the *Problem-Solving Plan.*

*Step D* Check your work.

- Is my answer reasonable? Does my answer make sense?
- Is my method of solving the problem efficient?
- Did I check my answer in the original problem?
- Will I obtain the same answer if I use another strategy?
- Have I solved the problem?

- Continue to record other suggestions for this part of the *Problem-Solving Plan.*

*Step E* Make a final statement.

- Did I answer the question asked in the original problem?
- Did I choose the correct units?
- Will my answer be understood by someone else reading it?
- Did I round-off correctly? Is the accuracy of my answer consistent with the given information?

- Continue to record other suggestions for this part of the *Problem-Solving Plan.*

# 1.12 PSP Problem-Solving: Right Triangles and Pythagoras

In your study of mathematics, the following procedure often occurs.

| You learn a skill, method, or a strategy. | $\Longrightarrow$ | You apply the skill, method or strategy to solve the problem. |

- To solve a problem you need a plan. Review the suggested *Problem-Solving Plan* in the previous section.
- To solve a problem you need to make a decision.
  I Is the strategy for solving the problem immediately evident?
  II Is the strategy for solving the problem not immediately evident?

Trace the steps of the *Problem-Solving Plan* as they are applied to the solution of the following example.

**Example**

The guy wire for a tower is 48.0 m. It is secured, as shown, 23.0 m from the base of the tower. Calculate the height of the tower to 1 decimal place.

Plan: Answer the questions in Step A. A diagram is provided. Use the Pythagorean Relationship to find the missing side of the triangle.

**Solution**

Let $h$, in metres, represent the height of the tower.

Plan: Answer the questions in Step B. Introduce a variable. You need to use an equation to record the Pythagorean Relationship.

Thus, $h^2 + (23.0)^2 = (48.0)^2$
$$h^2 + 529 = 2304$$
$$h^2 = 1775$$

Since $h$ is a length, then
$$h = \sqrt{1775}$$
$$\doteq 42.1 \text{ (to}$$
$$1 \text{ decimal place)}$$

Plan: Do Step C. Solve the equation. How will I round my answer?

Plan: Do Step D. Check the answer. $(42.1)^2 + (23.0)^2 = (48.0)^2$ Solution checks. ✓

Thus, the height of the tower is 42.1 m (to 1 decimal place).

Plan: Do Step E. Did I answer the question asked in the original problem? Is the accuracy consistent with the given information?

As you learn new skills and strategies
in this text, you will be able to develop your plan for problem-solving, and to add to the list of questions that occur in the chart for the *Problem-Solving Plan*.

## 1.12 Exercise

**A** A diagram has already been drawn for each problem. Make a sketch of your own. Record the given information.

1 Calculate the length of the guy wire, *d*, in metres, for each diagram.

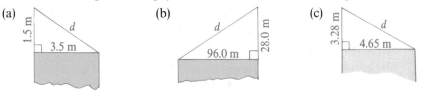

(a) 1.5 m — 3.5 m — *d*

(b) *d* — 96.0 m — 28.0 m

(c) 3.28 m — 4.65 m — *d*

2 Boats A and B leave an island situated at point O, at the same time. If each square represents 1 km², find the distance between the boats.

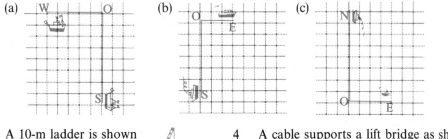

(a) W — O — S

(b) O — E — S

(c) N — O — E

3 A 10-m ladder is shown resting against a wall. Calculate how far up the wall the ladder will reach.

10.0 m — 2.5 m

4 A cable supports a lift bridge as shown. How high above the lift bridge is the cable fastened?

28.5 m — 25.6 m

5 Jennifer may take a short cut and walk along the diagonal rather than along Main Street and James Street. How much shorter is her short cut?

MAIN STREET
116.0 m

JAMES STREET
86.0 m

6 A diagram is used to record the following information:
(a) How far apart will the boats be after 3 h?
(b) If the cruiser travelled at the speed of the tugboat, how far apart would they be after 3 h?

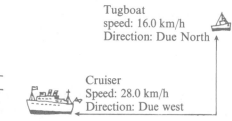

Tugboat
speed: 16.0 km/h
Direction: Due North

Cruiser
Speed: 28.0 km/h
Direction: Due west

**B** Solve each problem. Plan your solution. Refer to the steps in the chart for the *Problem-Solving Plan.*

7  How far should the base of a ladder be placed from a wall so that an 8.0-m ladder will reach 7.5 m up the wall?

8  John leaned his 6.0-m ladder against the wall with the base of the ladder 1.5 m from the wall. How far up the wall will the ladder reach?

9  Scarlett is 136.0 km due south of Stoney Creek. Windham Centre is 116.0 km due east of Stoney Creek. Find the distance between Scarlett and Windham to the nearest kilometre.

10  John rows at a speed of 6.0 km/h. Jean rows at the same rate.

(a) If John goes due west and Jean goes due north, how far apart will they be after 3 h?

(b) If Jean were to row 1 km/h faster, by how much would the distance increase?

11  Three ships leave an island at the same time.

|        | Direction | Speed     |
|--------|-----------|-----------|
| Ship A | Due west  | 23.0 km/h |
| Ship B | Due east  | 18.0 km/h |
| Ship C | Due south | 12.0 km/h |

(a) How far apart are ships B and C after 4 h?

(b) How far apart are ships A and C after 4 h?

(c) How far apart are ships A and B after 4 h?

12  A cruiser leaves an island at a speed of 14.0 km/h and heads due south. A sailboat leaves the island at the same time and heads due west at a speed of 8.0 km/h.

(a) How far apart will they be after 6 h?

(b) If the sailboat were to go 1 km/h slower, by how much would the distance change in (a)?

(c) What assumption do you make in finding your answer in (a)?

**C** 13  Find the sides of a square whose area would be equal to the area of a rectangle whose dimensions are 42.0 m by 28.0 m.

# 1.13  PSP  Problem-Solving: Strategies

As you solve problems, you learn new strategies that you record in the *Problem-Solving Plan* shown at the right. Remember: To solve a problem you need to make a decision.

   I Is the strategy for solving the problem immediately evident?

   II Is the strategy for solving the problem not immediately evident?

As you acquire and practise strategies for problem-solving, the more frequently you will be able to answer "*Yes, the strategy for solving the problem is immediately evident.*" The examples that follow illustrate some strategies for problem-solving that you can record in your *Problem-Solving Plan.*

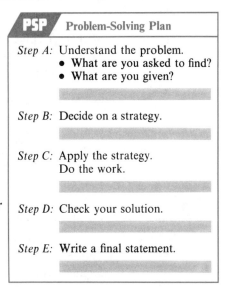

**PSP**  Problem-Solving Plan

*Step A:* Understand the problem.
- What are you asked to find?
- What are you given?

*Step B:* Decide on a strategy.

*Step C:* Apply the strategy. Do the work.

*Step D:* Check your solution.

*Step E:* Write a final statement.

---

**Example 1**  What is the last digit of the value for $2^{50}$?

*Which Strategy do I use?*
To solve this problem, a useful strategy is to ask "Can I answer a simpler problem?" A simpler problem would be

$$2^6 = \underbrace{2 \times 2 \times 2 \times 2 \times 2 \times 2}_{\text{6 factors}} = 64$$

The last digit is 4.

However, to find the last digit of the value for $2^{50}$, you can continue to test simpler problems. This procedure then results in a *pattern*, which you can then study, as shown in the following solution.

**Solution**  Think of a simpler problem to solve.
Find the last digit of the value for $2^1$, $2^2$, $2^3$, $2^4$, and so on.

The value of these powers of 2 have

| | | | |
|---|---|---|---|
| last digit 2 $\longrightarrow$ | $2^1 = 2$ | $2^5 = 32$ | $2^9 = 512$   and so on |
| last digit 4 $\longrightarrow$ | $2^2 = 4$ | $2^6 = 64$ | $2^{10} = 1024$ |
| last digit 8 $\longrightarrow$ | $2^3 = 8$ | $2^7 = 128$ | $2^{11} = 2048$ |
| last digit 6 $\longrightarrow$ | $2^4 = 16$ | $2^8 = 256$ | $2^{12} = 4096$ |

Think: Use a pattern to decide on the last digit of the value for $2^{50}$.

From the pattern, $2^{48}$ has last digit 6
$2^{49}$ has last digit 2
$2^{50}$ has last digit 4

Thus, the last digit of the value for $2^{50}$ is 4.

**PSP**  Remember: Record the strategies in your chart for the *Problem-Solving Plan.*

Very often, you will be overwhelmed by the amount of information that a problem presents. Sometimes you can use a chart to sort the given information, as shown in the following example.

**Example 2**     Michael, Debbie and Freddy hold the offices of President, Treasurer and Secretary on the Student's Council. Freddy dates Michael's sister. He also likes meeting with the president and the council. The treasurer never attends any meetings and has no brothers or sisters. Which positions do Freddy, Debbie and Michael hold on the Student's Council?

*Which strategy do I use?*
At first reading, the given facts are unorganized. To solve this problem, a chart is used to record positions that cannot be held by various people, based on the given facts.

**Solution**     Construct a chart to record the results.

× means the position is not held by that person.

The chart is then completed in stages, based on the facts given in the original problem.

|          | President | Secretary | Treasurer |
|----------|-----------|-----------|-----------|
| Michael  |           |           | ×         |
| Debbie   |           |           |           |
| Freddy   | ×         | ✓         | ×         |

Michael has a sister. The treasurer has no brothers or sisters. Thus Michael is not the treasurer (×).

The treasurer never attends any meetings.
Freddy likes meeting with the president.
Thus, Freddy is not the president (×).
Thus, Freddy is not the treasurer (×).
Thus, Freddy must be the secretary (✓).

|          | President | Secretary | Treasurer |
|----------|-----------|-----------|-----------|
| Michael  | ✓         | ×         | ×         |
| Debbie   | ×         | ×         | ✓         |
| Freddy   | ×         | ✓         | ×         |

Michael and Freddy cannot be treasurer. Thus, Debbie is the treasurer (✓). This means Debbie is neither the secretary (×) nor the president (×).

Since Freddy is the secretary (✓), then Michael is not (×). Thus, Michael is the president (✓).

Based on the results in the chart, Michael is the president, Debbie is the treasurer, and Freddy is the secretary.

 Remember: Record the strategy of *using a chart* in your *Problem-Solving Plan.*

## 1.13 Exercise

**B** 1   What is the last digit of the value for each power?

(a) $2^{80}$       (b) $2^{191}$       (c) $2^{5032}$

2   What is the last digit of the value for each power? Justify your answers.

(a) $3^{12}$       (b) $3^{65}$       (c) $7^{20}$       (d) $11^{121}$

3   (a) What is the first digit of the value for $2^{50}$?

(b) What is the first digit of the value for $3^{100}$?

4   (a) How many squares occur in the figure at the right?

Use the chart to record
the number of squares.

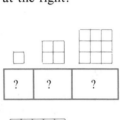

| Number of squares | | |
|---|---|---|
| ? | ? | ? |

(b) Use your answer in (a). How many
squares are in the original figure?

(c) Use a pattern. How many squares
are in this figure?

5   Morris, Kevin, and Jacques are married to Melanie, Terry, and Sonja, but not in this order. Each weekend, they plan tennis doubles but the wives and husbands are not partners. Terry and Jacques were partners and Kevin was with Morris's wife. If Kevin and Sonja were partners, who is married to whom?

6   How many equilateral triangles, in all, occur in this figure?

7   One hundred tennis players decide to have a tournament to see who is best. When one player loses a game, the player is out of the tournament. How many games must be played to find out who is the best?

---

Problem-Solving   **PSP**

In subsequent sections and chapters look for additional strategies for problem-solving, as well as tips for problem-solving suggested by the symbol **PSP**. The symbol **PSP** is also used to remind you to check with your *Problem-Solving Plan*.

# PSP  Problem-Solving Strategy: Using Counter Examples

You can help yourself remember mathematics by asking yourself these questions.

A  How are the properties, skills, strategies alike?

B  How are they different?

In your earlier work you dealt with these sets of numbers. You could compare their properties by asking: How are they alike? How do they **differ**?

$N$, Natural numbers   $W$, Whole numbers   $O$, Odd numbers
$\{1, 2, 3, \ldots\}$   $\{0, 1, 2, 3, \ldots\}$   $\{1, 3, 5, 7, \ldots\}$

$E$, Even numbers   $I$, Integers
$\{2, 4, 6, 8, \ldots\}$   $\{\ldots, -3, -2, -1, 0, 1, 2, 3, \ldots\}$

$R$, Reals   $Q$, Rationals   $\bar{Q}$, Irrationals

To explore their properties, certain vocabulary is used. To solve problems in mathematics, you need to understand the meaning of the vocabulary. For example, a set, $S$, is said to be **closed** for the operation of addition, if the following is true:

For any $m, n \in S$, then $m + n \in S$.

Often the choice of a specific example can be used to show that a property or statement is not true. The choice of a **counter example** to test whether a statement is false is a useful strategy for solving problems.

| *Statement* | *Counter Example* |
|---|---|
| Is the set of odd numbers, $O$, closed with respect to addition? | Choose $1, 3 \in$ Odd Numbers. Then $1 + 3 = 4$ which is an even number. Conclusion: The set of odd numbers is *not* closed with respect to addition. |

However, a numerical example cannot be used to show that a statement is true. For example, to prove that the set of even numbers, $E$, is closed with respect to addition, you need to show that, for any choice of numbers in $E$, their sum is also a member of $E$. To do so, you use the fact that any even number can be shown in the form $2(n)$ where $n$ is a natural number.

Choose any two even numbers. They are of the form $2k$ and $2m$.
Then add them.     $2k + 2m = 2(k + m)$

Since $k + m$ is a natural number, then $2(k + m)$ is an even number.
Conclusion: The set $E$ is closed with respect to addition.

To explore the properties of the real numbers, you need to know the meanings of the terms used to describe the properties. Each term is illustrated numerically.

- The operation of multiplication for integers is **commutative**.
$$(-2)(-3) = (-3)(-2)$$

- For the integers, multiplication **distributes** over subtraction.
$$(-3)[(-2) - (-3)]$$
$$= (-3)(-2) - (-3)(-3)$$

- The rationals have an **additive identity** namely, 0.
$$0 + \left(-\frac{2}{3}\right) = \left(-\frac{2}{3}\right) + 0 = -\frac{2}{3}$$

- Each member of $Q$ has a **multiplicative inverse**.
$\frac{2}{3}$ is the multiplicative inverse of $\frac{3}{2}$
since $\left(\frac{2}{3}\right)\left(\frac{3}{2}\right) = 1$

- The operation of addition for rationals is **associative**.
$$-\frac{1}{2} + \left(\frac{-3}{4} + \frac{2}{3}\right) = \left(-\frac{1}{2} + \frac{-3}{4}\right) + \frac{2}{3}$$

- For the integers, division does not distribute over addition.
$$(-8) \div [(-2) + (-2)]$$
$$\neq (-8) \div (-2) + (-8) \div (-2)$$

- The rationals have a **multiplicative identity**, namely 1.
$$\frac{4}{5} \times 1 = 1 \times \frac{4}{5} = \frac{4}{5}$$

- Each member of $I$ has an **additive inverse**.
$-2$ is the additive inverse of $+2$
since $(+2) + (-2) = 0$.

## 1.14 Exercise

1 The chart that follows is used to summarize the properties of the various sets of numbers. Make a copy of the chart. Then complete the chart by using examples to test whether to write *Yes* or *No* in the appropriate spaces in the chart. Some answers have been included in the chart where possible. Use a counter example to show a property is not true.

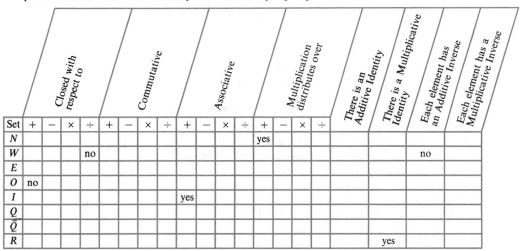

| Set | Closed with respect to + | − | × | ÷ | Commutative + | − | × | ÷ | Associative + | − | × | ÷ | Multiplication distributes over + | − | × | ÷ | There is an Additive Identity | There is a Multiplicative Identity | Each element has an Additive Inverse | Each element has a Multiplicative Inverse |
|---|---|---|---|---|---|---|---|---|---|---|---|---|---|---|---|---|---|---|---|---|
| N | | | | | | | | | | | | | yes | | | | | | | |
| W | | | no | | | | | | | | | | | | | | | | no | |
| E | | | | | | | | | | | | | | | | | | | | |
| O | no | | | | | | | | | | | | | | | | | | | |
| I | | | | | | yes | | | | | | | | | | | | | | |
| Q | | | | | | | | | | | | | | | | | | | | |
| Q̄ | | | | | | | | | | | | | | | | | | | | |
| R | | | | | | | | | | | | | | | | | | yes | | |

## Practice and Problems: Review

1 Simplify.
   (a) $-(-2)(-3)^2$

   (b) $[(-2)(-3) + (-4)(-6)] \div (-6)$

   (c) $\dfrac{1}{-3} - \dfrac{1}{8}$

   (d) $6 - \dfrac{-1}{5} - \dfrac{1}{-2}$

   (e) $\dfrac{-2}{3} \div \dfrac{-4}{5} + \dfrac{-5}{6}$

2 Simplify.   (a) $2\sqrt{8} - 5\sqrt{2}$   (b) $3\sqrt{48} - 2\sqrt{27}$   (c) $3\sqrt{8} - 2\sqrt{50}$
   (d) $2\sqrt{2}(2\sqrt{12} - 3\sqrt{18}) - 3\sqrt{3}(4\sqrt{27} - 3\sqrt{12})$

3 A rectangular field is 236 m by 312 m. What is the length of a diagonal path to the nearest metre?

4 Use the digits 0 to 9 only once each in the spaces provided so that the addition question is correct. Find at least two different answers.

$$\begin{array}{ccc} ? & ? & ? \\ ? & ? & ? \\ \hline ? & ? & ? & ? \end{array}$$

## Practice Test

1 Simplify.
   (a) $8^0$

   (b) $4^{\frac{1}{2}}$

   (c) $3^{-2}$

   (d) $27^{-\frac{1}{3}}$

   (e) $3^0 + 2^{-1} + \left(\dfrac{1}{2}\right)^{-2} - 4^0\left(2^{-2} + \dfrac{3}{4}^{-1}\right)$

2 Simplify.
   (a) $3\sqrt{2} - 3\sqrt{8} + \sqrt{2}$   (b) $8\sqrt{6} - 3\sqrt{24} - 3\sqrt{150}$   (c) $3\sqrt{2}(3\sqrt{5} - 4\sqrt{2})$
   (d) $-2\sqrt{3}(4\sqrt{12} - 5\sqrt{48})$   (e) $3\sqrt{45} - 2\sqrt{27} + 2\sqrt{20} + 5\sqrt{48}$

3 (a) Simplify   (i) $\dfrac{2\sqrt{75}}{\sqrt{3}}$   (ii) $\dfrac{2\sqrt{72}}{-\sqrt{24}}$   (iii) $\dfrac{3}{2\sqrt{12}} - \dfrac{5}{\sqrt{27}}$
   (b) Calculate the value of (i) to (iii) to 2 decimal places.

4 Find the rational number represented by $0.\overline{24}$ and $0.2\overline{43}$.

5 Two helicopters leave a building at the same time. One helicopter flies due north at 112.0 km/h. The other helicopter flies to the west at 89.0 km/h. Find how far apart they are after one hour.

6 Find the product $\left(1 - \dfrac{1}{2}\right)\left(1 - \dfrac{1}{3}\right)\left(1 - \dfrac{1}{4}\right)\left(1 - \dfrac{1}{5}\right)\cdots\left(1 - \dfrac{1}{100}\right)$.

   Hint: Refer to your *Problem-Solving Plan* PSP

# 2 Polynomials: Operations and Factoring

Language of mathematics, polynomials, operations with polynomials, solving equations, common factor, factoring trinomials, difference of squares, solving quadratic equations, solving problems, applications, strategies and problem solving

## Introduction

When you study mathematics, it is like learning about people who have contributed to the knowledge of mathematics. The list of such people is long. The study of mathematics has been influenced by many brilliant and dedicated persons. As you continue your study of mathematics, you will learn about some of the many interesting people and historical events that have shaped the development of mathematics. A partial list of them is shown below.

| | | | | |
|---|---|---|---|---|
| Newton | Galileo | Euler | Fourier | Einstein |
| Thales | Appolonius | Cardan | Pascal | Ptolemy |
| Sacrobosco | Pythagoras | Fibonacci | Plato | Archimedes |
| da Vinci | DeMoivre | Copernicus | Aristotle | Fermat |
| Viète | Cayley | Recorde | Hipparchus | Leibniz |

When people develop mathematics the results are often named after them in their honour. For example, the Cartesian Plane is named after René Déscartes (1596–1650). He made important contributions to the study of mathematics. It is said that many of his brilliant ideas came to him while he was resting in bed. If you discover original mathematics, and publish your discovery, it may be named after you. Many of these mathematicians were ordinary people who became interested in pursuing some aspect of mathematics, and in some cases their interest became their life-long pursuit.

Often one person was influenced by the mathematical interests, thinking steps, and thought processes of another. For example, Pythagoras, who has an important theorem named after him, was influenced by the work of Thales, another Greek mathematician. In your study of mathematics, you will share the methods of many great thinkers.

Not only does mathematics build upon the thoughts of individual people, but also its collective influence touches every aspect of modern society.

## 2.1 Multiplying by a Monomial

The skills learned in algebra and in arithmetic are similar.

*Arithmetic*
- $3 + 3$ can be written as $2 \times 3$.
- $4 \times 5$
- $2^3$ means $2 \times 2 \times 2$.
- $-3$ is the opposite of 3.
- $\dfrac{1}{3}$ and $\dfrac{2 \times 1}{2 \times 3}$ are equivalent.

*Algebra*
- $x + x$ can be written as $2x$.
- $xy$ means $x \times y$.
- $x^3$ means $x \times x \times x$.
- $-x$ is the opposite of $x$.
- $\dfrac{z}{y}$ and $\dfrac{xz}{xy}$ are equivalent.

It is important to learn the vocabulary of algebra. The expression $3x$ is called a **term**.

This part is called the
**numerical** (number) **coefficient**.

$3x$

This part is called the
**literal** (letter) **coefficient**.

There is a special vocabulary for describing expressions that consist of sums and differences of terms.

| *Vocabulary* | | *Example* |
|---|---|---|
| *mono*mial | ⟵ 1 term ⟶ | $3x, 4m^2, 2xy$ |
| *bi*nomial | ⟵ 2 terms ⟶ | $3a - 2b, 2a^2 + 5$ |
| *tri*nomial | ⟵ 3 terms ⟶ | $2a + 3c + b, 2x^2 + 3x + 5$ |

**Polynomial** is used as a collective word for monomials, binomials, trinomials, and so on.

Once you learn a skill in mathematics, you can use that skill in any other topic of mathematics. Thus, you can use the laws of exponents to multiply monomials.

$$(2x^3y)(3x^2y^3) = 6x^5y^4$$

Think: You can multiply the factors in any order you wish.

Multiply the numerical
coefficients.
$2 \times 3 = 6$

Multiply the literal
coefficients.
$(x^3)(x^2) = x^5 \quad (y)(y^3) = y^4$

You will need your skills with integers and exponents to multiply monomials.

**Example 1**  Find the product $(-4ab)(2a^2b)$.

**Solution**

$$(-4ab)(2a^2b) = (-4ab)(2a^2b)$$

Think: Multiply numerical coefficients.

Then multiply literal coefficients.

$$= -8a^3b^2$$

You need to use your substitution skills to simplify expressions.

**Example 2**  Find the value of $(-5a^2b)(-2ab^3)$ for $a = 2, b = -1$.

**Solution**

*Step 1* Simplify.
$$(-5a^2b)(-2ab^3)$$
$$= 10a^3b^4$$

*Step 2* Substitute.
$$10a^3b^4$$
$$= 10(2)^3(-1)^4$$
$$= 80$$

$a = 2, b = -1$

To **expand** a product of a monomial and a polynomial means to remove brackets by multiplying. In the next example, the distributive property is used to expand the expression.

**Example 3**  Expand $-2a(3a - 4ab + b)$.

**PSP** Be sure you understand the meaning of each word.

**Solution**
$$-2a(3a - 4ab + b)$$
$$= -6a^2 + 8a^2b - 2ab$$

Multiply each term by $-2a$.

## 2.1  Exercise

**A** Remember: Review your skills with integers and exponents.

1 For each of the following write the
   • numerical coefficient   • literal coefficient.

   (a) $4y$  (b) $-6x^2$  (c) $\dfrac{2x}{3}$  (d) $-12ab$

   (e) $36x^2y$  (f) $\dfrac{2}{3}kp$  (g) $-16p^2$  (h) $-\dfrac{3xy}{5}$

2 Identify each polynomial as a monomial, binomial, or trinomial.
   (a) $5x^3 + 3x - 4$  (b) $3ab^2c - 6a$  (c) $4x^2y$  (d) $5 - 6xy^2$
   (e) $-x + 3y - z$  (f) $a^2b^4 - 16$  (g) $-yx^2z^3$  (h) $2a + 3a^2b - c$

3   Find each product. What do you notice about your answers?
    (a) $(3a^2b)(2ab^2)$           (b) $(-3ab^2)(-2a^2b)$           (c) $(6a^3)(b^3)$

4   (a) Write $(-2xy^2)(4x^3y)$ as one term.
    (b) Evaluate the expression in (a) for $x = -1$, $y = 1$.

5   (a) Find the square of $-2ab^2$.
    (b) Evaluate the expression in (a) for $a = -3$, $b = 2$.

6   (a) Expand $3xy(2x + 3y - 2xy)$.
    (b) Evaluate the expression in (a) for $x = -3$, $y = -2$.

7   Find the product of each pair of monomials.
    (a) $3y, -2y$          (b) $6x^3, 2x$          (c) $-6a, -3a$          (d) $-6m^3, 4m$
    (e) $4a, -7a$          (f) $6y, -3y^2$          (g) $2a^2, -3a$          (h) $-4x, -3x^2$

B   Remember: To simplify means to express in simplest terms.

8   Simplify each product.
    (a) $(2x)(-3y)$                 (b) $(-3x)(-3x)$                 (c) $(-4xy)(-2xy)$
    (d) $-(3ab)(2ab)$              (e) $(3x^2)(-4x^2)$             (f) $(-3y^2)(-2y)$
    (g) $-(2x^2y)(-3xy^2)$         (h) $(3a^2b)(-3ab)$            (i) $(-6a^3)(2ab^2)$
    (j) $-(-3mn)(-2m^2n)$          (k) $(6pq)(-p^3q^2)$           (l) $-(4ab^2)(2a^3b)$

9   Find the square of each monomial.
    (a) $-3x$        (b) $2a^2$        (c) $-4xy$        (d) $2mn$        (e) $3mn^2$        (f) $-2x^2y$

10  Simplify.
    (a) $(3mn)(-2m)(4n^2)$          (b) $-(2x^3)(-3x)(-2x^2)$      (c) $(-2xy)(-y^2)(xy^2)$
    (d) $(3x^3y)(-2xy^2)(xy)$       (e) $-(2ab)(-a)(-6ab^2)$      (f) $(-3m)(2mn)(mn^2)$

11  Find the value of each of the following for $x = 3$ and $y = -2$.
    (a) $(x^2y)(y)$                 (b) $(4xy)(-5x^2y^2)$      (c) $-(xy^2)(4xy)$        (d) $y(x^3y^3)$
    (e) $(7x)(3x^3y^4)$             (f) $(2x^2y)(-y^3)$        (g) $(-5xy^2)(y)$         (h) $(3xy)(7y^2)$

12  Find the value of each of the following for $a = 3.2$ and $b = -1.5$.
    (a) $(3a)(-2b)$                 (b) $(3a)(-4b^2)$                 (c) $(2ab)(-3ab^2)$
    (d) $(0.5ab)(1.2a^2)$           (e) $(-1.5b^2)(0.4a^2b)$          (f) $(0.8a^2b)(-0.5ab)$

13 Expand.

(a) $3(x + 2)$
(b) $-4(k - 2)$
(c) $-6x(x - 3)$
(d) $-2y(y - 5)$
(e) $2x(x + y)$
(f) $-3x(2x - y)$
(g) $-3(x^2 - 2x - 5)$
(h) $-3x(4 + 2x - 6x^2)$
(i) $4(3 - 2y - y^2)$
(j) $-6y(2 - 3y - 4y^2)$
(k) $-3ab(a^2b - 2b^2)$
(l) $2p^2q(p^2 - q^2 + 1)$

14 Evaluate each expression for the given values.

(a) $-3pq(p - q)$,   $p = -1, q = 2$
(b) $2a^2b(a^2 + 2a - 1)$,   $a = 3, b = -2$
(c) $-3x^2y(x^2 - 2xy + y^2)$,   $x = -2, y = -1$

15 Evaluate each expression for the given values.

(a) $2ab(a^2 - b)$,   $a = 2.5, b = -3.2$
(b) $-3xy(x^2 + y^2)$,   $x = 0.6, y = -0.5$
(c) $2p^2q(p + q + q^2)$,   $p = 1.25, q = -0.75$

16 The dimensions of a rectangle are given in variable form. Calculate the area for each pair of values.

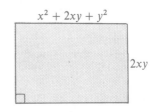

(a) $x = 3, y = 2$
(b) $x = 2, y = 3$
(c) $x = 3, y = 3$
(d) $x = 1.2, y = 0.5$
(e) $x = 3.25, y = 0.75$

17 Find an expression for each area. Simplify the expression.

(a) Square

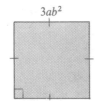

(b) Rectangle

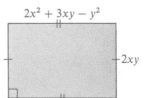

C 18 The diagram represents a rectangle whose dimensions are given in variable form. What is the greatest possible area if the variables have these possible values?

$x = 2, 3, 4, 5$
$y = 1, \frac{1}{2}, \frac{1}{3}, \frac{1}{4}$

**PSP** Do you see a pattern?

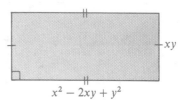

## 2.2 Dividing by a Monomial

You need to be able to divide by a monomial in order to solve the following problem.

The area of a rectangle, and its length, are shown. What is the width of the rectangle?

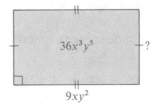

Think: Width $= \dfrac{\text{Area}}{\text{Length}}$

$\qquad\quad = \dfrac{36x^3y^5}{9xy^2}$

$\qquad\quad = ?$

You need to use the laws of exponents to divide by a monomial.

$$a^m \div a^n = a^{m-n} \ (a \neq 0)$$

Analyze this example.

Think: You can divide the factors in the numerator by the factors in the denominator in any order you want.

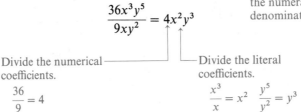

$$\frac{36x^3y^5}{9xy^2} = 4x^2y^3$$

Divide the numerical coefficients.

$\dfrac{36}{9} = 4$

Divide the literal coefficients.

$\dfrac{x^3}{x} = x^2 \quad \dfrac{y^5}{y^2} = y^3$

**Example 1**  Simplify $(-9x^3y^2) \div (3xy^2)$.

**Solution**

$(-9x^3y^2) \div (3xy^2)$ — Think: Divide the numerical coefficients.

— Think: Then divide the literal coefficients.

$= -3x^2$

Remember to use your skills with integers and with exponents to divide monomials.

**Example 2**  Divide $-12a^3b^2$ by $-4ab^2$.

**Solution**

$\dfrac{-12a^3b^2}{-4ab^2} = 3a^2 \qquad$ Think: $\dfrac{a^3}{a} = a^2, \dfrac{b^2}{b^2} = 1$

Think: $\dfrac{-12}{-4} = 3$

You need to use your skills with substitution to simplify expressions.

**Example 3**   Find the value of $(12x^3y^2) \div (-4x^2y)$, for $x = 2$, $y = -3$.

**Solution**   *Step 1* Simplify.                *Step 2* Substitute.

$$\frac{12x^3y^2}{-4x^2y} = -3xy$$

$$-3xy = -3(2)(-3)$$
$$= 18$$

You can use the distributive property to divide a polynomial by a monomial. Each term of the polynomial is divided by the monomial.

**Example 4**   Divide $12a^3b^2 - 6ab^3 + 18a^2b$ by $3ab$.

**Solution**

$$\frac{12a^3b^2 - 6ab^3 + 18a^2b}{3ab}$$

$$= 4a^2b - 2b^2 + 6a$$

Think: Divide each term by $3ab$.

$$\frac{12a^3b^2}{3ab} - \frac{6ab^3}{3ab} + \frac{18a^2b}{3ab}$$

## 2.2   Exercise

**A** Review your skills with integers and exponents.

1   Find each quotient.

(a) $\dfrac{x^6}{x^2}$

(b) $\dfrac{4a^3}{2a^2}$

(c) $\dfrac{-12x^3}{-4x}$

(d) $\dfrac{16y^3}{-4y^2}$

(e) $\dfrac{6p^5}{-3p^3}$

(f) $\dfrac{-8q^3}{-2q}$

(g) $\dfrac{9m^3}{3m^2}$

(h) $\dfrac{-12n^4}{4n^4}$

2   (a) Write $(-12a^3b^2) \div (-4ab)$ as one term.
    (b) Evaluate the expression in (a) for $a = -1$, $b = 2$.

3   Use $a = -1$. Evaluate each of the following.

(a) $\dfrac{2a^3}{a^2}$

(b) $\dfrac{(2a)^3}{a^2}$

(c) $\left(\dfrac{2a}{a}\right)^3$

(d) $\dfrac{-2a^3}{a^2}$

4   (a) What would be your first step in evaluating $\dfrac{-6p^3q}{3pq}$ for $p = -3$, $q = 2$?

    (b) Evaluate the expression in (a).

5 (a) Why may $\dfrac{12p^2q - 18pq}{6pq}$ be written as $\dfrac{12p^2q}{6pq} - \dfrac{18pq}{6pq}$?

(b) Simplify the expression in (a).

**B** Remember to simplify the expression before evaluating it.

6 Divide.

(a) $\dfrac{3x}{x}$     (b) $\dfrac{xy}{x}$     (c) $\dfrac{-6xy}{2x}$     (d) $\dfrac{8x^2y}{-2y}$     (e) $\dfrac{3abc}{-ab}$

(f) $\dfrac{-25mn}{-5m}$     (g) $\dfrac{-48ab}{-8a}$     (h) $\dfrac{-18a^2b}{9ab}$     (i) $\dfrac{-14x^2y}{-7xy}$     (j) $\dfrac{-3a^3}{a^2}$

(k) $\dfrac{-8m^4}{-2m^2}$     (l) $\dfrac{16m^2n}{-4mn}$     (m) $\dfrac{-36x^4y^3}{6x^2y}$     (n) $\dfrac{-36a^3b}{-6ab}$     (o) $\dfrac{-49\,m^2t}{-7mt}$

7 Find each quotient.

(a) $\dfrac{-24a^2b}{6ab}$     (b) $\dfrac{-18ab^3}{-6ab^2}$     (c) $\dfrac{-25a^3b}{-5ab}$     (d) $\dfrac{12a^3b^3}{-4a^2b}$

(e) $\dfrac{49m^2t^3}{-7mt}$                 (f) $(-14x^3y^2) \div (-2xy)$

(g) $(-28m^2n^3) \div (14mn^2)$          (h) $(-64m^3n) \div (8m^2n)$

8 If $x = 2$, $y = -3$, find the value of each of the following.

(a) $\dfrac{3xy}{y}$             (b) $\dfrac{-2x^2y}{xy}$           (c) $\dfrac{-6xy^2}{-2xy}$

(d) $\dfrac{4x^2y^2}{-2y}$          (e) $\dfrac{-18x^4y^3}{-9x^3y^2}$        (f) $\dfrac{27x^5y^3}{-3x^2y^3}$

(g) $(-25xy^2) \div (5xy)$     (h) $(-18xy^2) \div (3x)$     (i) $(-36x^4y^2) \div (-18x^3y^2)$

9 Find the following quotients.

(a) $\dfrac{(2x)(-4xy)}{2x^2}$       (b) $\dfrac{(3xy)(-4x^2y)}{-12xy^2}$       (c) $\dfrac{(-6a)(3ab)}{-9a}$

(d) $\dfrac{(3ab)(2a)(-3b)}{-6a^2b}$     (e) $\dfrac{(-20m)(-3m^3)}{-15m^3}$     (f) $\dfrac{(-8x^2)(-2x)(-3x)}{-12x^3}$

(g) $\dfrac{(-2ab)(-6ab)}{(-3a^2)(2b^2)}$     (h) $\dfrac{(-16xy)(xy)}{(-4x)(4y^2)}$     (i) $\dfrac{(3m^2)(-2mn)}{(6mn)(-m)}$

10 Simplify.

(a) $\dfrac{3y - 6y^2}{3y}$

(b) $\dfrac{8mn - 4m^2n}{2mn}$

(c) $\dfrac{-25mx + 5xy}{-5x}$

(d) $\dfrac{8x^2 + 16x^3}{-4x}$

(e) $\dfrac{12xy^2 - 16xy}{-4xy}$

(f) $\dfrac{24ax^2 - 16a^2x}{-8ax}$

(g) $\dfrac{50mn^2 - 25m^2n}{-5mn}$

(h) $\dfrac{xy^2 - xy + x^2y}{xy}$

(i) $\dfrac{a^2b - a^3b - 3ab^2}{-ab}$

(j) $\dfrac{6x^2y - 4xy^2 + 10x^2y^2}{-2xy}$

(k) $\dfrac{9a^2m^2 - 6am^2 - 18a^2m}{-3am}$

(l) $\dfrac{15p^3q^2 - 3pq^5 + 12p^2q^2}{-3pq^2}$

11 If $x = -2$, $y = -3$, find the value of each expression.

(a) $\dfrac{-3x^2y - 6xy^2}{-3xy}$

(b) $x + 2y$

(c) What do you notice about your answers in (a) and (b)? Why is this so?

12 Evaluate each expression for the values given.

(a) $\dfrac{6xy - 3xy^2}{3xy}$, $x = 2$, $y = -3$

(b) $\dfrac{2ab^2 - 4a^2b}{-2ab}$, $a = -2$, $b = 3$

(c) $\dfrac{8x^2y^2 - 4x^3y^2}{-2x^2y^2}$, $x = -1$, $y = 2$

(d) $\dfrac{12m^2n^3 - 9mn^3}{-3mn^3}$, $m = 3$, $n = -1$

13 Since $(3xy^2)(-2xy) = -6x^2y^3$, then both $(3xy^2)$ and $(-2xy)$ are factors of $-6x^2y^3$. Thus $\dfrac{-6x^2y^3}{3xy^2} = -2xy$ or $\dfrac{-6x^2y^3}{-2xy} = 3xy^2$. Find the missing factor for each of the following.

(a) $(-6a^2) = (?)(-a^2)$

(b) $10m^5 = (-5m)(?)$

(c) $6x^4 = (-2x^3)(?)$

(d) $(-36x^5y^3) = (?)(4x^2y)$

(e) $-24ab^3 = (?)(-24ab)$

(f) $-6a^2b^4 = (-3a^2b)(?)$

(g) $12a^2b^3 = (?)(-4ab)$

(h) $-18a^5b^2 = (?)(6a^4b)$

14 These letters belong: A, H, I, M, O, ?, ?—but these do not: B, C, D, E, F. What are the next two letters? Give reasons for your answer.

C 15 Which expression, A or B, has the greater value for $m = -2$, $n = -1$?

A $\dfrac{(6m^2n)(-3mn^3)}{(-3mn)(2m^2n)}$

B $\dfrac{(25mn^3)(60m^3n)}{(-20m^2n^2)(-15m^2n)}$

## 2.3 Operations With Polynomials: Addition, Subtraction

You need to know the following vocabulary.

- **Like Terms** are terms which have the same literal coefficients.

  $$3a, \; -2a, \; -30a, \; 2.5a$$

  same literal coefficients

- **Unlike Terms** are terms which have different literal coefficients.

  $$3a, \; -2y, \; -30x, \; 2.5k$$

  different literal coefficients

To simplify polynomials, you collect like terms.

**Example 1**  Simplify $2x - 4y + 5x - 3y$.

**Solution**  $2x - 4y + 5x - 3y = 2x + 5x - 4y - 3y$
$$= 7x - 7y \longleftarrow \text{This expression cannot be}$$
simplified further because $7x$ and $7y$ are unlike terms.

To add or subtract polynomials, you collect like terms. To evaluate a polynomial, first, you need to simplify it.

**Example 2**  If $a = -3$, $b = 2$, and $c = -2$, find the value of the expression
$$(5a - 3b) + (2a + b - c).$$

**Solution**

*Step 1* Simplify.
$$(5a - 3b) + (2a + b - c)$$
$$= 5a - 3b + 2a + b - c$$
$$= 7a - 2b - c$$

*Step 2* Evaluate.
$$7a - 2b - c$$
$$= 7(-3) - 2(2) - (-2)$$
$$= -21 - 4 + 2$$
$$= -23$$

The expression $7a - 2b - c$ and $(5a - 3b) + (2a + b - c)$ in Example 2 are equivalent since they have equal values when they are evaluated for values of the variables $a$, $b$, and $c$.

**Example 3**  Simplify $(7p^2 - 6pq + 5q^2) - (p^2 + 3pq - q^2)$.

**Solution**

$$(7p^2 - 6pq + 5q^2) - (p^2 + 3pq - q^2)$$
$$= 7p^2 - 6pq + 5q^2 - p^2 - 3pq + q^2$$
$$= 6p^2 - 9pq + 6q^2$$

Remember: Just as you did with integers, to subtract a polynomial, add its opposite.

The distributive property can be used to simplify expressions. First expand, then collect like terms.

**Example 4**  Simplify.

(a) $3(x - 2y) - 2(2x - 4y)$        (b) $3x(2x - 3) - 2(4 - 3x)$

**Solution**

(a)   $3(x - 2y) - 2(2x - 4y)$
   $= 3x - 6y - 4x + 8y$
   $= -x + 2y$

(b)   $3x(2x - 3) - 2(4 - 3x)$
   $= 6x^2 - 9x - 8 + 6x$
   $= 6x^2 - 3x - 8$

These powers of $x$ are written in **descending** order of the exponents.

## 2.3   Exercise

**A** Your skills with integers are important for simplifying polynomials.

1   Write each of the following as a single term.
   (a) $p + 2p + 3p$         (b) $y + 2y - y$         (c) $3y - 2y + y$
   (d) $-12x - 6x + 8x$       (e) $6p - 3p + 8p$       (f) $-2s + 5s + 8s$

2   Simplify each of the following.
   (a) $3a - 2b + 2a$         (b) $5x - 3y + 3x$       (c) $-4m - 2n + 5m$
   (d) $3x - 2y + 2x + y$     (e) $2p + 3q - 2q + 3p$  (f) $-2m + 3p - 3p + 3m$

3   Simplify.
   (a) $3x - 2y + 4x - y$         (b) $4a - 5b - 3b - 2a$       (c) $6m - 2n - 3m + 2n$
   (d) $x^2 - 3x - 2 + 4x^2 - 2x + 5$       (e) $3y^2 - 4y - 6 - 3 - 2y - 3y^2$

4   (a) Simplify $(3a - 2b) + (5a - 4b)$.        (b) Simplify $(6a - 3b) + (2a - 3b)$.
   (c) Why are the answers in (a) and (b) called equivalent expressions?

5   (a) What is the first step in evaluating the expression
         $(x^2 - 2xy) - (3xy + y^2)$ for $x = -2$, $y = 3$?
   (b) Evaluate the expression in (a).

6   (a) Simplify $(2x^2 - 3x) + (5x - 8)$.
   (b) Write your answer in (a) in descending powers of the variable.

7   (a) Simplify $(3y^2 - 2y) - (3y + 4)$.
   (b) Write your answer in (a) in ascending powers of the variable.

**B** Remember: Before you can do mathematics, you must know the vocabulary. **PSP**
Review the meaning of any words that you have learned in this section.

8  Simplify.
  (a) $(6x - 2y) - (3x - 4y)$
  (b) $(7p - 9q) + (3q + p)$
  (c) $(2a + 3b) - (a - b) - (a + 4b)$
  (d) $(2x - 3y) + (5x - 5y) - (2y - 3x)$
  (e) $a - b - (3a - 2b) - (6a - 5b)$
  (f) $(4m - 2n) - (3m - n) - (2n - 5m)$
  (g) $(x^2 - 2x) - (x^2 - 3x) - (2x^2 - 10)$
  (h) $(y^2 - 4) + (3y^2 - 8y) - (2y + 4)$

9  Expand and simplify.
  (a) $3(x - y) - 2(x + y)$
  (b) $2(a - 3b) + 3(a - 2b)$
  (c) $-2(3m - 2n) - 4(m + n) - 3(m - n)$
  (d) $3(x - 2y + z) + 2(2x - 3y + z)$
  (e) $4(2a - 4b - c) - 3(3a - 2b - 3c)$

10  Simplify. Write your answers in descending powers of the variable.
  (a) $2(x^2 - 3x - 4) - 3(2x^2 - 4x - 1)$
  (b) $-6(y^2 - y + 5) + 3(2y^2 - 2y - 6)$
  (c) $3x(x + 2) - 2x(x - 1) - x(3 - x)$
  (d) $4y(2 - y) + 2y(y - 1) - 3(y^2 - y)$

11  Evaluate the polynomial $2a(a - b) - 3b(b - a) + 2a(2a - 3b)$
  for the following values of the variables.
  (a) $a = -3, b = 2$
  (b) $a = -6, b = -3$
  (c) $a = 2.5, b = 3.2$
  (d) $a = 0.8, b = -0.4$
  (e) $a = 1.25, b = -2.25$
  (f) $a = -3.6, b = 4.5$

12  Simplify each of the following.
  (a) $3x - 2y - (x + y)$
  (b) $5x - 6y - 3(x - y)$
  (c) $2(10x + 3y) - 9(2x + y)$
  (d) $3y - 4x + 8(x - y) - 2(x - y)$

13  Why can the polynomials in Question 12 be described as equivalent?

14  Evaluate each of the following for $x = -3, y = 2$.
  (a) $2(x - 2y) - 3(2x - y)$
  (b) $4(x - 3y) - 2(x - 5y) - 4(x - 2y)$
  (c) $3(2x^2 - 4x - 5) - 6(x^2 - 4x + 5)$
  (d) $2x(x - 2) - 3x(4 - x) - 6x(x - 5)$

15  If $x = -3, y = 2$, which polynomial, A or B, has the greater value?
  A    $-2y - 2(x + y) + 5(x - y)$
  B    $3x - 6(x - y) - 2(y - x)$

**C** 16  If $m = -1, n = 1$, which polynomial, A or B, has the lesser value?
  A    $3m(m - n) - 3n(2n - m) + mn$
  B    $-3(2n - 3m) - 2(m - n) + 12(2n - m)$

## Applications: Perimeters and Areas

Sometimes, manufacturers use variables to represent the dimensions of the shapes of the containers of different products.

The perimeter of the rectangle, in units, is given by

$$x + (8 - 2x) + x + (8 - 2x) = 16 - 2x$$

The area of the rectangle, in square units, is given by

$$x(8 - 2x) = 8x - 2x^2$$

Questions 17 and 18 refer to the above rectangle.

**17** Find the perimeter, if
(a) $x = 1$      (b) $x = 2$      (c) $x = 3$
(d) What is the greatest integral value of $x$ that can be used to find the perimeter? Why?

**18** Find the area if
(a) $x = 1$      (b) $x = 2$      (c) $x = 3$
(d) Which of the above values of $x$ gives the maximum area?
(e) Why is it not permissible to use $x = 4$?

**19** (a) Write an expression for the perimeter of the rectangle.
(b) Write an expression for the area.
(c) Find values of the area, and the perimeter, when $x = 1$, $x = 2$.

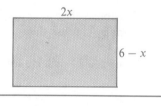

In Questions 20 and 21, $n$ represents a natural number.

**20** (a) Find the value of $n$ for which the rectangle has maximum area.
(b) What is the maximum area in square units?
(c) What is the value of the perimeter when the area is maximum?

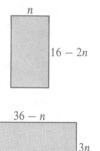

**21** (a) Find the value of $n$ for which the rectangle has maximum area.
(b) What is the value of the perimeter when the area is maximum?

## 2.4 Solving Equations

Finding solutions to equations is an important skill needed to solve problems that otherwise might be too difficult to solve. These properties of equality are used to solve equations.

- If equals are added to equals, the resulting sums are equal.
- If equals are subtracted from equals, the resulting differences are equal.
- If equals are multiplied by equals, the resulting products are equal.
- If equals are divided by equals, the resulting quotients are equal.

**Example 1**  Solve $1 + 3x(x + 6) = x(3x + 1) + 18$

**Solution**
$$1 + 3x(x + 6) = x(3x + 1) + 18$$
$$1 + 3x^2 + 18x = 3x^2 + x + 18$$
$$1 + 18x = x + 18$$
$$17x = 17$$
$$x = 1$$

Think: Subtract $3x^2$ from each side of the equation.

Think: What is the next step?

Think: To check whether any error has been made, verify $x = 1$ in the original solution.

Left Side (L.S.) $1 + 3x(x + 6)$
$= 1 + 3(1)(1 + 6)$
$= 22$

Right Side (R.S.) $x(3x + 1) + 18$
$= (1)[3(1) + 1] + 18$
$= 22$       L.S. = R.S. checks ✓

To express the value of $t$ in terms of the other variables in the following formula, you use the same properties of equations.

**Example 2**  Solve for $t$ in the formula $v = u + at$

**Solution**
$$v = u + at$$
$$v - u = u + at - u$$
$$v - u = at$$

Think: Subtract $u$ from each side

$$\frac{v - u}{a} = \frac{at}{a}$$

Think: Divide each side by $a$.

$$\frac{v - u}{a} = t \text{ or } t = \frac{v - u}{a}$$

---

## 2.4 Exercise

**B 1**  Find the roots of each equation. Verify your answer.

(a) $4(y - 2) - 3(y + 1) = 1 - 3y$        (b) $3(y - 10) = 5(4 - 3y) - 14$

2 Solve.
(a) $4y - 3 = 2y + 9$     (b) $7x - 6 = 5x - 28$     (c) $3(x + 4) = 5x$
(d) $12m - 3 = 5(2m + 1)$           (e) $3(y + 1) = 4(6 - y)$
(f) $3(y - 10) = 5(4 - 3y) - 14$      (g) $4(y - 5) - 7 = -15$
(h) $-2(2m - 3) = 16 + 6m$        (i) $15 + 5(y - 20) = 3(y - 1)$.

3 Solve.

(a) $\dfrac{2}{3}y - \dfrac{1}{3}y = 8$       (b) $\dfrac{2}{3}x - 2 = \dfrac{1}{3} - \dfrac{1}{2}x$       (c) $\dfrac{1}{2}(x - 5) = \dfrac{x}{4}$

(d) $\dfrac{1}{5}(x + 3) = \dfrac{1}{6}(x + 7)$            (e) $\dfrac{m}{6} + \dfrac{1}{4}(m + 5) = \dfrac{1}{3}(m + 8)$

4 Solve the formula for the variable indicated. You may first need to simplify the formula.

(a) $F = ma$, $m$     (b) $V = \dfrac{M}{D}$, $M$     (c) $C = 2\pi r$, $r$     (d) $E = IR$, $R$

(e) $v^2 = u^2 + 30t$, $t$     (f) $S = 180(n - 2)$, $n$     (g) $t = 3(p + s)$, $p$

(h) $P = 2(l + w)$, $l$     (i) $y = mx + b$, $m$     (j) $y = m(x - a)$, $a$

(k) $S = \left(\dfrac{u + v}{2}\right)t$, $u$     (l) $\dfrac{P - 2l}{2} = w$, $P$     (m) $\dfrac{v - u}{a} = t$, $a$

5 To find $t$ for different values of $u$ and $v$ in an experiment, a calculator is to be used. Express $t$ in terms of the other variables, $u^2 = v^2 - 30t$ and then find the values of $t$ for each of the following values of $u$ and $v$.

(a) $u = 28$, $v = 36$     (b) $u = 23.2$, $v = 28.5$     (c) $u = 146.3$, $v = 189.8$

Refer to your *Problem-Solving Plan*. Solve the following problems.

6 At the December concert, 209 tickets were sold. There were 23 more student tickets sold than twice the number of adult tickets. How many of each were sold?

7 The length of a box when decreased by 6 cm is equal to the width. If the perimeter is 68 cm, find its dimensions.

8 How would you divide $33 000 among 3 people so that the first person has twice as much as the second person and three times as much as the third person?

9 The greater of two numbers is equal to 3 times the lesser. The smaller number, increased by 5, equals the greater number decreased by 45. Find the numbers.

10 George paid a bill using only quarters. If nickels had been used to pay the bill, then 72 more nickels would have been needed. How much was the bill?

11 An amount of money which is invested at 8% earns the same as an amount $800 greater invested at 6%. How much money is invested at 8%?

## 2.5 Multiplying Binomials

As your knowledge of mathematics grows, new skills build upon known skills. For example, you can use the distributive property to find the product of binomials.

$$(x + y)(x + 2y) = (\ x + y\ )(x + 2y)$$
$$= (x + y)x + (x + y)(2y)$$
$$= x^2 + xy + 2xy + 2y^2$$
$$= x^2 + 3xy + 2y^2$$

You can interpret the product of the binomials above by drawing a diagram. **PSP**

Area of the whole rectangle $= (x + y)(x + 2y)$

Sum of the areas of the parts of the rectangle
$$= x^2 + xy + 2xy + 2y^2 \text{ or } x^2 + 3xy + 2y^2$$

Thus, $(x + y)(x + 2y) = x^2 + 3xy + 2y^2$

| | $x$ | $2y$ | |
|---|---|---|---|
| | $x^2$ | $2xy$ | $x$ |
| | $xy$ | $2y^2$ | $y$ |

However, you need to learn a more efficient method of multiplying binomials.

*Step 1* You obtained the following result by using the distributive property, or by using a diagram.

$$(x + y)(x + 2y) = x^2 + 3xy + 2y^2$$

*Step 2* Study the result in Step 1 to obtain a more efficient method of multiplying binomials. Analyze the result.

$$(x + y)(x + 2y) = x^2 + 3xy + 2y^2$$

Mentally find the result.

$$xy + 2xy = 3xy$$

You could summarize Step 2 by using a memory device called FOIL.

$$(x + y)(x + 2y)$$

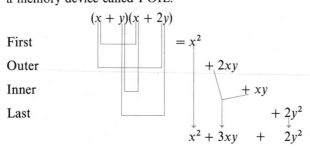

First $= x^2$

Outer $+ 2xy$

Inner $+ xy$

Last $+ 2y^2$

$$x^2 + 3xy \quad + \quad 2y^2$$

You need to be able to multiply binomials before you can simplify polynomials such as the one given in the following example.

**Example 1**   Simplify $(x - 3y)(2x + y) - (x + y)^2$.

**Solution**

$(x - 3y)(2x + y) - (x + y)^2$ ⟵————— Remember
$= 2x^2 - 5xy - 3y^2 - (x^2 + 2xy + y^2)$   $(x + y)^2 = (x + y)(x + y)$
$= 2x^2 - 5xy - 3y^2 - x^2 - 2xy - y^2$   In this step, write the
$= x^2 - 7xy - 4y^2$   product again with brackets, as shown. Why?

Often, polynomials are used in industry and in engineering to represent dimensions. Thus, a computer program can be written to calculate dimensions for different values of the variables.

**Example 2**   Find an expression, in simplest terms, for the shaded area. Find its area when $n = 4$.

**Solution**

Area of shaded region
$=$ Area of Rectangle ABCD $-$ Area of Rectangle EFGH
$= (2n + 1)(3n - 1) - (n + 1)(n + 2)$
$= 6n^2 + n - 1 - (n^2 + 3n + 2)$
$= 6n^2 + n - 1 - n^2 - 3n - 2$
$= 5n^2 - 2n - 3$

For $n = 4$   $5n^2 - 2n - 3 = 5(4)^2 - 2(4) - 3$
$= 80 - 8 - 3$
$= 69$

The area of the shaded region is 69 square units.

## 2.5   Exercise

**A**  Review the skills needed to multiply two binomials.

1   Multiply.

(a) $(y + 3)(y + 2)$ 　　　　(b) $(k + 1)(k + 6)$ 　　　　(c) $(y + 6)(y - 7)$

(d) $(y - 3)(y - 2)$ 　　　　(e) $(x - 3)(x + 2)$ 　　　　(f) $(a - 5)(a + 3)$

(g) $(y - 6)(y + 7)$ 　　　　(h) $(y - 7)(y + 7)$ 　　　　(i) $(x + y)(x - y)$

2   Use a diagram to illustrate each of the following.
   (a) $(x + 2y)(x + 2y) = x^2 + 4xy + 4y^2$
   (b) $(x - y)^2 = x^2 - 2xy + y^2$                     (c) $(2x - y)^2 = 4x^2 - 4xy + y^2$

3   (a) Simplify $2(x - 1)^2$.        (b) Simplify $(2x - 1)^2$.
   (c) Why do the answers in (a) and (b) differ?

4   Find the products. How long did it take you?
   (a) $(y + 3)(3y - 5)$          (b) $(2a + 4)(3a - 7)$          (c) $(3t + 3)(t - 3)$
   (d) $(y - 4)(y + 4)$          (e) $(x - 6)(x + 2)$          (f) $(m + 7)(m + 2)$
   (g) $(4x - 2)(x + 7)$          (h) $(x - 9y)(2x + y)$          (i) $(x + 1)(x + 8)$
   (j) $(4 + k)(6 + k)$          (k) $(3k - 2)(3k + 2)$          (l) $(3x - 1)(3x + 1)$

5   Simplify each of the following.
   (a) $3(x - 1)(x - 4)$          (b) $-4(x - 3)(2x - 5)$          (c) $3(3k + 1)^2$
   (d) $8(2y - 6)(3y + 1)$          (e) $-2(x - y)^2$          (f) $-3(2x - y)(2x + y)$
   (g) $-2(k - 6)(k + 8)$          (h) $-(2m - 3)(m - 3)$          (i) $3(x - 5)^2$
   (j) $2(3p - q)(2p - q)$          (k) $2(2x - y)^2$          (l) $-2(a - 5)(a + 6)$

   B   Review the method that helps you multiply binomials mentally.

6   Expand.
   (a) $(x^2 - 8)(x^2 - 3)$          (b) $(8 + 2a)(1 + a)$          (c) $(2y^2 - 1)(6y^2 + 7)$
   (d) $\left(x + \dfrac{1}{4}\right)\left(x - \dfrac{1}{4}\right)$          (e) $(2x - 1)^2$          (f) $(3y - 5)^2$
   (g) $(ab - 6)(ab + 6)$          (h) $\left(2x - \dfrac{1}{2}\right)^2$          (i) $\left(4x - \dfrac{5}{2}\right)^2$

7   (a) Simplify $2(x - 1)^2 + 2(x - 3)(x + 2)$.
   (b) Simplify $2(x - 1)^2 - 2(x - 3)(x + 2)$.
   (c) Why do the answers in (a) and (b) differ?

8   Simplify.
   (a) $(x - 4)(x - 3) - 2(x - 4)(x + 5)$          (b) $3(2 - y)(3 + y) - 4(y - 6)(y + 5)$
   (c) $(a - 3)(2a - 2) + 2(2a + 3)(2a - 1)$          (d) $3(5m + 4)(m - 6) - 2(m - 6)(3m + 7)$
   (e) $(3x - 5)^2 - 2(x - 5)(x + 5)$          (f) $2(a - 1)^2 - (a + 1)^2$
   (g) $3(x - y)^2 - 3(x + y)(x - 2y)$          (h) $2(a - 2b)^2 - 3(b - 2a)^2$
   (i) $3(x - 1)^2 - 2(x + 1)^2$          (j) $(3x - 1)^2 - (2x + 1)^2$
   (k) $3(x - 4y^2) - 4(2x + 5y)(2x - 3y)$          (l) $(3 - y)^2 - 2(4 - y)^2$

9   Expand and simplify.
    (a) $(x + y)(2x - y)(x + y)$               (b) $(2a - b)(3a + b)(a - b)$
    (c) $(3x - 2)(2x^2 - 2x + 1)$          (d) $(a - 2b)(3a^2 - 2ab + b^2)$
    (e) $(x - y)^3$         (f) $(2m + 1)^3$         (g) $(3a - 2b)^3$

10  Evaluate each of the following for $x = -2$, $y = 3$.
    (a) $(2x - 3)^2 + (x - 1)^2 + (x - 5)^2$
    (b) $(x - 1)^2 - (x - 2)^2 + (x - 3)^2 - (x - 4)^2$
    (c) $2(y - 5)^2 - 3(y - 2)^2 - 3y(y - 4)$
    (d) $y(y - 3) - (y - 3)^2 - 3(y - 2)^2$
    (e) $-(x - y)^2 + (x + y)^2 - 2(x - y)^2 - 2x(y - x)$

11  In a computer program, the area, $A$, of a cardboard region is given by
    $$A = 2(3n - 2)^2 - 3(n - 1)^2, \ n \in N.$$
    Calculate the area for
    (a) $n = 2$             (b) $n = 3$             (c) $n = 4$

12  Refer to the previous question. Use an efficient procedure on a calculator
    to obtain the value of $A$ for each value of $n$.
    (a) $n = 1.8$          (b) $n = 2.65$          (c) $n = 23.82$

13  (a) Write a computer program to evaluate the expression
        $$3(2p - 1)^2 - 2(3p + 2)^2.$$
    (b) Test your program for specific inputs for $p$.

14  (a) Find an expression for the area of
        the rectangle in simplest terms.
    (b) Find the area when $x = 4$.

15  (a) Find the area of each rectangle.

    **PSP**
    It is often helpful to use
    specific values to test
    your solution to a problem.

    (b) By how much does the area of A exceed that of B?

## 2.6 Finding Common Factors

When you are learning mathematics, it is helpful to look for similarities and differences. For example, compare the meaning of **expand** and **factor**.

**Expand**

To *expand* means to write a product of polynomials as a sum or difference of terms.

$2x(x + 2) = 2x^2 + 4x$
$ab(a - b) = a^2b - ab^2$

**Factor**

To *factor* means to write a sum or difference of terms as a product of polynomials.

$2x^2 + 4x = 2x(x + 2)$

$2x$ is the **greatest common factor** of the terms.

$a^2b - ab^2 = ab(a - b)$

$ab$ is the **greatest common factor** of the terms.

Expanding and factoring are inverse operations.

$\xrightarrow{\hspace{2cm}\text{Expanding}\hspace{2cm}}$

$3ab(a - b + 3) = 3a^2b - 3ab^2 + 9ab$

$\xleftarrow{\hspace{2cm}\text{Factoring}\hspace{2cm}}$

**Example 1**  Factor each expression.
(a) $2ab + 4c$  (b) $-3b^2 - 9b$  (c) $3x^3 + 6x^2 - 9x$

**Solution**  (a) $2ab + 4c = 2(ab + 2c)$

$2$ is the greatest common factor of the terms.

(b) $-3b^2 - 9b = -3b(b + 3)$

$-3b$ is the greatest common factor of the terms.

(c) $3x^3 + 6x^2 - 9x = 3x(x^2 + 2x - 3)$
$\qquad\qquad\qquad\quad = 3x(x + 3)(x - 1)$

$3x$ is the greatest common factor of the terms.

You can check your answers by expanding mentally.
For example, $3x(x^2 + 2x - 3) = 3x^3 + 6x^2 - 9x$
This is the original polynomial. Checks ✓

The skills you learn in mathematics are often extended to develop new skills. For example, compare the following.

$$mx + my = m(x + y) \qquad (a + b)x + (a + b)y = (a + b)(x + y)$$

monomial common factor    binomial common factor

The above suggests the following pattern.

$$\boxed{\phantom{xx}}(x + y) = \boxed{\phantom{xx}}x + \boxed{\phantom{xx}}y$$

↑
represents a polynomial

**Example 2**    Express in factored form $3x(x - 2) - 2(x - 2)$.

**Solution**    $3x(x - 2) - 2(x - 2)$         Think: What is the common factor?
$= (x - 2)(3x - 2)$         $(x - 2)$ is a common factor of each term.

## 2.6  Exercise

**A** When you are factoring polynomials your first step is to remove the common factors.

1    What is the greatest common factor of each of the following polynomials?
   (a)  $3x(x - 2)$ (b)  $2a(a - 1)$ (c)  $-3x(x + 3)$
   (d)  $3y(2y + 5)$ (e)  $5xy(x - y)$ (f)  $-2x(x - y)$
   (g)  $-3x^2y(x + y)$ (h)  $2a^2b(a - b)$ (i)  $3x(x^2 - 3x - 1)$
   (j)  $-3a(a^2 - 2a - 1)$ (k)  $-3x(2x^2 - 3x - 1)$ (l)  $-2m(m^2 - 3mn + n^2)$
   (m)  $-a^2(2a - 3b + c)$ (n)  $-2x(x - y - z)$ (o)  $-p(3p^2 - pq + q)$

2    Find the greatest common factor of each of the following groups of terms.
   (a)  $-12xy, 16xy$ (b)  $-20x^2y, 16xy^2$ (c)  $-24ab, 16ab$
   (d)  $6x^3, 9x^2$ (e)  $ay^2, -2by^2, -3cy^2$ (f)  $5m^3, -25m^2, 15m$
   (g)  $5a^2, -2ab, a$ (h)  $-6a^3, -18a^2, 6a$ (i)  $50ax^2, 75axy$

3    Find the missing factor.
   (a)  $8xy = (?)(-2x)$ (b)  $-6axy = (2a)(?)$
   (c)  $-6x^4 = 2x^2(?)$ (d)  $24a^2b^2c = (?)(-8abc)$
   (e)  $-12a^2b^3 = (?)(-6ab^2)$ (f)  $8x^5y^3 = (?)(-2x^2y)$
   (g)  $-8y^5 = (?)(-4y^3)$ (h)  $-12x^3y^3 = (4xy^2)(?)$

4   (a) Factor the expression $-2x^2 + 2xy$.

    (b) How would you check your factors in (a)?

 Once you do the work, think of a method of checking it.

B After you factor an expression, check your work.

5   Find the missing factor.

    (a) $3x - 3y = (?)(x - y)$               (b) $mx - my = m(?)$
    (c) $2xa + 8xb = (?)(a + 4b)$            (d) $18a^5 - 27a^4 = 9a^4(?)$
    (e) $x^5 - 5x^4 + 3x^3 = (?)(x^2 - 5x + 3)$
    (f) $2xya - 4xyb + 6xyc = (?)(a - 2b + 3c)$
    (g) $2\pi x^3 - 4\pi x^2 + 6\pi x = 2\pi x(?)$
    (h) $4a^2b^2c^3 - 6a^2b^3c^2 - 8a^3b^2 = 2a^2b^2(?)$

    How would you check your answers?

6   Factor.

    (a) $-12x + 4y$    (b) $4xa - 8xb$    (c) $2a^2 - 6a$      (d) $-13ab - 39ac$
    (e) $18a^4 - 27a^3$    (f) $6x^2 - 4x$    (g) $15xy - 10xy^2$    (h) $6a - 12a^5$
    (i) $28a^2 - 4ab$             (j) $49mn - 14m^2n^2$       (k) $64x^6y^2 - 32x^4y^4$

    How would you check your answers above?

7   Express each of the following in factored form.

    (a) $x^4 - 5x^3 + 3x^2$       (b) $x^2 + 4xy - x$         (c) $12x^2 - 24x + 30$
    (d) $abx^2 + 6aby - 8aby^2$   (e) $ax^3 - 5ax^2 + 3ax$    (f) $10x^3 - 50x^2 + 30x$
    (g) $4m^3 - 8m^2 + 6m$        (h) $3x^2 - 12xy + 9y^2$    (i) $45a^2b - 15ab^2 - 60ab$
    (j) $10a^3b^3 - 20a^2b^2 - 10ab$  (k) $6p^2q^2 + 3p^3q^2 - 9p^2q^3$  (l) $9ax^2 - 18axy + 6ay^2$

8   For each of the following
    • identify the common factor,
    • express in factored form.

    (a) $x(a + b) + y(a + b)$            (b) $2x(a - b) - y(a - b)$
    (c) $3x(x + 1) - 2(x + 1)$           (d) $a(2a - 3b) - b(2a - 3b)$
    (e) $2x(2x - 5y) - 3y(2x - 5y)$      (f) $a(a - 3b) + 2b(a - 3b)$

9   Part of the solution is provided where the terms of a polynomial are grouped to find a common factor. Complete the solution.

$$2ax - 3by - 3ay + 2bx = \underline{2ax + 2bx} - \underline{3ay - 3by}$$
$$= 2x(a + b) - 3y(a + b)$$
$$= ?$$

10  Factor each of the following. (You may need to group the terms.)

(a) $2ax - 3bx - 2ay + 3by$  (b) $a^2 - ab + ac - bc$

(c) $am + an + bm + bn$  (d) $6am - 9an - 2bm + 3bn$

(e) $bc - ab + b^2 - ac$  (f) $x^2 + y - xy - x$

(g) $2mx + 4x + 2my + 4y$  (h) $3mxy - 6mx - 3nxy + 6nx$

11  Use $a = 3$ and $b = -4$ to calculate the following.

(a) $a^2b - ab^2$  (b) $ab(a - b)$

(c) Why are the answers in (a) and (b) the same?

(d) Which required fewer calculations? Why?

12  Evaluate each expression if $x = -2$ and $y = 2$. How many can you do mentally?

(a) $6x - 12x^2$  (b) $4x^2 - 8x$

(c) $3xy - 6y^2$  (d) $6x^2y - 12x^3y^2$

(e) $6xy^2 - 12xy + 6x^2y$  (f) $-24x^3y^3 - 36x^2y^2 + 12xy$

13  The surface area, $S$, of an oil drum is given by the formula $S = 2\pi r^2 + 2\pi rh$, $\pi \doteq 3.14$.

radius, $r$
height, $h$

(a) Calculate the surface area, $S$, for $r = 10.2$ (in metres) and $h = 9.6$ (in metres).

(b) Factor the expression for $S$. Now calculate $S$ for the values in (a).

14  (a) Calculate the surface area of a cylindrical water reservoir with a radius of 7.4 m and a height of 11.5 m.

(b) By how much does the surface area of the cylindrical reservoir increase if the radius is increased by 1.2 m?

15  (a) A stainless steel cylindrical silo has a radius of 2.25 m and a height of 14.2 m. Calculate its surface area.

(b) Use an efficient method on your calculator of finding your answer in (a).

Calculator Tip

Your calculator may have a constant feature. If you push any of the keys $\boxed{+}$ $\boxed{-}$ $\boxed{\times}$ or $\boxed{\div}$ twice you establish a constant. Read your calculator manual. Try the calculator steps shown.

$\boxed{C}$ $4.6$ $\boxed{\times}$ $\boxed{\times}$

| Input | | Output |
|---|---|---|
| 3.8 | $\boxed{=}$ | 17.48 |
| 4.6 | $\boxed{=}$ | 21.16 |
| 9.3 | $\boxed{=}$ | 42.78 |

## Applications: Track and Field

Have you ever wondered why runners do not line up exactly at the start of a race, but always cross the same finish line?

*The distance around the outside of the track is longer than the distance around the inside of a track. To ensure that the length of the race is the same for each runner, some runners seem to be given a head start.*

A circular race track is shown. A runner on the outside track will run further than a runner on the inside track.

$$D = 2\pi R - 2\pi r$$

└── additional distance

To use a calculator effectively, factor the expression.

$$2\pi R - 2\pi r = 2\pi(R - r)$$

---

16. (a) Use $D = 2\pi R - 2\pi r$ to find $D$ to 1 decimal place for $R = 25.0$ m, $r = 20.0$ m, and $\pi \doteq 3.14$. How many calculations did you do to find the answer?

    (b) Use $D = 2\pi(R - r)$ for the data in (a). How many calculations did you do to find the answer?

    (c) Which expression is more suitable to calculate $D$, $2\pi R - 2\pi r$ or $2\pi(R - r)$? Give reasons why.

17. Two runners are to run a 1500-m race on a circular track. How much of a head start should the runner on the outside lane get so that they run the same distance? Use $R = 30.0$ m, $r = 28.0$ m.

18. Two relay teams are to race in the 1500-m relay on the track shown. One team uses the inside of the track, while the other uses the outside of the track. How much of a head start should the team on the outside be given?

100.0 m

$R = 25.0$ m
$r = 21.0$ m

Finish line

## PSP Strategy: Factoring Trinomials

Sometimes, you can develop a strategy for solving a problem, by looking at the final result, and working backwards. For example, in your earlier work, you multiplied binomials to obtain a trinomial. What if you are given a trinomial? How can you find its factors?

Examine results A and B of your earlier work.

**A:** *Specific Example*

**B:** *General Example*

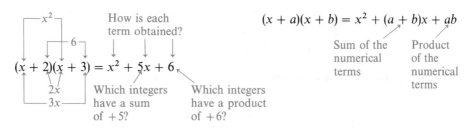

Now you can interpret results A and B to obtain a strategy for factoring a trinomial.

Factor $x^2 + 14x + 48$             $(x + 6)(x + 8)$

Ask     → Which integers have      Which integers have    → The integers
yourself:     a sum of $+14$?         a product of $+48$?      are $+6$ and $+8$.

To factor a trinomial, ask these two key questions.   **PSP**   When doing mathematics remember the key questions to ask yourself.

Which integers have this sum?

$$x^2 + 8x + 12 = (x + 2)(x + 6)$$
$$x^2 - 8x + 12 = (x - 2)(x - 6)$$
$$x^2 - 4x - 12 = (x + 2)(x - 6)$$
$$x^2 + 4x - 12 = (x - 2)(x + 6)$$

Which integers have this product?

**Example 1**    Factor $x^2 - 6xy - 27y^2$.

**Solution**     $x^2 - 6xy - 27y^2 = (x - 9y)(x + 3y)$

Think: The sum of     Think: The product of     The integers are
the integers is $-6$.     the integers is $-27$.     $-9$ and $+3$.

**Example 2**   Factor $a^2 - 10ab + 25b^2$.

**Solution**   $a^2 - 10ab + 25b^2 = (a - 5b)(a - 5b)$

The sum of the integers is $-10$.

The product of the integers is $+25$.

The integers are $-5$ and $-5$.

## 2.7 Exercise

**A 1** (a) For the trinomial $a^2 + 5a + 6$, what two integers have a sum of $+5$. What two integers have a product of $+6$?

(b) Use your answers in (a) to write the factors of the trinomial.

**2** Copy and complete the chart.

| | | What two integers have | | |
|---|---|---|---|---|
| | Trinomial | this sum? | this product? | The integers are |
| (a) | $m^2 - 12m + 36$ | $-12$ | $+36$ | ? |
| (b) | $k^2 + 8k + 16$ | $+8$ | $+16$ | ? |
| (c) | $p^2 + 2px - 48x^2$ | $+2$ | $-48$ | ? |
| (d) | $x^2 - 6xy - 72y^2$ | $-6$ | $-72$ | ? |

(e) Write the factors of the trinomials in (a) to (d).

**3** Find the missing factor.

(a) $m^2 + 12m + 27 = (?)(m + 9)$

(b) $x^2 - 11x + 30 = (x - 5)(?)$

(c) $y^2 - 3y - 18 = (?)(y - 6)$

(d) $m^2 + 2m - 24 = (?)(m + 6)$

(e) $x^2 - xy - 30y^2 = (x - 6y)(?)$

(f) $a^2 + 6ab + 9b^2 = (?)(a + 3b)$

**4** Write the numbers with the following properties.

(a) product is $+56$ and sum is $+15$

(b) product is $-16$ and sum is $-6$

(c) product is $-12$ and sum is $-1$

(d) product is $-35$ and sum is $+2$

**5** Find two numbers so that

| | (a) | (b) | (c) | (d) | (e) | (f) | (g) | (h) | (i) |
|---|---|---|---|---|---|---|---|---|---|
| product is | $+16$ | $+9$ | $-20$ | $-15$ | $-18$ | $-10$ | $+14$ | $-26$ | $+48$ |
| sum is | $+10$ | $-10$ | $-1$ | $-2$ | $+3$ | $+3$ | $+15$ | $+11$ | $-14$ |

**B 6** Find the missing term if each of the following trinomials is a perfect square.

(a) $(?) + 2a + 1$

(b) $m^2 + (?) + 4$

(c) $(?) - 12x + 4$

(d) $4p^2 - 4p + (?)$

(e) $16a^2 - 16a + (?)$

(f) $9a^2 - (?) + 16$

7  Write each of the following as a perfect square.

    (a) $y^2 + 8y + 16$          (b) $m^2 - 6m + 9$          (c) $x^2 - 2xy + y^2$

    (d) $a^2 + 2a + 1$          (e) $4x^2 + 36x + 81$       (f) $25y^2 - 20y + 4$

    (g) $4a^2 + 4a + 1$        (h) $25a^2 - 40ab + 16b^2$

8  Factor each of the following. Which have a common factor?

    (a) $x^2 + 8x + 15$    (b) $y^2 - y - 30$    (c) $3a^2 + 9a + 6$    (d) $x^2 - 2xy + y^2$

    (e) $x^2 + 3xy + 2y^2$  (f) $2a^2 + 8a + 8$    (g) $2x^2 + 2x - 4$    (h) $x^2 + 4x - 5$

9  Express each trinomial in factored form.

    (a) $x^2 - 9x + 20$         (b) $m^2 - 13m + 42$        (c) $a^2 + 6a + 9$

    (d) $25 - 10x + x^2$        (e) $a^2 - 3ab - 10b^2$     (f) $3x^2 + 3x - 6$

    (g) $x^2 + 4x - 21$         (h) $9x^2 - 12xy + 4y^2$    (i) $18 - 9x + x^2$

    (j) $m^2 + 8mn + 15n^2$     (k) $50a^2 + 20ab + 2b^2$    (l) $3y^2 + 12y - 15$

10  In translating word problems involving motion, use algebraic expressions
    to solve the problem. Copy and complete the chart.

|  | Distance (km) | Time (h) | Speed (km/h) |
|---|---|---|---|
| (a) | $y^2 + 12y + 35$ | $y + 5$ | |
| (b) | $x^2 + x - 6$ | | $x + 3$ |
| (c) | $y^2 + 10y + 9$ | $y + 9$ | |

11  (a) The trinomial $x^2 - 4x + k$ is to be a perfect square. Find $k$, $k > 0$.

    (b) The trinomial $x^2 - kx + 16$ is to be a perfect square. Find $k$, $k > 0$.

    (c) The trinomial $x^2 + kx + 16$ is to be a perfect square. Find $k$, $k > 0$.

PSP  12  How many different ways can you spell SUSAN?

                                                            S
                                                       U  U
                                                    S  S  S
                                                     A  A
                                                     N

C  13  You know these results of           $(2x + 1)(4x + 3) = 8x^2 + 10x + 3$
        multiplying binomials. Examine      $(2x - 1)(4x - 3) = 8x^2 - 10x + 3$
        these results and your own.         $(2x + 1)(4x - 3) = 8x^2 - 2x - 3$
                                           $(2x - 1)(4x + 3) = 8x^2 + 2x - 3$

    Suggest a method of finding the factors of trinomials such as

    A: $3y^2 + 10y + 3$                B: $3x^2 - 19x - 14$

    Find the factors of these trinomials.

## 2.8 Working Backwards: Factoring Trinomials

An important strategy in solving certain problems is to use a *known result* to solve *what is not known*.

| Use a known result to develop a method of solving a problem. | → | Then apply the method to the solution of a problem. |

For example, you have already obtained this known result:

$$(2x + 1)(4x + 3) = 8x^2 + 10x + 3$$

Now analyze the result.

- $8x^2 + 10x + 3$

  Product is $+24$.

  $(2x + 1)(4x + 3)$

  $+2 \times +1 \times +4 \times +3 = +24$

- $8x^2 + 10x + 3$

  $6x + 4x$

  $+6$ and $+4$ are factors of $+24$.

  $(2x + 1)(4x + 3)$

  $+4x$

  $+6x$

### Method

*Step A:* Thus, to find the factors of $8x^2 + 10x + 3$, ask yourself: What two integers have

- a product of $+24$?
- a sum of $+10$?

Answer is $+6$ and $+4$.

*Step B:* Use the answer $+6$ and $+4$ to decompose the trinomial.

$$\begin{aligned} 8x^2 + 10x + 3 &= 8x^2 + 4x + 6x + 3 \\ &= 4x(2x + 1) + 3(2x + 1) \\ &= (2x + 1)(4x + 3) \end{aligned}$$

This method is called the **method of decomposition**.

**Example 1**    Factor $6y^2 + 19y + 15$.

**Solution**
$$\begin{aligned} & 6y^2 + 19y + 15 \\ =\ & 6y^2 + 9y + 10y + 15 \\ =\ & 3y(2y + 3) + 5(2y + 3) \\ =\ & (2y + 3)(3y + 5) \end{aligned}$$

Think: What two integers have a product of $+90$ and a sum of $+19$? The numbers are $+9$ and $+10$.

In the previous example, if you write the numbers $+9$ and $+10$ in a different order, you obtain the same factors.

$$6y^2 + 19y + 15 = 6y^2 + 10y + 9y + 15$$
$$= 2y(3y + 5) + 3(3y + 5)$$
$$= (2y + 3)(3y + 5)$$

**Example 2**   Factor $2x^2 - 7x - 15$.

**Solution**   $2x^2 - 7x - 15 = 2x^2 - 10x + 3x - 15$
$$= 2x(x - 5) + 3(x - 5)$$
$$= (x - 5)(2x + 3)$$

Which two integers have a product of $-30$?
Which two integers have a sum of $-7$?
The numbers are $-10$, $+3$.

## 2.8   Exercise

**A** Remember: In order to factor a trinomial, you need to ask two key questions.

1   (a) For the trinomial $3x^2 + 5x + 2$, what two integers have
   • a sum of $+5$?   • a product of $+6$?
   (b) Use your answers in (a) to write the factors of the trinomial.

2   Complete the chart.

| | Trinomial | What two integers have this sum? | this product? | The integers are |
|---|---|---|---|---|
| (a) | $6y^2 - 7y - 3$ | $-7$ | $-18$ | ? |
| (b) | $6y^2 + 7y + 2$ | $+7$ | $+12$ | ? |
| (c) | $10y^2 - 17y + 3$ | $-17$ | $+30$ | ? |
| (d) | $8y^2 + 2y - 15$ | $+2$ | $-120$ | ? |

(e) Write the factors of the trinomials in (a) to (d).

**PSP**
Ask yourself key questions.

3   Two integers have the following properties. What are the numbers?
   (a) product $+27$, sum $+12$        (b) product $-64$, sum $-12$
   (c) product $-48$, sum $+2$         (d) product $-10$, sum $-3$

4   Find two integers with the following properties.

| | (a) | (b) | (c) | (d) | (e) | (f) | (g) | (h) | (i) | (j) |
|---|---|---|---|---|---|---|---|---|---|---|
| product | $+15$ | $-27$ | $-8$ | $-40$ | $-15$ | $-54$ | $-27$ | $+56$ | $-48$ | $+16$ |
| sum | $-8$ | $-6$ | $-7$ | $+3$ | $+2$ | $-3$ | $-6$ | $-15$ | $-13$ | $-10$ |

5   (a) To factor the trinomial        $6x^2 + 13x + 5$
                                        $\uparrow$   $\uparrow$   $\uparrow$
                                        $A$   $B$   $C$

   how are the coefficients $A$, $B$, and $C$ used to help you find the factors?
   (b) Factor the trinomial.

**B** Remember: The first step in factoring is to look for a common factor.

6 Each of the following were obtained by the method of decomposition. Write the factors of the original trinomial.

(a) $3x(x - 2) + 2(x - 2)$       (b) $2a(a - 3) - 3(a - 3)$

(c) $2x(x - y) - y(x - y)$       (d) $m(2n - 1) - 3(2n - 1)$

(e) $x(x - 5y) - 5y(x - 5y)$       (f) $p(p + 3q) + 2q(p + 3q)$

7 Factor each of the following.

(a) $4x^2 + 8x + 3$       (b) $4x^2 - 8x + 3$       (c) $4x^2 + 4x - 3$

(d) Use your work in (a) to (c) to factor the trinomial $4x^2 - 4x - 3$.

8 Factor each of the following.

(a) $9x^2 + 15x + 4$       (b) $9x^2 - 15x + 4$       (c) $9x^2 - 9x - 4$

(d) Use your work in (a) to (c) to factor the trinomial $9x^2 + 9x - 4$.

9 Express each of the following in factored form.

(a) $2y^2 + 3y + 1$       (b) $3x^2 - 5x - 2$       (c) $2y^2 + 5y - 12$

(d) $6x^2 + 5x + 1$       (e) $5x^2 - 11x + 2$       (f) $6m^2 - 11m - 10$

(g) $2y^2 + 5y + 2$       (h) $6y^2 - 13y + 6$       (i) $10m^2 + m - 3$

10 Factor.

(a) $3x^2 - 19xy - 14y^2$       (b) $3m^2 + 13m + 4$       (c) $10x^2 - 28x + 16$

(d) $3y^2 + y - 30$       (e) $8y^2 + 14y - 15$       (f) $4x^2 - 17xy - 15y^2$

11 Which of the trinomials have like factors?

(a) $3x^2 + 10x + 7$       (b) $2x^2 - 3x - 14$       (c) $2x^2 - 7x + 6$

(d) $7x^2 + 13x - 2$       (e) $6x^2 - 17x + 5$       (f) $7x^2 - 22x + 3$

(g) $3x^2 - 20x + 25$       (h) $6x^2 + 20x - 50$       (i) $2x^2 - 7x - 4$

(j) $6x^2 + 15x - 36$       (k) $3x^2 + 13x - 10$       (l) $7x^2 - 13x - 2$

**PSP** **C** 12 (a) Write the next two lines of the following pattern.

$$1 - x^2 = (1 - x)(1 + x)$$
$$1 - x^3 = (1 - x)(1 + x + x^2)$$
$$1 - x^4 = (1 - x)(1 + x + x^2 + x^3)$$

(b) Use the pattern in (a) to write the factors of each polynomial.

$1 - x^{10}$                 $1 - x^{100}$

(c) Use the pattern in (a) to find the sum $1 + 2 + 4 + 8 + 16 + \cdots + 2^{15}$.
(Hint: $1 = 2^0$)

## 2.9 Factoring a Difference of Squares

Many number tricks are often explained by using factoring skills. For example, these calculations can be done mentally with the help of factoring skills.

$$24^2 - 16^2 \qquad 99 \times 101 \qquad \text{Can you do them mentally?}$$

To see how factoring skills apply to the above, note that each of the following binomial products has a common property.

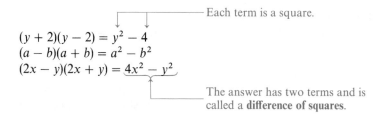

Each term is a square.

$$(y + 2)(y - 2) = y^2 - 4$$
$$(a - b)(a + b) = a^2 - b^2$$
$$(2x - y)(2x + y) = 4x^2 - y^2$$

The answer has two terms and is called a **difference of squares**.

To factor a **difference of squares**, write each term as a square as the following example shows.

**Example 1**   Factor $25a^2 - 16b^2$.

**Solution**
$$25a^2 - 16b^2 = (5a)^2 - (4b)^2$$
$$= (5a + 4b)(5a - 4b)$$

One factor is a difference of the two terms.
The other factor is the sum of the two terms.

To factor the following expression completely, check whether each resulting factor needs to be factored again. Then you must do an additional step.

**Example 2**   Factor completely $x^4 - y^4$.

**Solution**
$$x^4 - y^4 = (x^2)^2 - (y^2)^2 \longleftarrow$$
$$= (x^2 + y^2)(x^2 - y^2)$$
$$= (x^2 + y^2)(x + y)(x - y)$$

Think: Write each term as a square. Eventually, you will do this step mentally.

This factor cannot be factored again. Only a *difference* of squares can be factored.

 **PSP**
Understand the meaning of key words.

Skills for factoring a difference of squares, $a^2 - b^2$, can be used to do the calculations from the beginning of the section mentally.

$$24^2 - 16^2 = (24 + 16)(24 - 16) \qquad 99 \times 101 = (100 - 1)(100 + 1)$$
$$= 40 \times 8 \qquad\qquad\qquad = 100^2 - 1$$
$$= 320 \qquad\qquad\qquad\qquad = 9999$$

You must be able to recognize when a polynomial is in the form of a difference of squares.

**Example 3**  Factor each of the following.
(a) $(x + 3)^2 - y^2$            (b) $(x - 2)^2 - (y - 6)^2$

**Solution**  (a)    $(x + 3)^2 - y^2$       (b)    $(x - 2)^2 - (y - 6)^2$
           $= (x + 3 - y)(x + 3 + y)$       $= (x - 2 + y - 6)(x - 2 - y + 6)$
                                       $= (x + y - 8)(x - y + 4)$

## 2.9 Exercise

**A** To factor a difference of squares, you must be able to recognize when a polynomial is a difference of squares.

1    Find the following products. What property do they have in common?
     (a) $(x - 5)(x + 5)$         (b) $(3 - y)(3 + y)$         (c) $(2x + 3y)(2x - 3y)$
     (d) $(3m - 1)(3m + 1)$     (e) $(k + 4m)(k - 4m)$     (f) $(5y + 2x)(5y - 2x)$

2    Complete each of the following by first writing each term as a square and then writing the factors.
     (a) $4x^2 - y^2 = (?)^2 - y^2$    (b) $m^2 - 9 = m^2 - (?)^2$    (c) $x^2 - 49y^2 = x^2 - (?)^2$
     (d) $36 - 49x^2 = (?)^2 - (?)^2$          (e) $16a^2 - 25b^2 = (?)^2 - (?)^2$

3    Factor each of the following.
     (a) $x^2 - 25$            (b) $n^2 - 16$            (c) $k^2 - 49$
     (d) $a^2 - 64$            (e) $c^2 - 100$         (f) $m^2 - 81$

4    Write each in factored form.
     (a) $9x^2 - 4$           (b) $64y^2 - 1$         (c) $25p^2 - 49$
     (d) $4m^2 - 9$          (e) $25s^2 - 36$       (f) $400r^2 - 49$

5 Factor.

(a) $x^2 - 4y^2$      (b) $25k^2 - p^2$      (c) $m^2 - 100n^2$

(d) $100a^2 - 49b^2$      (e) $36y^2 - 25x^2$      (f) $16p^2 - 25q^2$

6 (a) What is the first step in factoring?

(b) Use your answer in (a) to factor $18a^2 - 8$.

7 (a) Write the factors of $x^4 - 1$.

(b) Check each factor in (a). How many factors did you get?

**B** Remember: Your first step of factoring is to check for a common factor.

8 For each of the following,
- write each term as a square.
- find the factors.

(a) $y^2 - 4$      (b) $1 - 4m^2$      (c) $16x^2 - 9$      (d) $a^2 - 36$

(e) $9x^2 - 1$      (f) $16x^2 - 25y^2$      (g) $49y^2 - 1$      (h) $9 - 25x^2$

(i) $4m^2 - 25t^2$      (j) $x^2y^2 - 4$

9 Factor each of the following. Remember to check for a common factor.

(a) $a^2 - b^2$      (b) $2x^2 - 2y^2$      (c) $3a^2 - 12b^2$      (d) $16p^2 - 1$

(e) $1 - 36a^2b^2$      (f) $2x^2 - 2$      (g) $10x^2 - 640$      (h) $81m^2 - 4n^2$

(i) $3 - 75y^2$      (j) $16a^2 - 9b^2$      (k) $1 - 4a^2$      (l) $-y^2 + 49$

(m) $64 - x^2y^2$      (n) $16 - 9y^2$      (o) $2x^2y^2 - 8$

10 (a) How are each of the following alike? How are the terms different?

$$x^2 - s^2 \qquad\qquad (x + y)^2 - s^2$$

(b) Factor the expressions in (a).

11 (a) How are each of the following alike? How are they different?

$$m^2 - 4n^2 \qquad\qquad m^2 - 4(n + t)^2$$

(b) Factor the expressions in (a).

12 (a) How are each of the following alike? How are they different?

$$x^2 - y^2 \qquad\qquad (x + a)^2 - (y + b)^2$$

(b) Factor the expressions in (a).

13 Factor completely.

(a) $(a + b)^2 - c^2$      (b) $(a - b)^2 - c^2$      (c) $x^2 - (y + k)^2$

(d) $x^2 - (y - h)^2$      (e) $c^2 - (2a - b)^2$      (f) $c^2 - 4(2a - b)^2$

(g) $(a + b)^2 - (x + y)^2$      (h) $(a - b)^2 - (x - y)^2$

14 Factor each of the following completely. Which two cannot be factored?

(a) $m^2 - s^2$      (b) $a^2 - 4b^2$      (c) $4s^2 - 9t^2$      (d) $4a^2 - b^2$

(e) $y^2 - x^2$      (f) $x^2 + 1$      (g) $x^2 - \dfrac{1}{4}$      (h) $18k^2 - 32m^2$

(i) $4t^2 - 25s^2$      (j) $\dfrac{x^2}{25} - 1$      (k) $x^4 - 1$      (l) $-25x^2 + 16y^2$

(m) $-9m^2 + 49$      (n) $9 - (a - b)^2$      (o) $-1 - 16y^2$

(p) $2m^2n^2 - 50$      (q) $1 - 64y^4$      (r) $25x^2y^2 - 1$

(s) $9(a - b)^2 - 1$      (t) $a^2 - (a - b)^2$      (u) $(x - y)^2 - 4$

(v) $16x^4 - 4b^4$      (w) $(a - b)^2 - 4(a + b)^2$      (x) $81 - 16x^4$

15 Complete each of the following and then calculate.

(a) $21 \times 19 = (20 + ?)(20 - ?)$      (b) $29 \times 31 = (? - 1)(? + 1)$

(c) $61 \times 59 = (60 + 1)(? - 1)$      (d) $102 \times 98 = (100 + ?)(100 - ?)$

16 Calculate each of the following by using your skills with $a^2 - b^2 = (a + b)(a - b)$. How many can you do mentally?

(a) $19^2 - 9^2$      (b) $29^2 - 19^2$      (c) $38^2 - 28^2$      (d) $48^2 - 18^2$

(e) $35^2 - 25^2$      (f) $45^2 - 15^2$      (g) $75^2 - 25^2$      (h) $96^2 - 4^2$

17 (a) A square is shown with another square piece removed. Find the area of the shaded area in terms of $a$ and $b$.

(b) Use the diagram at the right to explain why $(a - b)(a + b) = a^2 - b^2$.

18 (a) Find an algebraic expression for the area of the shaded region. ABCD and EFGH are squares.

(b) Write your algebraic expression in (a) in factored form.

C 19 (a) Write 3 factors for $a^4 - 1$.     **PSP**

(b) Write the factors of $a^8 - 1$.

(c) Write the factors of $a^{16} - 1$.

(d) Use your pattern in (a), (b), (c) to predict the factors for $a^{32} - 1$. How can you check your prediction?

## Applications: Pipe Construction

Under every major city is a network of concrete storm sewer pipes that can carry heavy volumes of water after a rain storm.

To calculate the amount of material, $V$, in each pipe, use

Volume = shaded area × length of pipe
$V = (\pi R^2 - \pi r^2)L$, where $\pi \doteq 3.14$.

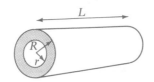

*The pipes are large enough to safely carry any great surge of water away from our homes after a severe rainstorm. Without these pipes it would not take long for a city to become flooded.*

Use factoring skills to write
$$V = \pi(R^2 - r^2)L$$
$$= \pi(R - r)(R + r)L.$$

---

20  Use $R = 75.0$ cm, $r = 71.0$ cm, $L = 100.0$ cm.

  (a) Use $V = (\pi R^2 - \pi r^2)L$ and calculate $V$.

  (b) Use $V = \pi(R - r)(R + r)L$ and calculate $V$.

  (c) Which method (a) or (b) do you prefer? Give reasons why.

21  Calculate the amount of concrete needed to construct this pipe.

22  How much concrete is needed to make this flower pot?

Outside diameter
120.0 cm
Inside diameter
108.0 cm

125.0 cm

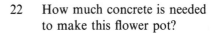
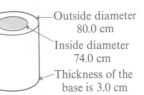

40.0 cm

Outside diameter
80.0 cm
Inside diameter
74.0 cm
Thickness of the
base is 3.0 cm

23  The measurements of an underground pipe are length 1.85 m, inside diameter 1.36 m, outside diameter 1.52 m

  (a) Calculate the volume of concrete needed to construct each pipe.

  (b) After each concrete pipe is fitted to another pipe, it has an effective length of 1.73 m.

    (i) Calculate how many pipes, fitted together, give an effective length of 1 km of underground pipe.

    (ii) What is the maximum volume of water that the pipe in (i) can hold?

## 2.10 Inventory: Factoring Skills

Sometimes it is necessary to use more than one factoring skill to factor certain algebraic expressions.

**Example**  Factor $a^4 - 5a^2 - 36$.

**Solution**  $a^4 - 5a^2 - 36 = (a^2 - 9)(a^2 + 4)$   Think: Check to see if any factors can be factored again.

$$= (a - 3)(a + 3)(a^2 + 4)$$

## 2.10 Exercise

**B** You must be able to recognize which skills must be used to factor a polynomial. When you factor the following polynomials, always check for a common factor first. There are at least two expressions that cannot be factored. Can you find others?

| | | | | | |
|---|---|---|---|---|---|
| 1. | $3a^2 + 6a$ | 2. | $2x - 8xy$ | 3. | $36a^3 - 4a^2$ |
| 4. | $25a^4 - 9y^4$ | 5. | $x^2 + 7x + 12$ | 6. | $3a^2 - 3b^2$ |
| 7. | $y^2 - 11y + 28$ | 8. | $16x^2 - 8x + 1$ | 9. | $a^2 - ab - 56b^2$ |
| 10. | $4x^2 - 11x + 6$ | 11. | $-1 + 9k^2$ | 12. | $1 + 18y + 32y^2$ |
| 13. | $2y^2 - 8y^3$ | 14. | $x^2 + 6x + 8$ | 15. | $56x^2 + 9x - 2$ |
| 16. | $-16 - 9x^2$ | 17. | $16 - 28x + 10x^2$ | 18. | $m^4 - 16$ |
| 19. | $8 - 14y + 5y^2$ | 20. | $-(1 - a^4)$ | 21. | $m^4 - 5m^2 - 36$ |
| 22. | $6a^2 + 5a + 1$ | 23. | $x^4 - y^4$ | 24. | $p^2 - 2pq - 63q^2$ |
| 25. | $m^4 + 3m^2 - 4$ | 26. | $x^2 - xy$ | 27. | $x^2 + 3xy - x$ |
| 28. | $a^2 - 144$ | 29. | $3a^2 - 36a + 36$ | 30. | $(a + b)^2 - c^2$ |
| 31. | $-a^2 - 2ab - b^2$ | 32. | $x^3 + 5x^2 - 6$ | 33. | $x^4 + 18x^2 + 32$ |
| 34. | $m^4 - 9m^2 - 112$ | 35. | $x^8 - 1$ | 36. | $2y^2 - 2y - 24$ |
| 37. | $2x^2 - 8$ | 38. | $4y^2 + 8y - 60$ | 39. | $m^4 - 16$ |
| 40. | $2x^2 - 16x + 32$ | 41. | $x^3 - xy^2$ | 42. | $x^4 - 5x^2 + 4$ |
| 43. | $-48 - 3y^2$ | | | 44. | $x^2y^3z - 2xy^2$ |
| 45. | $(x - y)^2 - (x + y)^2$ | | | 46. | $9(a + b)^2 - (a - b)^2$ |
| 47. | $(a - b)^2 - 16(a + 2b)^2$ | | | 48. | $25(2x + 1)^2 - (9x - 1)^2$ |
| 49. | $4(x - y)^2 - 16(x + y)^2$ | | | 50. | $25(x + 2y)^2 - 9(x - 2y)^2$ |

## 2.11 Solving Quadratic Equations

Equations of the form $ax^2 + bx + c = 0$, $a \neq 0$, are called **quadratic equations**. The solution of quadratic equations depends on the following property of numbers.

**PSP** When you are solving a problem, be sure to note all possibilities.

If $ab = 0$, then one of 3 possibilities is true.

I    $a = 0$      or      II    $b = 0$      or      III    $a = 0$ and $b = 0$

To solve the equation $x^2 - 7x + 12 = 0$, $x \in R$, you write its factors.

$$x^2 - 7x + 12 = 0$$
$$(x - 4)(x - 3) = 0 \longleftarrow \text{Since the product of two factors is equal}$$

If $x - 4 = 0$   or   If $x - 3 = 0$     to 0, at least one of the factors is equal to 0.
$$x = 4 \qquad\qquad x = 3$$

Check in the original equation.

If $x = 4$                     If $x = 3$

L.S. $= x^2 - 7x + 12$        L.S. $= x^2 - 7x + 12$

     $= 16 - 28 + 12 = 0$          $= 9 - 21 + 12 = 0$

R.S. $= 0$                  R.S. $= 0$

Thus, 4 is a root.            Thus, 3 is a root.

If an equation has 1 root, it is a **first degree** equation. If an equation has 2 roots, it is an equation of the **second degree**.

**Example 1**     Solve $3x^2 - 14x - 5 = 0$, $x \in R$.

**Solution**
$$3x^2 - 14x - 5 = 0$$
$$(3x + 1)(x - 5) = 0$$
$$3x + 1 = 0 \qquad \text{or} \qquad x - 5 = 0$$
$$x = -\frac{1}{3} \qquad\qquad x = 5$$

Think: To solve the equation, factor the trinomial.

The roots of the equation are 5 and $-\frac{1}{3}$.

Remember to check the values in the original equation.

To solve a quadratic equation, the trinomial expression must be equated to zero.

**Example 2**    Find the solution set for $2x^2 - 17x = 9$, $x \in R$.

**Solution**

$$2x^2 - 17x = 9$$
$$2x^2 - 17x - 9 = 0$$
$$(2x + 1)(x - 9) = 0$$

$2x + 1 = 0$    or    $x - 9 = 0$

$$x = -\frac{1}{2} \qquad\qquad x = 9$$

The solution set is $\left\{-\frac{1}{2}, 9\right\}$.

Think: Write the equation in the form $ax^2 + bx + c = 0$.

**PSP**
An important strategy is to consider whether to rewrite the problem in a form you are already familiar with.

If you are given the roots of a quadratic equation, you can form the equation.

| Roots | Equation | |
|---|---|---|
| $4, -3$ | Use the variable $x$. | $(x - 4)[x - (-3)] = 0$ |
| | | $(x - 4)(x + 3) = 0$ |
| | | $x^2 - x - 12 = 0$ |

## 2.11   Exercise

**A** All variables represent real numbers.

1    What are the roots of each equation?
   (a) $(x - 3)(x + 4) = 0$
   (b) $(y - 6)(y + 2) = 0$
   (c) $(m - 3)(2m + 1) = 0$
   (d) $(x + 5)(x + 5) = 0$
   (e) $(3y - 1)(y + 2) = 0$
   (f) $x(x - 3) = 0$

2    Solve each equation.
   (a) $(y + 1)(y - 3) = 0$
   (b) $(2x + 1)(x - 3) = 0$
   (c) $(2m - 1)(3m + 2) = 0$
   (d) $(m + 6)(3m - 5) = 0$
   (e) $(5k - 1)(k - 3) = 0$
   (f) $2y(y - 6) = 0$

3    Solve each equation.
   (a) $x^2 - 2x - 8 = 0$
   (b) $y^2 + 11y = -30$
   (c) $m^2 - 6m - 16 = 0$
   (d) $p^2 - 5p - 36 = 0$
   (e) $x^2 - x - 20 = 0$
   (f) $t^2 - 49 = 0$

4    Find the roots of each equation.
   (a) $y^2 - 15y + 50 = 0$
   (b) $m^2 - 5m - 24 = 0$
   (c) $s^2 + 9s + 18 = 0$
   (d) $b^2 - 11b + 30 = 0$
   (e) $g^2 + 7g - 18 = 0$
   (f) $4m^2 - 9 = 0$

5    Find the solution set of each equation.
   (a) $x^2 - 9x + 20 = 0$
   (b) $p^2 - 4p - 96 = 0$
   (c) $y^2 + 21y - 100 = 0$
   (d) $x^2 + 11x + 30 = 0$
   (e) $s^2 - 4s - 12 = 0$
   (f) $25m^2 - 16 = 0$

6  (a) The roots of a quadratic equation are 3, $-8$. Form the equation.
   (b) The solution set of an equation is $\{-2, 6\}$. Form the equation.

7  Each pair of roots is a solution of a quadratic equation. Form each equation.

   (a) 4, 5             (b) $-3, 8$          (c) $-4, -4$         (d) 9, $-3$

   (e) $1, \dfrac{2}{3}$        (f) $-\dfrac{3}{2}, 2$        (g) 0.6, 0.9         (h) $\dfrac{1}{2}, -\dfrac{1}{3}$

**B** Remember: Check the answers you obtain in the *original* equation.

8  (a) What is the first step in solving $x^2 = 14x + 72$?   **PSP**
   (b) Solve the equation in (a). Check your solution.

9  (a) What should be the first step in solving $3x^2 - 6x - 72 = 0$?
   (b) Solve the equation in (a). Check your solution.

10  Solve.

   (a) $x^2 + 2x - 48 = 0$        (b) $x^2 - 4x - 21 = 0$        (c) $x^2 - 4x = 12$
   (d) $3x^2 + x - 30 = 0$        (e) $6x^2 - 7x + 1 = 0$        (f) $12x^2 + 11x = 15$

11  Find the roots of each of the following.
   (a) $x^2 + x - 6 = 0$          (b) $x^2 - x - 42 = 0$          (c) $x^2 + 7x = 18$
   (d) $8x^2 + 14x = 15$          (e) $3x^2 + 13x = 10$          (f) $4 = 8x - 3x^2$

12  Find the solution set.
   (a) $x^2 + 8x + 15 = 0$        (b) $x^2 - 9x + 20 = 0$        (c) $x^2 - x = 30$
   (d) $6x^2 - 5x - 1 = 0$        (e) $17x + 15 = 4x^2$          (f) $10x^2 = 29x - 10$

13  Solve.

   (a) $3(x^2 - 5) + 4x = 0$      (b) $26p = 5p^2 + 24$          (c) $y^2 - 10 = \dfrac{y}{3}$

   (d) $4k^2 + \dfrac{11}{3}k = 5$        (e) $5(2m + 5) = -m^2$          (f) $6 + y - y^2 = 0$

**C** 14  One root of each equation is given.
   *Step 1*  Find the value of $n$.                    *Step 2*  Find the other root.
   (a) $nx^2 + 5x - 3 = 0$, $x = -3$                    (b) $3p^2 + np - 2 = 0$, $p = -2$

   (c) $6y^2 - y + n = 0$, $y = \dfrac{1}{2}$                    (d) $4m^2 + 4mn - 3 = 0$, $m = -\dfrac{1}{2}$

## Solving Problems: Quadratic Equations

You can use skills with quadratic equations to solve problems, such as the following.

**Example**    Two positive numbers differ by 4 and the sum of their squares is 136. What are the numbers?

**Solution**    Let the numbers be represented by $n$ and $n + 4$.

$$n^2 + (n + 4)^2 = 136$$
$$n^2 + n^2 + 8n + 16 = 136$$
$$2n^2 + 8n - 120 = 0$$
$$n^2 + 4n - 60 = 0$$
$$(n + 10)(n - 6) = 0$$
$$n = -10 \text{ or } n = 6$$

**PSP** Based on the given information, write the appropriate equation.

Since the numbers are positive, then the numbers are 10 and 6.

Check: **PSP**
The numbers differ by 4. Checks ✓
Sum of squares is $10^2 + 6^2 = 136$.
Checks ✓

---

15    Two numbers differ by 8 and the sum of their squares is 274. What are the numbers?

16    A rectangular courtyard has a length 4 m greater than its width. If the area of the courtyard is 96 m², then find the dimensions of the courtyard.

17    Two consecutive integers are squares and the sum of these squares equals 313. What are the integers?

18    The length of a rectangle is 6 m more than its width. The area of the rectangle is 27 m². What are the dimensions of the rectangle?

19    The perimeter of a right triangle is 120 cm. If the length of the hypotenuse is 50 cm, find the length of the other two sides.

# 2.12 PSP Problem-Solving: Strategies

In Chapter 1, various problem-solving strategies were dealt with and you listed them in your *Problem-Solving Plan* PSP. Place the following strategies in your list for PSP.

▶ **Drawing a diagram or a physical model:** A diagram or model is often helpful for recording the given information. As well, a diagram may reveal a pattern or suggest that you try a simpler program or diagram. In your work with geometry, adding an extra part to the diagram, such as a line or a diagonal, often may help you connect the given information with what you are trying to prove.

▶ **Guessing and Testing:** You may need to solve some problems where a direct strategy cannot be used. You may need to make a reasonable guess at the answer and then test it. As you repeat the strategy of guess and test, a list of your answers may reveal a pattern or suggest another strategy.

▶ **Missing Information:** To solve some problems you need to obtain missing information.

---

Review your *Problem-Solving Strategies* PSP. Solve these problems.

1  (a)  Four points are drawn on a circle. How many line segments can be drawn to connect 4 points?

   (b)  In (a) there are 6 points. How many line segments can be drawn?

2  Five people are standing in line to purchase tickets for a rock show. How many different ways can the people form a line?

3  How many rectangles can you show on a chessboard?

4  The number 8 is an even number and can be written as a sum of two prime numbers, $8 = 5 + 3$. Can every even number be written as the sum of two prime numbers?

5  How many different committees of 3 persons can you form out of 9 people?

6  When a line is drawn through a square, two regions are formed. How many regions can be formed when 3 lines are drawn? 5 lines are drawn? What is the maximum number of regions when 5 lines are drawn?

7  Eight people walk into a room and sit around a round table. How many different ways can the seating plan be arranged?

## Practice and Problems: Review

1 Simplify.
(a) $3(x^2 - 2) - 3(x^2 + 2) - 3(2x^2 - 1)$ (b) $(2x - 3y)(x + 2y)$
(c) $4a(a - b) - 3b(b - a) - 2a(2b - 3a)$ (d) $(3a - 2b)^2$

2 Write each of the following in factored form.
(a) $2a - 8ab$ (b) $x^2 - 16x + 28$ (c) $9m^2 - 1$
(d) $x^4 - 3x^2 - 4$ (e) $36(a - b)^2 - 9(a + b)^2$

3 Solve the formula for the variable indicated.
(a) $A = \left(\dfrac{a + b}{2}\right)t,\ a$ (b) $\dfrac{v - u}{a} = t,\ u$ (c) $y = \dfrac{1}{3}x - 2,\ x$

4 Find the roots of
(a) $x^2 - 8x + 15 = 0$ (b) $\dfrac{1}{8}(4 - 3y) + 2 = \dfrac{1}{2}(y - 5) - y$

5 (a) Solve the problem.

At this year's lottery, John, Liz and Nick won $100\,000$. They also won $2500 last year in the same lottery. Since each person paid different amounts for the ticket, this year John received $400 more than twice what Liz received. Nick received $600 less than what Liz received. How much did each person receive?

(b) What information is not needed to solve the problem in (a)?

## Practice Test

1 Simplify.
(a) $(-6a^2b)(-5ab)$ (b) $(-8a^2b^3) \div (-2ab)$ (c) $(-3xy)(4x^2y)$

2 Find each solution set. Verify your answer.
(a) $2(y - 3) + 5 = 3(y + 2) - 4$ (b) $x^2 - 8x + 12 = 0$
(c) $2(y - 1)(y + 1) - 2(2y - 1)^2 = -9 - 2(y + 1)^2,\ y \in R.$

3 Write each of the following in factored form.
(a) $2x^2 - 8x^3$ (b) $y^2 + 9y + 8$ (c) $k^4 - 16$ (d) $x^4 - 5x^2 - 36$

4 If $a = -3$ and $b = 2$, find the value of
$(2a - 3b)(a + 2b) - 3(a + 5b)(2a - b) - (a - b)^2.$

5 (a) Subtract $3(x^2 - 2x - 5)$ from the sum of $2(2x^2 - 5)$ and $-3(2x^2 + 5)$.
(b) By how much does the product of $3x$ and $3x - 2$ exceed $3(x - 5)$?

6 The sum of two numbers is 20. Their product is 96. Find the numbers.

# 3 Applying Skills: Rational Expressions

Essential skills, factoring, rational expressions, operations with rational expressions, solving equations and inequations, solving problems, applying skills, strategies and problem-solving

## Introduction

An important characteristic of mathematics is extending skills you have learned in one branch of mathematics to the learning of skills in another branch. Compare the following.

| Arithmetic | | Algebra |
|---|---|---|
| $3 + 3$ | How are each of these alike? | $x + x$ |
| $4^2$ | | $x^2$ |
| $2(3) - 6$ | How are they | $2x - 6$ |
| $2(6) + 3(8)$ | different? | $2x + 3y$ |

Algebra uses a language of symbols. Once you learn the meanings of the symbols, and how to use them, you can use algebra to solve problems that you might otherwise not be able to solve. The language of algebra has developed over many years. Read the newspaper article shown at the right.

Each skill in algebra is very important for solving problems related to the weather, economics, medicine, space travel, etc. Skills with algebra are used to solve many scientific problems. Advanced algebra is used to describe the paths travelled by space probes.

In this chapter, you will continue to develop skills with algebraic expressions. Throughout the chapter, try to compare the skills you learn in algebra with those you learn in arithmetic. They are closely related.

### People of Algebra

Many people have contributed to Algebra, the branch of mathematics in which letters are used to represent arithmetic relations. The oldest surviving mathematical document, The Rhind Papyrus, (Egypt, 2000 B.C.), contains problems dealing with quadratic equations. Even the Babylonians practised advanced algebra. The Greek Diophantus studied many aspects of algebra. The word algebra comes from the title of an Arabic publication Al-jabr-w'al-muqabalah, written by the Arab, Al KHWarizmi.

People of many nationalities have contributed to the study of algebra. The Italians Luca Pacioli (1450–1520), Nicolo Tartaglia (1500–57) and Geralamo Cardano (1501–76) improved the understanding of equations by introducing negative and complex numbers. A Frenchman, Francois Viete (1540–1603), introduced notation useful in the study of algebra. Englishmen John Wallis (1616–1703), Brook Taylor (1685–1731) and Sir Isaac Newton (1643–1727) also made important contributions, especially Newton for the branch of mathematics called calculus. The German, Karl F. Gauss contributed important proofs in algebra, while the Norwegian Niels H. Abel made important contributions about the structure of algebra. Others who have made significant contributions to the study of algebra are Joseph L. Lagrange, Paolo Ruffini, Evariste Galois, Gottfield W. Leibniz, Augustin L. Cauchy, Karl G. Jacobi, Arthur Cayley, James J. Sylvester, Richard Dedekind, etc.

Near the end of the nineteenth century, Benjamin Pierce and his son Charles combined algebra with logic and gave birth to Boolean Algebra, named in honour of George Boole.

As problems became more and more complicated, so more and more algebra was invented. The impact of algebra on the study of mathematics is considered to be greater than the impact of computers on today's society.

# 3.1 Essential Skills: Factoring

This pattern occurs in your study of mathematics.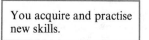

Step A

| You acquire and practise new skills. |
|---|

Step B

| You apply these skills to develop new skills or to solve problems. |
|---|

Before you factor, you must be able to recognize which skills to use.

Throughout the following exercise,
- look for common factors first.
- check your factors to see if any of them can be factored again.

## 3.1 Exercise

**B** List the various skills for factoring that you know. Then factor each of the following. Two of them cannot be factored.

1. $y^2 - 2y - 24$
2. $2m^2 - 2$
3. $m^2 - 11m + 28$
4. $a - 4a^2$
5. $pqr + pqs$
6. $x^2 - 144$
7. $k^2 + 4k$
8. $x^2 - 24x + 80$
9. $p^2 + 7p + 12$
10. $2y^2 + 11y + 12$
11. $2y^2 + 4$
12. $m^3 - 9m^2 - 10m$
13. $3a^2 - 3b^2$
14. $36y^3 - 9y^2$
15. $25m^4 - 16y^4$
16. $y^4 - 13y^2 + 36$
17. $2m^2 - 11m + 12$
18. $x^2 + 2x - 8$
19. $16y^2 - 8y + 1$
20. $2x^2 - 8x^3$
21. $10x^2 - 29x + 10$
22. $-x^2 - 2xy - y^2$
23. $2m^2 + 3m + 1$
24. $90x^2 - 1000$
25. $3y^2 - 36y + 36$
26. $-y^2 + 144$
27. $25m^2 - 16n^2$
28. $12x^2 - 7x - 10$
29. $m^4 - 5m^2 - 36$
30. $2a^3 - 4a$
31. $25x^4 - y^4$
32. $-30y + 62y^2 + 48y^3$
33. $8x^2 - 24y^2$
34. $m^4 - 3m^2 - 4$
35. $2y^3 + 8y^2$
36. $10x^2 - 19x - 15$
37. $\frac{1}{4}x^2 - x + 1$
38. $x^2 - 21x + 108$
39. $x^4 - y^4$
40. $24y^2 - 13y - 2$
41. $b^2 - 15b + 56$
42. $16x^2 + y^2$
43. $x^3 - xy^2$
44. $y^4 - 17y^2 + 16$
45. $-1 + 9n^2$
46. $x^2 + 3x - 18$
47. $36y + 9$
48. $4x^3y + 21x^2y^2 - 18xy^3$
49. $2x^2 - 16x + 32$
50. $x^4 - x^2y^2$
51. $2x^2 + 9x - 35$
52. $-(1 - y^4)$
53. $36m^2 + 25n^2$
54. $1 + 38x + 72x^2$
55. $(y^2 - 4y)^2 - 144$
56. $4(x + y)^2 - (x - y)^2$
57. $9(x - \frac{1}{2})^2 - 4(x + \frac{1}{2})^2$
58. $(m^2 - 5m)^2 - 36$

## 3.2 Simplifying Rational Expressions

Expressions such as $\dfrac{x + y}{x}$ and $\dfrac{x^2 + 6x + 5}{x + 1}$ are rational expressions. Since division by zero is not permissible, then the denominator of rational expressions must not equal zero. When you are working with rational expressions, you must note the restrictions on the variables.

$$\frac{x + y}{x}, \; x \neq 0 \qquad \frac{x^2 + 6x + 5}{x + 1}, \; x + 1 \neq 0 \text{ or } x \neq -1$$

You can use your skills with factoring to simplify rational expressions.

**Example**  Simplify $\dfrac{x^2 + 6x + 5}{x + 1}$.

**Solution**  $\dfrac{x^2 + 6x + 5}{x + 1} = \dfrac{(x + 1)(x + 5)}{x + 1}$  ⟵ Think: Make a note of any restrictions. Factor any expressions.

$$x \neq -1$$

$$= \frac{\overset{1}{\cancel{(x + 1)}}(x + 5)}{\underset{1}{\cancel{x + 1}}}$$  ⟵ Divide numerator and denominator by the same expression.

$$= x + 5, \; x \neq -1$$

## 3.2 Exercise

**A** Before you factor any expression, make a note of any restrictions on the variables.

1  Identify the restrictions on the variables of each rational expression.

(a) $\dfrac{5}{z}$

(b) $\dfrac{a + 2}{a}$

(c) $\dfrac{2x}{y - 1}$

(d) $\dfrac{7}{3m + 6}$

(e) $\dfrac{8a}{ab}$

(f) $\dfrac{-36m}{mn^2}$

(g) $\dfrac{3w - 9}{w(w + 3)}$

(h) $\dfrac{2a + 6}{1 - 2a}$

2  Identify the restrictions on the variables of each rational expression.

(a) $\dfrac{b}{b^2 - 1}$

(b) $\dfrac{3mn}{(m + n)(m - n)}$

(c) $\dfrac{xy - 1}{(x - 2)(y - 3)}$

(d) $\dfrac{\frac{1}{2}c}{2c(c - \frac{1}{2})}$

(e) $\dfrac{4pq}{pq(r - 1)}$

(f) $\dfrac{2k}{(k - 2)(k + 2)}$

(g) $\dfrac{2w + 3}{(2w + 3)(w - 1)}$

(h) $\dfrac{m - 3}{(3m - 6)(2m + 1)}$

(i) $\dfrac{(a^2 - 4)(a + 3)}{(a + 3)(a - 2)}$

3 Factor each of the following. What are the restrictions on the variables?

(a) $\dfrac{y^2 - 16}{y^2 + 4y - 32}$

(b) $\dfrac{y^2 - 9}{y^2 - 6y + 9}$

(c) $\dfrac{y^2 - 5y + 6}{y^2 - 4}$

(d) $\dfrac{10ab - 15a^2b}{12a^2 - 8a}$

4 (a) Find the value of $\dfrac{x^2 + 6x + 5}{x + 1}$ if $x = 8$.

(b) Find the value of $x + 5$ if $x = 8$.

(c) Why are the answers the same in (a) and (b)?

5 (a) Simplify $\dfrac{x^2 - 2x - 48}{x + 6}$.　　　(b) Evaluate the expression in (a) if $x = -4$.

**B** Remember: Note the restrictions on the variables, before you simplify an expression.

6 For each of the following expressions
  • note the restrictions on the variables.
  • simplify the expression.

(a) $\dfrac{x^2 - 2x - 15}{4x - 20}$

(b) $\dfrac{2y - 2}{y^2 - 3y + 2}$

(c) $\dfrac{2y - 7}{2y^2 - y - 21}$

(d) $\dfrac{6x^2 - x - 1}{4x^2 - 1}$

(e) $\dfrac{x^2 + 10xy + 25y^2}{x + 5y}$

(f) $\dfrac{6x^2 - 5xy + y^2}{6x^2 - xy - y^2}$

(g) $\dfrac{x^2 + 4x + 3}{x^2 - 2x - 3}$

(h) $\dfrac{2p^2 + 3pq + q^2}{3p^2 + 2pq - q^2}$

(i) $\dfrac{25x^2 - 9y^2}{5x^2 + 8xy + 3y^2}$

7 Evaluate each of the following. Use $x = -1$, $y = 3$.

(a) $\dfrac{x^2 - 5x + 6}{x - 3}$

(b) $\dfrac{y^2 - 7y + 6}{y - 6}$

(c) $\dfrac{x^2 - 9x + 20}{x - 5}$

(d) $\dfrac{x^2 - 5xy - 24y^2}{x - 8y}$

(e) $\dfrac{x^2 - y^2}{3x^2 + 2xy - y^2}$

(f) $\dfrac{2x^2 + xy - y^2}{4x^2 - y^2}$

8 Use $a = x + y$, and $b = x - y$. Simplify each of the following.

(a) $\dfrac{3a^2 + 12ab + 12b^2}{a + 2b}$

(b) $\dfrac{a^2 - b^2}{3a^2 - 2ab - b^2}$

(c) $\dfrac{10a^2 - 9ab - 9b^2}{2a - 3b}$

9 Which expression has the greatest value for $x = -3$, $y = 2$?

A: $\dfrac{8x^2 + 2xy - 15y^2}{2x + 3y}$

B: $\dfrac{x^2 + 4xy + 3y^2}{x^2 - y^2}$

C: $\dfrac{2xy + 4y^2}{16x^2 - 64y^2}$

## 3.3 Monomial Denominators

Your skills in arithmetic extend to skills in algebra. Compare the
following. How are these examples alike? How are they different?
In arithmetic you deal
with numbers, whereas
in algebra you deal
with algebraic
expressions.

*Arithmetic*

$$\frac{1}{2} + \frac{1}{3} = \frac{3}{6} + \frac{2}{6}$$

$$= \frac{5}{6}$$

*Algebra*

$$\frac{1}{x} + \frac{1}{y} = \frac{y}{xy} + \frac{x}{xy}$$

$$= \frac{y + x}{xy}$$

**Example 1**   Simplify $\dfrac{5}{4ab} + \dfrac{-2}{3a} - \dfrac{-3}{2b}$.

Think: To add or subtract
find the least common
denominator.

**Solution**

$$\frac{5}{4ab} + \frac{-2}{3a} - \frac{-3}{2b} = \frac{5}{4ab} + \frac{-2b}{3ab} - \frac{-3a}{2ab} \text{, where } a, b \ne 0.$$

$$= \frac{15}{12ab} + \frac{-8b}{12ab} - \frac{-18a}{12ab}$$

The least common
multiple of $4ab$,
$3a$ and $2b$ is $12ab$.

$$= \frac{15 - 8b + 18a}{12ab}$$

This expression cannot be
simplified any further.

To simplify the following expressions, you follow the same procedure.

**Example 2**   Simplify $\dfrac{x-1}{3} - \dfrac{x-2}{4}$.

**Solution**

$$\frac{x-1}{3} - \frac{x-2}{4} = \frac{4(x-1)}{12} - \frac{3(x-2)}{12}$$

Think: What is the least
common denominator?

$$= \frac{4x - 4 - 3x + 6}{12}$$

$$= \frac{x+2}{12}$$

## 3.3 Exercise

**A 1**   To add or subtract rational expressions, you need to find the least
common denominator. How is the least common denominator for
$\dfrac{-3}{2ab} - \dfrac{2}{3a}$ related to the least common multiple of $2ab$ and $3a$?

2   Find the least common multiple of each of the following.

   (a) $4m, 6m$          (b) $3x, 2x$          (c) $xy, x$          (d) $x^2y, xy^2$

   (e) $3x, x, 6x$       (f) $a, b, 2ab$       (g) $x, x^2, 2x$      (h) $xy, x, x^2y$

3   Simplify.

   (a) $\dfrac{3x}{2} + \dfrac{5x}{4}$

   (b) $\dfrac{3}{2a} + \dfrac{5}{4a}$

   (c) $\dfrac{3x}{2a} + \dfrac{5x}{4a}$

   (d) $\dfrac{4x}{3} + \dfrac{2x}{5}$

   (e) $\dfrac{4}{3a} + \dfrac{2}{5a}$

   (f) $\dfrac{4x}{3a} + \dfrac{2x}{5a}$

4   Simplify each of the following.

   (a) $\dfrac{-3}{4m} + \dfrac{2}{6m}$

   (b) $\dfrac{-4y}{3x} - \dfrac{3y}{2x}$

   (c) $\dfrac{2x}{m} - \dfrac{3x}{n}$

   (d) $\dfrac{-2}{xy} + \dfrac{6}{x}$

   (e) $-\dfrac{8}{x^2y} - \dfrac{6}{xy^2}$

   (f) $\dfrac{4x}{a} - \dfrac{3x}{2a^2}$

5   Simplify.

   (a) $\dfrac{3x}{2} - \dfrac{5x}{4} + \dfrac{3x}{2}$

   (b) $\dfrac{3x}{2} + \dfrac{5x}{3} + \dfrac{2x}{6}$

   (c) $\dfrac{3x}{2} - \dfrac{5x}{4} + \dfrac{2x}{5}$

6   Simplify.

   (a) $\dfrac{3}{a} - \dfrac{5}{2a} + \dfrac{3}{a}$

   (b) $\dfrac{3x}{a} - \dfrac{5x}{2a} + \dfrac{3x}{a}$

   (c) $\dfrac{2}{x} - \dfrac{5}{xy} - \dfrac{6}{y^2}$

   (d) $\dfrac{2a}{x} - \dfrac{5a}{xy} - \dfrac{6a}{x^2}$

7   Simplify each of the following.

   (a) $\dfrac{x}{3} - \dfrac{x}{5}$

   (b) $\dfrac{a}{6} - \dfrac{2a}{9}$

   (c) $\dfrac{m}{5} + \dfrac{3m}{2}$

   (d) $\dfrac{x}{4} + \dfrac{x+5}{3}$

   (e) $\dfrac{y+1}{6} - \dfrac{3}{4}$

   (f) $\dfrac{x-1}{3} - \dfrac{3}{2}$

8   Simplify.

   (a) $\dfrac{6x+1}{3} + \dfrac{x-2}{4}$

   (b) $\dfrac{2m-1}{6} - \dfrac{m+1}{9}$

   (c) $\dfrac{6y+4}{3} - \dfrac{y-2}{2}$

   (d) $\dfrac{2x+1}{6} - 3$

   (e) $\dfrac{8x-2}{9} - \dfrac{x-3}{6}$

   (f) $\dfrac{2t-1}{6} + \dfrac{3t+1}{4}$

   (g) $\dfrac{x-1}{3} + \dfrac{x-2}{2} - \dfrac{x-3}{6}$

   (h) $\dfrac{2x-1}{6} + \dfrac{3x+1}{4} - \dfrac{2x-5}{2}$

**B** Remember: When you add or subtract, you need to find the least common denominator.

9   You can write a rational expression in these equivalent ways.

$$\frac{-6}{xy} = -\frac{6}{xy} = \frac{6}{-xy}$$

Simplify each of the following. Use positive denominators.

(a) $\dfrac{2a}{x} + \dfrac{3b}{-2y}$

(b) $\dfrac{-2}{xy} - \dfrac{6}{-x}$

(c) $\dfrac{8}{x^2y} - \dfrac{8}{xy^2}$

(d) $\dfrac{6}{-a^2} + \dfrac{4}{a}$

(e) $\dfrac{-3}{-4xy^2} - \dfrac{-2}{6x^2y}$

(f) $\dfrac{2a}{xy^2} - \dfrac{-3b}{-x^2y}$

(g) $\dfrac{5}{2a} + \dfrac{-8}{-3a} - \dfrac{4}{6a}$

(h) $\dfrac{my}{2x} - \dfrac{-2mx}{3y} + \dfrac{m}{-6xy}$

(i) $\dfrac{-4}{x} - \dfrac{5}{-x^2} - \dfrac{6}{2x}$

10   Simplify.

(a) $\dfrac{2}{3x} - \dfrac{4}{x} + \dfrac{5}{6x}$

(b) $\dfrac{x}{a} - \dfrac{2x}{b} + \dfrac{3x}{2ab}$

(c) $\dfrac{a}{3m} + \dfrac{b}{2m} - \dfrac{2c}{6n}$

(d) $\dfrac{-3}{x} + \dfrac{4}{x^2} - \dfrac{7}{2x}$

(e) $\dfrac{6a}{xy} - \dfrac{4a}{x} + \dfrac{-8a}{x^2y}$

(f) $\dfrac{m}{pq} - \dfrac{2m}{p} - \dfrac{3m}{q^2}$

11   Simplify.

(a) $\dfrac{2m+3}{4m} + \dfrac{3m+2}{2m}$

(b) $\dfrac{3x+2}{5x} - \dfrac{4x-1}{2x}$

(c) $\dfrac{2a-b}{3a} + \dfrac{a+b}{2b}$

(d) $\dfrac{3x+y}{2x^2y} - \dfrac{2x-y}{4xy}$

(e) $\dfrac{x-3}{2x} - \dfrac{x^2-1}{4x^2}$

(f) $\dfrac{2-3y}{3y} + \dfrac{2y^2+1}{2y^2}$

12   (a) Find the sum of $\dfrac{2x}{3y}$, $\dfrac{-x}{-2y}$, and $\dfrac{x}{-6y}$.

(b) Subtract $\dfrac{3a^2}{5ab}$ from $\dfrac{a}{6b}$.

(c) Find the product of $\dfrac{2x^2y}{3a}$ and $\dfrac{-6a}{5xy}$.

(d) Divide $\dfrac{6x^2k}{-7xy}$ by $\dfrac{-7k}{3y}$.

13   (a) What are the next two numbers in the pattern?

2, 12, 40,    ?, ?

(b) What are the next two letters in the pattern?

T, F, S, E, T, T, ?, ?

**C** 14   (a) You are given $a^2 + \dfrac{1}{a^2} = 3$. Find the value of $\left(a + \dfrac{1}{a}\right)^2 - \left(a - \dfrac{1}{a}\right)^2$.

(b) If $b^2 + \dfrac{1}{b^2} = 6$, find a value for $\left(b + \dfrac{1}{b}\right)^4$.

## 3.4 Rational Expressions: Adding and Subtracting

Look for similarities and differences to help you remember how to do mathematics. For example, in the previous section you simplified expressions with monomial denominators.

PSP

The process used in this section is the same. Only the algebraic expressions are different. In the following example, the denominators are like binomials. Thus, you can add the numerators.

**Example 1**   Simplify $\dfrac{2x + 1}{x - 3} + \dfrac{3x - 1}{x - 3} - \dfrac{x + 1}{x - 3}$.

**Solution**

$\dfrac{2x + 1}{x - 3} + \dfrac{3x - 1}{x - 3} - \dfrac{x + 1}{x - 3}$ ⟵ The denominators are like and $x \neq 3$.

$= \dfrac{(2x + 1) + (3x - 1) - (x + 1)}{x - 3}$ ⟵ Thus, add the numerators.

$= \dfrac{2x + 1 + 3x - 1 - x - 1}{x - 3}$

$= \dfrac{4x - 1}{x - 3}$

In the next example, the denominators are not like. You need to use your factoring skills to obtain the least common denominator.

**Example 2**   Simplify $\dfrac{-a^2}{a^2 - b^2} + \dfrac{a}{a - b} - \dfrac{b}{a + b}$.

**Solution**

$\dfrac{-a^2}{a^2 - b^2} + \dfrac{a}{a - b} - \dfrac{b}{a + b}$ , $a \neq b, a \neq -b$     Think: Find the least common denominator.

$= \dfrac{-a^2}{(a - b)(a + b)} + \dfrac{a(a + b)}{(a - b)(a + b)} - \dfrac{b(a - b)}{(a - b)(a + b)}$

$= \dfrac{-a^2 + a^2 + ab - ba + b^2}{(a - b)(a + b)}$     Remember: $a^2 - b^2 = (a - b)(a + b)$

$= \dfrac{b^2}{(a - b)(a + b)}$

The exercise that follows develops your skills with adding and subtracting rational expressions. These skills are important for solving equations that involve rational expressions.

## 3.4 Exercise

**A** Remember: You can add the numerators only if the denominators are the same.

1 List the restrictions on the following denominators.

(a) $\dfrac{5}{x} - \dfrac{4}{x-4}$

(b) $\dfrac{3}{a+1} - \dfrac{3}{a}$

(c) $\dfrac{4}{x+4} + \dfrac{5}{x-2}$

(d) $\dfrac{3}{x+1} - \dfrac{5}{x-2}$

(e) $\dfrac{6}{x-y} - \dfrac{7}{x+y}$

(f) $\dfrac{4}{x-6} + \dfrac{3}{x+5}$

(g) $\dfrac{6}{x-3} + \dfrac{2}{2x}$

(h) $\dfrac{4}{x-2y} - \dfrac{8}{x+2y}$

2 (a) Simplify $\dfrac{1}{x} + \dfrac{x+1}{2x}$.

(b) Simplify $\dfrac{1}{x-1} + \dfrac{x+1}{2(x-1)}$.

(c) How are the expressions in (a) and (b) alike? How do they differ?

3 (a) Simplify $\dfrac{x+1}{x} + \dfrac{x^2+1}{x^2}$.

(b) Simplify $\dfrac{x+1}{x-1} + \dfrac{x^2+1}{(x-1)^2}$.

(c) How are the expressions in (a) and (b) alike? How do they differ?

4 (a) Simplify $\dfrac{a+b}{a} - \dfrac{b-a}{b}$.

(b) Simplify $\dfrac{a+b}{a-b} - \dfrac{b-a}{a+b}$.

(c) How are the expressions in (a) and (b) alike? How do they differ?

5 (a) Simplify $\dfrac{3}{a} + \dfrac{4}{a+2}$.

(b) Simplify $\dfrac{3}{a} + \dfrac{4}{a^2+2a}$.

(c) How are (a) and (b) alike? How are they different?

6 (a) Simplify $\dfrac{8}{y-2} - \dfrac{4}{y+2}$.

(b) Simplify $\dfrac{8}{y-2} - \dfrac{4}{y^2-4}$.

(c) How are (a) and (b) alike? How are they different?

**B** When you have completed your work, check whether your answer can be simplified any further.

7 Simplify each of the following.

(a) $\dfrac{3}{x-2} + \dfrac{x}{x-1}$

(b) $\dfrac{3y}{y-3} - \dfrac{2}{y+5}$

(c) $\dfrac{3}{a-b} - \dfrac{4}{a+b}$

(d) $\dfrac{3}{x-6} + \dfrac{4}{2x-3}$

(e) $\dfrac{2}{y-5} - \dfrac{3y}{y+5}$

(f) $\dfrac{2x}{x+5} - \dfrac{3}{x-3}$

8   Simplify.

(a) $\dfrac{5}{a} - \dfrac{3}{a-2}$   (b) $\dfrac{5}{a} - \dfrac{3}{a^2 - 2a}$   (c) $\dfrac{8}{y+1} - \dfrac{6}{y}$   (d) $\dfrac{8}{y^2 + y} - \dfrac{6}{y}$

(e) $\dfrac{3}{x-3} + \dfrac{8}{x+3}$   (f) $\dfrac{4}{x-2} + \dfrac{6}{x+2}$   (g) $\dfrac{3}{x^2 - 9} - \dfrac{2}{x+3}$   (h) $\dfrac{5}{x^2 - 4} - \dfrac{1}{x+2}$

9   Remember that $-(a-b) = b-a$. Simplify each of the following.

(a) $\dfrac{3}{x-1} + \dfrac{x}{1-x}$   (b) $\dfrac{2}{x+1} - \dfrac{x}{1-x^2}$   (c) $\dfrac{3}{5-a} - \dfrac{a}{a^2 - 25}$

(d) $\dfrac{a}{a^2 - 4} - \dfrac{4}{2+a}$   (e) $\dfrac{2x - 3y}{x^2 - y^2} - \dfrac{1}{y-x}$   (f) $\dfrac{3}{3-a} - \dfrac{2-a}{9-a^2}$

(g) $\dfrac{2x}{x^2 - y^2} - \dfrac{x}{y-x} + \dfrac{y}{y+x}$   (h) $\dfrac{3m}{m+n} + \dfrac{2n}{n-m} - \dfrac{6}{m^2 - n^2}$

10   Use $x = 3$. Find the value of each expression.

(a) $\dfrac{1}{x-1} - \dfrac{x}{x^2 - 1}$   (b) $\dfrac{1}{x^2 - 1}$

(c)   What do you notice about your answers in (a) and (b)? Why is this so?

11   Evaluate each expression for the given value.

(a) $\dfrac{4}{y^2 - 4} - \dfrac{2}{y+2}$, $y = 3$   (b) $\dfrac{3}{a-3} - \dfrac{2}{a^2 - 9}$, $a = 2$

(c) $\dfrac{3a}{a-3} + \dfrac{4a^2}{a^2 - 6a + 9}$, $a = -1$   (d) $\dfrac{2}{x-1} - \dfrac{3}{x+1} + \dfrac{4}{x^2 - 1}$, $x = 2$

12   Use $x = -2$. Evaluate each of the following.

(a) $\dfrac{x-6}{x^2 - 8x + 16} + \dfrac{4x + 20}{x^2 + 12x + 35}$   (b) $\dfrac{x+1}{2x^2 - 5x + 6} - \dfrac{x-3}{2x^2 - x - 3}$

## Problem-Solving

An important strategy in solving some problems is organized trial and error. Solve the following problem.

▶ A 4 × 4 square as shown is cut into two congruent parts. Find as many ways as you can of cutting the square into congruent parts.

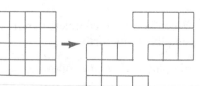

▶ To solve any problem in mathematics you must understand the meaning of the words used. Refer to Chapter 8 to find the meaning of **congruent**.

# 3.5 Combining Operations: Monomials

Often, you need to make decisions when you are simplifying expressions. It is useful to plan your steps before proceeding with the simplification. For example, to simplify the following expressions, you can simplify your work by looking for like factors.

**Example 1** Simplify. (a) $\dfrac{-24k^2}{45} \times \dfrac{-9}{15k}$ (b) $\dfrac{-3x^2y}{4a^2} \div \dfrac{9xy}{-5a}$

**Solution**

(a) $\dfrac{-24k^2}{45} \times \dfrac{-9}{15k} = \dfrac{\overset{-8\ \ k}{-24k^2}}{\underset{5}{45}} \times \dfrac{\overset{-1}{-9}}{\underset{5\ \ 1}{15k}}$, where $k \neq 0$.

$$= \dfrac{-8k}{5} \times \dfrac{-1}{5}$$

$$= \dfrac{8k}{25}$$

(b) $\dfrac{-3x^2y}{4a^2} \div \dfrac{9xy}{-5a} = \dfrac{\overset{-1\ x\ \ 1}{-3x^2y}}{\underset{a}{4a^2}} \times \dfrac{\overset{1}{-5a}}{\underset{3\ 1\ 1}{9xy}}$, where $x, y, a \neq 0$.

$$= \dfrac{-x}{4a} \times \dfrac{-5}{3}$$

$$= \dfrac{5x}{12a}$$

In the next example, first simplify the expression in parentheses.

**Example 2** Simplify $\dfrac{2x^2}{5}\left(\dfrac{5}{x} - \dfrac{-3}{2x^2}\right)$.

**Solution** $\dfrac{2x^2}{5}\left(\dfrac{5}{x} - \dfrac{-3}{2x^2}\right) = \dfrac{2x^2}{5}\left(\dfrac{10x + 3}{2x^2}\right)$, where $x \neq 0$.

$$= \dfrac{\overset{1}{2x^2}}{5}\left(\dfrac{10x + 3}{\underset{1}{2x^2}}\right)$$

$$= \dfrac{10x + 3}{5}$$

Always ask yourself: Is my final answer in simplest form?

## 3.5  Exercise

**A** Remember to check your final answer to see if it is in simplest form.

1  Find the products.

(a) $\dfrac{m}{n} \times \dfrac{b}{a}$

(b) $\dfrac{-m}{n} \times \dfrac{-a}{b}$

(c) $\left(\dfrac{-a}{m}\right)\left(\dfrac{-m}{b}\right)$

(d) $\dfrac{-6}{5} \times \dfrac{-x}{3}$

(e) $\dfrac{x^2}{-4} \times \dfrac{8}{x}$

(f) $\dfrac{x}{y} \times \dfrac{-3y}{k}$

(g) $\dfrac{3a}{2} \times \dfrac{5m}{6}$

(h) $-3m^2\left(-\dfrac{5}{6m}\right)$

(i) $\dfrac{-6x}{3} \times \dfrac{-3}{-6x}$

2  Simplify each of the following.

(a) $\dfrac{-y^2}{2} \times \dfrac{y^2}{3}$

(b) $\dfrac{3x^2}{2y} \times \dfrac{-2y}{3}$

(c) $\dfrac{a^2}{3} \times \dfrac{a^4}{6}$

(d) $\left(\dfrac{x}{3m}\right)\left(\dfrac{-3m}{-y}\right)$

(e) $\left(\dfrac{3a^2}{5b^2}\right)\left(\dfrac{10b}{4b^3}\right)$

(f) $\left(\dfrac{6}{x^2y}\right)\left(\dfrac{x^3y^2}{x}\right)$

3  Simplify. Watch for like factors.

(a) $\dfrac{xy}{-5} \times \dfrac{-10}{x} \times \dfrac{-2}{y}$

(b) $m \times \dfrac{-m}{8} \times \dfrac{4k}{-m}$

(c) $\dfrac{2x}{y} \times \dfrac{-6x}{5y} \times \dfrac{y^2}{-3x}$

(d) $\left(\dfrac{4a}{-3y}\right)\left(\dfrac{-3}{8ab}\right)\left(\dfrac{3b}{2}\right)$

4  Multiply each of the following.

(a) $\dfrac{12x}{-5x^2} \times \dfrac{-x^2}{6x^2} \times \dfrac{-10x}{3x}$

(b) $\dfrac{-2x^3}{3} \times \dfrac{3x^2}{-2y^3} \times \dfrac{4y^2}{x}$

(c) $\left(\dfrac{-16m^2}{5}\right)\left(\dfrac{-15}{4m^2}\right)\left(\dfrac{m}{3}\right)$

(d) $\dfrac{-x^2}{6y} \times \dfrac{12xy}{-x} \times \dfrac{2y}{-x^2}$

5  Write the reciprocal of each of the following.

(a) $\dfrac{3y}{-x}$

(b) $\dfrac{-2x^2}{y}$

(c) $2y$

(d) $-\dfrac{2x}{3}$

(e) $\dfrac{5y}{4}$

(f) $\dfrac{-3x}{5y}$

6  Divide each of the following.

(a) $\dfrac{x}{y} \div \dfrac{a}{b}$

(b) $\dfrac{-x}{y} \div \dfrac{-a}{b}$

(c) $\dfrac{-a}{-b} \div \left(-\dfrac{a}{y}\right)$

(d) $\dfrac{-2}{7} \div \dfrac{3}{-x}$

(e) $6 \div \left(\dfrac{-3}{y}\right)$

(f) $\dfrac{-6}{y} \div \dfrac{5}{k}$

7    Simplify each of the following.

(a) $\left(\dfrac{-x}{4}\right) \div \left(\dfrac{-5}{16y}\right)$

(b) $\dfrac{-2}{3y} \div \dfrac{5y}{-6}$

(c) $\dfrac{2x}{-5} \div \dfrac{x^2}{-10}$

(d) $\dfrac{x^2}{4} \div \dfrac{20x^2 y}{-16}$

(e) $\left(\dfrac{-x}{ab}\right) \div \left(\dfrac{-x}{ab}\right)$

(f) $-6 \div \dfrac{-15}{ab}$

**B** Remember: The order of operations applies to your work with rational expressions.

8    Simplify.

(a) $\dfrac{ab}{-3} \div \dfrac{a}{-9} \times \dfrac{-b}{3}$

(b) $\dfrac{3a}{-b} - \dfrac{-a^2}{b^2} \times \dfrac{b}{-a}$

(c) $\dfrac{-5}{a} \times \dfrac{-a^3}{-ab} - \dfrac{3a}{-2b}$

(d) $\left(\dfrac{x}{10y}\right)\left(\dfrac{-2x}{y^2}\right) \div \left(\dfrac{-1}{5y^2}\right)$

9    Simplify each of the following.

(a) $\dfrac{-4x^2}{y^2} \times \dfrac{y}{-8x} \div \dfrac{y}{2x}$

(b) $\dfrac{-10a^2}{b} \times \dfrac{-b^2}{5a} \div \left(\dfrac{b}{2a}\right)$

(c) $\dfrac{3a}{-b} \times \dfrac{b^2}{6a} \div (-a)$

(d) $\left(\dfrac{-x}{4k}\right)\left(-\dfrac{5}{3x}\right) \div \left(\dfrac{x}{12k}\right)$

(e) $\left(\dfrac{x}{10y}\right)\left(\dfrac{-2x}{y^2}\right) \div \left(\dfrac{-1}{5y^2}\right)$

(f) $-\dfrac{16m^3}{n} \times \dfrac{-1}{4m^2} \div \dfrac{-n^2}{4m}$

10    Simplify.

(a) $\dfrac{-4x^2}{5}\left(\dfrac{-5}{x} - \dfrac{-3}{2x}\right)$

(b) $\left(\dfrac{-2}{3x} + \dfrac{8}{-2y}\right) \div \dfrac{-3y}{x^2}$

(c) $\left(\dfrac{-5}{2x} + \dfrac{-2}{3x}\right) \div \left(\dfrac{-3}{x} + \dfrac{5}{-4x}\right)$

(d) $\left(\dfrac{3}{2a} - \dfrac{2}{-3b}\right) + \left(\dfrac{2}{b} - \dfrac{3}{-a}\right)$

11    If $x = \dfrac{-4a}{5b}$ and $y = \dfrac{-3a}{2b}$, find an expression for

(a) $xy$      (b) $x^2$      (c) $y^2$      (d) $x + y$      (e) $x - y$

(f) $y - x$      (g) $2x + y$      (h) $3y - x$      (i) $-x - y$

**C 12**    (a) Prove $\left(\dfrac{x}{-y} \times \dfrac{-y^2}{2x}\right) \times \dfrac{y^2}{-x} = \dfrac{x}{-y} \times \left(\dfrac{-y^2}{2x} \times \dfrac{y^2}{-x}\right).$

(b) Prove $\left(\dfrac{-2b}{3a} \div \dfrac{-b}{-a}\right) \div \dfrac{3a}{-2b} \neq \dfrac{-2b}{3a} \div \left(\dfrac{-b}{-a} \div \dfrac{3a}{-2b}\right).$

# 3.6 Rational Expressions: Multiplying and Dividing

The skills you used to simplify expressions in the previous section, can be extended to the simplification of rational expressions involving polynomials. To simplify such expressions, you need to factor the numerators and denominators.

**Example 1**    Simplify $\dfrac{a^2 - 4a}{a^2 + 5a} \times \dfrac{a^2 + 7a + 10}{3a - 12}$.

**Solution**    $\dfrac{a^2 - 4a}{a^2 + 5a} \times \dfrac{a^2 + 7a + 10}{3a - 12} = \dfrac{a(a - 4)}{a(a + 5)} \times \dfrac{(a + 5)(a + 2)}{3(a - 4)}$

Make a note of the restrictions.
$a \neq 0, 4, \text{ or } -5.$

$$= \dfrac{\overset{1}{\cancel{a}}\overset{1}{\cancel{(a - 4)}}}{\cancel{a}\cancel{(a + 5)}} \times \dfrac{\overset{1}{\cancel{(a + 5)}}(a + 2)}{3\cancel{(a - 4)}}$$

$$= \dfrac{a + 2}{3}$$

You need to plan ahead if you are going to simplify rational expressions involving more than one operation. Compare the steps you use for simplifying in the next example with the steps you would use to simplify $\dfrac{2}{3} \times \dfrac{6}{5} \div \dfrac{4}{15}$.

**PSP**   Look for comparisons with previous problems you have solved.

**Example 2**    Simplify $\dfrac{y^2 + y}{y^2 - 4y} \times \dfrac{y^2 - 4y - 21}{y + 3} \div \dfrac{y^2 - 6y - 7}{y^2 - y - 12}$.

**Solution**    $\dfrac{y^2 + y}{y^2 - 4y} \times \dfrac{y^2 - 4y - 21}{y + 3} \div \dfrac{y^2 - 6y - 7}{y^2 - y - 12}$

$$= \dfrac{y(y + 1)}{y(y - 4)} \times \dfrac{(y - 7)(y + 3)}{y + 3} \div \dfrac{(y - 7)(y + 1)}{(y - 4)(y + 3)}$$

$$= \dfrac{\overset{1}{\cancel{y}}\overset{1}{\cancel{(y + 1)}}}{\cancel{y}\cancel{(y - 4)}} \times \dfrac{\overset{1}{\cancel{(y - 7)}}\overset{1}{\cancel{(y + 3)}}}{\cancel{y + 3}} \times \dfrac{\overset{1}{\cancel{(y - 4)}}(y + 3)}{\cancel{(y - 7)}\cancel{(y + 1)}}$$

Note the restrictions.
$y \neq -3, \pm 2, -1, 0, 4, 7$

$$= y + 3$$

## 3.6 Exercise

**A** Remember: When you simplify rational expressions, look for like factors.

1   (a) What is the first step in simplifying $\dfrac{a^2 - b^2}{a^2 - 2ab + b^2}$?

(b) What restrictions apply in (a)?     (c) Simplify the expression.

2   For each expression,
   • list the restrictions on the variable.     • simplify the expression.

(a) $\dfrac{-4x^2(x - y)}{2x(x - y)}$     (b) $\dfrac{-4(a + b)}{2(a + b)}$     (c) $\dfrac{-4x^3 - 4x^2 y}{-4x - 4y}$

(d) $\dfrac{s^2 - 2s - 15}{4s - 20}$     (e) $\dfrac{2m^2 + 5m - 3}{2m^2 - 7m + 3}$     (f) $\dfrac{x^2 - 16}{2x - 8}$

(g) $\dfrac{a^2 - 10ab + 25b^2}{a^2 - 25b^2}$     (h) $\dfrac{4m^2 - 36m + 72}{m^2 - 36}$

3   (a) What is the first step in simplifying $\dfrac{y + 1}{y^2 - 1} \div \dfrac{3y}{y - 1}$?

(b) Simplify the expression in (a). What restrictions apply?

4   For each of the following
   • simplify the expression.     • list the restrictions that apply.

(a) $\dfrac{36}{y^2 + 2y} \times \dfrac{y + 2}{9}$     (b) $\dfrac{x - 1}{3x} \div \dfrac{x^2 - 1}{x}$     (c) $\dfrac{y + 2}{8} \div \dfrac{y^2 - y - 6}{16}$

(d) $\dfrac{a^2 - b^2}{a^2 - 16} \times \dfrac{a - 4}{a - b}$     (e) $\dfrac{x + 1}{x^2 - 1} \div \dfrac{x}{x - 1}$     (f) $\dfrac{3x - 12}{4x + 20} \times \dfrac{x^2 + 5x}{x^2 - 4x}$

5   (a) Simplify $\dfrac{x^2 - 9}{-(x - 3)}$.     (b) Simplify $\dfrac{x^2 - 9}{3 - x}$.

(c) What do you notice about your answers in (a) and (b)?

6   When you are simplifying expressions, remember that $-(x - y) = y - x$.
Simplify each of the following.

(a) $\dfrac{-(y - x)}{y - x}$     (b) $\dfrac{x - y}{-(y - x)}$     (c) $\dfrac{-(y - x)}{-(x - y)}$     (d) $\dfrac{-(y - x)}{x - y}$

(e) $\dfrac{x + y}{y + x}$     (f) $\dfrac{m^2 - n^2}{n - m}$     (g) $\dfrac{4a^2 - b^2}{2a - b}$     (h) $\dfrac{x^2 + xy - 2y^2}{y^2 - x^2}$

**B** Review the various skills for factoring. Remember: Always check for a common factor first.

7    Simplify.

(a) $\dfrac{y-3}{2-y} \times \dfrac{y-2}{3-y}$

(b) $\dfrac{x^2y}{2x-2} \times \dfrac{2}{xy^2}$

(c) $\dfrac{x-1}{6} \div \dfrac{1-x}{8}$

(d) $\dfrac{4}{y^2-9} \div \dfrac{8}{3-y}$

(e) $\dfrac{x-y}{16} \times \dfrac{8}{x^2-y^2}$

(f) $\dfrac{x+1}{x^2-1} \times \dfrac{x-1}{x}$

8    Simplify each of the following.

(a) $\dfrac{x^2-1}{x^2+6x+9} \div \dfrac{x^2+2x-3}{x^2+6x+9}$

(b) $\dfrac{a^2+3a+2}{a^2-3a} \times \dfrac{3-a}{a^2+7a+6}$

(c) $(4a^2-9b^2) \div \dfrac{3ab+2a^2}{2}$

(d) $\dfrac{2a^2-7a-4}{a^2-7a+12} \times \dfrac{2a-6}{4a^2-1}$

9    Simplify.

(a) $\dfrac{x+1}{x-1} \times \dfrac{x+3}{1-x^2} \times \dfrac{1-x}{(x+3)^2}$

(b) $\dfrac{x^2-y^2}{x^2+xy} \times \dfrac{(x+y)^2}{xy} \div \dfrac{x^2-xy}{x^2+xy}$

(c) $\dfrac{a^2-a}{6a^2+15} \times \dfrac{4a^2+10}{a^2-7a+12} \times \dfrac{a^2-4a}{2a}$

(d) $\dfrac{2x+x^2}{4-x^2} \times \dfrac{x^2-2x}{x^2-4x} \times \dfrac{x^2-6x+8}{x^2-16}$

(e) $\dfrac{x^3+4x^2}{x^2-1} \times \dfrac{x^2-5x+6}{x^2-3x} \div \dfrac{x^2+2x-8}{x^2-1}$

10    If $a = -2$, which expression, A or B, has the greater value?

A:    $\dfrac{a^2+a}{a+3} \times \dfrac{a^2-4a-21}{a^2-4a} \div \dfrac{a^2-6a-7}{a^2-a-12}$

B:    $\dfrac{a^3+4a^2}{a^2-1} \times \dfrac{a^2-5a+6}{a^2-3a} \div \dfrac{a^2+2a-8}{a^2-1}$

**C** 11    If $x$ decreases in value from 2 to 1, how does the value of the following expression change?

$$\dfrac{x^2+7x+6}{x^2+6x+5} \div \dfrac{x^3+6x^2}{x^2+5x}$$

## 3.7 Applying Skills: Solving Equations

The process by which you learn mathematics is shown in the diagram.

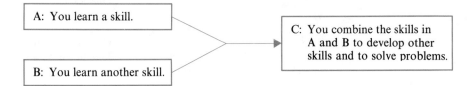

In this section you will combine your skills in solving equations (Skill A) with your skills in simplifying equations (Skill B) to solve another type of equation (Skill C).

**Example 1**   Solve $\dfrac{4x-3}{6} - \dfrac{2x-5}{8} = \dfrac{7x}{16}$, $x \in R$.

**Solution**
$$\frac{4x-3}{6} - \frac{2x-5}{8} = \frac{7x}{16}$$

$$\frac{\overset{8}{48}(4x-3)}{\underset{1}{6}} - \frac{\overset{6}{48}(2x-5)}{\underset{1}{8}} = \frac{\overset{3}{48}(7x)}{\underset{1}{16}}$$

Think: Multiply the equation by the least common multiple of the denominators, which is 48.

$$8(4x-3) - 6(2x-5) = 3(7x)$$
$$32x - 24 - 12x + 30 = 21x$$
$$32x - 12x - 21x = -6$$
$$-x = -6$$
$$x = 6$$

Check in the original equation.

$$\text{L.S.} = \frac{4x-3}{6} - \frac{2x-5}{8} \qquad\qquad \text{R.S.} = \frac{7x}{16}$$

$$= \frac{4(6)-3}{6} - \frac{2(6)-5}{8} \qquad\qquad = \frac{7(6)}{16}$$

$$= \frac{21}{8} \qquad\qquad\qquad\qquad = \frac{21}{8}$$

L.S. = R.S. checks ✓

Equations using rational expressions are needed to solve geometric problems involving ratio. Remember, as you solve each equation, note the restrictions on the variables.

**Example 2** Solve $\dfrac{x+5}{x-3} = \dfrac{x+3}{x-4}$, $x \in R$.

**Solution**

$$\dfrac{x+5}{x-3} = \dfrac{x+3}{x-4} \longleftarrow \text{Think: Multiply the equation by } (x-3)(x-4), \ x \neq 3, 4.$$

$$(x-3)(x-4)\dfrac{x+5}{x-3} = (x-3)(x-4)\dfrac{x+3}{x-4} \ \leftarrow \text{This step may be done mentally.}$$

$$(x-4)(x+5) = (x-3)(x+3)$$
$$x^2 + x - 20 = x^2 - 9$$
$$x - 20 = -9$$
$$x = 11 \qquad \text{Check} \quad \text{L.S.} = \text{R.S. checks } \checkmark$$

To solve the many different problems that may occur in geometry on the co-ordinate plane and also in real-life applications, you must be able to solve equations of many different types.

## 3.7 Exercise

**A** All variables represent real numbers.

1. (a) What is your first step in solving the equation $\dfrac{2}{3y} + \dfrac{3}{5} = \dfrac{1}{4y}$?

   (b) Solve the equation in (a).

2. (a) Solve the equation $\dfrac{x+18}{4} - x = \dfrac{x-5}{2} + 2$.

   (b) Solve the equation $\dfrac{x+18}{x} - x = \dfrac{x-5}{2-x} + 2$.

   (c) How are the solutions in (a) and (b) alike? How do they differ?

3. (a) What are the restrictions on the variable of the equation $\dfrac{3}{x} + 2 = \dfrac{2x+3}{x-1}$?

   (b) Find the solution set in (a).

   (c) Check your answer in (a). Verify your solution.

4. (a) What is your first step in solving the equation

   $$\dfrac{x+1}{2} - \dfrac{2x-1}{3} = -1?$$

   (b) What is the solution set of the equation in (a)? Verify your answer.

5 (a) What is the root of the equation given by

$$\frac{80}{x} - 3 = \frac{200}{5x} - 1?$$

(b) Write your answer in (a) in two other forms.

6 (a) Find the solution set for $\dfrac{3x - 1}{2x} = \dfrac{5}{4}$.

(b) Write your answer in (a) in two other forms.

**B** Remember to verify your answer.

7 Solve. Verify your answer.

(a) $\dfrac{m - 3}{2} - \dfrac{m - 4}{3} = \dfrac{m - 2}{4}$

(b) $\dfrac{1}{3}(2y - 1) + \dfrac{y + 1}{2} = \dfrac{y - 2}{6}$

8 Find each solution set.

(a) $\dfrac{5 - s}{2} + \dfrac{s + 18}{4} = s + 2$

(b) $\dfrac{x - 2}{2} + \dfrac{3(x + 2)}{10} = 2 - \dfrac{4(x - 1)}{5}$

9 Solve and verify. What are the restrictions?

(a) $\dfrac{3x + 2}{3x + 4} = \dfrac{x - 1}{x + 1}$

(b) $\dfrac{y + 5}{y - 3} = \dfrac{y + 3}{y - 4}$

10 Find the roots.

(a) $\dfrac{2x - 1}{3x} = 1$

(b) $\dfrac{3x - 1}{x} = \dfrac{5}{2}$

(c) $\dfrac{x - 3}{x + 3} = 2$

(d) $\dfrac{x + 8}{x + 3} = \dfrac{x}{x - 3}$

(e) $\dfrac{y - 1}{y} = \dfrac{y + 1}{y + 3}$

(f) $\dfrac{y + 1}{y - 2} = \dfrac{y + 3}{y - 4}$

11 Solve.

(a) $\dfrac{x - 2}{x} + \dfrac{1}{5} = -\dfrac{4}{5x}$

(b) $\dfrac{3}{a} = \dfrac{2a + 3}{a - 1} - 2$

(c) $\dfrac{1}{x} = \dfrac{2}{x + 1} + \dfrac{1}{1 - x}$

(d) $\dfrac{y - 1}{y} - \dfrac{1}{4} = \dfrac{5}{3y}$

(e) $\dfrac{2y - 2}{y + 2} = 2 + \dfrac{5 - y}{2 + y}$

(f) $\dfrac{3m}{m - 3} = \dfrac{3m - 1}{m + 3} - 2$

**C** 12 One of the roots of the following equation is 3.

$$\frac{x + 6}{x} = \frac{x + k}{x - k} - k.$$

(a) Find the value of $k$.   (b) What other roots does the equation have?

## Problem-Solving: Using Rational Expressions

Now you can apply your skills in solving equations involving rational expressions to the solution of problems. You need to organize your work before you solve a problem.

**Problem-Solving Plan**

*Step A* Read the problem carefully. Answer these two important questions:
  I What information am I asked to find? (information I don't know)
  II What information am I given? (information I know)
  Be sure to understand what it is you are to find, then introduce the variables.
*Step B* Translate from English to mathematics and write the equations.
*Step C* Solve the equations.
*Step D* Check the answer in the original problem.
*Step E* Write a final statement as the answer to the problem.

You need to form an equation involving rational expressions in order to solve the following problem.

**Example** A plane travels 5 times as fast as a passenger train. To travel 400.0 km, the train requires 4 more hours than the plane. Find the speed of the train and the plane.

**Solution** Let $x$ km/h be the speed of the train. Then $5x$ km/h is the speed of the plane.

Use a chart to record the given information.

Remember: Use time $= \dfrac{\text{distance}}{\text{speed}}$.

|  | $d$ | $t$ | $s$ |
|---|---|---|---|
| train | 400.0 | $\dfrac{400.0}{x}$ | $x$ |
| plane | 400.0 | $\dfrac{400.0}{5x}$ | $5x$ |

$$\frac{400.0}{x} - 4 = \frac{400.0}{5x} \qquad x \neq 0$$

$\longleftarrow$ Think: Use the given information. The train requires 4 more hours. Write the equation.

$$5x\left(\frac{400.0}{x}\right) - 5x(4) = 5x\left(\frac{400.0}{5x}\right)$$

$\longleftarrow$ Multiply each term of the equation by $5x$.

$$2000.0 - 20x = 400.0$$
$$1600.0 = 20x$$
$$80.0 = x \quad \text{or} \quad x = 80.0$$

Thus, • the speed of the train is 80.0 km/h.
  • the speed of the plane is 400.0 km/h.

You may check your answers.

# 3.8 Exercise

**B** Remember: Use a chart to help you organize the given information.

1 Read the following problem.

If a boat's speed is 6.0 km/h slower than usual, it needs 1 more hour to travel a distance of 36.0 km between two islands. How fast does the boat usually go?

(a) Copy and complete the chart.

|  | distance (km) | speed (km/h) | time (h) |
|---|---|---|---|
| usual rate | 36.0 | $s$ | ? |
| slower rate | 36.0 | $s - 6.0$ | ? |

(b) Use the chart above to aid you in writing a complete solution for the problem.

2 If a car travels 30.0 km/h slower, it will take 3.0 h more to travel 700.0 km. How fast is the car travelling now?

(a) Complete the chart.

|  | distance (km) | speed (km/h) | time (h) |
|---|---|---|---|
| present rate | 700.0 | $s$ | ? |
| slower rate | 700.0 | $s - 30.0$ | ? |

(b) Write a complete solution to the problem using the chart as an aid.

3 If Jan could increase her speed by 1.0 m in 10.0 s she could cut 20.0 s off her time for a 60.0 m swim. Find her present swimming speed.

(a) Copy and complete the chart.

|  | distance (km) | speed (m/s) | time (s) |
|---|---|---|---|
| present rate | 60.0 | $s$ | ? |
| faster rate | 60.0 | $s + 0.1$ | ? |

(b) Use the chart as an aid in solving the problem.

4 A train travelled 672.0 km. If it had travelled 12.0 km/h slower, it would take 1.0 h longer to cover the same distance. Find the speed of the train.

5 Going at its usual speed, a boat travels 72.0 km from port to port. If it were to go 6.0 km/h faster then it would take 1.0 h less. Find its usual speed.

6 A taxi made a trip of 480.0 km. If it had gone 16.0 km/h faster, it would have broken the speed limit but would have taken 60.0 min less.

(a) How fast did the taxi go?      (b) What was the faster speed?

7    Samuel paddled a rubber dinghy 12.0 km down the French River.
     Paddling up the river took 20.0 min longer because he paddled 6.0 km/h
     slower than before. Find his speed down the river.

8    The Grand Lake River system is about 160.0 km long. If Joanne and
     her crew were to go 4.0 km/h faster than their leisurely rate, they could
     complete the trip in 3 h 20 min less time.
     (a) What is their usual leisurely speed for canoeing?
     (b) What assumption(s) do you make in solving this problem?

9    Lesley is travelling from Edmonton to Winnipeg to visit friends. She can
     leave today by bus or she can leave tomorrow by express train which
     travels 25.0 km/h faster, saving her 2.8 h. Determine how long each trip
     would take her if the distance between Edmonton and Winnipeg is
     1400.0 km.

10   Jim, a cross-country runner, trains all year round and finds that in the
     winter with slippery road conditions he slows down by 2.0 km/h, so that
     it takes him 2.0 h longer to run the 48.0-km course. How fast does he run
     (a) in the winter?          (b) in the summer?

11   Supplies at the campsite became low so some of the campers had to go to
     the outfitters to pick up more food. If 3 campers had paddled instead
     of 2 they would have increased their speed by 2.0 km/h and saved 1.0 h.
     How long did it take the canoe to travel the 40.0-km distance to the
     outfitters?

---

## Math Tip

It is important to clearly understand the vocabulary of mathematics when
solving problems. *You cannot solve problems if you don't know what the
clues are.*

▶ Make a list of all the words you learn in this chapter.
▶ Continue to add the remaining new words to your list. Provide a simple
  example to illustrate the meaning of each word.

---

## Calculator Tip

Review the use of each of the following keys on your calculator. Remember:
Refer to the manual provided with your calculator.

$$\boxed{\sqrt{\phantom{x}}}\ \boxed{x^2}\ \boxed{1/x}\ \boxed{x^y}\ \boxed{\pi}\ \boxed{\%}\ \boxed{\text{Min}}\ \boxed{\text{MR}}\ \boxed{+/-}$$

# 3.9 Solving Inequations

Often in mathematics your results can be summarized in a concise way. For example, the properties of equality may be written as shown.

If $a = b$, $a$, $b \in R$, then for any real number $c$,

$$a + c = b + c \qquad c \times a = c \times b$$

$$a - c = b - c \qquad \frac{a}{c} = \frac{b}{c}$$

**PSP**

Ask yourself:
How are they alike?
How are they different?

You have used the above equalities to solve equations. In a similar way the properties of inequality may be written as shown except for one major difference.

If $a > b$, $a$, $b \in R$, then for any real number $c$,

$$a + c > b + c \qquad c \times a > c \times b$$

$$a - c > b - c \qquad \frac{a}{c} > \frac{b}{c}$$

($c$ must be positive.)

This simple example shows why $c$ must be positive. The inequality is reversed if you multiply or divide by a negative number.

| original inequality | multiply by a negative number | divide by a negative number |
|:---:|:---:|:---:|
| $4 > 2$ | $-2 \times 4 < -2 \times 2$ | $\dfrac{4}{-2} < \dfrac{2}{-2}$ |
| | $-8 < -4$ | $-2 < -1$ |

Your earlier skills in multiplying binomials are needed to solve the following inequation.

**Example 1**   Find the solution set of
$$2(2y - 3)(y - 5) \geq (2y - 5)(2y + 5) + 3, \ y \in R.$$

**Solution**
$$2(2y - 3)(y - 5) \geq (2y - 5)(2y + 5) + 3$$
$$2(2y^2 - 13y + 15) \geq 4y^2 - 25 + 3$$
$$4y^2 - 26y + 30 \geq 4y^2 - 22$$
$$-26y \geq -52$$

Why?

$$\frac{-26y}{-26} \leq \frac{-52}{-26}$$
$$y \leq 2$$

The solution set is $\{y \mid y \leq 2, y \in R\}$.

In order to solve the following equation, you need to simplify the terms of the equation.

**Example 2**    Solve $\dfrac{y+6}{2} > \dfrac{y-2}{3} + 5$, $y \in R$.

**Solution**

$$\dfrac{y+6}{2} > \dfrac{y-2}{3} + 5$$

Think: Multiply all terms by the least common denominator, namely, 6.

$$6\left(\dfrac{y+6}{2}\right) > 6\left(\dfrac{y-2}{3}\right) + 6(5)$$
$$3(y+6) > 2(y-2) + 30$$
$$3y + 18 > 2y - 4 + 30$$
$$3y - 2y > 8$$
$$y > 8$$

Thus, the solution set is $\{y \mid y > 8, \, y \in R\}$.

## 3.9 Exercise

**A** Review your skills with inequations. The domain of all the equations is the real numbers.

1 (a) Solve $6y + 12 = 3y - 6$.          (b) Solve $6y + 12 \leq 3y - 6$.

(c) How are the solutions in (a) and (b) alike? How do they differ?

2 (a) Solve $2(y - 6) + 8 < 4(y + 7)$, $y \in R$.

(b) Draw the solution set in (a).

3 (a) What is your first step in solving the inequation    **PSP**    Have a plan.
$$\dfrac{3y - 1}{3} \geq \dfrac{13}{6} - \dfrac{2y - 3}{2}?$$

(b) Find the solution set in (a).

4 (a) What is your first step in solving the inequation
$$4(y - 5)^2 - 2(y + 2)^2 \leq 2(1 - y)^2 - 2?$$

(b) Solve the inequation in (a).

5 Solve.

(a) $\dfrac{2p + 3}{5} \geq -2$

(b) $\dfrac{x - 1}{2} < \dfrac{7 + x}{10}$

(c) $\dfrac{y}{3} < \dfrac{3(y - 1)}{4}$

(d) $\dfrac{y}{3} - \dfrac{1}{4} > \dfrac{2y + 9}{12}$

**B** Remember: The inequality is reversed when you multiply or divide by a negative number.

6   Solve and verify.

(a) $\dfrac{y - 5}{4} \geqq \dfrac{1}{3} - \dfrac{y - 5}{12}$

(b) $\dfrac{y}{2} - \dfrac{2y - 5}{10} < -\dfrac{1}{10}$

(c) $\dfrac{m + 1}{2} - \dfrac{1}{6} < \dfrac{m}{6} - \dfrac{m - 5}{3}$

(d) $\dfrac{m + 1}{4} + 1 \geqq \dfrac{2m + 1}{2}$

7   Solve.

(a) $y - \dfrac{10}{3} \geqq \dfrac{2(y - 3)}{3}$

(b) $\dfrac{k - 3}{3} + \dfrac{5}{6} < \dfrac{k + 2}{2} - \dfrac{2}{3}$

(c) $\dfrac{1}{3}(2k - 1) - \dfrac{4}{3} \leqq \dfrac{5 - k}{2} - \dfrac{13}{2}$

(d) $\dfrac{y - 10}{5} > \dfrac{4 - 3y}{3} - \dfrac{14}{15}$

(e) $\dfrac{x + 1}{3} + \dfrac{x}{2} < \dfrac{2x + 3}{3} + \dfrac{1}{3}$

(f) $\dfrac{2y - 1}{3} - \dfrac{1}{5} \leqq \dfrac{y + 2}{5}$

8   Solve.

(a) $(x + 1)(x - 6) - x^2 < x + 18$

(b) $(k + 4)(2k - 5) > 2k(k - 3) - 38$

(c) $(m - 3)(3m - 1) - 3m(m - 5) \leqq 28$

(d) $2(p - 3)(2p - 4) \geqq 148 + 4(p - 3)^2$

(e) $(2y - 3)(y + 5) - (3 - y)(4 - 2y) < 7$

9   (a) Solve $\dfrac{y}{2} - \dfrac{5}{3} \leqq \dfrac{y - 3}{3}$.

**PSP** Remember: To do mathematics, you need to know the meaning of each word.

(b) Which of the following are equivalent to the inequation in (a)?

A $\dfrac{12 - y}{3} + \dfrac{1}{3} \geqq \dfrac{y + 2}{3}$

B $\dfrac{y + 2}{3} \geqq -\dfrac{8 + y}{6}$

C $\dfrac{y + 1}{3} \leqq 2 - \dfrac{y - 2}{6}$

D $\dfrac{y - 1}{2} - 1 \geqq \dfrac{6 - y}{4}$

**C** 10   If $a > 0$, $a \in R$, which of the following are true?

(a) $2a + a > 3$

(b) $2(a + 1) < 1$

(c) $2(a + 3) + 3 < 5 + a$

(d) $6(4a - 3) > -4(5 - a) + 2$

11   If $b < 0$, $b \in R$, which of the following are false?

(a) $2(b - 3) > 3(b + 3)$

(b) $3(b - 1) > 4(b - 1)$

(c) $2(b + 7) - 4(b + 3) < 15(b - 1)$

(d) $(3b + 1)^2 - 3(b - 2)^2 < 6b^2 - 11$

## Practice and Problems: Review

1 Simplify. (a) Subtract $\dfrac{2x-5}{2x}$ from $\dfrac{x+2}{3x}$.    (b) Add $\dfrac{3n-7}{8n}$ to $\dfrac{2n-4}{3n}$.

2 Express each of the following in simplest terms.

(a) $\dfrac{y^2-11y+18}{y^2-12y+27}$    (b) $\dfrac{5y-20}{y^2-6y+8}$    (c) $\dfrac{25x^2-1}{10x^2+8x-2}$

3 Use $a=2$, $b=-1$ to evaluate $\dfrac{a^2-ab-6b^2}{a^2-5ab+6b^2} - \dfrac{3a^2+13ab+4b^2}{a^2+ab-12b^2}$.

4 Solve

(a) $\dfrac{y-2}{2} - 2 = \dfrac{4(y+1)}{5} - \dfrac{(y+2)}{10}$    (b) $\dfrac{2b-1}{b^2-9} - 1 = \dfrac{b-4}{b+3}$

5 (a) Use $x=2$, $y=-3$, $a=3$, and $b=-4$. Find the value of (i) $\dfrac{x}{y} + \dfrac{a}{b}$ (ii) $\dfrac{x+a}{y+b}$

(b) Use your answer in (a) to show why $\dfrac{x}{y} + \dfrac{a}{b} \neq \dfrac{x+a}{y+b}$?

(c) Use other numerical values for $x$, $y$, $a$, and $b$ to show that $\dfrac{x}{y} + \dfrac{a}{b} \neq \dfrac{x+a}{y+b}$

## Practice Test

1 Express each in simplest terms.

(a) $\dfrac{10ab-15a^2b}{12a^2-8a}$    (b) $\dfrac{p^2+2p-3}{3p^2+9p}$    (c) $\dfrac{16-4d}{2d^2-7d-4}$

2 Simplify.

(a) $\dfrac{3}{y-5} + \dfrac{y}{y^2-25}$    (b) $\dfrac{6y}{(y+3)^2} - \dfrac{3}{y+3}$    (c) $\dfrac{x-2}{x^2-2x+1} - \dfrac{3}{x-1}$

3 Simplify.

(a) $\dfrac{a^2-b^2}{a^2+b^2} \times \dfrac{a^2+ab}{b^2-a^2}$    (b) $\dfrac{a^2-a-2}{3a^2} \times \dfrac{a^2+a-2}{7a} \div \dfrac{a^4-5a^2+4}{9a^4}$

4 If $x=-2$, find the value of $\dfrac{x^2+6x+5}{x^2+7x+12} \times \dfrac{x^2+2x-8}{x^2-25} \div \dfrac{x^2-x-2}{x^2-2x-15}$

5 A trawler travels 4 times as fast as a tugboat. The tugboat requires 14.0 h more to travel 70.0 km than the trawler. Find the speed of each boat.

# 4 *Essential Skills: Co-ordinate Geometry*

Skills on the co-ordinate plane, vocabulary of relations, graphing equations and inequations, graphing regions, distance on the plane, distance formula, finding midpoints, solving problems, using slope, properties of lines, strategies and problem-solving

## Introduction

One of the main reasons for learning mathematics is to acquire skills and strategies for solving problems. Skills and strategies based on co-ordinate geometry are essential for solving many problems in mathematics. The more problems you solve, the better you will be at solving problems you have never met before.

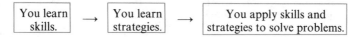

The skills and strategies of co-ordinate geometry can be applied to the solution of problems that occur in unrelated situations.

- comparing the performance of various teams in professional sports.

- analyzing the profit or loss of different businesses.

# 4.1 Essential Skills: Co-ordinate Plane

Important developments in mathematics often occur as a result of someone's need to develop skills to solve a problem. Some years ago, René Descartes (1596–1650) invented the co-ordinate plane so that he could describe mathematics in a visual way.

*René Descartes spent the better part of his life re-examining current ideas in mathematics, and subsequently building new ones. As a result, his valuable contribution of analytic geometry has influenced significantly the study of mathematics.*

An **ordered pair** of real numbers is used to identify any point A on the number plane by using a pair of axes drawn at right angles, as shown.

$(3, -2)$

Shows the horizontal co-ordinate (often called the **abscissa** or *x* **co-ordinate**).

Shows the vertical co-ordinate (often called the **ordinate** or *y* **co-ordinate**).

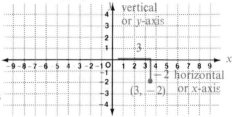

The horizontal co-ordinate always comes first. The origin is given the letter O and its co-ordinates are (0, 0).

Co-ordinates allow you to draw geometric shapes on the co-ordinate plane and study them. When you plot the points represented by the ordered pairs, you are drawing the **graph** of the ordered pairs.

**Example 1**   Rectangle ABCD has vertices at A(2, 6), B(8, 6), C(8, 2), and D(2, 2). Find its area.

**Solution**   Draw the graph.

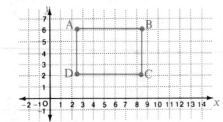

From the graph, BC = 4 units and DC = 6 units. Thus, area of rectangle ABCD is 24 square units.

You can also use the co-ordinate graph to record data. For example, in an experiment, the data collected are recorded as ordered pairs. Each component of the ordered pair is interpreted as shown.

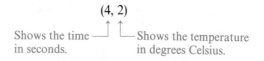

(4, 2)

Shows the time — in seconds.          └─ Shows the temperature in degrees Celsius.

In an experiment, two different sets of data were collected. Then they were accidentally dropped and mixed up.

A(2, 8)    B(2, 1)    C(5, 8)
D(10, 5)   E(11, 2)   F(14, 7)
G(2, 5)    H(8, 2)    I(8, 4)
J(11, 8)   K(8, 8)    L(6, 3)
M(5, 2)    N(4, 2)    P(2, 2)
Q(11, 5)   R(12, 6)

The graph shows the data in a visual form.

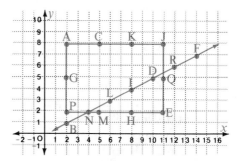

By recording the data on a co-ordinate plane it is possible to sort the data into their original groups.

The scientist may use a graph to predict new information. The next example suggests a pattern from which you can predict new information.

**PSP**

**Example 2**    Data from an experiment are recorded as these ordered pairs: (1, 2), (3, 4), (2, 3), (0, 1).

(a) Draw a graph of the data.

(b) Use the graph to predict two other ordered pairs that seem to fit the pattern.

**Solution**    (a)

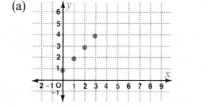

(b) From the graph it seems that (4, 5) and (5, 6) *may* fit the pattern.

Often, when solving a problem, a visual interpretation of the given data will help you find the answer. For example, the following problem is more difficult to solve if you do not draw a graph. Once the vertices are plotted, the problem is more easily solved.

**PSP**

**Example 3**    A parallelogram has its vertices in each of the quadrants. Only three of them are given: A($-8$, 2), B(2, 2), and C(7, $-1$). Name the co-ordinates of the missing vertex.

**Solution**

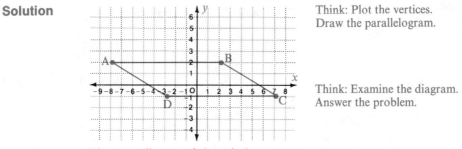

Think: Plot the vertices.
Draw the parallelogram.

Think: Examine the diagram.
Answer the problem.

The co-ordinates of the missing vertex are ($-3$, $-1$).

The four quadrants of the Cartesian plane are named as shown. This will enable you to refer to specific regions of the Cartesian plane.

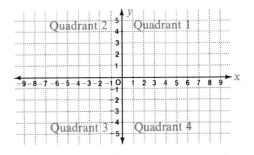

**PSP**   List the meanings of words used in mathematics.

## 4.1    Exercise

**A** So that you can draw graphs accurately, interpret the given information correctly.

Questions 1 to 8 are based on the following diagram.

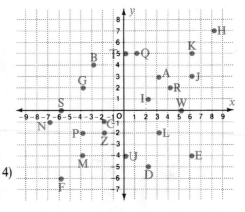

1   What are the co-ordinates of these points?
   (a) G            (b) A            (c) D
   (d) M            (e) Q            (f) E
   (g) What are the co-ordinates of the origin?

2   What letter is shown by these co-ordinates?
   (a) $(-3, 4)$        (b) $(4, 2)$        (c) $(-4, 2)$
   (d) $(0, -4)$        (e) $(-4, -2)$        (f) $(3, -2)$
   (g) $(6, -4)$        (h) $(0, 5)$        (i) $(-4, -4)$
   (j) $(6, 3)$        (k) $(5, 0)$        (l) $(-6, 0)$

3   What are the co-ordinates of these points?

   (a) T         (b) S         (c) U

   (d) What property do these points have in common?

4   What are the co-ordinates of these points?

   (a) M        (b) N        (c) P

5   What are the co-ordinates of these points?

   (a) F         (b) M        (c) A

   (d) What property do these points have in common?

6   Name the points whose $x$ co-ordinate is (a) 2    (b) $-2$  (c) $-4$

7   Name the points whose $y$ co-ordinate is (a) 3    (b) $-2$  (c) $-4$

8   (a) Name the points whose co-ordinates are both negative.

   (b) In which quadrant do they lie?

9   (a) Name a point that has a negative co-ordinate.

   (b) How many other points have the property in (a)?

   (c) In which quadrants are these points?

10  (a) Name the points whose co-ordinates are opposite in sign.

   (b) In which quadrants are these points?

11  (a) Name the points for which the $x$ co-ordinate is greater than the $y$
       co-ordinate by 1.

   (b) Name the points for which the $y$ co-ordinate or $x$ co-ordinate is equal to 0.

12  Name the point(s) in the third quadrant for which the

   (a) $y$ co-ordinate is equal to $-1$.     (b) the $x$ and $y$ co-ordinates are equal.


**B** Be sure to label your axes correctly when drawing graphs.


13  For each of the following rectangles, three vertices are given. Find the
    co-ordinates of the missing vertex.

   (a) A(6, 3)            B(6, $-3$)         C(2, $-3$)

   (b) E($-5$, $-5$)       F($-5$, 4)       G(3, 4)

   (c) I(2, 6)             J(7, 1)          K($-1$, $-7$)

14 (a) Plot the points shown by these ordered pairs.

$\left(-4, \frac{1}{2}\right)$    (8, 3)    $\left(1, -\frac{1}{2}\right)$    (−9, −2)    $\left(-2, \frac{3}{2}\right)$

$\left(0, \frac{5}{2}\right)$    (0, −1)    (6, 3)    (−2, −2)    (4, 3)

(−7, −2)    (−7, −1)    (1, 3)    $\left(5, \frac{3}{2}\right)$    (2, 0)

(b) What geometric figure are you reminded of in (a)?

15 In an experiment to cool a liquid these ordered pairs were recorded.

time in minutes ⌐    ⌐ temperature in degrees Celsius

(10, 2)    (0, 10)    (6, 4)    (8, 2)
(4, 6)    (12, 2)    (16, 2)    (18, 2)

(a) Plot the ponts.
(b) Name two other points that seem to fit the data.

16 (a) Plot the points shown by

A(−1, −2)    B(3, 6)    C(−3, −4)
D(2, 4)    E(−3, −6)    F(0, 0)    G(1, 2)

(b) Which ordered pair does not belong? Why is this so?

17 Which ordered pair does not belong? Why is this so?

A(1, 2)    B(0, 0)    C(2, 4)    D(−2, 4)    E(−3, 6)
F(4, 6)    G(−1, 2)    H(4, 8)    I(−4, 8)

18 Two different sets of data, recorded as ordered pairs, were accidentally combined.

A(−3, 4)    B(−8, −4)    C(1, −4)    D(2, 1)
E(−4, 6)    F(4, 2)    G(6, 3)    H(2, −6)
I(−1, 0)    J(−6, −3)    K(0, −2)    L(8, 4)
M(−2, −1)    N(−2, 2)    O(0, 0)    P(−4, −2)

Which data belong together?

C 19 The data from an experiment are recorded as ordered pairs.

(3, −2)    (−1, 4)    (−3, −2)    (−1, −2)    (3, 4)
(−3, 4)    (3, 0)    (1, −2)    (3, 2)    (−3, 2)

(a) Graph the data
(b) Use your graph to predict two other ordered pairs that fit the pattern.

## Applications: Using Graphs

When you walk at a constant speed, the relation of the distance travelled, $d$, the time taken, $t$, and your speed, $v$, is shown at the right. For a speed of 5 km/h ($v = 5$), the above formula is written as $d = 5t$. The data can be recorded as ordered pairs.

$d = vt$

distance travelled ⎯⎯⎯⎯⎯⎯ time taken in travelling
speed

Time taken is 4 h. ⎯⎯⎯ (4, 20) ⎯⎯⎯ Distance travelled is 20 km.

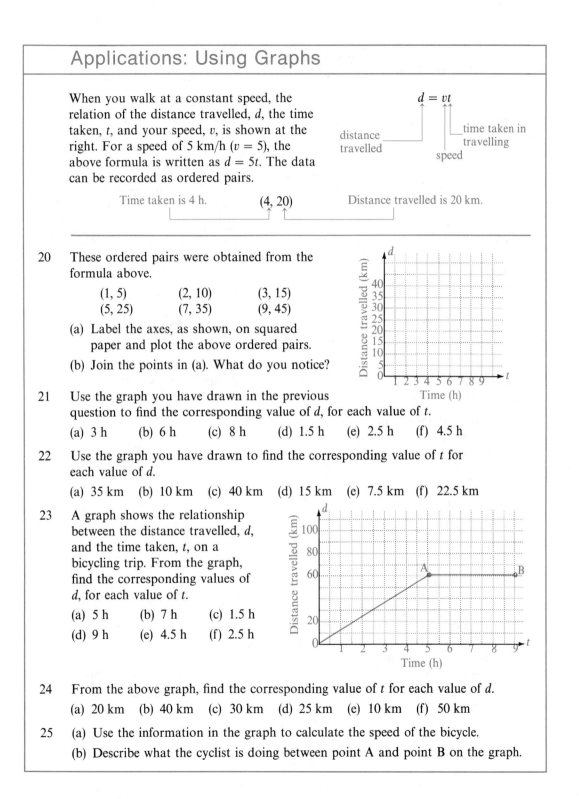

20  These ordered pairs were obtained from the formula above.

(1, 5)　　　(2, 10)　　　(3, 15)
(5, 25)　　　(7, 35)　　　(9, 45)

(a) Label the axes, as shown, on squared paper and plot the above ordered pairs.

(b) Join the points in (a). What do you notice?

21  Use the graph you have drawn in the previous question to find the corresponding value of $d$, for each value of $t$.

(a) 3 h　　(b) 6 h　　(c) 8 h　　(d) 1.5 h　　(e) 2.5 h　　(f) 4.5 h

22  Use the graph you have drawn to find the corresponding value of $t$ for each value of $d$.

(a) 35 km　(b) 10 km　(c) 40 km　(d) 15 km　(e) 7.5 km　(f) 22.5 km

23  A graph shows the relationship between the distance travelled, $d$, and the time taken, $t$, on a bicycling trip. From the graph, find the corresponding values of $d$, for each value of $t$.

(a) 5 h　　(b) 7 h　　(c) 1.5 h
(d) 9 h　　(e) 4.5 h　　(f) 2.5 h

24  From the above graph, find the corresponding value of $t$ for each value of $d$.

(a) 20 km　(b) 40 km　(c) 30 km　(d) 25 km　(e) 10 km　(f) 50 km

25  (a) Use the information in the graph to calculate the speed of the bicycle.

(b) Describe what the cyclist is doing between point A and point B on the graph.

## 4.2 Vocabulary of Relations

Often, words that you use in your study of mathematics also occur in your everyday language. For example when you first think of relations you may think of

John is an uncle of Marie.       Lucia is the sister of Greg.

When you read newspaper sports summaries, you can see many relations among the numbers listed in the team standings. You can see relations such as

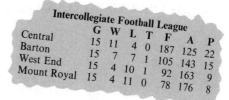

| Intercollegiate Football League | | | | | | | |
|---|---|---|---|---|---|---|---|
| | G | W | L | T | F | A | P |
| Central | 15 | 11 | 4 | 0 | 187 | 125 | 22 |
| Barton | 15 | 7 | 7 | 1 | 105 | 143 | 15 |
| West End | 15 | 4 | 10 | 1 | 92 | 163 | 9 |
| Mount Royal | 15 | 4 | 11 | 0 | 78 | 176 | 8 |

• Central has won 4 more games than Barton.
• Mount Royal has scored 8 points.
• West End has 9 points.

What other relations do you see?

When you think of numbers, you might think of relations such as

6 is greater than 4       8 is less than 12

Symbols are used to help you express mathematical ideas. Often there are several ways of expressing the same concept. For example, the following are different ways of showing the relation among numbers.

A: A **table of values** can be used to list the numbers that are related.

| x | y |
|---|---|
| 0 | 0 |
| 1 | 2 |
| 2 | 4 |
| 3 | 6 |

How are the numbers x and y related?

B: The symbol ⟶ can be used to show how the numbers are related.

0 ⟶ 0
1 ⟶ 2
2 ⟶ 4
3 ⟶ 6

C: You can use **ordered pairs** to show the relation.

(0, 0)
(1, 2)
(2, 4)
(3, 6)

D: If you want to see the relation, you can **draw a graph** by plotting the points. What property do you notice about this relation?

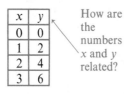

E: You can use an **arrow diagram** to show the relation for the numbers.

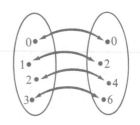

You could use some of these ways to record teams standings.

- **As a table**

| Team | Points |
|------|--------|
| Central | 22 |
| Barton | 15 |
| West End | 9 |
| Mount Royal | 8 |

- **As ordered pairs**

(Central, 22),
(West End, 9),
(Barton, 15)
(Mount Royal, 8)

How are these
components related?

- **As an arrow diagram**

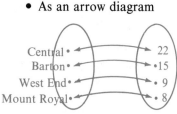

A **relation** is a set of ordered pairs. Some relations can be described by using an equation such as

$$y = 2x + 1, \ x \in N \longleftarrow \text{defining equation of the relation}$$

The symbol $\longrightarrow$ can be used to show the relation in the form

$$x \longrightarrow 2x + 1, \ x \in N$$

To draw a graph of this relation ordered pairs are listed and then plotted.

*Step 1* List the ordered pairs of the relation.

| $x$ | $y$ |
|-----|-----|
| 1 | 3 |
| 2 | 5 |
| 3 | 7 |
| 4 | 9 |

*Step 2* Plot the ordered pairs.

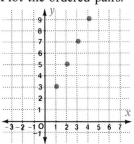

Two important words that are used with relations are **domain** and **range**.

ordered pairs of the relation

The set of all first components of the ordered pairs is called the **domain** of the relation.

(1, 3),
(2, 5),
(3, 7), . . .

The set of all second components of the ordered pairs is called the **range** of the relation.

## 4.2 Exercise

**A** Review the meaning of the new words you have learned in this section.

1 List the domain and range for each of the relations given by the ordered pairs.

(a) $\{(2, 1), (-1, 3), (4, 2), (3, -2)\}$ (b) $\{(0, 2), (-1, -1), (3, 2), (2, 3)\}$

(c) $\{(4, 1), (1, 4), (-2, 3), (3, -2)\}$

2 (a) What is the domain and the range of the relation given by this table of values?

| x | 2 | 3 | 4 | 5 | 3 | 4 | 5 | 4 | 5 | 5 |
|---|---|---|---|---|---|---|---|---|---|---|
| y | 1 | 1 | 1 | 1 | 2 | 2 | 2 | 3 | 3 | 4 |

(b) Draw a graph of the relation.

3 (a) What is the domain and the range of the relation given by these ordered pairs?

$(-3, -1)$, $(-5, 0)$, $(-6, -1)$, $(-3, 1)$, $(-6, -2)$, $(-3, -2)$,
$(-3, 0)$, $(-4, 1)$, $(-3, 2)$, $(-4, -2)$, $(-5, -2)$, $(-7, -2)$

(b) Draw a graph of the relation.

4 A relation is given by an arrow diagram.

(a) Write the ordered pairs of the relation.

(b) What is the domain of the relation?

(c) What is the range of the relation?

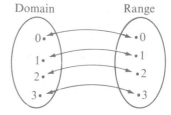

5 A relation is given by the ordered pairs.

(0, 0), (1, 1), (2, 4), (3, 9)

(a) Draw an arrow diagram.  (b) Write the members of each set: domain, range.

6 (a) Draw an arrow diagram for the relation given by (0, 0), (1, 1), (2, 2), (3, 3).

(b) Draw an arrow diagram for the relation given by (0, 1), (1, 1), (2, 3), (3, 3).

(c) How are the diagrams in (a) and (b) alike? How are they different?

7 (a) Draw an arrow diagram for the relation given by (4, 6), (4, 7), (5, 8), (5, 9).

(b) Draw an arrow diagram for the relation given by (4, 6), (5, 7), (6, 8), (7, 9).

(c) How are the diagrams in (a) and (b) alike? How are they different?

B Review the meaning of domain, range, and relation.

8 The graph of a relation is shown. Write

(a) the ordered pairs of the relation.

(b) the domain of the relation.

(c) the range of the relation.

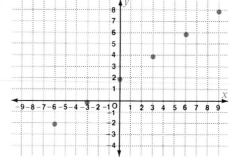

9    For each relation shown on a graph, write
  • the ordered pairs of the relation.
  • the domain of the relation.
  • the range of the relation.

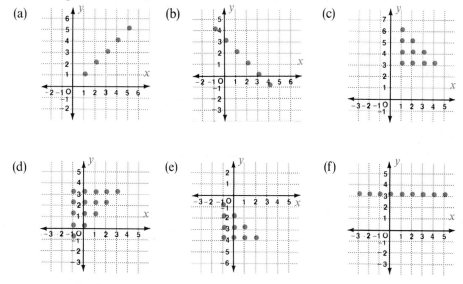

(a)    (b)    (c)

(d)    (e)    (f)

10   (a) Draw the graph defined by $x - y = 2$, $x, y \in N$.
  (b) Use the graph in (a). Predict other pairs, $(x, y)$, that are on the graph. How can you check your prediction?

11   (a) Draw the graph defined by $2x + y = 6$, $x, y \in N$.
  (b) Use the graph in (a). Predict other pairs, $(x, y)$, that are on the graph. How can you check your prediction?

12   (a) Draw the graph defined by each equation.

    A    $x + y = 10$, $x, y \in N$
    B    $x + y = 10$, $x, y \in I$

    **PSP**    Ask yourself the key questions.

  (b) How are the graphs of A and B alike? How are they different?

13   Draw the graph defined by each equation. $x, y \in I$.
  (a) $x + 2y = 3$          (b) $x - 3y = 5$          (c) $x + 4y = -2$
  (d) $y = x$               (e) $x - 2y = -4$         (f) $y = 2x$
  (g) $x - 4y = -3$         (h) $3x - 2y = -1$        (i) $3x - y = -9$

14 Standings are shown in the chart.

(a) What relation is shown by the ordered pairs, (Oakdale, 2), (Meadowvale, 3), (Eastdale, 6)?

(b) Write another ordered pair that belongs to the relation in (a).

(c) What relation is shown by the following: (Meadowvale, 219), (Crescent, 213), (Eastdale, 162)?

(d) Write another ordered pair that belongs to the relation in (c).

**Girls Basketball**

|            | W | L | T | F   | A   |
|------------|---|---|---|-----|-----|
| Oakdale    | 7 | 2 | 0 | 222 | 155 |
| Meadowvale | 6 | 3 | 0 | 219 | 146 |
| Crescent   | 5 | 4 | 0 | 213 | 204 |
| Eastdale   | 3 | 6 | 0 | 162 | 213 |

15 Refer to the standings in the previous question.

(a) Express the following relation in words: (Oakdale, 155), (Meadowvale, 146), etc.

(b) Draw an arrow diagram for the relation in (a).

(c) Each ordered pair belongs to the same relation. Find the missing components. (Crescent, 5), (Meadowvale. ?), (?, 7).

(d) Draw an arrow diagram for the relation in (c). What is the domain, the range?

**C** 16 Use the standings shown.

(a) Choose a relation shown in the chart. Write the ordered pairs.

(b) Draw an arrow diagram for the relation you have chosen in (a).

**National Football League**
**American Conference**

|             | W | L | T | F   | A   |
|-------------|---|---|---|-----|-----|
| Denver      | 6 | 3 | 0 | 143 | 110 |
| Oakland     | 5 | 4 | 0 | 173 | 154 |
| Seattle     | 4 | 5 | 0 | 190 | 206 |
| San Diego   | 3 | 6 | 0 | 169 | 202 |
| Kansas City | 2 | 7 | 0 | 141 | 208 |

## Math Tip

Remember: a very serious, and very common error when working with inequalities is to forget to change the sense of the inequality when you multiply or divide by a negative number. Don't make this error.

Multiply

$$-x < 6$$
$$(-1)(-x) > (-1)(6)$$
$$x > -6$$

Divide

$$-x < 6$$
$$\frac{-x}{-1} > \frac{6}{-1}$$
$$x > -6$$

## Problem-Solving

To go from P to Q you can only go right or up. How many different paths are possible from P to Q. Refer to your *Problem-Solving Plan*. A path is already shown.

# 4.3 Graphing Equations and Inequations

The principles of graphing occur over and over in your study of mathematics.

To draw the graph of the relation defined by

$$y = 2x + 1, \ x \in I \longleftarrow \text{The domain is the set of integers.}$$

you construct a table of values

Since only a part of the relation is shown, the graph is often referred to as a **partial graph**.

| $x$ | $y$ |
|-----|-----|
| $-1$ | $-1$ |
| $0$ | $1$ |
| $1$ | $3$ |
| $2$ | $5$ |

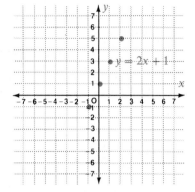

If the domain is the set of real numbers, $R$, then you draw the graph as shown at the right.

- How are the two graphs alike?
- How do the graphs differ?

**PSP**

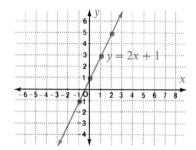

Since the graph of this relation is a straight line, it is called a **linear relation**. However, the following example shows the graph of a relation which is **non-linear**.

**Example 1**  Draw the graph of the relation given by $y = x^2$, $x, y \in R$.

**Solution**  *Step 1* Use a table to show related values of $x$ and $y$.

| $x$ | $-3$ | $-2$ | $-1$ | 0 | 1 | 2 | 3 |
|-----|------|------|------|---|---|---|---|
| $y$ | 9 | 4 | 1 | 0 | 1 | 4 | 9 |

*Step 2* Draw the graph of the above table by plotting the points and then drawing a smooth curve through them.

Think: Representative points are plotted to sketch the position of the graph. Then a smooth curve is drawn.

Think: Since the graph is not linear, you need to plot enough points to draw the curve.

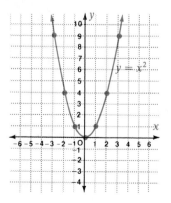

Not every ordered pair that satisfies the above non-linear relation can be shown on a Cartesian plane. As before, the graph shows only part of the set of the ordered pairs for the relation and is thus a **partial** graph. However, the partial graph provides enough information to work with the relation. From its partial graph you can see that the domain is all the real numbers. The range is given by the set of all positive $y$-values. The range may be expressed in the form $\{y \mid y \geq 0, y \in R\}$.

Relations may also be defined by inequations as the next example shows. Again, you can follow the steps with which you are familiar.

**Example 2**   Draw the graph of the relation given by
$y > x$, $x \in \{1, 2, 3\}$ and $y \in \{1, 2, 3, 4, 5\}$.

**Solution**   *Step 1*   Find the ordered pairs of the relation.

| $x = 1$ | $x = 2$ | $x = 3$ |
|---------|---------|---------|
| (1, 2)  | (2, 3)  | (3, 4)  |
| (1, 3)  | (2, 4)  | (3, 5)  |
| (1, 4)  | (2, 5)  |         |
| (1, 5)  |         |         |

*Step 2*   Plot the points. The graph of the relation is shown.

---

## 4.3   Exercise

**A** Review the meaning of *linear* and *non-linear*.

1   List the domain and the range of the relation shown by each graph.

(a)          (b)

(c)          (d)

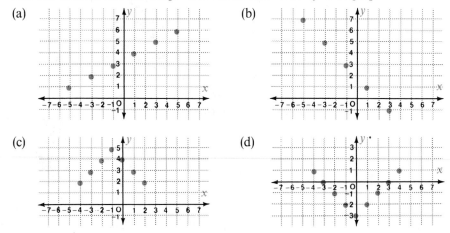

2   List the domain and the range of the relation shown by each of the
    following graphs.

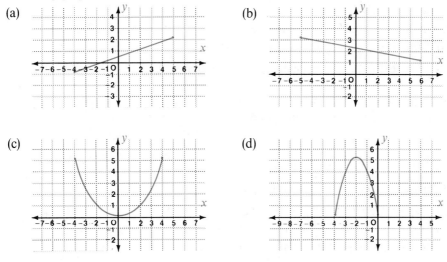

(a)     (b)

(c)     (d)

3   A relation is defined by $y = 2x - 1$, $x, y \in I$.
    (a) Write the domain of the relation.    (b) Write the range of the relation.
    (c) Draw the graph of the relation.

4   A relation is given by $x + y = 8$, $x, y \in R$.
    (a) Write the domain of the relation.    (b) Write the range of the relation.
    (c) Draw the graph of the relation.

5   A relation is given by
        $y > x - 1$, $x, y \in \{0, 1, 2, 3, 4, 5, 6\}$.
    (a) Write the ordered pairs of the relation.    (b) Write the domain of the relation.
    (c) Write the range of the relation.            (d) Draw the graph of the relation.

6   Draw a graph of each of the following relations.
    (a) $y = x + 1$, $x, y \in \{-2, -1, 0, 1, 2, 3\}$
    (b) $y = x + 1$, $x, y \in I$                    (c) $y = x + 1$, $x, y \in R$
    (d) How are the graphs in (a), (b), and (c) alike? How are they different?

7   (a) Draw the graph of the relation given by each of the following.
            A   $y = x^2 + 1$, $x \in I$              B   $y = x^2 + 1$, $x \in R$
    (b) What is the domain and the range of relations A and B?
    (c) How are the graphs of A and B alike? How are they different?

**B** Remember: You must interpret accurately, the meanings of these symbols.

$I, R, <, >, \leq, \geq$.

8   A relation is defined by $2x + y \leq 1$, $x, y \in \{-4, -3, -2, \ldots, 3, 4, 5\}$.
   (a) Write the ordered pairs of the relation.
   (b) Write the range of the relation.     (c) Draw the graph of the relation.

9   Refer to the set $S = \{-3, -2, -1, 0, 1, 2, 3\}$.
   Draw the graph of each of the following.
   (a) $\{(x, y)\,|\,x = -2,\ x, y \in S\}$          (b) $\{(x, y)\,|\,y = 3,\ x, y \in S\}$
   (c) $\{(x, y)\,|\,x < 2,\ x,\ y \in S\}$          (d) $\{(x, y)\,|\,y > -1,\ x,\ y \in S\}$

10   Refer to the set $M = \{-2, -1, 0, 1, 2\}$.
   (a) Write the elements of $\{(x, y)\,|\,y > x + 1,\ x, y \in M\}$
   (b) Write the domain of the relation in (a).
   (c) Write the range of the relation in (a).

11   If $T = \{-6, -5, -4, \ldots, 4, 5, 6\}$ then draw the graph of each of the
   following.
   (a) $\{(x, y)\,|\,x - y = 3,\ x, y \in T\}$          (b) $\{(x, y)\,|\,2y = x + 4,\ x, y \in T\}$
   (c) $\{(x, y)\,|\,y + x < 1,\ x, y \in T\}$          (d) $\{(x, y)\,|\,x \geq y + 1,\ x, y \in T\}$

12   You can often write a relation with only the domain shown. For each
   relation write the range of the relation.
   (a) $y = 2x + 1$, $x \in \{1, 2, 3, 4, 5, 6,\ 7\}$
   (b) $x + 3y = 2$, $x \in \{-1, 0, 1, 2, 3, 4, 5\}$
   (c) $x > y + 1$, $x \in \{-6, -5, -4, \ldots, 4, 5, 6\}$
   (d) $2y < x - 1$, $x \in \{-5, -4, \ldots, 3, 4, 5\}$
   (e) $y \geq 2x + 1$, $x \in \{0, 1, 2, \ldots, 9, 10\}$

   **PSP** To solve problems in mathematics, you must understand the meaning of symbols and words.

13   Draw the graph of each relation.
   (a) $2x - y = 3$, $x \in R$          (b) $y = x^2 - 1$, $x \in R$
   (c) $y = \dfrac{x + 2}{3}$, $x \in R$          (d) $y = -x^2 + 1$, $x \in R$

   Which of the above relations are linear? Which are non-linear?

14   (a) Draw the graph of each relation on the same set of axes.

   A: $y = \dfrac{1}{2}x^2$, $x \in \{-4, -2, 0, 2, 4\}$          B: $y = x^2$, $x \in \{-4, -2, 0, 2, 4\}$

   (b) How are A and B alike?          (c) How do A and B differ?

# 4.4 **PSP** Problem-Solving: Strategy for Checking

After you have drawn the graph of a relation, it is important that you check your work. To do this, you need to decide whether or not an ordered pair satisfies a relation. For example, when the graph, defined by the equation

$$2x - 3y = 5, \ x, y \in R$$

is drawn, you obtain a straight line. For this straight line you know the two important facts A and B.

A: Any ordered pair of numbers that satisfies $2x - 3y = 5$ lies on the line.

For example, if you chose $(1, -1)$ then

$$\text{L.S.} = 2x - 3y \qquad \text{R.S.} = 5$$
$$= 2(1) - 3(-1) \qquad \text{—— Right side of the equation}$$
$$= 2 + 3 = 5$$

Since L.S. = R.S., then $(1, -1)$ lies on the line.

B: Any ordered pair of numbers *not* on the line does *not* satisfy the equation given by $2x - 3y = 5$.

For example, if you chose $(3, -1)$ then

$$\text{L.S.} = 2x - 3y \qquad \text{R.S.} = 5$$
$$= 2(3) - 3(-1)$$
$$= 6 + 3 = 9$$

Since L.S. $\neq$ R.S. then $(3, -1)$ does not lie on the line.

It is very useful to know how to decide whether an ordered pair of numbers does or does not satisfy a relation.

**Example 1**     Decide whether A(3, 4) satisfies the relation
$2x - 3y \leq 1, \ x, y \in R.$

**Solution**     For A(3, 4) use $x = 3$ and $y = 4$
$$\text{L.S.} = 2x - 3y \qquad \text{R.S.} = 1$$
$$= 2(3) - 3(4)$$
$$= 6 - 12 = -6$$

Thus for A(3, 4), L.S. $\leq$ R.S.
Thus A(3, 4) satisfies the relation $2x - 3y \leq 1$.

In the next example, if you know that the ordered pair satisfies the relation then you can find the value of $k$.

**Example 2**   Find the value of $k$ if $(-3, 2)$ satisfies the relation $3x + ky = 5$, $x, y \in R$.

**Solution**   Since $(-3, 2)$ satisfies the equation given by $3x + ky = 5$, then

$$3(-3) + k(2) = 5$$
$$-9 + 2k = 5$$
$$2k = 14$$
$$k = 7$$

Thus the equation is

$$3x + 7y = 5.$$

*Check*   $\text{L.S.} = 3x + 7y$    $\text{R.S.} = 5$
$\phantom{\text{L.S.}} = 3(-3) + 7(2)$
$\phantom{\text{L.S.}} = -9 + 14$
$\phantom{\text{L.S.}} = 5$
$\text{L.S.} = \text{R.S.}\checkmark\text{checks}$

## 4.4   Exercise

**A** Review the meanings of the symbols $<, >, \leqq, \geqq$.

1   A relation is given by $2x - y = 6$, $x, y \in R$. Which of the following satisfy the relation?

A$(0, -6)$    B$(-1, -9)$   C$(6, 6)$     D$(3, 0)$     E$(-2, -10)$  F$(-4, 14)$

2   A relation is given by $x - 3y \geq 2$, $x, y \in R$. Which of the following satisfy the relation?

P$(9, 2)$     Q$(-5, -2)$   R$(3, -1)$    S$(4, 0)$     T$(10, 3)$     U$(5, 1)$

3   A relation is given by $y = 2x^2 - 1$, $x, y \in R$. Which of the following satisfy the relation?

D$(2, 3)$     E$(-1, 1)$    F$(0, 1)$     G$(1, -1)$    H$(-2, -7)$   K$(3, 17)$

4   A relation is given by $x^2 + y^2 = 100$, $x, y \in R$. Which of the following satisfy the relation?

M$(6, 8)$     N$(4, 6)$     P$(10, 0)$    T$(-8, -6)$   R$(8, 2)$      S$(0, -10)$

5   For each relation two ordered pairs are given. Decide which ordered pair satisfies each given relation, $x, y \in R$.

(a) $3x - y = 8$,        $(2, 2), (3, 1)$

(b) $y < 2x - 1$,        $(2, 3), (3, 4)$

(c) $y = x^2 - 2$,        $(2, 2), (-2, -6)$

(d) $2x = 3(y - 5)$,    $(0, 5), (5, 9)$

(e) $3(x - 2) < y + 3$,  $(3, 1), (4, 2)$

(f) $y^2 = x + 1$,        $(-2, 1), (8, 3)$

(g) $3x + 2y \leq 25$,   $(-4, -2), (7, 3)$

(h) $x^2 + y^2 = 25$,    $(3, 4), (20, 5)$

(i) $y > x^2$,            $(2, 4), (3, 10)$

(j) $y < 3x - 1$,         $(1, 1), (-1, 1)$

**B** Be sure you complete the solution with a final statement.

6   Which of the following ordered pairs satisfy *both* relations $2x - y \leq 3$, $x + y \geq 1$, $x, y \in R$?

$\quad$ A(0, 1) $\qquad\qquad$ B($-3$, 2) $\qquad\qquad$ C(2, 3)

7   Which of the following ordered pairs satisfy *both* relations $x + y = 14$, $x^2 + y^2 = 100$, $x, y \in R$?

$\quad$ D(8, 6) $\qquad\qquad$ E(10, 4) $\qquad\qquad$ F(12, 2)

8   For each of the following decide which ordered pair satisfies both relations. $x, y \in R$.

$\quad$ (a) $x + 2y = 7$, $x - y = -2$, $\qquad$ $(1, -3)$, $(1, 3)$
$\quad$ (b) $x - y < 1$, $y + x > 3$ $\qquad\qquad$ $(1, 3)$, $(4, 3)$
$\quad$ (c) $x = y + 2$, $2(x - 1) = y + 6$, $\quad$ $(4, 2)$, $(6, 4)$
$\quad$ (d) $2x + y > 1$, $x \leq y$, $\qquad\qquad$ $(1, 3)$, $(4, 2)$
$\quad$ (e) $y - 2x \geq 2$, $x + y > 1$, $\qquad$ $(-3, 1)$, $(2, 6)$
$\quad$ (f) $3x - 2y = 0$, $x + y = 5$, $\qquad$ $(3, 2)$, $(2, 3)$
$\quad$ (g) $y > 2$, $x + y < 6$, $\qquad\qquad$ $(3, 2)$, $(2, 3)$
$\quad$ (h) $3x - 2y \leq 1$, $x + y > 0$, $\qquad$ $(-1, 2)$, $(-1, 1)$

9   (a) If $(2, -1)$ satisfies the relation given by $\dfrac{y - 3}{x + 2} = m$, $x, y \in R$, then find the value of $m$.
$\quad$ (b) Find two other ordered pairs that satisfy the relation in (a).

10  (a) If $(2, 2)$ satisfies the relation given by $2x + ky = 6$, $x, y \in R$, find the value of $k$.
$\quad$ (b) Find two other ordered pairs that satisfy the relation in (a).

11  For each of the following relations, an ordered pair is given that satisfies it. Find the value of $k$.

$\quad$ (a) $2x + ky = 8$ $\quad$ $(3, 1)$ $\qquad\qquad$ (b) $2(x - 1) = ky$ $\quad$ $(-2, 3)$
$\quad$ (c) $3y = 8 + 2kx$ $\quad$ $(1, 5)$ $\qquad\qquad$ (d) $2k = 2x - y$ $\qquad$ $(6, 4)$
$\quad$ (e) $k(y - x) = 3$ $\quad$ $(-3, 0)$ $\qquad\qquad$ (f) $3x - 2ky = 9$ $\quad$ $(0, -2)$

**C** 12  (a) If $(-2, 3)$ satisfies the relation given by $(k - 1)x + 3ky = 9$, $x, y \in R$, then find the value of $k$.
$\quad$ (b) Find two other ordered pairs that satisfy the relation in (a).

## 4.5 Inequations and Regions

When the graph of a straight line is drawn, the co-ordinate plane is separated into 3 regions, as shown at the right,

   I one region above the line
  II one region below the line
 III points on the line that satisfy
     the condition that $x + 2y = 8$

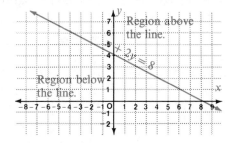

In the region *above* the line the $y$ co-ordinate of any ordered pair, $(x, y)$, is greater than the corresponding $y$ co-ordinate for a point *on* the line. Thus, $x + 2y > 8$.

In the region *below* the line the $y$ co-ordinate of any ordered pair, $(x, y)$, is less than the corresponding $y$ co-ordinate for a point *on* the line. Thus, $x + 2y < 8$.

The corresponding inequations and their graphs are shown.

$x + 2y > 8$                                                $x + 2y < 8$

A broken line is used to show that the region does not include the boundary.

When the boundary is not included, the region is often called an **open half plane**.

If the boundaries are included then the inequations that define the regions are $x + 2y \geq 8$ and $x + 2y \leq 8$. Their graphs are as shown.

$x + 2y \geq 8$                                               $x + 2y \leq 8$

When the boundary is included in the region, the region is often called a **closed half plane**.

To draw the region defined by an inequation, such as, $3y - x \geq 6$, first you need to locate the boundary. The boundary is defined by $3y - x = 6$. To check the accuracy of your work of drawing the graph defined by an inequation, you need to use the skills you learned in the previous section.

**Example**    Draw the graph of $3y - x \geq 6$.

**Solution**    Draw the graph of the equation $3y - x = 6$. Use a table of values.

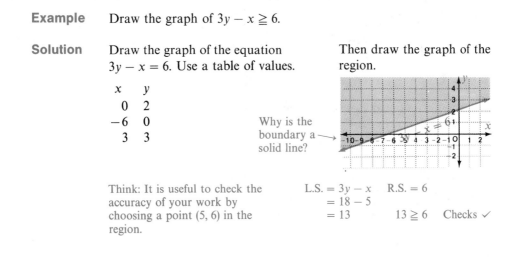

Then draw the graph of the region.

| x | y |
|---|---|
| 0 | 2 |
| −6 | 0 |
| 3 | 3 |

Why is the boundary a → solid line?

Think: It is useful to check the accuracy of your work by choosing a point (5, 6) in the region.

L.S. $= 3y - x$     R.S. $= 6$
$= 18 - 5$
$= 13$          $13 \geq 6$    Checks ✓

## 4.5  Exercise

**A** 1   (a) Which of the following describes the region shown?

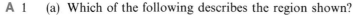

A  $x + y = 4$     B  $x + y < 4$
C  $x + y \leqq 4$     D  $x + y > 4$     E  $x + y \geqq 4$

Give reasons for your choice.

(b) Draw a graph for each of the other regions given in (a). How are they alike? How are they different?

2   Which of the following points are in the given region?

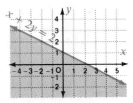

(a) (3, 1)    (b) (0, 0)    (c) (−3, −3)
(d) (−3, 3)   (e) (0, 4)    (f) (2, 0)

3   Which point would be the most useful point to check the accuracy of the graph that is drawn?

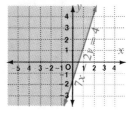

A(0, 0)         B(5, 0)         C(0, 6)

Give reasons for your answer.

4    In each of the following graphs, the equation shows the line used to
     indicate the boundary of the region. What is the inequation that describes
     each region?

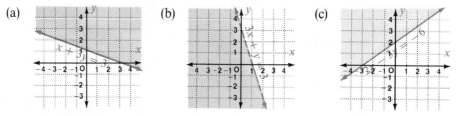

(a)          (b)          (c)

**B 5**  A region is graphed for each defining inequation. Which of the given points
     are in the region?

(a) $2x - y \geq 5$            A(4, 2)            B(2, 2)

(b) $3x + y < -2$            C(-2, 3)            D(-1, 2)

(c) $2y + 3x > -11$          E(-2, -4)          F(-3, 0)

(d) $y - 2x \leq 3$            G(-1, 1)            H(2, 9)

(e) $x + 3y < 8$             I(5, 2)            J(0, 2)

(f) $2x + 5y \geq 7$          O$\left(\dfrac{1}{2}, \dfrac{1}{5}\right)$          P$\left(\dfrac{3}{2}, \dfrac{4}{5}\right)$

(g) $2x - y < -4$            Q(-2, 2)           R(0, 0)

6    (a) Draw the region given by $2x + y \geq 3$.

     (b) Choose an appropriate point in your region to test the accuracy of your work.

7    Draw the region defined by each of the following.

(a) $x + y > 1$    (b) $x + y \leq 1$    (c) $2x + y \geq 1$   (d) $2x + y < 1$   (e) $x \geq 2$

(f) $y > 3$        (g) $x \leq -4$       (h) $y \leq -3$       (i) $x < -4$       (j) $y > -6$

8    (a) Draw the region given by $x - y \geq 8$.

     (b) Draw the region given by $y \leq x - 8$.

     (c) Why are the regions in (a) and (b) the same?

     (d) Which inequation is more helpful when drawing the above region?

          A: $x - y \geq 8$                      B: $y \leq x - 8$

     (e) What error might be made in drawing the region in (a) when the
         inequation is in the form $x - y \geq 8$?

**C 9**  For each of the following

     • write the defining inequation in the form $y = mx + b$.

     • graph the region.

(a) $2x + y > 8$            (b) $x - y < 6$            (c) $2x - y \leq 4$

(d) $2y - x \leq 6$          (e) $y - 3x \geq 9$          (f) $3x - y < 6$

## 4.6　An Essential Skill: Calculating Distance

An essential skill in working with co-ordinate geometry is the ability to calculate the distance between two points on the plane.

The distance between two islands A and B is shown.

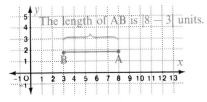

The distance between island A and island C is shown.

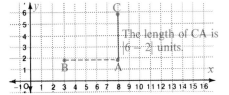

With co-ordinate geometry you can use some algebraic tools to solve problems. To find the distance between islands B and C you can use a useful tool, the Pythagorean Theorem.

$$BC^2 = AC^2 + AB^2$$
$$BC^2 = 4^2 + 5^2$$
$$= 16 + 25$$
$$= 41$$

Thus, $BC = \sqrt{41}$ or 6.4 (to 1 decimal place)

Thus the distance between the islands B and C is $\sqrt{41}$ units (or 6.4 units to 1 decimal place).

Use these steps on your calculator to find a square root.

Output

| c | 41 | $\sqrt{\phantom{x}}$ | 6.4031242 |

You need to decide to what accuracy you are to give your answer.

You can find the distance between points given in any quadrant, as shown in the following example.

**Example 1**　Find the distance between the points R(−5, 6) and S(3, −5)

**Solution**　From the diagram

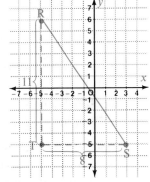

$$ST = |3 - (-5)| \qquad RT = |6 - (-5)|$$
$$= 8 \qquad\qquad\quad = 11$$

Use Pythagoras Theorem
$$RS^2 = ST^2 + RT^2$$
$$= 64 + 121$$
$$= 185$$
$$RS = \sqrt{185}$$

Thus, the distance between R and S is $\sqrt{185}$ units.

It is often necessary to combine more than one skill when solving a mathematical problem. This is demonstrated in Example 2.

**Example 2**   A triangle has vertices A($-1$, $-4$), B(12, $-4$), and C(4, 4). Find its area.

Think: Sketch the information on a diagram to help you visualize the solution to the problem.

**Solution**   From the diagram, the co-ordinates of point D are (4, $-4$).

$$AB = |12 - (-1)| \quad CD = |4 - (-4)|$$
$$= 13 \qquad\qquad = 8$$

$$\text{Area of } \triangle ABC = \tfrac{1}{2} \times \text{base} \times \text{height}$$
$$= \tfrac{1}{2} \times AB \times CD$$
$$= \tfrac{1}{2}(13)(8)$$
$$= 52$$

Thus, the area of $\triangle ABC$ is 52 square units.

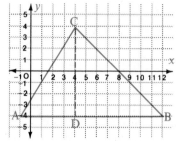

## 4.6   Exercise

**A 1**   Find the length of each line segment.

**2**   Find the length of the sides of each figure.

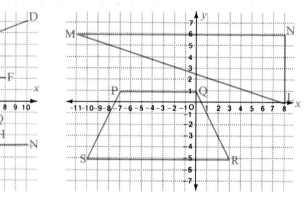

**3**   A line segment AB is given by the co-ordinates of its end points A(3, 4) and B($-2$, $-1$).

(a) Sketch a diagram of the information.

(b) Find the length of AB.

**4**   Refer to the diagram.

(a) What information do you need to find the area of ABCD?

(b) Calculate the area of ABCD.

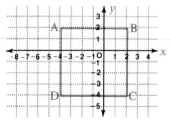

5   Refer to the diagram.

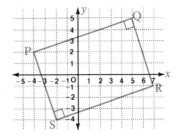

   (a) What information do you need to find
       the area of PQRS?

   (b) Calculate the area of PQRS. Express
       your answer as a radical.

   (c) Express your answer in (b) as a decimal
       to 1 decimal place.

**B** For each of the following problems, be sure to make a final statement.   `PSP`

6   Find the length of each line segment given by the pairs of points.
   (a) $(8, 3), (8, -8)$      (b) $(13, 3), (13, -8)$      (c) $(9, -2), (3, -2)$
   (d) $(6, -9), (6, -8)$      (e) $(3, 2), (8, 4)$      (f) $(5, 2), (4, -3)$

7   Which line segment is longer?
       AB      $A(4, 8), B(-2, 2)$      or      CD      $C(5, -2), D(-2, 5)$

8   Three vertices of a rectangle PQRS are given.
       $P(-4, 3)$          $Q(8, 7)$          $R(10, 1)$
   (a) Find the lengths of the sides.      (b) Find the length of the diagonal.

9   (a) Draw the rectangle with vertices as follows.
           $A(4, -1)$      $B(-4, -1)$      $C(-4, 4)$      $D(4, 4)$
   (b) What is the area of the rectangle?

10  The vertices of a triangle are $P(-4, 8), Q(8, 2)$ and $R(-4, 4)$. Find the length of
   (a) PQ          (b) RP          (c) QR
   (d) What type of triangle is it: scalene, isosceles, or equilateral?

11  A triangle has vertices: $A(2, 3), B(7, -8), C(-4, -3)$. Find its area.

12  (a) Plot points $A(0, 6), B(-2, 0), C(2, 0), D(-4, -6)$, and $E(4, -6)$.
   (b) Find the lengths of AB and BD. What do you notice?
   (c) Find the lengths of AC and CE. What do you notice?
   (d) Find the lengths of BC and DE. What do you notice?

**C** 13  For the points $A(-5, -7), B(-1, 1)$, and $C(3, 9)$, find
   (a) AB          (b) BC          (c) AC
   (d) Use your results above to help you explain why B is the midpoint of AC.

## 4.7 Process of Mathematics: Distance Formula

If you wanted to find the distance on a plane and you had to make this calculation many times, you could use a computer. However, you would need a formula so that the computer could be programmed to accept many inputs. These inputs would be the co-ordinates of the end points.

In order to develop a formula, you use the same steps that you used to find the distance between two points for co-ordinates of numerical values.

Choose the following co-ordinates to represent any two points on the Cartesian plane.

$P_1(x_1, y_1)$          $P_2(x_2, y_2)$

These numbers are called subscript numbers, and are the same for each point.

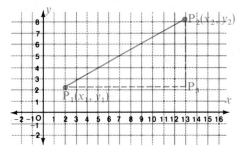

You can see from the diagram that the co-ordinates of $P_3$ are $(x_2, y_1)$.
The distance between $P_2$ and $P_3$ is given by $(y_2 - y_1)$.
The distance between $P_1$ and $P_3$ is given by $(x_2 - x_1)$.
$\Delta P_1 P_2 P_3$ is a right triangle. Thus, you can use the Pythagorean Property for its sides.

$$P_1P_2{}^2 = P_1P_3{}^2 + P_2P_3{}^2$$
$$= (x_2 - x_1)^2 + (y_2 - y_1)^2$$
Thus, $P_1P_2 = \sqrt{(x_2 - x_1)^2 + (y_2 - y_1)^2}$

Thus, the distance between two points $P_1(x_1, y_1)$ and $P_2(x_2, y_2)$ is
$$P_1P_2 = \sqrt{(x_2 - x_1)^2 + (y_2 - y_1)^2}$$

You could now program a computer to calculate the distance between any two points $P_1$ and $P_2$.

**Example**   Find the distance between $A(-2, 5)$ and $B(-7, -10)$.
You may leave your answer in radical form.

**Solution**   Use $A(-2, 5) = (x_1, y_1)$ and $B(-7, -10) = (x_2, y_2)$.
Then $AB = \sqrt{[-7 - (-2)]^2 + (-10 - 5)^2}$
$= \sqrt{(-5)^2 + (-15)^2}$
$= \sqrt{25 + 225}$
$= \sqrt{250}$
$= 5\sqrt{10}$  ⟵ Express your answer in simplest form.
Thus, the distance between A and B is $5\sqrt{10}$ units.

## 4.7 Exercise

**A** Throughout the exercise, you may express your answer in radical form unless otherwise indicated.

1   A line segment, AB, has endpoints A(1, 3) and B(2, 4).
   (a) Sketch a diagram to show this information.
   (b) Find the length of AB.

2   A line segment, CD, has end points C($-3$, 2) and D(2, $-3$).
   (a) Sketch a diagram to show this information.
   (b) Find the length of CD.

3   Line segment, PQ, has end points P($-3$, 4) and Q(2, 5).
   (a) Find the length PQ. Express your answer in radical form.
   (b) Express your answer to (a) to 1 decimal place.

4   Refer to the diagram.
   Calculate the length of each line segment.

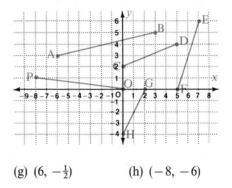

5   Find the distance from the origin, O(0, 0), to each point. Leave your answer in radical form.
   (a) (3, $-2$)           (b) ($-5$, 2)
   (c) (1, 6)            (d) ($-2$, $-9$)
   (e) (11, 2)           (f) ($-1\frac{1}{2}$, $-4$)       (g) (6, $-\frac{1}{2}$)           (h) ($-8$, $-6$)

6   Find the distance between each pair of points.
   (a) (2, 2), (7, 4)         (b) (6, $-6$), (2, $-3$)        (c) (3, 8), ($-3$, $-8$)
   (d) (4, 4), (9, 9)         (e) ($-3$, 0), (8, $-5$)        (f) (9, $-3$), (12, $-4$)

**B** Use a sketch of the information, if necessary, to help you solve the problem.   **PSP**

7   The co-ordinates of points are shown.

   A(10, 8)       B(14, 4)       C(6, 3)        D(3, $-3$)
   E(1, $-6$)      F($-2$, 0)      G($-3$, $-4$)    H($-7$, $-8$)
   I($-8$, 6)      J($-4$, 2)      K($-3$, 2)      L(3, 5)

   Which of the following have the same lengths?
   (a) AB       (b) KL        (c) GH       (d) EF        (e) CD       (f) IJ

8   A triangle has vertices A(2, 4), B(5, −5), and C(−4, −2). Find the lengths of the sides to determine what type of triangle △ABC is.

9   △PQR has vertices P(5, 10), Q(8, 6) and R(−7, 1). Find its perimeter.

10   Three vertices of a rectangle are S(2, 5), T(5, −1), and U(−3, −5).
    (a) What are the co-ordinates of the missing vertex?
    (b) Find the lengths of the sides.       (c) What is the area of the rectangle?

11   Three islands are located by the following co-ordinates: F(−10, 4), Q(2, 8), R(7, −7). Which island is closer to Q?

12   Various ports on islands are shown by these co-ordinates.
       P(6, 6)       Q(−4, 4)       R(5, −5)       S(−3, 0)       T(11, 0)       U(−3, −9)
    How far did the ship travel if the ship visited the ports in the order given below?
    (a) P, T, S          (b) R, S, U          (c) R, P, S          (d) T, R, S

13   Three vertices of a rectangle are P(−1, −10), Q(11, −6), and S(−5, 2).
    (a) What are the co-ordinates of the missing vertex R?
    (b) Find the area of the rectangle.
    (c) Name the co-ordinates of the midpoint of QR.
    (d) Name the co-ordinates of the point at which the diagonals intersect.

14   A(−4, 0), B(0, 1), and C(4, 2) are points on the co-ordinate plane.
    (a) Find the length of AB, BC, and AC.
    (b) Calculate AB + BC. How does your answer compare to your answers in (a)?
    (c) Based on your results in (a) and (b), what conclusion can you make?

C 15   Show that points K(6, 3), L(−10, −5) and M(2, 11) lie on the circle with centre C(−4, 3).

## Problem Solving

Each step of the solution seems to logically follow, but there is definitely a problem. What is wrong with the solution?

$$n = 1 \quad ①$$
$$n + 1 = 2$$
$$n(n + 1) = 2n$$
$$n^2 + n = 2n$$
$$n^2 + n - 2 = 2n - 2 \qquad \text{Since } n = 1 \text{ from } ①$$
$$(n + 2)(n - 1) = 2(n - 1) \qquad \text{Then } n + 2 = 2$$
$$n + 2 = 2 \qquad\qquad\qquad 1 + 2 = 2$$
$$\text{or} \quad 3 = 2 \quad ?$$

# 4.8 **PSP** Problem-Solving: Finding the Midpoint

In mathematics, a solution to a simple problem very often suggests a solution to a more advanced problem. For example, these three calculations suggest a general method of finding the midpoint of a line segment.

I The line segment, AB, has end points with co-ordinates A(2, 3), B(6, 3).

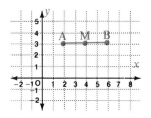

From the diagram, the midpoint is M(4, 3) which suggests that the x co-ordinate was found by

$$x = \frac{2 + 6}{2}$$

$= 4$    In other words, 4 is the average of 2 and 6.

II The line segment, CD, has end points with co-ordinates C(2, 3), D(2, −1)

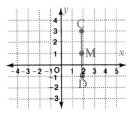

From the diagram, the midpoint is M(2, 1) which suggests that the y co-ordinate is found by

$$y = \frac{3 + (-1)}{2}$$

$= 1$    In other words, 1 is the average of 3 and (−1).

III From the diagram, the co-ordinates of the midpoint appear to be found by finding the average of the x co-ordinates and also of the y co-ordinates of the end points.

    midpoint = M(3, 2)

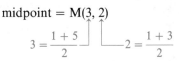

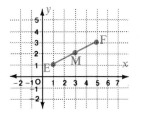

The previous examples suggest that for any two points $P_1(x_1, y_1)$ and $P_2(x_2, y_2)$, the midpoint, M, has co-ordinates

$$M\left(\frac{x_1 + x_2}{2}, \frac{y_1 + y_2}{2}\right)$$

In fact, this is indeed the case, and this formula can be used to find the co-ordinates of the midpoint of a line segment.

**Example**   Find the midpoint, M, of the line segment, PQ, with end points P(3, −7) and Q(−5, 11).

**Solution**   Use $(x_1, y_1) = (3, -7)$ and $(x_2, y_2) = (-5, 11)$.

Use $M = \left( \dfrac{x_1 + x_2}{2}, \dfrac{y_1 + y_2}{2} \right)$

$= \left( \dfrac{3 - 5}{2}, \dfrac{-7 + 11}{2} \right)$

$= \left( \dfrac{-2}{2}, \dfrac{4}{2} \right)$

$= (-1, 2)$

The midpoint, M, of line segment, PQ, has co-ordinates $(-1, 2)$.

## 4.8   Exercise

**A** Review the method of finding the co-ordinates of the midpoint of a line segment.

1   Line segment, PQ, has end points P(8, 4) and Q(2, 6).
   (a) Sketch the information on a diagram.
   (b) What are the co-ordinates of the midpoint?

2   Find the co-ordinates of the midpoint of the line segment with these end points.
   (a) A(1, 6), B(9, 6)       (b) D(−3, 3), E(−9, 3)       (c) G(6, −1), H(6, −7)
   (d) M(−7, 4), N(−7, −4)   (e) P(4, 4), Q(8, 4)         (f) R(3, 8), S(3, 4)

3   Find the midpoint of each line segment given by the co-ordinates of the end points.
   (a) (−1, −2), (−7, 10)     (b) (6, 4), (0, 0)          (c) (5, −1), (−2, 9)
   (d) (0, 0), (6, 4)         (e) (4, −5), (9, −6)        (f) (0, −4), (12, 0)
   (g) (−2, 3), (3, 5)        (h) (5, 0), (−8, −3)        (i) (−7, −11), (−5, 0)

4   Find the midpoint of each of the following.
   (a) AB   A(5, 3), B(1, 5)   (b) CD   C(−4, −5), D(2, 3)   (c) EF   E(−6, 3), F(6, −7)

**B** Remember: When you answer a problem, make a final statement.   **PSP**

5   (a) A diameter of a circle has end points A(9, −4) and B(3, −2). Find the centre of the circle.
   (b) The end points of AB are A($\sqrt{72}$, −$\sqrt{12}$) and B($\sqrt{32}$, −$\sqrt{48}$). Find the midpoint.

6   Find the midpoint of each side of $\triangle ABC$ whose vertices are A(12, 4), B(−6, 2), and C(−4, −2).

7   One end point of line segment AB is A(−2, 4). If the co-ordinates of the midpoint are (−1, 7), find the co-ordinates of B.

8   If the midpoint of a segment is (−1, −8) and one end point is (7, −9), find the co-ordinates of the remaining end point.

9   D(−5, 8), E(−5, −6), and F(9, 8) are the vertices of $\triangle DEF$.
    (a) Find the midpoint M of DE.      (b) Find the midpoint N of DF.
    (c) Find the length of MN.          (d) Find the length of the base EF.
    (e) How do the lengths of MN and EF compare?

10  The vertices of $\triangle ABC$ are A(2, 8), B(−2, −8), and C(−14, 4).
    P and Q are the midpoints of AB and AC.
    (a) Sketch a diagram of the given information.      **PSP**
    (b) Use co-ordinates to show that $PQ = \dfrac{1}{2} BC$.

11  B(−2, 16), C(10, 4), D(−2, −8), and E(−14, 4) are the vertices of a square.
    (a) Show that the diagonals are equal in length.
    (b) Show that the diagonals bisect each other.

**PSP** 12  If 2893 digits are used to number the pages of a book, how many pages does the book have?

C 13  Show that in $\triangle PQR$, given by P(6, 4), Q(8, −4), and R(10, 6), the line segment joining the midpoints of any two sides is half the length of the third side.

---

## Calculator Tip

The value of $\pi$ is given by expression   $4(1 - \frac{1}{3} + \frac{1}{5} - \frac{1}{7} + \cdots)$.
How many terms are needed in the above expression to obtain the value of $\pi$ accurate to 3 decimal places?

> Use your calculator. You may need to use the memory in and memory recall features on your calculator. Refer to your manual.

# 4.9 Working With Slope

In the previous section, you worked with an important property of a line segment, namely, its length. Another property of a line segment, or a line, is its **slope**. The term slope is often used when describing steepness. When a cottage is built the roof must have a certain amount of steepness to it so that the snow will slide off, rather than building up on the roof. A jet, as shown in the photograph, must maintain a certain slope for a successful take-off.

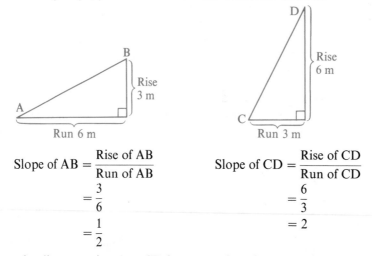

*The Lockheed L-1011 is a wide-bodied jet that carries 256 passengers. It must maintain a certain slope for a successful take-off. This jet is so large that there is a galley in which the meals are prepared to be taken up to the passengers by 2 elevators.*

In calculating slope, you need to know the terms **rise** and **run**.

$$\text{Slope of AB} = \frac{\text{Rise of AB}}{\text{Run of AB}}$$
$$= \frac{3}{6}$$
$$= \frac{1}{2}$$

$$\text{Slope of CD} = \frac{\text{Rise of CD}}{\text{Run of CD}}$$
$$= \frac{6}{3}$$
$$= 2$$

From the diagrams, it seems CD is steeper than AB. How do their slopes compare?

You can calculate the slopes of lines and line segments on the Cartesian plane.

**Example** Calculate the slope of AB and CD.

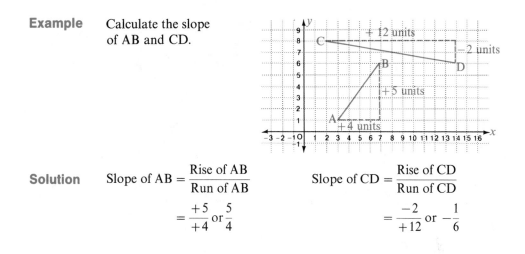

**Solution** 

$$\text{Slope of AB} = \frac{\text{Rise of AB}}{\text{Run of AB}}$$

$$= \frac{+5}{+4} \text{ or } \frac{5}{4}$$

$$\text{Slope of CD} = \frac{\text{Rise of CD}}{\text{Run of CD}}$$

$$= \frac{-2}{+12} \text{ or } -\frac{1}{6}$$

The symbols $\Delta x$ and $\Delta y$ were invented to help describe slope. ($\Delta y$ is read delta $y$.) You can also think of slope as follows.

$$\text{Slope} = \frac{\text{amount of vertical change}}{\text{amount of horizontal change}}$$

$$= \frac{\Delta y}{\Delta x} \longleftarrow \text{Change in } y.$$
$$\longleftarrow \text{Corresponding change in } x.$$

**PSP**

Be sure you know the meaning of each symbol you use when you are doing mathematics.

# 4.9 Exercise

**A** Review the meaning of *rise*, *run*, and *slope*. Be sure you know how these terms are related.

1 Calculate the slope of each line segment.

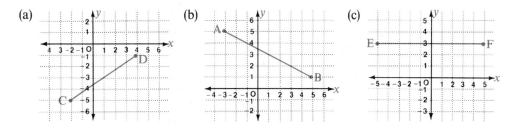

2   Calculate the slope of
    each line segment.

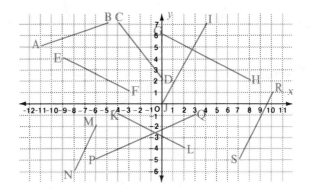

3   A line segment has end points P($-3$, 1) and Q(2, 5).
    (a) Sketch a diagram.
    (b) Calculate the rise, run, and slope of the line segment.

4   Find the slope of each line segment with the following end points.
    (a) $(-1, 8)$, $(7, -3)$       (b) $(2, -4)$, $(8, 10)$       (c) $(1, 3)$, $(-4, 5)$
    (d) $(9, 4)$, $(-3, -7)$       (e) $(1, 6)$, $(-3, 7)$       (f) $(-3, 5)$, $(1, -8)$

5   Calculate the slope of the roof shown
    in the diagram. (The slope of a roof
    is often referred to as the *pitch* of the
    roof.)

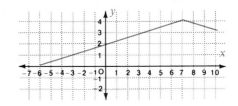

**B** Be sure to express your answer in simplest terms.

6   Use the graph of the line given.
    A, B, C, D are points on the line.
    Calculate the slope of

    (a) AB          (b) CD

    (c) What do you notice about the
        answers in (a) and (b)?

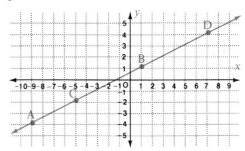

7   Calculate the slope of each line.
    (a)

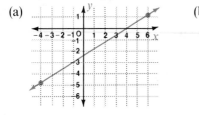

    (b)

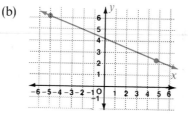

8    Calculate the slope of each line.

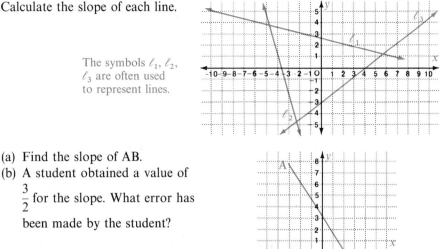

The symbols $\ell_1$, $\ell_2$, $\ell_3$ are often used to represent lines.

9    (a) Find the slope of AB.
     (b) A student obtained a value of $\frac{3}{2}$ for the slope. What error has been made by the student?

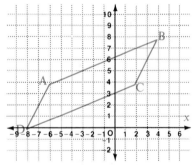

10   (a) What is the slope of lines parallel to the *x*-axis? Give reasons for your answer.
     (b) Why is the slope not defined for line segments or lines parallel to the *y*-axis?

11   Refer to the diagram. A parallelogram has opposite sides parallel.
     (a) Calculate the slope of each side of the parallelogram.
     (b) What do you notice about the slopes of the opposite sides of the parallelogram?
     (c) Write a probable conclusion about the slopes of parallel lines.

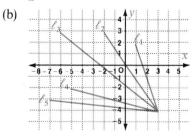

C 12  Calculate the slopes of the line segments in each diagram.

     (a)                          (b)

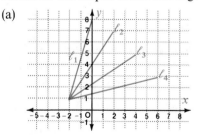

     (c) Based on your results in (a) and (b), what conclusion can you make about
        • lines with positive slopes?    • lines with negative slopes?

# 4.10   Properties of Lines: Slope

To find the slope of a line, you need to know the co-ordinates of two points of the line.

**Example 1**   Calculate the slope of the line given by the equation
$2x + y = 6$.

**Solution**   Think: Sketch a graph.

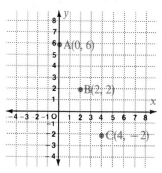

Choose two points on the line, say A and C.

$$\text{Slope}_{AC} = \frac{\Delta y}{\Delta x}$$

$$= \frac{-2 - 6}{4 - 0}$$

$$= \frac{-8}{4}$$

$$= -2$$

The slope of $2x + y = 6$ is $-2$.

From the diagram in Example 1 note that

$$\text{Slope}_{AB} = \frac{\Delta y}{\Delta x} \qquad\qquad \text{Slope}_{BC} = \frac{\Delta y}{\Delta x}$$

$$= \frac{2 - 6}{2 - 0} \qquad\qquad = \frac{-2 - 2}{4 - 2}$$

$$= \frac{-4}{2} \qquad\qquad = \frac{-4}{2}$$

$$= -2 \qquad\qquad = -2$$

For the line in Example 1,   $\text{Slope}_{AB} = \text{Slope}_{BC} = \text{Slope}_{AC}$.

These calculations illustrate important properties of a line.

A   The calculation of the slope of a line is independent of the choice of the points used to calculate the slope. *The slope of a line is constant* and is called the **constant slope property** of a line. The symbol $m$, is used to represent the slope. You can write

$$m_{AB} = m_{BC} = m_{AC}$$

In general, if $P(x_1, y_1)$ and $Q(x_2, y_2)$ are points on a line then

$$\text{Slope}_{PQ} = \frac{y_2 - y_1}{x_2 - x_1}$$

**B** Since $m_{AB} = m_{BC}$ then the points A, B, C are on the same line. Three points are said to be **collinear** if they lie on the same straight line. You can use the fact $m_{AB} = m_{BC}$ to show points are collinear.

Based on the property of a line, you can determine whether or not 3 given points are collinear, as shown in the next example.

**Example 2**  Three points are given on a plane.

$$M(-3, 7) \qquad N(-8, 1) \qquad P(2, 13)$$

Show that M, N and P are collinear.

**Solution**

| For points M and N | For points M and P | For points N and P |
|---|---|---|
| $m_{MN} = \dfrac{1-7}{-8-(-3)}$ | $m_{MP} = \dfrac{13-7}{2-(-3)}$ | $m_{NP} = \dfrac{13-1}{2-(-8)}$ |
| $= \dfrac{-6}{-5}$ or $\dfrac{6}{5}$ | $= \dfrac{6}{5}$ | $= \dfrac{12}{10}$ or $\dfrac{6}{5}$ |

Thus $m_{MN} = m_{MP} = m_{NP} = \dfrac{6}{5}$.

Points M, N, and P are collinear.

## 4.10   Exercise

**A** Remember: To calculate the slope of a line, you need to use the co-ordinates of two points on the line.

1   A line passes through each pair of points. Find the slope of each line.
   (a) $(2, -6), (-4, 6)$ 　　　(b) $(0, -2), (4, 6)$ 　　　(c) $(-3, 8), (2, -2)$
   (d) $(12, -3), (2, 7)$ 　　　(e) $(6, 8), (-2, -4)$ 　　　(f) $(-4, 0), (6, 8)$

2   Calculate the slope of each line.
   (a)
   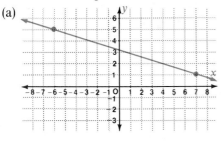
   (b)
   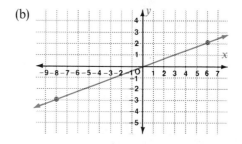

3   A line is defined by $y = 3x - 1$, $x \in R$.

   (a) Draw a graph of the line. 　　　(b) Calculate its slope.

**B** Remember: The co-ordinates of a point on a line satisfy the equation of the line.

4 Calculate the slope of each line defined by

(a) $y = 2x - 1$

(b) $y = 3x + 5$

(c) $2y = 3x + 1$

(d) $2x - y = 8$

(e) $3y - 1 = 2x$

(f) $\dfrac{1}{2}x + y = 6$

5 A line is constructed through a point $(3, 2)$ with slope $\dfrac{4}{3}$. Why does the line pass through the point with co-ordinates $(6, 6)$?

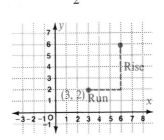

6 For each line, a point and its slope, $m$, are given. Draw each line on squared paper.

(a) $(-1, 3)$, $m = \dfrac{2}{3}$

(b) $(2, 3)$, $m = -\dfrac{4}{3}$

(c) $(3, -2)$, $m = -\dfrac{3}{2}$

(d) $(-2, -1)$, $m = -4$

7 (a) A line passes through the points $(4, 3)$ and $(-2, k)$. Why is the slope of the line given by $\dfrac{k - 3}{-2 - 4}$?

(b) The slope of the line in (a) is $\dfrac{1}{2}$. Find the value of $k$.

8 (a) A line passes through the points $(2, k)$ and $(-3, 2k)$. If the slope of the line is $-\dfrac{1}{2}$, find $k$.

(b) A line passes through the points $(2, -3)$ and $(4, y)$. Find $y$ if the slope of the line is $\dfrac{2}{3}$.

9 A line passes through the following points and has a slope $m$. Find the value of $k$.

(a) $(2, k)$, $(3, -2)$, $m = 2$

(b) $(-3, 1)$, $(4, k)$, $m = \dfrac{1}{2}$

(c) $(-8, k)$, $(2, 3k)$, $m = -3$

(d) $(1, -k)$, $\left(-\dfrac{1}{2}k, -5\right)$, $m = -\dfrac{1}{4}$

10 Points A($-8$, 1), B($-2$, 5), and C(4, 9) are given on a plane. Calculate

(a) the slope of AB                 (b) the slope of BC

Based on your results in (a) and (b) what conclusion can you make about the points A, B, and C?

11 Points D($-8$, $-7$), E(12, 6), and F(6, 2) are given on the plane.

(a) Use your work with slope to determine if the points D, E, and F are collinear.

(b) Check your answer in (a) by plotting the points.

12 Decide which of these sets of points are collinear. Give reasons why or why not.

(a) A($-3$, $-4$)       B(2, 0)           C(12, $-8$)     **PSP**

(b) D(11, 9)           E(3, 6)            F(7, 5)

(c) G(2, $-6$)        H($-10$, $-4$)     I(14, $-8$)

13 A(3, $-4$), B(9, 2), C(14, $-3$), and D(8, $-9$) are the vertices of a rectangle.

(a) Calculate the slopes of the opposite sides.

(b) What do you notice about your answers in (a)?

14 (a) Decide on a strategy to show why the figure given by the points     **PSP**

R($-5$, 1), S(5, 3), T(2, $-1$), and U($-8$, $-3$) is a parallelogram.

(b) Use your strategy in (a) and show your work.

C 15 Which of the following figures are parallelograms?

(a) A(2, 5), B(6, 1), C(6, $-6$), D($-6$, 5)

(b) E($-5$, $-4$), F($-5$, 1), G(7, 4), H(7, $-1$)

## Computer Tip

The computer may be used to perform calculations in any branch of mathematics. For example, it can do tedious calculations in finding answers in co-ordinate geometry. The computer program shown finds the co-ordinates of the midpoint of a line segment if we know the co-ordinates of the end points.

```
10 INPUT X1, Y1, X2, Y2
20 LET M1 = (X1 + X2)/2
30 LET M2 = (Y1 + Y2)/2
40 PRINT "MIDPOINT IS" M1, M2
50 END
```

## Math Tip

It is important to clearly understand the vocabulary of mathematics when solving problems.

• Make a list of all the words you have met in this chapter.

• Provide a sample of your own to illustrate each word.

## Practice and Problems: Review

1 (a) Draw the graph of each relation on the same set of axes.

A: $y = x^2$, $x \in \{-2, -1, 0, 1, 2\}$   B: $y = -x^2$, $x \in \{-2, -1, 0, 1, 2\}$

(b) How are A and B alike?   (c) How do A and B differ?

2 The co-ordinates of three vertices of a rectangle are A(2, 10), B(8, 4), and C(−1, −5). Find the co-ordinates of the missing vertex.

3 Draw the region defined by each of the following.

(a) $x - y > 1$   (b) $x + y \leq 1$   (c) $x + 2y > 1$   (d) $2x - y \leq 1$   (e) $y \geq 1$

4 The vertices of a parallelogram are D(−12, 2), E(−2, 4), F(−5, −2), and G(−15, −4).

(a) Calculate the slopes of the opposite sides.

(b) What do you notice about your answers in (a)?

5 (a) Draw the rectangle with vertices A(11, 0), B(7, −8), C(−5, −2), and D(−1, 6).

(b) Find the area of the rectangle. You may leave your answer in radical form.

(c) Find the co-ordinates of the midpoint of each side.

## Practice Test

1 The data from an experiment are recorded as ordered pairs.
(1, 2) (5, 10) (2, 4) (3, 5) (3, 6) (4, 8)

(a) Plot the ordered pairs.   (b) Which ordered pair does not seem to fit?

(c) Use your graph to predict two other ordered pairs that seem to fit the pattern.

(d) What is the domain and the range of the relation above?

2 Draw the graph of each relation, $x \in R$. Which relations are linear? non-linear?

(a) $x \longrightarrow 2x - 3$   (b) $x \longrightarrow x^2 - 2$   (c) $x \longrightarrow 3 - 2x$   (d) $x \longrightarrow -x^2 + 2$

3 If (−2, 3) satisfies the relation given by $3kx - 2y = 1$, then find the value of $k$.

4 Draw the graph of each region given by

(a) $y < x - 1$   (b) $x - 2y \geq 2$   (c) $x < 1$

5 Three vertices of rectangle ABCD are A(−2, −1), B(10, 3), and C(11, 0). Find the

(a) co-ordinates of the midpoint of each side of the rectangle.

(b) length of each diagonal of the rectangle.   (c) slopes of each side of the rectangle.

6 Two forestry stations are located at (−5, −2) and (9, 5). Which station is closer to a fire located at the point with co-ordinates (−3, 9)?

# 5 The Straight Line: Patterns and Process

Meaning of functions, vertical line test, properties of linear functions, graphing techniques, patterns with slopes and intercepts, using $y = mx + b$, properties of parallel and perpendicular lines, writing equations of lines, solving problems, applications, strategies, and problem solving

## Introduction

Various mathematical symbols are used in mathematics to show entities, relations or operations. The origin and development of some of the symbols you use today are unclear. Historians can only guess at the origin of some symbols. In early times, the processes and development of mathematics were hindered because proper symbols had not been established. Sometimes confusion occurred because different people used different symbols. For example, to indicate subtraction, Diophantus, a Greek, used the symbol $\nearrow$, the Hindus used a dot, and the Italians used M or m. The mathematical symbols $+$ and $-$ were first introduced in 1489 by Johann Widman of Germany and have been used ever since. Refer to the other symbols shown at the right.

Symbols are intended to simplify the study of mathematics.

$=$ This symbol was used for the first time by the mathematician Robert Recorde in 1557. He used two equal parallel lines $(=)$ "because no things can be more equal".

$>$ These symbols, first used by
$<$ Thomas Harriot (1560–1621), were not accepted as suitable symbols by others at the time.

$\times$ The symbol for multiplication was introduced by William Oughtred (1574–1660) but it was not readily adopted since it too closely resembled the variable $x$.

Often a symbol used in mathematics is credited to a particular person. For example, Leonhard Euler (1707–1783) is given credit for a symbol used in this chapter and throughout mathematics, namely, $f(x)$. Euler, blind from 1768, was one of the most prolific writers in the history of mathematics, and, in some way or another, his name occurs almost in every branch of mathematics. His notation allows a linear function to be represented in different forms as follows:

▶ equation, $y = 2x + 1$      ▶ mapping notation, $f : x \longrightarrow 2x + 1$
▶ ordered pairs, $(x, 2x + 1)$      ▶ function notation, $f(x) = 2x + 1$

The mathematics you study is the result of much human activity, and touches every discipline in some way or another.

# 5.1 Functions and Forms

In doing mathematics **PSP**
- you often look for patterns and similarities to help you learn mathematics.
- you need to know the meaning of special words and concepts precisely.
- you need to recognize that a symbol or form in mathematics often represents a lot of useful information.
- you often develop additional mathematics based on your previously acquired skills.

For example, from your earlier work with relations, the graphs of two relations are drawn where $x, y \in \{0, 1, 2, 3, 4\}$.

$A: y = x + 1$
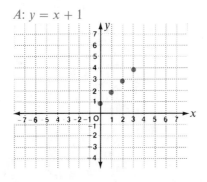

$B: y \geq x + 1$
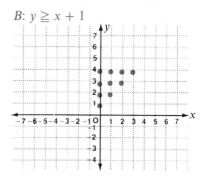

- For every $x$ co-ordinate in the above graph, there is *only* one corresponding $y$ co-ordinate.

- For some $x$ co-ordinates in the above graph, there is *more than one* $y$ co-ordinate.

These observations about graphs is the basis of the nature of a special relation called a **function**.

> A relation is a function if for every $x$ co-ordinate there is one and only one corresponding $y$ co-ordinate.

There are different ways of deciding whether a relation is a function. For example, a relation is a function if
- no two different ordered pairs have the same first (or $x$) co-ordinate, or
- for every first (or $x$) co-ordinate, there is only one second (or $y$) co-ordinate, or
- for every element in the domain, there is only one element in the range.

Thus the relation in graph A is a function, while the relation shown by graph B is not a function.

**Example 1**   Which graph represents a function?

(a)

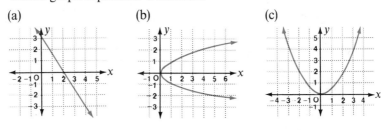

(b)

(c)

**Solution**

(a) For each $x$ value there is one and only one corresponding $y$ value. Thus, this graph represents a function.

(b) For some $x$ values there is more than one corresponding $y$ value. Thus, this graph does not represent a function.

(c) For each $x$ value there is one and and only one corresponding $y$ value. Thus, this graph represents a function.

The solution in the previous example suggests a method of testing whether a relation is or is not a function. This test is called the **vertical line test**.

---

**The Vertical Line Test**

To determine whether or not a relation is a function, draw a line parallel to the $y$-axis to intersect the graph.
- If the vertical line cuts the graph at most once, the relation is a function.
- If the vertical line cuts the graph more than once, the relation is not a function.

---

A graph is used in Example 1 to show the function. Symbols can also be used to show a function. For example,

- as an equation $y = x + 1$, $x \in \{0, 1, 2, 3\}$
- as ordered pairs $\{(0, 1), (1, 2), (2, 3), (3, 4)\}$
- in arrow or mapping notation

$f : x \xrightarrow{\phantom{aa}} x + 1$, $x \in \{0, 1, 2, 3\}$
$\uparrow$

This is read as "$f$ maps $x$ onto $x + 1$".

- by an arrow diagram

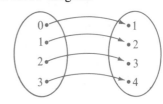

A function can also be represented by the notation

$f(x) = x + 1$, $x \in \{0, 1, 2, 3\}$. If $x = 2$, then $f(x) = x + 1$
$\uparrow$
Read this as $f$ at $x$.
$\qquad\qquad\qquad\qquad\qquad\qquad f(2) = 2 + 1$
$\qquad\qquad\qquad\qquad\qquad\qquad\quad\; = 3$

**Example 2**  If $f(x) = 2x - 3$, find the value of

(a) $f(1)$                    (b) $f(-1)$                    (c) $f(1.5)$

**Solution**

(a) Use $x = 1$.
$$f(x) = 2x - 3$$
$$f(1) = 2(1) - 3$$
$$= 2 - 3$$
$$= -1$$

(b) Use $x = -1$.
$$f(x) = 2x - 3$$
$$f(-1) = 2(-1) - 3$$
$$= -2 - 3$$
$$= -5$$

(c) Use $x = 1.5$.
$$f(x) = 2x - 3$$
$$f(1.5) = 2(1.5) - 3$$
$$= 3 - 3$$
$$= 0$$

## 5.1 Exercise

**A** Review the procedure of the vertical line test.

1  A relation is shown by the graph.

(a) Write the domain of the relation.

(b) Write the range of the relation.

(c) Determine whether the relation is a function. Give reasons why.

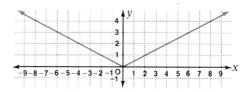

2  A relation is shown by the graph.

(a) Write the domain of the relation.

(b) Write the range of the relation.

(c) Determine whether the relation is a function. Give reasons why.

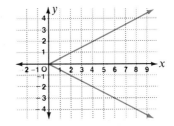

3  For each of the following, write the domain and the range. Then determine which are functions. Give reasons why.

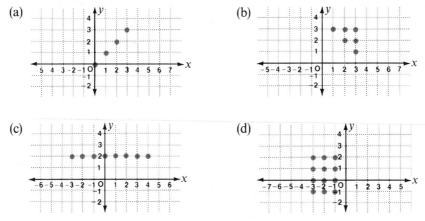

(a)

(b)

(c)

(d)

4   Use the vertical-line test to determine which of the following graphs are functions. Give reasons why.

(a) (b) (c)

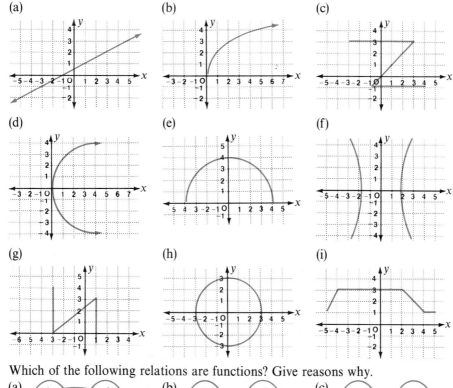

(d) (e) (f)

(g) (h) (i)

5   Which of the following relations are functions? Give reasons why.

(a) (b) (c)

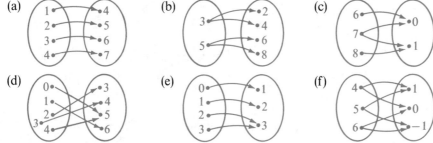

(d) (e) (f)

6   (a) A function is given by $f : x \longrightarrow 3x + 2,\ x \in R$.
       Write three other forms that represent the function.

    (b) A function is given by $f(x) = 3x - 2,\ x \in R$.
       Use four other forms that represent the above function.

**B**  Review the different forms that you can use to represent a function.

7   These relations are defined by ordered pairs. Determine whether or not they are functions. Give reasons why.

(a) $(1, 3), (2, 3), (3, 2), (1, 4), (4, 1)$     (b) $(3, 1), (2, 1), (-3, 1), (3, 2), (1, 2)$

(c) $(-1, 2), (4, 1), (3, 1), (2, 1), (-1, 3)$   (d) $(4, 3), (-2, 1), (1, -2), (-1, -2), (-4, 3)$

8   (a) Draw the graph of the function $f : x \longrightarrow 3x - 2$, $x \in \{-2, -1, 0, 1, 2\}$.
    (b) Give reasons why $f$ can be called a function.

9   Draw the graphs of the following functions.
    (a) $f : x \longrightarrow 2x - 3$, $x \in \{-1, 0, 1, 2, 3\}$
    (b) $g : x \longrightarrow 8 - 3x$, $x \in \{-2, -1, 0, 1, 2\}$
    (c) $f : x \longrightarrow \dfrac{3}{2} x + 1$, $x \in \{0, 1, 2, 3, 4\}$

10  (a) Draw a graph of the relation. $g(x) = \dfrac{1}{4} x^2$, $|x| \leq 8$, $x \in R$  $\qquad$ A compact form of writing $-8 \leq x \leq 8$.

    (b) Determine whether the relation in (a) is a function. Give reasons why.

11  (a) Draw the graph of the function. $f(x) = 3x - 1$, $-5 \leq x \leq 5$, $x \in R$
    (b) How would you use absolute value symbols to write $-5 \leq x \leq 5$ more compactly?

12  Determine which of the following are functions. Give reasons why.
    (a) $f : x \longrightarrow 3x + 1$, $x \in \{-3, -2, -1, 0, 1\}$ $\quad$ (b) $y > x - 1$, $x$, $y \in \{-4, 3, -2, 1\}$
    (c) $2x < y - 1$, $x$, $y \in \{-4, -3, \ldots, 3, 4\}$ $\quad$ (d) $g(x) = 2x^2$, $-3 \leq x \leq 3$, $x \in R$
    (e) $y = -3x + 2$, $-2 \leq x \leq 2$, $x \in R$ $\quad$ (f) $x = -2y^2$, $y \in R$
    (g) $\{(x, y) \,|\, y = 3, \, y \in R\}$ $\quad$ (h) $\{(x, y) \,|\, x = 6, \, x, \, y \in R\}$

13  If $f(x) = 3x - 2$, find the value of each of the following.
    (a) $f(0)$ $\quad$ (b) $f(-1)$ $\quad$ (c) $f(1)$ $\quad$ (d) $f(3)$ $\quad$ (e) $f(-2)$ $\quad$ (f) $f(4)$

14  If $f(x) = 4 - 2x$ and $g(x) = 3x + 1$ find the value of each of the following.
    (a) $f(0)$ $\quad$ (b) $g(0)$ $\quad$ (c) $f(-1)$ $\quad$ (d) $g(-1)$ $\quad$ (e) $f(-2)$
    (f) $g(-3)$ $\quad$ (g) $f(-2) + g(-2)$ $\quad$ (h) $f(-3) - g(-3)$

15  If $g(x) = 2x^2 + 1$, evaluate each of the following.
    (a) $g(-3)$ $\quad$ (b) $g(0)$ $\quad$ (c) $g(1)$ $\quad$ (d) $g(2)$ $\quad$ (e) $g(-2)$ $\quad$ (f) $g(4)$

16  If $g(x) = 2x + 3$, then find the value of $x$ that makes $g(x)$ equal to
    (a) 3 $\qquad$ (b) 5 $\qquad$ (c) $-3$ $\qquad$ (d) 13 $\qquad$ (e) 1

PSP 17  Joey, Jeff and Amy have either a dog, a cat or a mouse as a pet. Jeff is allergic to dogs and Joey also likes horses. If neither boy owns a cat, to whom does each pet belong?

C 18  (a) $h(x) = 2x + 3$ and $k(x) = 3 - 2x$. For what value of $x$ is $h(x) = k(x)$?
    (b) $g(x) = x^2$ and $f(x) = 2 - x$. For what value(s) of $x$ is $f(x) = g(x)$?

## 5.2 The Linear Function

Very often, seemingly unrelated phenomena can be related by mathematics. For example, the following graphs are drawn.

A The corresponding values of volume and mass for different substances are written as ordered pairs (volume, mass).

The results are graphed.

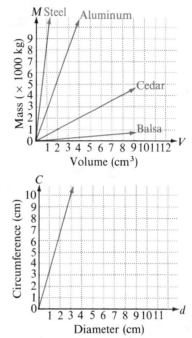

B The **linear function** often occurs in other surprising places. If the ordered pairs for corresponding values of the circumference of a circle and its diameter (diameter, circumference) are plotted the result is another example of a linear function. Again, the slope of the line has an important significance. It represents the value $\pi$.

In the process of mathematics, the specific examples A and B above are written in a general form for the linear function

$Ax + By = C$ where $A$, $B$, $C$, are constants, $A$, $B$, $C$, $x$, $y \in R$

The mathematician studies the general form of the linear function and its defining equation and then applies this general knowledge to specific examples of the linear function as they occur in science, measurement, etc.

You will see in this chapter, and in subsequent chapters, the concept of intercepts is associated with a graph. For example,

$x + 2y = 8$, $x$, $y \in R$

defines a linear function, and its graph is a straight line.

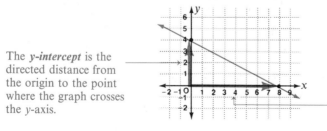

The **y-intercept** is the directed distance from the origin to the point where the graph crosses the y-axis.

The **x-intercept** is the directed distance from the origin to point where the graph crosses the x-axis.

You can use your skills in algebra to find the $x$- and $y$-intercepts.

$x$-intercept  Let $y = 0$. Then
$$x + 2y = 8$$
$$x + 0 = 8$$
$$x = 8$$

The $x$-intercept is 8.

$y$-intercept  Let $x = 0$. Then
$$x + 2y = 8$$
$$0 + 2y = 8$$
$$y = 4$$

The $y$-intercept is 4.

In general, for any curve, the intercept is the directed distance from the origin to the point where the curve crosses the axis. If the slope and either of the intercepts of a line are known, the graph of the line may be drawn.

**Example**  The $x$-intercept of a line is $-4$ and its slope is $\dfrac{3}{2}$. Draw its graph.

**Solution**  Since the $x$-intercept is $-4$, then the line passes through the point $(-4, 0)$.

Use slope $= \dfrac{3}{2}$.

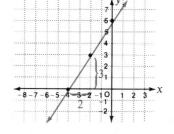

---

## 5.2  Exercise

**A** Review the meaning of $x$-*intercept* and $y$-*intercept*.  **PSP**  You must learn the meanings of words.

1   Refer to the following graphs. For each, what is the value of the
   • $x$-intercept?              • $y$-intercept?              • slope?
   (a)                          (b)                          (c)

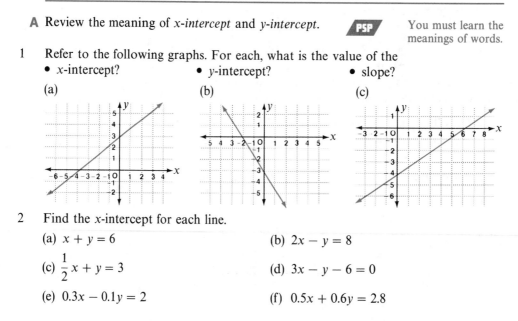

2   Find the $x$-intercept for each line.
   (a) $x + y = 6$

   (c) $\dfrac{1}{2}x + y = 3$

   (e) $0.3x - 0.1y = 2$

   (b) $2x - y = 8$

   (d) $3x - y - 6 = 0$

   (f) $0.5x + 0.6y = 2.8$

3   Find the *y*-intercept for each line.
   (a) $2x + y = 3$           (b) $y - 2x = 3$           (c) $2x - 3y = 6$
   (d) $x - 4y + 8 = 0$       (e) $0.5x + 0.3y = 3$      (f) $0.8x - 2.5y = 5.8$

4   Find the *x*- and *y*-intercept for each line.
   (a) $3x - y = 6$                        (b) $2x = 8 + y$
   (c) $4x - y + 8 = 0$                    (d) $3y - 2x = 6$
   (e) $2.5x + 3.5y = 6$                   (f) $1.3x + 0.6y = 4.5$

5   (a) Draw the graph given by $2x + 7y = 5$.
       What is the value of the *x*-intercept?
   (b) The graph crosses the *x*-axis at point A.
       What are the co-ordinates of point A?

6   (a) Draw the graph of $3x - y = 6$. What is the value of the *y*-intercept?
   (b) The graph crosses the *y*-axis at point B. What are the co-ordinates of
       point B?

7   (a) Draw the graph of $2x + 3y = 6$. What is the slope of the line?
   (b) What are the values of the intercepts?
   (c) What are the co-ordinates of the points where the graph crosses each
       axis?

   **B** To find the intercepts of a graph, you can use your skills with algebra.

8   Use the following equation. For each

       *Step A:* Find the *x*- and *y*-intercepts.
       *Step B:* Use the intercepts in Step A to draw the graph.

   (a) $x + 3y = 6$           (b) $2x + y = 4$           (c) $2x - y = 5$
   (d) $x - 2y = 3$           (e) $y = 2x + 5$           (f) $x = 3y - 2$
   (g) $y = \dfrac{3}{4}x + 2$   (h) $\dfrac{x}{2} + \dfrac{y}{3} = 6$   (i) $\dfrac{x}{3} - \dfrac{y}{4} = 12$

9   (a) A line with slope $\dfrac{3}{4}$ passes through $(3, 0)$. Draw the graph of the line.

   (b) What is the *x*-intercept of the graph?
   (c) What is the *y*-intercept of the graph?

10 (a) A line with slope $\frac{3}{2}$ passes through $(0, -3)$. Draw the graph of the line.

(b) What is the $x$-intercept of the graph?

(c) What is the $y$-intercept of the graph?

11 Draw the graph of each line.

(a) $x$-intercept $= 2$, slope $= \frac{3}{2}$ 　　　　(b) $y$-intercept $= -3$, slope $= -2$

(c) $x$-intercept $= -6$, slope $= -\frac{2}{3}$ 　　　(d) $y$-intercept $= 4$, slope $= \frac{3}{2}$

12 The path of a passenger ferry has slope $-\frac{3}{2}$ with $x$-intercept $-3$.

(a) Draw the graph of the ferry's path. 　　(b) What is the $y$-intercept?

(c) Which dock will the ferry go to, the dock at $A(-1, 3)$ or the dock at $B(-5, 3)$?

13 The path of a helicopter has slope $\frac{2}{3}$ and $y$-intercept 4.

(a) Draw the graph of the path. 　　(b) What is the $x$-intercept?

(c) Will the helicopter pass over any of these lagoons with co-ordinates shown?

lagoon A: $(3, 6)$ 　　　　lagoon B: $(-3, 2)$

14 A trawler is on a course with $x$-intercept 3 and $y$-intercept $-2$.

(a) Draw a graph of the path of the trawler. 　(b) What is the slope of its course?

(c) A school of fish is located at point $S(?, 4)$ which is on the path of the trawler. What is the missing co-ordinate?

## Calculator Tip

▶ A calculator is a useful tool for helping you to do mathematics. Do you know how to use each of these keys shown on a calculator? Refer to your manual.

| C | √ | +/− | AC |
|---|---|-----|----|
| Min | π | m+ | m− |
| 1/x | MR | $x^y$ | $x^2$ |

▶ These calculations occur frequently in your work with co-ordinates. Use an efficient procedure to do each calculation. Interpret the significance of these calculations.

A $\dfrac{3.6 - 2.1}{1.8 - 3.6}$ 　　B $\sqrt{(4.6 - 3.2)^2 + (1.8 - 1.6)^2}$

# Applications: Interpreting Slope

To find the average speed you use the relationship average speed $= \dfrac{\text{distance travelled}}{\text{time taken}}$

The distances and times recorded during a trip can be recorded on a graph. For example, the distances and times travelled by a school band during a concert tour is summarized on the graph.

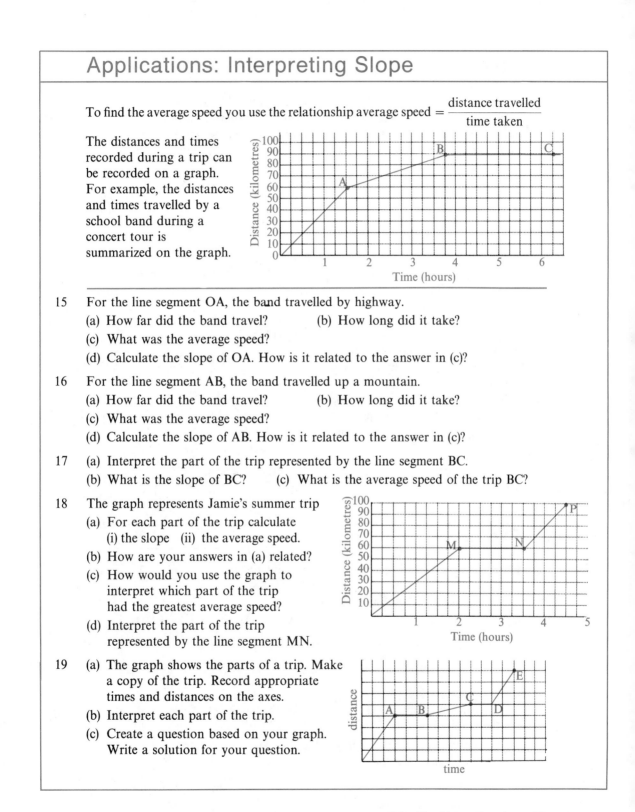

15 For the line segment OA, the band travelled by highway.
  (a) How far did the band travel?  (b) How long did it take?
  (c) What was the average speed?
  (d) Calculate the slope of OA. How is it related to the answer in (c)?

16 For the line segment AB, the band travelled up a mountain.
  (a) How far did the band travel?  (b) How long did it take?
  (c) What was the average speed?
  (d) Calculate the slope of AB. How is it related to the answer in (c)?

17 (a) Interpret the part of the trip represented by the line segment BC.
  (b) What is the slope of BC?  (c) What is the average speed of the trip BC?

18 The graph represents Jamie's summer trip
  (a) For each part of the trip calculate
    (i) the slope  (ii) the average speed.
  (b) How are your answers in (a) related?
  (c) How would you use the graph to interpret which part of the trip had the greatest average speed?
  (d) Interpret the part of the trip represented by the line segment MN.

19 (a) The graph shows the parts of a trip. Make a copy of the trip. Record appropriate times and distances on the axes.
  (b) Interpret each part of the trip.
  (c) Create a question based on your graph. Write a solution for your question.

## 5.3 Strategy: Graphing Techniques

As you study mathematics, you will find it useful to explore whether a skill you know can be used in another way. For example, in order to draw the graph of a straight line, you need to be able to find the co-ordinates of two points on the line. Two convenient points can be the values of the $x$- and $y$-intercepts.

- First, find the intercepts of the graph given by $2x - 3y = 6$.

*x-intercept*
Use $y = 0$. $2x - 3y = 6$
$$2x - 0 = 6$$
$$x = 3$$
The graph passes through A(3, 0).

*y-intercept*
Use $x = 0$. $2x - 3y = 6$
$$0 - 3y = 6$$
$$y = -2$$
The graph passes through B(0, -2).

- Use the points A and B.
  Draw the graph.

- Once the graph is drawn, check your work. Do this by choosing a point from the graph with integral co-ordinates, and checking to see if it satisfies the equation.

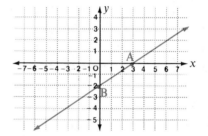

(6, 2) lies on the graph of the line.
$$2x - 3y = 6$$
$$2(6) - 3(2) = 6 \qquad \text{Thus, (6, 2) satisfies the equation.}$$

## 5.3 Exercise

**A** Review the method of finding the $x$- and $y$-intercepts.

1  For each equation, find the $x$- and $y$-intercepts.
   (a) $x - 2y = 6$
   (b) $3x + y = 9$
   (c) $y = 2x - 1$
   (d) $3x - 2y = 12$
   (e) $2x + y - 8 = 0$
   (f) $x - 2y + 10 = 0$
   (g) $3(x - 2) = y + 3$
   (h) $\frac{1}{2}x - 3y = 3$
   (i) $2x - \frac{3}{2}y = 2$

2  (a) Find the intercepts for $3x - y = 9$. Use the value $m$ to help you draw the graph of the line
   (b) Choose a point A on the graph that you have drawn. Do the co-ordinates of A satisfy the equation?

3   (a) Find the intercepts of $2x - y = 10$. Use them to draw the graph of the line.

    (b) Choose a point B on the graph that you have drawn. Do the co-ordinates of B satisfy the equation?

4   Find the co-ordinates of the point where $x - 2y = 8$ crosses each axis. Use them to find the slope of the line. How could you check your answer?

  **B** To answer the following questions you need to draw more than one graph.

5   A line passes through the points A(3, 1), B(−2, 3).

    (a) Draw the graph.    (b) Estimate the $x$- and $y$-intercepts.

6   (a) Draw the graph of the line passing through (3, 2) with $x$-intercept $-3$.

    (b) Estimate the $y$-intercept.

7   A ship passes through the points A(6, 12) and B(4, 8).

    (a) Draw the graph of the path of the ship.

    (b) Through what points on the $x$- and $y$-axes will the ship pass?

8   (a) Draw the graph of the line parallel to $y = 2x - 1$ and passing through $(-3, 1)$.

    (b) What is the $x$-intercept of the required line in (a)?

9   (a) Draw the graph of the line with the same $x$-intercept as $2x - 3y = 12$ and parallel to $x + y = 4$.

    (b) What is the $y$-intercept of the line you graphed in (a)?

**PSP** 10   Jennifer has two containers measuring 5 L and 8 L. How could she use these containers to measure out 7 L?

    List any assumptions you make in answering this question.

**C** 11   $\triangle ABC$ has vertices given by A(8, 8), B(0, −4), and C(−2, 6). What point in the interior of $\triangle ABC$ is equidistant from all vertices?

## Math Tip

Even famous mathematicians study the work of others. Gottfried Wilhelm Leibniz (1646–1716) studied the work of René Déscartes and Blaise Pascal. Their influence, and Leibniz's ingenuity provided the foundation for making important mathematical discoveries. By asking the right questions he discovered the expression $\dfrac{\pi}{4} = 1 - \dfrac{1}{3} + \dfrac{1}{5} - \dfrac{1}{7} + \dfrac{1}{9} - \dfrac{1}{11} + \dfrac{1}{13} - \cdots$, which provides a method for calculating the value of $\pi$ to as many decimal places as needed. The publication of his discoveries opened up new strategies to a number of mathematicians to solve problems they were currently working on.

# 5.4 PSP Patterns with Slopes and Intercepts

The lines in the graph shown are drawn parallel. An important aspect of studying mathematics is to explore properties of figures that share a common property. How are the slopes related for parallel lines?

Another important aspect of developing concepts and skills in mathematics is to explore how the equation of a graph can provide clues to its graph. For example, if the equation of a graph is known, can you predict certain properties of the graph? The following exercise explores what patterns there might be for the slopes and *y*-intercepts of a line and how the slope and *y*-intercept are related to the equation of the graph.

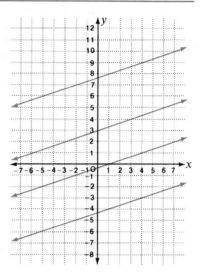

## 5.4 Exercise

**B** As you complete these questions, look for clues and patterns to help you work with graphs.   **PSP**

> **Exploration I:** Questions 1 to 3 explore the relations among parallel lines and their slopes.

1  (a) Find the slope of each line shown in the diagram above.

  (b) What do you notice about your answers in (a)?

  (c) Use your results in (a) and (b). Write a probable conclusion.

2  (a) Find the slope of each line.

  (b) What do you notice about your answers in (a)?

  (c) Use your results in (a) and (b). Write a probable conclusion.

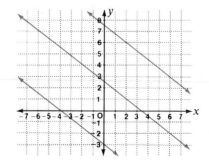

3   Use your results in Questions 1 and 2.

   (a) The lines in the diagram are parallel.
       Find the slope of line $p_1$.

   (b) Predict the slopes of line $p_2$ and $p_3$.

   (c) Verify your answers in (b). Find the
       slopes of $p_2$ and $p_3$ from the graph.

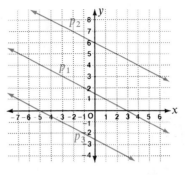

---

**Exploration II:** Questions 4 to 8 explore the relationship between the
slope of a line and its defining equation.

---

4   (a) Draw the graph of $y = 2x + 3$, $x$, $y \in R$.     (b) What is the slope of the line?

5   Draw the graph of each line. Then copy and complete the chart.

|     | equation | slope |
| --- | --- | --- |
| (a) | $y = 3x + 3$ | |
| (b) | $y = \dfrac{1}{2}x + 1$ | |
| (c) | $y = -2x + 5$ | |
| (d) | $y = -\dfrac{2}{3}x + 3$ | |

   Study the chart. How might the slope be related to the equation?

6   (a) Use your results of Question 5 to predict the slope of $y = -\dfrac{1}{2}x + 3$, $x \in R$.

   (b) Draw a graph of $y = -\dfrac{1}{2}x + 3$, $x \in R$. What is the slope?

   (c) How do your answers in (a) and (b) compare?

7   For each equation,
   *Step 1:* predict the slope of the line.
   *Step 2:* draw the graph of the line to check your prediction.

   (a) $y = -3x + 1$     (b) $y = -\dfrac{1}{2}x + 3$     (c) $y = 4x + 5$     (d) $y = x - 2$

8   Use your results in Questions 4 to 7 to suggest a method of finding the slope
   of the line from the equation of the line.

9   (a) Draw the graph of $y = 3x + 5$.   (b) What is the y-intercept of the line in (a)?

10  Draw the graph of each line.
    Then copy and complete the chart.
    Study the chart. How might the
    y-intercept be related to the
    equation?

| | equation | y-intercept |
|---|---|---|
| (a) | $y = 2x + 3$ | |
| (b) | $y = x - 1$ | |
| (c) | $y = -2x + 4$ | |

11  (a) Use your results of Question 10 to predict the y-intercept of $y = 2x - 3, x \in R$.
    (b) Draw a graph of $y = 2x - 3$. What is the y-intercept?
    (c) How do your answers in (a) and (b) compare?

12  Predict the y-intercept of each line. (How would you check your prediction?)

    (a) $y = \dfrac{1}{2}x + 4$        (b) $y = -2x - 4$        (c) $y = -\dfrac{1}{3}x + \dfrac{2}{3}$

13  Use the results of Questions 9 to 12 to suggest a method of finding the value of the y-intercept from the equation of a line.

## Problem-Solving

To solve some problems, you need to list all the possibilities. Try the following problem.

To win the championship in baseball, you need to win the *World Series*. To win the World Series, a team needs to win 4 out of seven games. One possibility is to win 4 games in a row. Another possibility is to win the first two and the last two games.

In how many different ways can a baseball team win the World Series?

## Math Tip

It is important to understand clearly the vocabulary of mathematics when solving problems.
A  Make a list of all the new words you meet in this chapter. Provide an example of your own to illustrate the meaning of each word.
B  Continue to build your understanding of the vocabulary throughout your work in mathematics. Repeat Step A for other chapters.

# 5.5 A Useful Form: $y = mx + b$

Once you explore patterns in mathematics, you apply them in order to simplify calculations or to draw graphs. For example, in Section 5.4, graphs such as the following suggested a pattern.

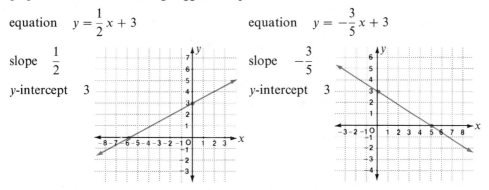

equation $\quad y = \dfrac{1}{2}x + 3$

slope $\quad \dfrac{1}{2}$

$y$-intercept $\quad 3$

equation $\quad y = -\dfrac{3}{5}x + 3$

slope $\quad -\dfrac{3}{5}$

$y$-intercept $\quad 3$

Examples such as those above suggest a useful form of the equation, one from which the slope and $y$-intercept can be found at a glance. This form is

$$y = mx + b$$

In the equation, $m$ and $b$ are **parameters**. A parameter represents a constant, and is shown by a letter such as $m$ or $b$.

$$y = mx + b$$

slope of the line    $y$-intercept of the line

$y$-intercept

$$y = -2x + 3 \qquad y = \dfrac{1}{3}x + 4$$

slope

An equation expressed in this form is called the **slope $y$-intercept form** of the equation. The equation of the straight line in this form tells you a great deal about the line without graphing it.

**Example 1**    Find the slope and the $y$-intercept of $2x + 3y = 6$, $x \in R$.

**Solution**   
$$2x + 3y = 6$$
$$3y = -2x + 6$$
$$y = -\dfrac{2}{3}x + 2$$

Think: Write the equation in the slope $y$-intercept form.

From this form of the equation you know that

the slope is $-\dfrac{2}{3}$ and the $y$-intercept is 2.

With the slope $y$-intercept form of the equation, you can solve the following problem. The strategy is to write both equations in the same form and compare the equations.

**Example 2**  The lines given by $x + 2y = k$ and $3x + 4y = 8$ have equal $y$-intercepts. Find the value of $k$.

**Solution**

$$x + 2y = k \qquad\qquad 3x + 4y = 8$$
$$2y = -x + k \qquad\qquad 4y = -3x + 8$$
$$y = \frac{-x}{2} + \frac{k}{2} \qquad\qquad y = -\frac{3}{4}x + 2$$

Think: write the equation in the slope $y$-intercept form.

Since the $y$-intercepts are equal then

$$\frac{k}{2} = 2$$
$$k = 4$$

Think: Compare the parts of the equation.

An important strategy for solving problems is to remember the following property of a line and its equation: **If a point is on the line, its co-ordinates satisfy the equation of the line**.

**Example 3**  If $(-3, 2)$ is on the line given by $y = mx + 8$, find the value of $m$.

**Solution**  Since $(-3, 2)$ is a point on the line, its co-ordinates satisfy the equation.

$$y = mx + 8$$
$$2 = m(-3) + 8$$
$$-6 = -3m \text{ or } 2 = m$$

You can interpret this result to mean that the slope of the line is 2.

## 5.5 Exercise

A Throughout this exercise the variables are $x, y \in R$.

1  Without drawing the graph, write the slope and $y$-intercept for each line.

(a) $y = 3x + 6$

(b) $y = -\frac{1}{2}x + 3$

(c) $x - y = 3$

(d) $2x = 3 - y$

(e) $3x + 2y = 6$

(f) $x = 2y - 3$

(g) $\frac{1}{2}x + \frac{1}{3}y = 4$

(h) $4x - 2y = 3$

(i) $x = 3y + 6$

(j) $2(x - 1) = y + 3$

(k) $3(y + 1) = 2x - 2$

(l) $\frac{x + y}{3} = 4$

2 Write the equation of each line for the given values of the slope $m$, and $y$-intercept $b$.

(a) $m = 2, b = 3$         (b) $m = 2, b = -3$         (c) $m = -2, b = 3$

(d) $m = \dfrac{1}{2}, b = -4$      (e) $m = -3, b = \dfrac{1}{2}$      (f) $m = -\dfrac{3}{4}, b = -\dfrac{1}{3}$

3 (a) Find the $y$-intercept of the line given by $3x + y = 8$.

  (b) Use a different method to find the $y$-intercept.

4 (a) At what point does the graph of $2x - 3y = 8$ cross the $x$-axis?

  (b) Write the co-ordinates of the point where the graph of $2y - 3x - 8 = 0$ meets the $y$-axis.

5 Write the co-ordinates of the point at which the graph crosses the indicated axis.

(a) $2x - y = 6$, $x$-axis              (b) $x - 3y + 9 = 0$, $y$-axis

(c) $\dfrac{x - 2y}{3} = 2$, $x$-axis        (d) $4(x - 1) = 3y + 6$, $y$-axis

6 Without drawing a graph, decide which lines are parallel.

(a) $y = 3x - 3$     (b) $y = -3x - 3$     (c) $y = -3x + 3$     (d) $y = 3x + 3$

**B** Remember: Use the strategy of writing an equation in the form $y = mx + b$.

7 Lines are given by the following equations. Which lines are parallel?

(a) $y = 3x - 2$             (b) $2x + y = 4$            (c) $x + 2y = 3$

(d) $\dfrac{x + y}{2} = 3$          (e) $2x + 6y = 3$          (f) $y + x = 4$

(g) $x = -\dfrac{1}{2}y + 3$     (h) $-\dfrac{1}{2}(x + 4) = y + 2$     (i) $3(y - 2) = 6 - x$

8 The slopes of 2 lines $\ell_1$ and $\ell_2$ are given as follows

       slope of $\ell_1 = m + 3$          slope of $\ell_2 = 3m - 5$

If the lines are parallel, find $m$.

9 (a) The lines $2x + y = 6$ and $8 - y = mx$ are parallel. Find the value of $m$.

  (b) The lines $\dfrac{4x - 2y}{3} = 3$ and $3x + y = 2 + kx$ are parallel. Find the value of $k$.

10  (a) The lines $3x + 2y = 8$ and $k - y = 2x$ have equal $y$-intercepts. Find the value of $k$.

    (b) Find the value of $k$ if the lines given by $2x - 3y = 4$ and $3x - 6k = 2y$ have the same $x$-intercept.

11  The lines given by the equations $x - 3y = 6 + k$ and $2x = 3y - 4k$ have equal $x$-intercepts. Find the value of $k$.

12  (a) The point $(2, 5)$ is on the line given by $y = 3x + k$. Find the value of $k$.

    (b) The point $(-2, 1)$ is on the line given by $y = mx + 3$. Find the slope.

13  (a) Find the slope of the line $kx - 2y = 6$ if $(-1, 0)$ is on the line.

    (b) The point $(-3, 1)$ is on the line given by $3x - ky = k$. Find the $x$-intercept.

14  A boat travels a path given by $3x - 2y = 6$. At what point will it dock on the $x$-axis?

15  The paths of two ships are given by $3y + x = 4$ and $x - k = y$. If the two ships are to meet at the same point on the $y$-axis, find the value of $k$.

16  A projectile is on a path given by $2x - ky = 1$. If it passes through $(1, 3)$, find the value of $k$.

17  Grey whales are tracked by a research team. A co-ordinate grid is used to record their path. One of these paths crossed the $x$-axis at $(-2, 0)$ and had a slope of $\dfrac{3}{2}$.

    (a) What is the equation of the path?

    (b) What assumption have you made in finding your answer in (a)?

C 18  An equation is given in the general form $Ax + By + C = 0$. Find an expression in terms of the parameters in the equation.

    (a) for its slope                  (b) for its $y$-intercept

## Problem-Solving  PSP

In your study of mathematics, it is useful to generalize results. For example, $Ax + By + C = 0$ is the equation of a line where $A$, $B$, or $C$ are real numbers.
- Describe the graph of the equation if one of $A$, $B$, or $C$ is equal to zero.
- Describe the graph if both $A$ and $C$ are equal to zero, or both $B$ and $C$ are equal to zero.

# Exploring Perpendicular Lines

Earlier, you drew graphs to help you explore an important property of parallel lines.

| Parallel lines have equal slopes |
| --- |

By drawing graphs, you can explore an important property of perpendicular lines. The following questions explore the relationship between the slopes of perpendicular lines.

19  (a) Find the slopes of each pair of perpendicular line segments.

(b) Find the product of each pair of slopes.

(c) What do you notice about your answer in (b)?

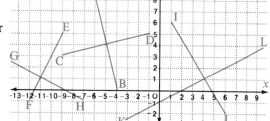

20  (a) Draw any two lines that are perpendicular to each other.

(b) Find their slopes.

(c) Find the products of the slopes in (b). What do you notice?

Repeat the above instructions for another pair of perpendicular lines.

21  (a) What are the slopes of $y = x - 3$ and $y = -x + 2$.

(b) Find the product of the slopes in (a).

(c) Draw the graphs of the lines in (a). What do you notice about the lines?

22  (a) Draw the graphs of $y = \dfrac{1}{2}x + 3$ and $y = -2x + 1$. What do you notice?

(b) Find the product of the slopes of the lines in (a).

23  (a) Based on the results of the questions on this page, write a probable conclusion about the slopes of lines that are perpendicular.

(b) Use your conclusion in (a). Decide which of the following lines are perpendicular to each other.

A  $y = \dfrac{1}{2}x + 3$       B  $y = -x + 2$       C  $y = -\dfrac{1}{2}x - 3$

D  $y = \dfrac{1}{3}x + 2$       E  $y = 2x + \dfrac{1}{2}$       F  $y = -3x - 4$

G  $y = -2x + 1$       H  $y = x - \dfrac{1}{3}$       I  $y = 3x + \dfrac{1}{2}$

# 5.6 Slope: Parallel and Perpendicular Lines

By calculating slopes of lines you can find properties of parallel and perpendicular lines.

**Parallel lines**
- Lines that have equal slopes are parallel.
- Lines that are parallel have equal slopes.

**Perpendicular lines**
By examining specific examples, you have observed a property of the slopes of perpendicular lines AB and CD.

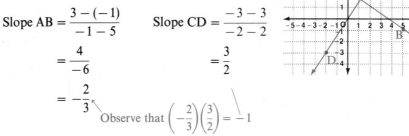

$$\text{Slope AB} = \frac{3 - (-1)}{-1 - 5} \qquad \text{Slope CD} = \frac{-3 - 3}{-2 - 2}$$

$$= \frac{4}{-6} \qquad\qquad\qquad = \frac{3}{2}$$

$$= -\frac{2}{3}$$

Observe that $\left(-\frac{2}{3}\right)\left(\frac{3}{2}\right) = -1$

In the above example, the product of the slopes is $-1$. Thus the slopes of AB and CD are said to be **negative reciprocals**.

From examples, such as the one above, the observation is made that
- lines that are perpendicular have slopes that are negative reciprocals.
- lines that have slopes that are negative reciprocals are perpendicular.

**Example** Show that the line PQ, given by P(3, 2) and Q(6, 1), is perpendicular to the line $3x - y = 2$.

**Solution** For PQ, slope $= \dfrac{2 - 1}{3 - 6}$

$$= \frac{1}{-3} \text{ or } -\frac{1}{3}$$

Write the line $3x - y = 2$ in the slope $y$-intercept form.
$$3x - y = 2$$
$$-y = 2 - 3x$$
$$y = 3x - 2$$

The slope is 3.

The product of the slopes is $\left(-\dfrac{1}{3}\right)(3) = -1$.

Thus, the lines are perpendicular.

## 5.6 Exercise

**A** If two lines are parallel or perpendicular, what do you know about the slopes?

1 Use the slopes given.

$$\text{slope of PQ} = \frac{2}{3} \quad \text{slope of RS} = -2 \quad \text{slope of DE} = \frac{-1}{3} \quad \text{slope of FG} = \frac{3}{4}$$

What is the slope of a line that is

(a) parallel to PQ?

(b) perpendicular to FG?

(c) parallel to DE?

(d) perpendicular to RS?

2 The slope of the line is $\frac{3}{4}$.

(a) What is the slope of a line that is parallel to this line?

(b) What is the value of the parameter in $y = mx + b$?

3 (a) The slope of a line is 2. What is the slope of a line perpendicular to it?

(b) What is the slope of a line perpendicular to a line with slope $m$?

4 The slope of each line is given. Write the slope of a line perpendicular to it.

(a) 2  (b) $\frac{1}{3}$  (c) $-4$  (d) $-\frac{1}{2}$  (e) $\frac{3}{2}$  (f) $3\frac{1}{2}$  (g) $k$  (h) $-\frac{1}{m}$

5 Each pair of numbers represent the slopes of a pair of lines. Are the lines parallel, perpendicular, or neither?

(a) $3, \frac{1}{3}$  (b) $\frac{1}{3}, \frac{1}{3}$  (c) $-3, -3$  (d) $\frac{3}{5}, -\frac{5}{3}$

(e) $8, -8$  (f) $-1, \frac{1}{2}$  (g) $\frac{2}{3}, \frac{3}{2}$  (h) $\frac{4}{3}, 1\frac{1}{3}$

6 For each diagram, what is the slope of lines that are

• parallel to AB?  • perpendicular to AB?

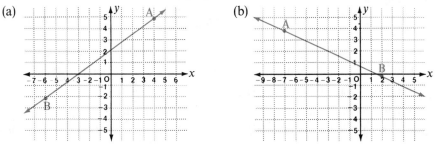

**B** Remember the meaning of the parameters $m$ and $b$ in $y = mx + b$.

7  (a) What is the slope of the line given by $y = 2x - 1$?
   (b) What is the slope of a line perpendicular to the line in (a)?

8  What is the slope of a line perpendicular to each line?

   (a) $y = 2x - 1$    (b) $y = \dfrac{2}{3}x + 3$    (c) $2x + y = 6$

   (d) $3x - y = 6$    (e) $x - 2y = 8$    (f) $4x - 2y = 3$

9  Which of the following pairs of lines are perpendicular? Why?

   (a) $y = 3x - 1$, $y = -\dfrac{1}{3}x + 4$    (b) $y = 2x + 5$, $y = -2x + 5$

   (c) $y = \dfrac{1}{4}x + 2$, $y = 4x + 5$    (d) $2x + y = 6$, $y = \dfrac{1}{2}x + 6$

   (e) $3x + y = 6$, $x - 3y = 4$

10  From the following list of equations, find pairs of lines that are
    • parallel                • perpendicular
    A: $3y - 2x + 3 = 0$    B: $4y + 3x - 2 = 0$    C: $4x - 3y + 6 = 0$
    D: $3y + 4x + 3 = 0$    E: $2x - 3y + 6 = 0$    F: $2y - 3x + 2 = 0$
    G: $4x - 3y - 2 = 0$    H: $2x + 3y + 6 = 0$    I: $3y + 2x + 8 = 0$

11  The slope of $\ell_1$ is $3k$ and $\ell_2$ is 4.
    (a) If $\ell_1$ and $\ell_2$ are perpendicular, explain why $(3k)(4) = -1$?
    (b) Solve for $k$ in (a). What is the slope of $\ell_1$?

12  The slope of $\ell_1$ is $2k$ and of $\ell_2$ is $8 + k$.
    (a) If $\ell_1$ and $\ell_2$ are parallel, explain why $2k = 8 + k$.
    (b) What are the slopes of $\ell_1$ and $\ell_2$?

13  The slopes of pairs of lines are given. If the lines are perpendicular, find each value of $k$.

    (a) $2k, \dfrac{1}{4}$    (b) $6, \dfrac{1}{2}k$    (c) $k + 1, 3$    (d) $6, \dfrac{k - 5}{2}$

14  (a) Find the slope of the line passing through each pair of points.
        (i) A(7, 3), B($-3$, 2)    (ii) C($-3$, $-8$), D(5, 8)
        (iii) E($-9$, 9), F($-2$, $-5$)    (iv) G(5, 9), H(6, $-1$)
    (b) Which lines in (a) are parallel?    (c) Which lines in (a) are perpendicular?

15  (a) Find the slope of the line passing through each pair of points.

     (i) M(4.7, 4.4), N(3.5, −0.4)      (ii) P(−3.2, 6), Q(1.8, 3.5)

     (iii) R(−4, 3.8), S(−6.4, −5.8)      (iv) T(1.4, 1.3), V(1.3, 1.1)

  (b) Which lines in (a) are parallel?

  (c) Which lines in (a) are perpendicular?

16  For the points given by

    A(5, 4)      B(7, 6)      C(3, 2)      D(11, −2)
    E(7, −3)     F(3, 5)      G(11, 1)     H(3, −3)

which pairs of lines are  • perpendicular?      • parallel?

  (a) AD, BC           (b) BC, EG           (c) DC, EF

  (d) AD, EG           (e) FE, BD           (f) FE, BG

17  The following 3 equations represent lines on the side of a triangle.

$$2x − 3y + 3 = 0 \qquad 3x + 2y + 2 = 0 \qquad 3x − y − 3 = 0$$

  (a) Decide whether the lines define a triangle that has a right angle.

  (b) What are the co-ordinates of the vertex of an acute angle of the triangle?

18  A figure is given by four vertices.

    A(11, −2)     B(7, −9)     C(−2, −2)     D(2, 4).

Why is the figure not a rectangle?

**PSP** 19  Which one of the following words does not belong?

  poles   nile   galen   xretev   kictet   gihrt

**C** 20  A right triangle has sides defined by the following equation.

$$kx − y + 2 = 0 \qquad 3x − 4y − 2 = 0 \qquad 4x − 3y − 3 = 0$$

What is the value of the parameter $k$?

## Problem-Solving

In this section, you have used specific examples to suggest a relationship among the slopes of parallel lines, and among the slopes of perpendicular lines. Often, to prove that a relationship is true, in general, a great deal of work is required. For example, to prove the following statements you need to draw on a number of skills and strategies you have acquired. Refer to your chart for the *Problem-Solving Plan*. Prove the following statements.

- Two lines are parallel if and only if they have equal slopes.
- Two lines are perpendicular if and only if their slopes are negative reciprocals.

## 5.7 Writing Equations of Lines

An important process in the study of mathematics is to look for an analogy as you learn mathematics.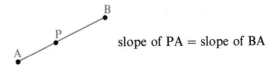

For example, you can graph a straight line on the co-ordinate plane if you know either of the following pieces of information.
- 2 points on the line or
- its slope and a point on the line.

Similarly, if you know these facts about a line, you can write the equation of the line. Use the important property of the slope of a line

slope of PA = slope of BA

to find the equation of the line.

**Example 1**    Find the equation of a line passing through the points A(4, 6) and B(5, 8).

**Solution**    Let any point on the line have co-ordinates P($x$, $y$).

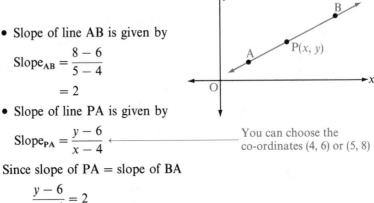

- Slope of line AB is given by

$$\text{Slope}_{AB} = \frac{8 - 6}{5 - 4}$$

$$= 2$$

- Slope of line PA is given by

$$\text{Slope}_{PA} = \frac{y - 6}{x - 4} \longleftarrow$$

You can choose the co-ordinates (4, 6) or (5, 8)

Since slope of PA = slope of BA

$$\frac{y - 6}{x - 4} = 2$$

$$y - 6 = 2(x - 4)$$
$$y - 6 = 2x - 8$$
$$y = 2x - 2 \longleftarrow$$

Check to see if points A and B satisfy this equation.

If you know 2 pieces of information about a line, you can find its defining equation. In the next example, you are given the slope and a point.

**Example 2** Find the equation of a line with slope 3 and passing through $(0, -2)$.

**Solution** Use $P(x, y)$ as any point on the line.
slope of PA = slope of the line

$$\frac{y - (-2)}{x - 0} = 3$$

$$y + 2 = 3x$$
$$3x - y = 2$$

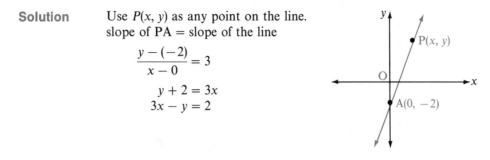

In the process of mathematics, you often need to review previous work you have done to review the principle on which you based the work. For example, the *fundamental* property of a straight line (that the slopes of its line segments are equal) allows you to find the equation of *any* line from first principles.

Slope PA = Slope PB = Slope AB

Often you may see equations written in different forms, each convenient in a different situation.

**Standard Form**
An equation written in the form $Ax + By + C = 0$ where $A, B, C$ are constants is said to be in *standard form*.

**Slope y-intercept Form**
If $m$ is the slope and $b$ the $y$-intercept, then the *slope y-intercept form* is given by $y = mx + b$.

## 5.7 Exercise

**A** Review the meaning of *slope, intercept*, and *standard form of an equation*. Throughout the exercise write the final equation of lines in standard form.

1 Find the slope of each of the following lines.
   (a) It passes through $(-1, 6)$ and $(1, 10)$.
   (b) It has $y$-intercept $-3$ and passes through $(4, 3)$.
   (c) It passes through $(-5, 2)$ and $(3, 4)$.
   (d) It has $x$-intercept 2 and passes through $(6, 2)$.
   (e) The $x$- and $y$-intercepts are $-6$ and 8 respectively.
   (f) It passes through $(4, -2)$ and has $x$-intercept $-3$.
   (g) The $x$- and $y$-intercepts are 4 and $-6$ respectively.

2   A line passes through the point A($-3$, 1) and has slope 2.

    (a) If P($x$, $y$) is any point on the line, why is the following true?

$$\frac{y-1}{x+3} = 2$$

    (b) Simplify the equation in (a).

3   A line passes through the points A(2, 1) and B(4, 3).

    (a) What is the slope of the line?

    (b) If P($x$, $y$) is any point on the line, why are the following true?

$$\frac{y-1}{x-2} = 1 \qquad \frac{y-3}{x-4} = 1$$

    (c) Simplify the equations in (b). What do you notice about your answers in (b)?

4   A line has slope $\frac{1}{2}$ and $y$-intercept $-1$.

    (a) What are the co-ordinates of a point on the line?

    (b) If P($x$, $y$) is any point on the line, why is the following equation true?

$$\frac{y+1}{x} = \frac{1}{2}$$

    (c) Simplify the equation in (b).

5   The $x$-intercept of a line is 2 and its slope is $-\frac{1}{2}$.

    (a) What are the co-ordinates of a point on the line?

    (b) If P($x$, $y$) is any point on the line, why is the following equation true?

$$\frac{y}{x-2} = -\frac{1}{2}$$

    (c) Simplify the equation in (b).

6   The $x$- and $y$-intercepts of a line are $-3$ and 2 respectively.

    (a) What is the slope of the line?

    (b) If P($x$, $y$) is any point on the line, why are the following true?

$$\frac{y-2}{x} = \frac{2}{3} \qquad \frac{y}{x+3} = \frac{2}{3}$$

    (c) Simplify the equations in (b). What do you notice about your answers in (b)?

7 Write each of the following equations in standard form $Ax + By + C = 0$.

(a) $\dfrac{y-1}{x+3} = \dfrac{3}{2}$     (b) $\dfrac{y-3}{x+2} = 2$     (c) $\dfrac{y+2}{x-3} = -3$     (d) $\dfrac{y+3}{x-3} = \dfrac{1}{2}$

(e) $\dfrac{y-1}{x+1} = -\dfrac{1}{3}$     (f) $\dfrac{y-2}{x} = \dfrac{3}{2}$     (g) $\dfrac{y}{x-3} = 4$     (h) $\dfrac{y+2}{x-1} = -\dfrac{4}{3}$

**B** Review the different facts about a line which you can use to write its equation.

8 Find the equation of each line in simplified form, if a point and its slope are given.

(a) $(4, 3)$, $2$     (b) $(2, 1)$, $-3$     (c) $(-3, 1)$, $\dfrac{1}{2}$     (d) $(0, -4)$, $-\dfrac{2}{3}$

9 Find the equation, in simplified form, of each line passing through the following points.

(a) $(4, 2)$, $(-1, 3)$           (b) $(2, 1)$, $(-1, -3)$

(c) $(4, 3)$, $(8, -1)$           (d) $(-2, -3)$, $(4, 5)$

10 For each line, the slope and $y$-intercept are given respectively. Find the equation of the line.

(a) $2$, $-3$     (b) $-3$, $2$     (c) $\dfrac{1}{2}$, $-3$     (d) $\dfrac{2}{3}$, $-\dfrac{1}{2}$

11 The $x$-intercept and slope of each line are given respectively. Find the equation of the line in simplified form.

(a) $2$, $-3$     (b) $-3$, $\dfrac{1}{2}$     (c) $\dfrac{2}{3}$, $2$     (d) $-\dfrac{4}{3}$, $-\dfrac{1}{2}$

12 Find the simplified equation of each line if its $x$- and $y$-intercepts are given respectively.

(a) $2$, $4$    (b) $-3$, $2$    (c) $0$, $5$    (d) $\dfrac{1}{2}$, $2$    (e) $3$, $-\dfrac{4}{3}$    (f) $-\dfrac{3}{4}$, $-\dfrac{2}{3}$

13 The equation of a line may be found using different facts. A line is shown. Find the equation of the line using

(a) a point and the $y$-intercept.

(b) another point and the $x$-intercept.

(c) the slope and the $y$-intercept.

(d) the slope and the $x$-intercept.

(e) What do you notice about your answers in (a) to (d)?

14 Find an equation for each line.

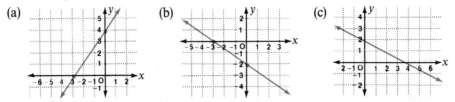

(a)   (b)   (c)

15 Write the equation of the $x$-axis and the $y$-axis.

16 Find the equation of each of the following lines passing through $(3, -1)$ if

(a) the slope is $\frac{1}{2}$.

(b) the $y$-intercept is $-2$.

(c) the $x$-intercept is $-1$.

(d) the line also passes through $(2, -3)$.

17 Find the equation of each line.

(a) It passes through $(-1, 3)$ and $(2, -2)$.

(b) It has slope 2 and passes through $(0, 6)$.

(c) It has $x$- and $y$-intercepts $-4$ and 2 respectively.

(d) It has slope $-\frac{2}{3}$ and $x$-intercept 3.     (e) It passes through $(4, 5)$ and $(-1, -1)$.

(f) It has $y$-intercept $\frac{3}{2}$ and slope $-2$.     (g) It has slope $-\frac{1}{2}$ and $x$-intercept $\frac{2}{3}$.

(h) It has slope 3 and passes through $(4, 5)$.

(i) It has slope 0 and passes through $(2, -3)$.

(j) It has an undefined slope and passes through $(-1, 2)$.

18 $\triangle ABC$ is given by the vertices $A(1, -2)$, $B(3, 4)$, and $C(-2, 3)$.

(a) Find the equations of the sides of the triangle.

(b) If $\angle B$ in $\triangle ABC$ is a right angle and A has new co-ordinates $(p, -1)$, find $p$.

19 $\triangle PQR$ is given by the co-ordinates $P(-4, 5)$, $Q(3, 7)$, and $R(0, -4)$.

(a) Find the equation of the line through P but parallel to RQ.

(b) Find the equation of the line through P, which is perpendicular to RQ.

C 20 The following equations represent the same line where $A$, $B$, $C$ are constants, $m$ is the slope, and $b$ is the $y$-intercept.

$$Ax + By + C = 0 \qquad y = mx + b$$

How are the parameters in the above two equations related?

# Problem-Solving: Using Given Information

To solve a problem you need to carefully analyze the given information. The given information often suggests a strategy for solving the problem.

**Example**
Find the equation that defines the line perpendicular to $y = 3x - 1$ and passing through the point $(-1, 2)$.

**PSP** Analyze the given information.

Think: Slope of $y = 3x - 1$ $\longrightarrow$ Think: Slope of line perpendicular
is 3. to $y = 3x - 1$ is $-\dfrac{1}{3}$.

Think: $(-1, 2)$ is a point on $\longrightarrow$ Think: Use P$(x, y)$ any point on the
the required line. line. Thus $\dfrac{y - 2}{x - (-1)} = -\dfrac{1}{3}$

Once you have analyzed the given information you can write the solution to the problem.

**Solution**
*Step 1:* Let P$(x, y)$ be any point on the line. The slope of the required

line is given by $\dfrac{y - 2}{x - (-1)}$ since $(-1, 2)$ is a point on the line.

*Step 2:* The slope of $y = 3x - 1$ is 3.

The slope of the required line is the negative reciprocal, $-\dfrac{1}{3}$.

Thus, the required equation is $\dfrac{y - 2}{x + 1} = -\dfrac{1}{3}$

$$3y - 6 = -x - 1$$

The equation, in standard form is $x + 3y - 5 = 0$

---

# 5.8 Exercise

**B** Write the equation you obtain in standard form.

1  (a) A line is parallel to $x = 3$ and passes through the point $(-4, 3)$. Write its equation.

(b) A line is parallel to $y = -2$ and passes through the point $(-2, -3)$. Write its equation.

2  (a) Find the equation of the line passing through $(3, 2)$ and parallel to the line $x - 2y + 3 = 0$.

(b) A line is parallel to $2x + y = 3$ and passes through $(-1, 3)$. Find its equation.

3   A line is perpendicular to $2x - y = 3$ and has $y$-intercept $-2$.
    (a) Find the equation of the line.
    (b) Which of the following points are also on the line?
        A$(-4, 4)$        B$(-2, -1)$        C$(4, 0)$

4   (a) A line is perpendicular to $y = 2x - 1$ and passes through $(2, -3)$. Find its equation.
    (b) A line has the same $x$-intercept as $2x + y = 8$ and passes through $(0, 1)$. Find its equation.
    (c) A line passes through $(-4, 2)$ and has the same $y$-intercept as $2x - y = 3$. Find its equation.

5   Find the equation of each side of each triangle.

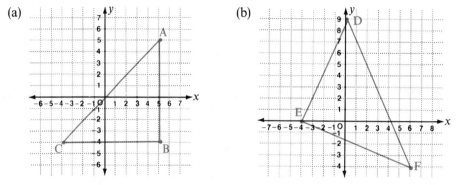

(a)        (b)

6   Points A$(-4, -3)$, B$(-2, 3)$, and C$(3, 0)$ are given.
    (a) Find the equation of the line AB.
    (b) Find the equation of the line through C perpendicular to AB.
    (c) Find the equation of the perpendicular bisector of AB.

7   A line passes through the point $(2, 3)$ and has $y$-intercept $-3$. Find its $x$-intercept.

8   What is the $y$-intercept of a line that has slope $\dfrac{2}{3}$ and passes through the point $(-1, 4)$?

9   Find the $y$-intercept of a line that has slope $\dfrac{1}{2}$ and has $x$-intercept $-3$.

10  A line has the same $x$-intercept as $3x - y = 9$ and the same $y$-intercept as $2y - x + 8 = 0$. Find its equation.

11  A line passes through the intersection of $2x - y = 7$ and $3x + y = 13$ and has slope $\dfrac{1}{2}$. Find its equation.

## 5.9  PSP  Strategy: Families of Lines

Often to solve a problem, different strategies are available. For example, in your earlier work, you have interpreted the significance of the parameters $m$ and $b$ in the equation $y = mx + b$.

- For $b = 3$, these lines are members of a family of lines with $y$-intercept of 3.

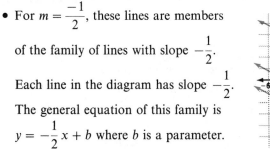

The general equation of the family of lines with $y$-intercept of 3 can thus be written as $y = mx + 3$, where $m$ is a parameter.

- For $m = \dfrac{-1}{2}$, these lines are members of the family of lines with slope $-\dfrac{1}{2}$.

Each line in the diagram has slope $-\dfrac{1}{2}$.

The general equation of this family is $y = -\dfrac{1}{2}x + b$ where $b$ is a parameter.

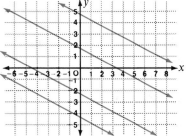

In each of the above examples, one of the parameters, either $m$ or $b$, is given a particular value and a family of lines is obtained. To obtain the equation of a specific member of the family, you need to be given one more specific piece of information about the line, as shown in the example.

**Example 1**    A line has $y$-intercept 3 and passes through the point $(-1, 5)$. What is the equation of the line?

PSP Refer to your *Problem-Solving Plan.*

**Solution**    *Step 1:* Let P$(x, y)$ be any point on the line.
Thus, the family of lines with $y$-intercept 3 is given by the equation   $y = mx + 3$.

*Step 2:* The required line passes through $(-1, 5)$.
Thus the co-ordinates of the point satisfy the equation   $y = mx + 3$.

Use $x = -1$, $y = 5$     $5 = m(-1) + 3$ or $m = -2$

Thus, the required equation of the line is $y = -2x + 3$.

The use of the equation, in the form, $y = mx + b$, is a useful strategy for solving problems about lines.

**Example 2**  Find the equation of a line with slope 3 and passing through the point (4, 1).

**Solution**  Use P($x$, $y$) as any point on the line.
Then, the family of lines with slope 3 is given by

$y = 3x + b$ ⟵ $b$ is the $y$-intercept.

Since (4, 1) is on the line, its co-ordinates satisfy the equation.

$$y = 3x + b$$
$$1 = 3(4) + b$$
$$-11 = b$$

The required equation is given by $y = 3x - 11$ (or $3x - y - 11 = 0$ in standard form).

The equation you obtain using the above strategy in Example 2 is the same, regardless of which method you use to solve the problem. For example, you could also use the following strategy to obtain the equation.

Use P($x$, $y$) as any point on the line. Since the line passes through (4, 1), then the slope of the line is given by $\dfrac{y - 1}{x - 4}$. Since the slope of a line is constant, then

$$\frac{y - 1}{x - 4} = 3$$
$$y - 1 = 3(x - 4)$$
$$y - 1 = 3x - 12$$
$$0 = 3x - y - 11 \qquad (\text{or } 3x - y - 11 = 0)$$

## 5.9  Exercise

**A** Review the meaning of a family of lines in the form $y = mx + b$.

1  Write the equation of the line that passes through (0, 3) and has the given slope.

(a) 2  (b) $-3$  (c) 1  (d) $-1$

(e) $\dfrac{1}{2}$  (f) 0.5  (g) $-\dfrac{2}{3}$  (h) $\dfrac{5}{2}$

2 A family of lines has slope $-3$. What is the equation of the line that passes through each point?

(a) $(0, 3)$         (b) $(0, -2)$         (c) $(0, 5)$         (d) $\left(0, \dfrac{1}{2}\right)$

(e) $(0. -0.5)$         (f) $\left(0, \dfrac{3}{2}\right)$         (g) $\left(0, -\dfrac{2}{3}\right)$         (h) $(0, 1.6)$

3 A family of lines is given by $y = 2x + b$. What is the equation of the line passing through each point?

(a) $(2, 3)$         (b) $(-1, 3)$         (c) $\left(-\dfrac{1}{2}, 2\right)$         (d) $(-3, 0.5)$

4 A family of lines is given by $y = mx - 3$. What is the equation of the line passing through each point?

(a) $(-4, 6)$         (b) $\left(3, \dfrac{1}{2}\right)$         (c) $(2, -1.5)$         (d) $(-3, -0.5)$

5 The family of lines with slope 3 is given by $y = 3x + b$.
(a) Find the member of the family with $y$-intercept $-2$.
(b) Find the member of the family passing through the point $(2, 1)$.
(c) Find the member of the family with $x$-intercept $-3$.

6 The family of lines with $y$-intercept $-2$ is given by $y = mx - 2$.
(a) Find the member of the family with slope $\dfrac{1}{2}$.

(b) Find the member of the family passing through $(-2, 3)$.
(c) Find the member of the family with $x$-intercept $-3$.

7 Write the equation of the family of lines for each property.

(a) slope 3         (b) $y$-intercept $-1$         (c) slope $-\dfrac{2}{3}$

(d) $y$-intercept 3         (e) $y$-intercept $-2$         (f) slope $-3$

8 Each equation represents a family of lines. What special property does each family have?

(a) $y = 3x + b$         (b) $y = mx - 2$         (c) $y = \dfrac{1}{2}x + b$

(d) $y = mx - \dfrac{2}{3}$         (e) $y = bx - 3$         (f) $y = mx + \dfrac{1}{3}$

(g) $\dfrac{y + 2}{x - 1} = m$         (h) $\dfrac{y - 2}{x} = m$         (i) $\dfrac{y}{x - 3} = m$

9    A family of lines is shown by each diagram. Use a parameter to write an equation for each family.

(a)                        (b)                        (c)

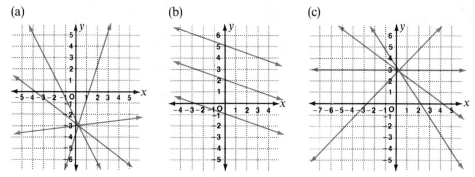

10    Write the equation for the families of lines that have the following properties.

(a) parallel to $2x + y = 3$                (b) with slope $\dfrac{1}{2}$

(c) perpendicular to $3x - y + 4 = 0$     (d) parallel to $y - x - 1 = 0$

(e) with slope $\dfrac{2}{3}$                     (f) perpendicular to $3x - 2y = 5$

11    (a) Write the equation of the family of lines with slope $-1$.

       (b) What is the equation of the member in (a) that passes through $(2, -1)$?

12    (a) Write the equation for each member of the family of lines with $y$-intercept 2.

       (b) Write the equation of the member in (a) that passes through the point $(4, -3)$.

13    (a) Use the *slope y-intercept* form to write the equation of the family of lines parallel to $2x + y = 6$.

       (b) Write the equation of the member in (a) that passes through the point $(3, -1)$.

       (c) Write the equation of the member in (a) that has $x$-intercept $-3$.

14    (a) Use the *slope y-intercept* form to write the equation of the family of lines perpendicular to $2x - y = 5$.

       (b) Write the equation of the member in (a) that passes through the point $(-2, 3)$.

       (c) Write the equation of the member in (a) that has $y$-intercept $-8$.

**B** Remember: Let the family of lines be represented in the form $y = mx + b$.

15 Use the equation of the form $y = mx + b$ to find the equation of the following lines.

(a) with slope 3 and passing through $(-1, -3)$

(b) passing through $(0, 4)$ with slope $\dfrac{1}{2}$   (c) with slope $\dfrac{2}{3}$ and $x$-intercept 3

(d) passing through $(0, 0)$ with slope 4   (e) passing through $(0, 8)$ and $(-4, 3)$

16 Write the equation of a line with the following properties.

(a) slope $\dfrac{1}{4}$, $y$-intercept 3   (b) $x$-intercept $-3$, slope 4

(c) passes through $(-4, 3)$ and $(2, 1)$   (d) $x$-intercept 3, passes through $(0, -4)$

(e) slope $-\dfrac{3}{2}$, $y$-intercept 5   (f) slope 0, passes through $(-4, -3)$

17 Find the equation for the line that has the following properties. Decide which family of lines is more suitable to use to find the answer.

(a) $y$-intercept $-3$, slope $\dfrac{2}{3}$   (b) parallel to $3x - y = 4$, $y$-intercept 5

(c) perpendicular to $2x - y = 5$, passes through $(-3, 0)$

(d) passes through $(-2, 1)$, parallel to the $x$-axis

(e) $x$-intercept $\dfrac{2}{3}$, slope 3   (f) perpendicular to $y = 2x$, $x$-intercept $-\dfrac{1}{2}$

(g) parallel to $2x + 2y = 3$, $x$-intercept $-1$

**PSP** You have different strategies that you can use to solve the following problems.

18 (a) Write the equation for each side of the parallelogram.

(b) Find the equation of each diagonal of the parallelogram.

(c) Determine whether the diagonals are perpendicular.

19 A line with slope $-3$ passes through the intersection of $x - 2y = -3$ and $3x - y = -4$. Find the equation of the line.

**C** 20 A line is a member of the family of lines $y = 2x + b$ and passes through the intersection of $3x - y = -7$ and $2x - 3y = -7$. What is the equation of the line?

## Strategy: Slope-Point Form

Often the information given in a problem suggests the strategy to use to solve the problem. The family of lines shown have the property that they all pass through the same point (2, 3). The general equation of the lines passing through (2, 3) is given by

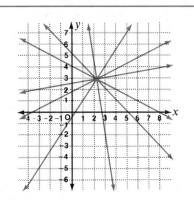

$$\frac{y - 3}{x - 2} = m \text{ where } m \text{ is the slope}$$

The general equation of a line through $(x_1, y_1)$ and with slope $m$ is given by

$$\frac{y - y_1}{x - x_1} = m \quad \text{or} \quad y - y_1 = m(x - x_1).$$

This equation is called the **slope-point form** of the equation.

21  Each equation shows a line in *slope-point* form. Write the point and the slope.

(a) $\dfrac{y - 3}{x + 1} = 2$       (b) $\dfrac{y + 2}{x - 3} = \dfrac{1}{2}$       (c) $y + 3 = 3(x - 1)$

(d) $y - 2 = -2(x + 1)$    (e) $\dfrac{y + 5}{x} = 3$       (f) $\dfrac{y}{x + 3} = \dfrac{2}{3}$

22  The *slope-point* form of an equation is given by $y + 3 = m(x + 2)$.

(a) Through what point does the line pass?

(b) If the line also passes through $(-2, 1)$, find the equation of the line in standard form.

23  A family of lines passes through the point $(0, -1)$.

(a) Use the *slope-point* form to find the equation of the member with slope 3.

(b) Use the *slope y-intercept* form to find the equation of the member with slope 3.

(c) Which method do you prefer, (a) or (b), to find the equation of the member?

24  (a) A family of lines passes through the point $(3, -1)$. Write the equation for the family.

(b) Write the equation for the member in (a) that

    (i) has slope $\dfrac{1}{2}$.       (ii) passes through $(-1, 4)$.

    (iii) has *y*-intercept 6.      (iv) has *x*-intercept $-2$.

# Practice and Problems: Review

1   If $f(x) = 8 - 3x$ and $g(x) = 6x - 1$, find the value of the following.
   (a) $f(0)$                  (b) $g(-1)$                  (c) $f(3) + g(3)$                  (d) $f(-1)g(3)$
   (e) For what value(s) of $x$ is $f(x) = g(x)$?

2   (a) Write the co-ordinates of the points at which the graph $2x + \dfrac{1}{3}(y + 6) = 4$
       crosses the axes.
   (b) Find the $y$-intercept if the point $(-1, 2)$ is on the line given by $2x - k = y$.

3   The slopes of pairs of parallel lines are given. Find the value of $k$.
   (a) $k + 2, 3$                  (b) $\dfrac{2}{3}k, 8$                  (c) $\dfrac{k - 1}{2}, k$                  (d) $5, \dfrac{3k + 1}{2}$

4   (a) Write the equation of the family of lines that passes through $(-2, 1)$.
   (b) If a member passes through the point $(-1, 3)$, find its equation.
   (c) Find the $y$-intercept of the line in (b).

5   $O(0, -4)$, $R(-4, 8)$, $S(8, 4)$, $T(12, -8)$ are the vertices of a quadrilateral.
   Show that the lines joining the midpoints of the sides form a rectangle.

# Practice Test

1   (a) If $g(x) = 3x - 5$, find $g(3)$, $g(0)$, and $g(-1)$.
   (b) Draw the graph of $g(x) = 3x - 5$. Is it a function? Justify your answer

2   Find the intercepts to draw the graph of each line.
   (a) $3x - 2y = 12$                          (b) $2x - 3 = 3(y + 1)$

3   Draw the graph of a line if it has the same $y$-intercept as $2x - y = 4$ and the same
   slope as $3x + y = 6$.

4   A line is parallel to $3x - y = 1$ and passes through $(2, 1)$.
   (a) Find the equation of the line.
   (b) Which of the points $A(1, -2)$, $B(2, -1)$, $C(3, 4)$ are also on the line?

5   Write the equation of each family of lines.
   (a) family with $y$-intercept $-6$                          (b) family with slope 3.

6   Find the equation for the line that has the following properties.
   (a) perpendicular to $x + \dfrac{1}{2}y = 3$ and has $y$-intercept $-3$.
   (b) parallel to $x - 3y = 1$ and has $x$-intercept $-4$.

7   $P(9, 1)$, $Q(11, -3)$ $R(0, -3)$ $S(-2, 1)$ are the vertices of a quadrilateral.
   (a) Find the lengths of the sides.                          (b) Find the slopes of the sides.
   (c) Classify the quadrilateral.

# Cumulative Review

1 Find the digit in the 11th place of the decimal form for each of

(a) $\dfrac{3}{7}$  (b) $\dfrac{2}{11}$  (c) $\dfrac{4}{21}$  (d) $\dfrac{6}{13}$  (e) $\dfrac{3}{15}$  (f) $\dfrac{49}{99}$

2 Simplify.

(a) $(x^3)^2(x^2)^3$  (b) $\left(\dfrac{x}{y}\right)^3 (xy)^2$  (c) $\dfrac{36x^3y^4}{-2xy}\left(\dfrac{x}{y}\right)^2$  (d) $(x^2)^m(x^m)^2x^{2m-2}$

3 Factor  (a) $6 + 13y + 6y^2$  (b) $81y^4 - 16x^4$  (c) $4y^2 - 2xy - 30x^2$

4 Simplify.

(a) $2(3x - 4y) - 4(x - 5) - 3y$  (b) $2(x^2 - 2x) + 3(2x - 1) - 5x(x - 3)$

(c) $2(x - 3)(x + 2) - 3(x + 1)(1 - x) + 2(x + 1)^2$

5 Simplify.  (a) $\dfrac{3a}{a-3} - \dfrac{2a}{a+3}$  (b) $\dfrac{ab}{ab - 2b^2} - \dfrac{5ab}{a^2 - 4b^2} + \dfrac{a}{a^2 + 2ab}$

6 If $x = 2$, find the value of  (a) $\dfrac{x^2 - 6x + 9}{6 - 2x}$  (b) $\dfrac{x+1}{x-1} \times \dfrac{x+3}{1-x^2} \div \dfrac{(x+3)^2}{1-x}$

7 Write a simplified expression for each answer.

(a) Find the sum of $\dfrac{6m-3}{6m}$ and $\dfrac{3m+1}{9m}$.

(b) By how much does $\dfrac{2a+3}{10a^2}$ exceed $\dfrac{6a-3}{15a^2}$?

(c) Solve and verify $\dfrac{x}{x-2} + 2 = \dfrac{5x}{x+2} + \dfrac{3x+1}{x^2-4}$.

8 The speed $V$ in metres per second at which sound travels in the air depends on the temperature, $t$, in degrees Celsius, and is given by $V = 20\sqrt{273 + t}$.

(a) Calculate the speed of sound to 1 decimal place when the temperature is $27°C$.

(b) Two persons A, B see the flash of a gun shot at S. If SA = 400.0 m, how long will it take A to hear the shot?

(c) If B hears the shot 3.5 s after A, how far apart are A and B?

9 Two row boats leave the dock of a cottage at the same time. One row boat goes due south at 8 km/h. The other row boat goes due west at 6 km/h. How far apart are the boats after 3 h?

# 6 *Using Systems of Equations: Problem-Solving*

Graphs of linear systems of equations, solving systems of equations, substitution method, method of comparison, addition and subtraction method, systems and computers, translation skills, organizational strategies, using charts, using diagrams, solving problems, applications, strategies and problem solving

## Introduction

Throughout your study of mathematics, you, like other people who have developed mathematics, will learn organizational skills that can be applied and used to solve problems. In mathematics, and in many other disciplines, two important problem-solving questions are those given below.

- What are you asked to find?
- What are you given?

These questions occur in a larger framework called *Problem-Solving Plan*, introduced to you in Chapter 1. If you haven't already done so, take a few minutes to review the questions that you have accumulated in the shaded parts of the *Problem-Solving Plan*.

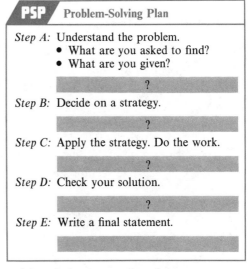

**PSP** Problem-Solving Plan

*Step A:* Understand the problem.
- What are you asked to find?
- What are you given?

    ?

*Step B:* Decide on a strategy.

    ?

*Step C:* Apply the strategy. Do the work.

    ?

*Step D:* Check your solution.

    ?

*Step E:* Write a final statement.

Throughout your work in this chapter and in others, you need a plan to solve a problem. The more mathematics you do and the more problems you solve, the more likely you are to begin to apply your skills of organizing the solution to a problem. You must develop a plan for solving problems whether the plan be your own or whether it be based on suggestions such as the one **PSP** shown above.

# 6.1 Graphing Systems of Equations

Computer techniques are used frequently as an aid in designing. Important points of the design are located by finding the intersection points of lines and curves. Many of the computer techniques for finding these points of intersection are based on mathematics. When solving problems in mathematics, you need to find intersection points. You can find the solution of a system of equations by drawing the graphs of the two lines, on the same set of axes, and thus obtaining the point of intersection.

**Example 1**   Draw the graphs defined by the equations. $x, y \in R$.

$$x + y = 8 \qquad\qquad x - y = 12$$

Write the co-ordinates of the point of intersection.

**Solution**   Think: Step 1   Construct a table of values.

$x + y = 8$

| $x$ | $y$ |
|-----|-----|
| $-1$ | $9$ |
| $0$ | $8$ |
| $1$ | $7$ |
| $8$ | $0$ |

$x - y = 12$

| $x$ | $y$ |
|-----|-----|
| $-1$ | $-13$ |
| $0$ | $-12$ |
| $1$ | $-11$ |
| $8$ | $-4$ |

The co-ordinates of the point of intersection are $(10, -2)$.

Think: Step 2   Draw the graphs.

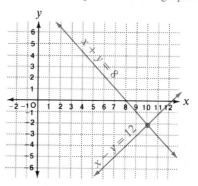

When you have located the co-ordinates of the point of intersection, check your work by substitution.

$$\text{L.S.} = x + y \qquad\qquad \text{L.S.} = x - y$$
$$\qquad = 10 + (-2) \qquad\qquad = 10 - (-2)$$
$$\qquad = 8 \qquad\qquad\qquad = 12$$
$$\qquad = \text{R.S.} \quad \text{Checks} \checkmark \qquad = \text{R.S.} \quad \text{Checks} \checkmark$$

The ordered pair $(10, -2)$ of Example 1 satisfies both equations. Thus, $(10, -2)$ is said to be a solution of the system of equations $x + y = 8$ and $x - y = 12$.

To **solve** a system of equations means to find the values of $x$ and $y$ that satisfy both equations. When you solved the equations in Example 1 you obtained $x = 10$ and $y = -2$. The solution can also be expressed as an ordered pair. Thus, $(x, y) = (10, -2)$ is another way of expressing the solution of the system of equations $x + y = 8$ and $x - y = 12$.

The skill of finding the co-ordinates of the point of intersection of graphs will be useful to you throughout your study of mathematics. One method of finding the intersection point is to draw the graphs.

**Example 2**  The paths of two ships are given by

$$\text{Ship A: } x + y = 8 \qquad\qquad \text{Ship B: } x - y = 4$$

Their paths intersect at an island. Write the co-ordinates of the location of the island.

**Solution**

$x + y = 8 \qquad x - y = 4$

| $x$ | $y$ |
|-----|-----|
| 0 | 8 |
| 8 | 0 |
| 4 | 4 |

| $x$ | $y$ |
|-----|-----|
| 0 | $-4$ |
| 4 | 0 |
| 5 | 1 |

The co-ordinates of the location of the island are (6, 2).

# 6.1 Exercise

**A** Remember: Check your solution in the *original* system of equations. All variables represent real numbers.

**PSP**

1  What is the solution of each system of equations? Check your answer in the original system.

(a)
(b)

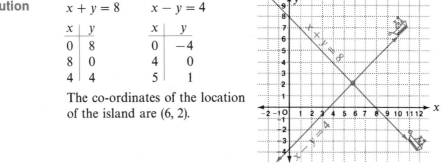

(c)
(d)

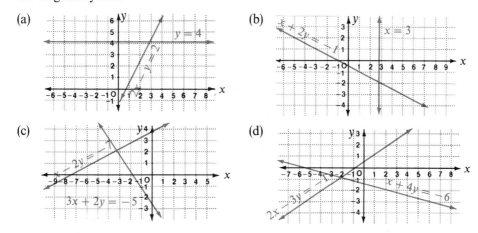

2   For each system of equations, decide whether the ordered pair given is a solution.

(a) $x - y = 4$
    $2x + y = 5$
    $A(3, -1)$

(b) $2x - y = 3$
    $x = -2y$
    $B(2, -1)$

(c) $2x = -y - 3$
    $x - 2y = 0$
    $C(-2, -1)$

(d) $3y - x = -9$
    $3x - y = 11$
    $D(3, -2)$

(e) $2x - 3y = -9$
    $3x + 2y = -9$
    $E(-3, 0)$

(f) $x = y + 6$
    $2y + 3x = -8$
    $F(-4, 2)$

3   For which of the following systems is the ordered pair $(3, -2)$ a solution?

(a) $x + y = 1$
    $x - y = 5$

(b) $2x + y = 4$
    $2y - x = -6$

(c) $3x = 5 - 2y$
    $x + y = 1$

(d) $5y + 3x = -1$
    $y = 2x - 8$

(e) $2x + 3y = 0$
    $x = 2y + 7$

(f) $y + 8 = 2x$
    $5x + 3y = 21$

4   (a) Draw a graph of $x + 2y = 8$.

(b) Use the same axes as you used in (a) and draw the graph of $x - 2y = -4$.

(c) What are the co-ordinates of the point of intersection? Check your solution.

5   For each system of equations,
    • use the method of graphing to solve it.      • check your solution.

(a) $x + 2y = 15$
    $2x - y = 0$

(b) $2x = y - 5$
    $y = x - 3$

**B** Remember to make a final statement when you state the solution to a problem.

6   Draw graphs. Solve each of the following system of equations.

(a) $x + 2y = 1$
    $2x - y = -3$

(b) $2y - x = -3$
    $y - x = -2$

(c) $x + 3y = 9$
    $x = y - 3$

(d) $2x + 3y = -6$
    $3x + 2y = -9$

(e) $x - 3y + 1 = 0$
    $2x + y = 4$

(f) $2x - 3y = 0$
    $x - y = -4$

7   Find the intersection point of the graph of the system of equations defined by

(a) $2x - 3y = 0$ and $x - 4y = -5$.      (b) $x - y = 4$ and $2x - y = 9$.

8   What are the co-ordinates of a point that lies on the graph of

(a) $x - 4y = 5$ and $3x + y = -11$?      (b) $x + 4y = 10$ and $x - y + 3 = -7$?

9   Find a pair of values for $x$ and $y$ that satisfy

(a) $x - 3y = 0$ and $2x + y = 7$.      (b) $3x + y = 7$ and $y = 4x$.

10   Two submarines are heading for a rendezvous (a meeting place). Their paths are given by

        Ship A: $x - y = -1$          Ship B: $x + y = 3$

Find the co-ordinates of their rendezvous. (Remember to check your answer.)

11   A tracking ship is on a course given by $2x - y = 4$. By collecting data, the ship has predicted the course of a submarine to be $x - 2y = -1$. Determine the co-ordinates of the point at which their paths cross.

12   (a) A ship travels on a course defined by $2x - y = 11$. Use a set of axes to draw its path.

    (b) Another ship travels on a course defined by $y = 3x - 15$. On the same set of axes as in (a), draw its graph.

    (c) At what point could the two ships meet?

13   A tug leaves Vancouver harbour located at $(8, 7)$ and sails along a course given by $x - y = 1$. A steamer leaves an island located at $(6, -4)$ and sails along $2x + y = 8$. If the ships are heading towards a rendezvous which boat has farther to travel?

14   The paths of two ships are given by the following equations.

        Ship A: $2x - 3y = 3$          Ship B: $4x = 9 + 6y$

Will the ships meet? Why or why not?

**PSP** 15   How many different ways can you spell WILLIAM?

```
            W
          I   I
        L   L   L
      L   L   L   L
        I   I   I
          A   A
            M
```

**C** 16   For each of the following systems,
   • draw the graph.
   • estimate the solution of the system from the graph.

(a) $x - 4y = 11$       (b) $x = 3y + 7$       (c) $y = 8 - 2x$
    $3x = 9 - y$           $2x + 5y = 8$         $3x - 2y = 7$

---

## Math Tip

As you know, it is important to clearly understand the vocabulary of mathematics when solving problems. You cannot speak the language of mathematics if you don't know the vocabulary.
   • Make a list of all the words you *review* and *learn* in this chapter.
   • Use an example of your own to illustrate the meaning of each word.

## 6.2 Equivalent Systems of Equations

The following equations are equivalent since they have the same solution set.

| Equivalent Equations | Solution Set |
|---|---|
| $3x - 4 = 2x + 1$ | $\{5\}$ |
| $2(x + 1) - 3 = x + 4$ | $\{5\}$ |
| $\dfrac{x + 1}{3} - \dfrac{2x + 2}{2} = -4$ | $\{5\}$ |

The word equivalent can also be applied to *systems* of equations. A system of two equations in two variables is equivalent to another system if both systems have the same solution set. The four systems of equations shown in these graphs are all equivalent to each other since they all have the same solution set. In other words, they all have the same point of intersection.

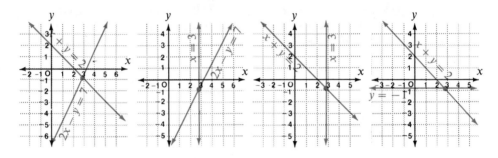

## 6.2 Exercise

**B** 1  (a) Draw the graph of each system of equations on the same set of axes.

   A   $2x + y = -10$     B   $x + 2y = -8$
       $x + 2y = -8$           $x - y = -2$

   (b) Why can the systems in (a) be called equivalent?

2  (a) Choose pairs of equations from the graph that give equivalent systems of equations.

   (b) Which of the equivalent systems in (a) give the equations in the simplest form?

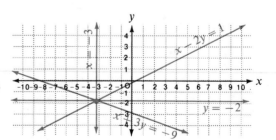

3   (a) Graph the line given by $2x - y = 7$.

    (b) Graph the line given by $4x - 2y = 14$.

    (c) What do you notice about your graphs in (a) and (b)?

    (d) How are the equations $2x - y = 7$ and $4x - 2y = 14$ related?

    (e) What is the solution set for the system of equations given by
$$2x - y = 7 \text{ and } 4x - 2y = 14?$$

4   (a) Draw the graph of $2x - y = 8$.    (b) Draw the graph of $2x - y = 10$.

    (c) What do you notice about the graphs in (a) and (b)?

    (d) Why can you not name an intersection point for
$$2x - y = 8 \text{ and } 2x - y = 10?$$

    (e) What is the solution set for the system of equations given by
$$2x - y = 8 \text{ and } 2x - y = 10?$$

5   (a) Draw the line given by $4x + 3y = 11$.    (b) Draw the line given by $3x - 2y = 4$.

    (c) Write the co-ordinates of the intersection point.

6   Refer to the previous question. The lines $4x + 3y = 11$ and $3x - 2y = 4$, intersect at $(2, 1)$. Draw the graph of each of the following.

    (a) $7x + y = 15$   Obtained by adding.   (b) $x + 5y = 7$   Obtained by subtracting.

$$\begin{array}{r} 4x + 3y = 11 \\ 3x - 2y = \ \ 4 \\ \hline 7x + \ \ y = 15 \end{array} \qquad \begin{array}{r} 4x + 3y = 11 \\ 3x - 2y = \ \ 4 \\ \hline x + 5y = \ \ 7 \end{array}$$

    (c) What do you notice about the intersection point of the graphs in (a) and (b)?

7   A system of equations is given by
$$2x + 3y = -1 \qquad ① \qquad \text{and} \qquad 3x - 5y = 8 \qquad ②$$
and intersects at $(1, -1)$. Find the resulting equation of each of the following and draw the graph of each resulting equation on the same set of axes.

    (a) $\begin{array}{l} 2x + \ \ 3y = -1 \ \ \longleftarrow 1 \times ① \\ 6x - 10y = \ \ 16 \ \ \longleftarrow 2 \times ② \end{array}$   means equation ② is multiplied by the value 2

      ? ▬▬▬▬▬

    (b) $\begin{array}{l} 4x + \ \ 6y = -2 \ \ \longleftarrow 2 \times ① \\ 9x - 15y = \ \ 24 \ \ \longleftarrow 3 \times ② \end{array}$   (c) $\begin{array}{l} 6x + \ \ 9y = -3 \ \ \longleftarrow 3 \times ① \\ 6x - 10y = \ \ 16 \ \ \longleftarrow 2 \times ② \end{array}$

      ? ▬▬▬▬▬       ? ▬▬▬▬▬

8   (a) Based on your results in the previous questions, describe a method of obtaining equivalent systems of equations.

    (b) Test your answer in (a). Write systems of equations that are equivalent to $3x - y = 2$ and $2x + y = 3$.

## Classifying Systems of Equations

In drawing the graphs of systems of equations, you will have noticed that there are three possible types of graphical results.

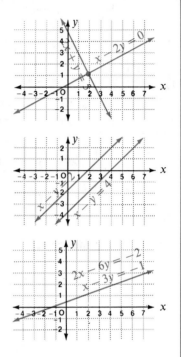

I There is one intersection point. This linear system has exactly one solution. Such a system is said to be **consistent and independent**.

$$x - 2y = 0 \qquad 2x + y = 5$$

II There is no intersection point, since the lines are parallel. This system has no solution. Such a linear system is said to be **inconsistent**.

$$x - y = 4 \qquad x - y = 2$$

III The graphs are co-incident. Any solution of one equation is a solution of the other. Thus, there is an infinite number of solutions. The linear system given by the equations

$$2x - 6y = -2 \text{ and } x - 3y = -1$$

has an unlimited number of solutions. The two equations represent the same line. Such a linear system is said to be **consistent and dependent**.

9  Draw the graph of $3x + 2y = 6$ and $x - y = 2$ on the same set of axes. How would you classify the system?

10  Draw the graph of $2x - 3y = -6$ and $2x - 3y = 15$ on the same set of axes. How would you classify the system?

11  Classify each of the following as
   • consistent   • inconsistent   • dependent   • independent

   You may wish to draw graphs to help you.

   (a) $2x - y = 2$
       $x + y = 4$

   (b) $x + 2y = 6$
       $x + 2y = 8$

   (c) $3x - 2y = 5$
       $6x - 4y = 10$

   (d) $2x - 3y = 5$
       $2x - y = -1$

   (e) $x - 3y = 5$
       $x = 3y + 8$

   (f) $2x - y = -3$
       $x + y = 0$

   (g) $x - y = 8$
       $3y = 3x - 24$

   (h) $y - 2x = -3$
       $4x = 2y + 6$

# 6.3 Method of Substitution: Solving Systems

You can find the solution of a system of linear
equations by drawing graphs. However, for some
systems, it is not possible to obtain the exact value
of the co-ordinates of the point of intersection.
For example, the graphs defined by the equations

$$10x + 5y = 14 \quad \text{and} \quad 5x - 10y = -3$$

are drawn on the same set of axes.

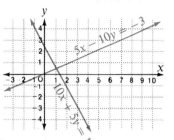

It is difficult to read the co-ordinates of the point of intersection
from the graph. You can only estimate the co-ordinates, and thus, you can
only estimate the solution of the system of equation. For this reason, you
need to develop algebraic methods of solving two equations in two variables.

You can solve this system of equations

$$x + 2y = 8 \quad ① \quad \text{and} \quad y = 3 \quad ②$$

by examining the graph of the system shown
at the right. By looking at the graph you
know that the ordinate of the point of
intersection is 3 since $y = 3$. To find $x$ you
substitute $y = 3$ in equation ①.

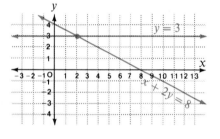

Use $y = 3$, $\qquad x + 2y = 8 \qquad ①$
$$x + 2(3) = 8$$
$$x + 6 = 8$$
$$x = 2 \qquad \text{Thus, the solution is } (x, y) = (2, 3).$$

In the example above, the value of one variable was substituted into the
other equation. The principle of the **substitution method** is to obtain an
expression for one of the variables and substitute this expression into the
other equation. For example, for this system you substitute as shown.

$$x + 2y = 5 \qquad ①$$
$$y = 3x - 1 \qquad ②$$

Use $y = 3x - 1$. Thus, $\qquad x + 2y = 5$
$$x + 2(3x - 1) = 5$$
$$x + 6x - 2 = 5$$
$$7x = 7$$
$$x = 1 \qquad ③$$

Once you have the value of one variable, $x$ or $y$, you can use it to find
the value of the other variable. For example:

Use $x = 1$ in ②. $\qquad\qquad y = 3x - 1$
$$= 3(1) - 1$$
$$= 2 \qquad \text{The solution is } (x, y) = (1, 2).$$

**Example**   Solve the system given by $2x + y = 5$ and $x - 3y = 6$.

**Solution**

$$2x + y = 5 \quad ① \qquad \text{Remember: You need to decide which}$$
$$x - 3y = 6 \quad ② \qquad \text{equation provides you with an}$$
expression that you can obtain **PSP**
From equation ① write   easily for a variable.

$$y = 5 - 2x \quad ③$$

Substitute $y = 5 - 2x$ from equation ③ into equation ②.

$$x - 3y = 6$$
$$x - 3(5 - 2x) = 6$$
$$x - 15 + 6x = 6$$
$$7x = 21 \qquad \text{Think: Use the value of } x \text{ in ④ and}$$
$$x = 3 \quad ④ \qquad \text{substitute into one of the } original \text{ equations.}$$

Use $x = 3$. $\quad 2x + y = 5$
$$2(3) + y = 5 \qquad \text{Think}$$
$$6 + y = 5 \qquad Check: \text{In equation ①} \quad \text{In equation ②}$$
$$y = -1 \qquad \text{L.S.} = 2x + y \qquad \text{L.S.} = x - 3y$$
Thus the solution is $\qquad\qquad = 2(3) + (-1) \qquad = 3 - 3(-1)$
$(x, y) = (3, -1)$. $\qquad\qquad = 5 \qquad\qquad = 6$
$$\text{R.S.} = 5 \text{ checks} \checkmark \quad \text{R.S.} = 6 \text{ checks} \checkmark$$

Very often, there are equivalent ways of expressing ideas in mathematics. For example, each of the following forms are equivalent solutions of the system of equations in the example.   **PSP**

A: $(x, y) = (3, -1)$ $\qquad\qquad$ B: $x = 3, y = -1$
C: The solution set is $\{(3, -1)\}$. $\quad$ D: The co-ordinates of the point
$\qquad\qquad\qquad\qquad\qquad\qquad\qquad$ of intersection are $(3, -1)$.

## 6.3   Exercise

**A** Throughout the exercise, use the method of substitution to solve the systems of equations. All variables represent real numbers.

1   This skill is essential in using the method of substitution. Express $x$ in terms of $y$.

(a) $x + 3y = 4$ $\qquad$ (b) $x - 2y = 8$ $\qquad$ (c) $3y - x = 5$
(d) $2y = 3 - x$ $\qquad$ (e) $2y = 8 - x$ $\qquad$ (f) $2x - y + 1 = 0$
(g) $2x - 5y = 1$ $\qquad$ (h) $3y = x - 5$ $\qquad$ (i) $7y - x + 5 = 0$

2   Express $y$ in terms of $x$.

(a) $3x + y = 2$ $\qquad$ (b) $y - 4x = 5$ $\qquad$ (c) $2x - y = 3$
(d) $3x = y + 6$ $\qquad$ (e) $2y - 2x = 8$ $\qquad$ (f) $3x - 2y = 4$
(g) $7x - 2y = 3$ $\qquad$ (h) $3x + 2y - 1 = 0$ $\qquad$ (i) $3x = 2y - 1$

3 Solve for the variable shown.

(a) $x - 3y = 5$, $x$     (b) $2x - y = 6$, $y$     (c) $3a = 4 - b$, $b$

(d) $4m - 2n - 5 = 0$, $n$     (e) $3a = 5 - b$, $b$     (f) $5x - 2y + 4 = 0$, $y$

4 For each system, use the given value of the variable to find the other variable.

(a) $x = 3$     (b) $y = 4$     (c) $x = 2y - 5$     (d) $3y = 1 - x$
$2x + y = 3$     $3x - y = 5$     $y = 3$     $x = -3$

(e) $a = 3$     (f) $2a - 3b = 5$     (g) $x = 4$     (h) $3a - b + 1 = 4$
$2b - 3a = 6$     $b = -6$     $3y - 2x = 1$     $a = 2$

5 Which of the following systems of equations has $(x, y) = (-1, -2)$ as a solution?

(a) $x - y = 1$     (b) $3x = y - 1$     (c) $y = 3x - 5$
$3x + 2y = -7$     $y + 2x = -4$     $2x + 5y = -12$

(d) $3x = 1 + 2y$     (e) $2x + 12 = -5y$     (f) $3x - 2y = 1$
$y + 3x = -5$     $x + y = -3$     $y = 4x + 6$

6 A system of equations is given by $2y = x - 3$ and $3x - y = 7$.

(a) Decide whether or not to express $y$ in terms of $x$ or $x$ in terms of $y$.

(b) Then solve the system of equations.     (c) Check your solution.

7 For each system of equations
- first decide whether or not to substitute an expression for $x$ or for $y$.
- then solve the system of equations.

(a) $2x + 3y = -4$     (b) $3x - y = 8$     (c) $3y = x + 11$
$y - 2x = 4$     $2y = x - 1$     $x = y - 5$

8 A system is defined by the equations

$$x + 3y = 6 \quad \text{①} \qquad\qquad 2x + y = 7 \quad \text{②}$$

(a) From ①, obtain an expression for $x$ and solve the system. What is the solution?

(b) From ②, obtain an expression for $y$ and solve the system. What is the solution?

(c) What can you conclude from your results in (a) and (b)?

B Remember: Verify your solution in the original equations.

9 Solve.

(a) $y = 3x - 8$     (b) $a = 2b + 2$     (c) $x = 2y + 1$     (d) $3m - 2n = -5$
$2x - y = 5$     $3a - b = 6$     $y - x = -1$     $m = n - 2$

(e) $2a - 3b = 9$     (f) $2x - 3y = 1$     (g) $2m - n = 4$     (h) $3x + 2y - 11 = 0$
$a = -6 - 2b$     $x = y + 1$     $n = m - 1$     $x = y - 3$

10     Solve each system of equations. (Remember: Decide for which variable you are going to obtain an expression.)

(a) $x - y = -2$
    $x + 2y = 7$

(b) $2q - p = 3$
    $q + 2p = 4$

(c) $3g = h + 10$
    $h = g - 4$

(d) $3x - z = -9$
    $z - 2x = 7$

(e) $3s + 2t = 6$
    $s + 2t = 6$

(f) $2m + 5n = -6$
    $m + 2n = -3$

(g) $2y = w + 5$
    $3w - y = 0$

(h) $2a - 3b - 1 = 0$
    $2a - b - 5 = 0$

11     Solve each system.

(a) $3.2x + 1.6y = 11.2$
    $4.8x - 3.2y = 0$

(b) $1.2x + 0.6y = 0$
    $9.6x - 4.2y = -18$

(c) $0.38x + 0.46y = -2.06$
    $0.87x - 0.35y = -1.91$

12     (a) Find the co-ordinates of the point of intersection of the graphs given by $3x - y = -7$ and $x - 2y = 1$.

(b) How can you check your answer in (a)?

13     Find the co-ordinates of the point of intersection of each of the following.

(a) $x - 2y = 1$
    $x + y = 2$

(b) $3x + y = 8$
    $2x - y = 7$

(c) $x + y = 5$
    $2y - x = 4$

(d) $3x - y = 4$
    $x - 2y = 3$

14     What are the co-ordinates of the point that lies on both of the lines?

(a) $y - 2x = -2$
    $x + y = 4$

(b) $2x - y = -1$
    $x - 2y = -5$

(c) $2x - y = -3$
    $x + y = 0$

(d) $3y = 2x - 5$
    $2x = y + 3$

15     (a) Two lines are given by $3x - y = 7$ and $x + 3y = 9$. Find the co-ordinates of the point of intersection.

(b) The paths of two ships are given by the equations $3x - y = 7$ and $x + 3y = 9$. At what point do their paths cross?

(c) A fire is located at the intersection of the lines of sight given by the equations $3x - y = 7$ and $x + 3y = 9$. At what point is the fire located?

(d) How are the questions in (a), (b), and (c) alike? How are they different?

C 16     A system of equations is given by these equations. Solve for $x$ and $y$.

$(x + 1)(y - 3) = (x - 2)(y + 3)$
$(x - 1)(y + 5) = (x + 2)(y + 4)$

## Problem-Solving

To solve some problems you may need to just exhaust all the numbers to find which ones satisfy the conditions of the problem. (A computer works somewhat like this.) Try this problem.

The number 121 has the property that by crossing out the digit 2, the remaining number, 11, is the square root of the original number. Find all numbers less than 1000 that have the same property.

# Applications: Problems Involving Systems of Equations

You can solve some problems by using two equations in two variables. For example, a system of equations has been obtained to answer the following problem.

The number of economy seats, $e$, and first class seats, $f$, on a jumbo jet are related by

$e + f = 390$ ⟵ There are 390 seats available.
$e = 5f + 30$

↑
The number of economy seats equals 30 more than 5 times the number of first class seats.

*The above photograph shows how large the interior of a jumbo jet really is. Would you believe some carry over 500 people.?*

17  Find the number of each of economy and first class seats available. Solve the problem using the information given above.

18  Two numbers, $m$ and $n$, are related by the following equations.
$m + n = 56$ ⟵ Their sum is 56.
$m = 3n - 8$ ⟵ One of the numbers is 8 less than 3 times the other.
Solve the equations to find the numbers.

19  Each of the following systems of equations describes the properties of two numbers, $m$ and $n$. Solve the equations to find the numbers.
(a) $m - 2n = 14$    (b) $2m - n - 3 = 0$    (c) $3m - 2n = -12$    (d) $3m - 44 = n$
    $n = 3m - 27$        $m + 1 = n$            $n = 2m + 7$            $m - 3n = 4$

20  The lines of sight of a hot air balloon from two boats are given as follows:
    Boat A: $x + 2y = 4$         Boat B: $x = y - 5$
Solve the equations to find the co-ordinates of the hot air balloon.

21  Sheila and Brian pooled unequal amounts of money and bought a raffle ticket. They won $1000. Each person's share of the winnings is related as follows:
$s + b = 1000$ ⟵ The total of the winnings is $1000.
$3s - 5b = 200$
↑
Three times Sheila's share less five times Brian's share is $200.
Solve the equations to find the amount of each person's share of the winnings.

## 6.4  Simplifying and Solving Systems

It is easier to solve some systems if you first simplify the equations by using your skills with polynomials. For example, the following system appears to be complex.

$$2(x - y) - 3(x + y) = -13 \qquad\qquad 5 - 2(2x - y) = 3(x - 2y)$$

By simplifying each equation, the system of equations is reduced to a simpler form which you already know how to solve.

$$\begin{aligned} 2(x - y) - 3(x + y) &= -13 \\ 2x - 2y - 3x - 3y &= -13 \\ -x - 5y &= -13 \\ \text{or} \quad x + 5y &= 13 \end{aligned} \qquad \begin{aligned} 5 - 2(2x - y) &= 3(x - 2y) \\ 5 - 4x + 2y &= 3x - 6y \\ -7x + 8y &= -5 \\ \text{or} \quad 7x - 8y &= 5 \end{aligned}$$

**Example**

Find the co-ordinates of the intersection point for the graphs defined by the equations

$$2(x - 1) + 3(y - 2) = 1$$
$$x - y = 2$$

**Solution**

$$\begin{aligned} 2(x - 1) + 3(y - 2) &= 1 \quad ① \\ x - y &= 2 \quad ② \end{aligned}$$

Simplify equation ①.

$$\begin{aligned} 2(x - 1) + 3(y - 2) &= 1 \\ 2x - 2 + 3y - 6 &= 1 \\ 2x + 3y &= 9 \quad ③ \end{aligned}$$

From equation ②, you can write

$$x = 2 + y \quad ④ \quad \longleftarrow$$

Substitute equation ④ in equation ③.

When using the method of substitution, use the most convenient expression for $x$ or for $y$. In this case, substitute an expression for $x$ from equation ②.

$$\begin{aligned} 2x + 3y &= 9 \\ 2(2 + y) + 3y &= 9 \\ 4 + 2y + 3y &= 9 \\ 5y &= 5 \\ y &= 1 \quad ⑤ \end{aligned}$$

Use the value of $y$ from equation ⑤ in equation ②.

$$\begin{aligned} x - y &= 2 \\ x - 1 &= 2 \\ x &= 3 \end{aligned}$$

Thus $x = 3$ and $y = 1$. $\longleftarrow$

Be sure to check in the original equations.

## 6.4 Exercise

**A** Remember: When you are checking your solution, verify in the *original* equations.

1. Simplify each of the following equations.

   (a) $3(x + 2) - y = 8$

   (b) $2(x - 3) - 3y = 2(x + 1)$

   (c) $4(x - y) - 2(x + y) = 6$

   (d) $-(x - 2) + 2(x - y) = 3$

   (e) $-2(x - y) = 3 - 2(x + y)$

   (f) $3(x + 3) - 8 = 5(y - 3)$

2. For each of the following
   - simplify each equation
   - express one variable in terms of the other.

   (a) $2(x - 1) + y = 4$

   (b) $3(x + 2) - 2(x - y) = -6$

   (c) $4(x - y) - 5(x - 2) = -4$

   (d) $3(x - 1) + 2(y + 1) = 5 + y$

   (e) $2(x - 3) - x = 6(y - 1) - 8$

   (f) $3(x - 3) - 2x = -2(y - 5) + 3$

3. (a) What is your first step in solving the following system?

   $$\frac{x}{2} + \frac{y}{2} = 3 \qquad 3x - 2y = 8$$

   **PSP**

   Have a plan.

   (b) Solve the system in (a).

4. (a) What is your first step in solving the following system?

   $$3(x + 2) - 2(x - y) = 8 \qquad x - y = 2$$

   (b) Solve the system in (a).

5. Two ordered pairs are given for each system of equations. Verify whether A or B is the solution of the given system.

   |  | A | B |
   |---|---|---|
   | (a) $x + y = 3$ <br> $3(x + 2) - y = 15$ | $(3, 0)$ | $(0, 3)$ |
   | (b) $2x - y = -1$ <br> $2(x - 3) - 3y = 2(x + 1) - 5$ | $(2, 3)$ | $(-1, -1)$ |
   | (c) $y + 2x = -2$ <br> $4(x - y) - 2(x + y) = 12$ | $(0, -2)$ | $(-3, 4)$ |
   | (d) $2x - 3y = -11$ <br> $3(x + 3) - 6 = 5(y - 3)$ | $(-4, 1)$ | $(-1, 3)$ |

**B** To solve each system, decide what the first step of your solution might be.

6. (a) Solve this system of equations.

   $$x - \frac{1}{3}y = 1 \qquad x + \frac{2}{3}y = 7$$

   (b) Verify your answer.

7   (a) Solve the following system of equations.
$$2(x - 1) + y = -4 \qquad\qquad 3x - 2y = -3$$
    (b) Verify your answer.

8   Solve each system of equations.
    (a) $3(x - 1) + 2(y + 1) = 5$
        $3x - y = -3$
    (b) $2x - y = 3$
        $2(x - 3) - 6(y - 1) = -8$
    (c) $3x - 2y = 1$
        $2(x - 3) - (y - 1) = -4$
    (d) $3m - n = -4$
        $2(m - 3) - 2(n + 1) = -12$

9   Solve each system of equations.
    (a) $\frac{1}{3}x - y = -2$
        $x - \frac{2}{3}y = 1$
    (b) $y + \frac{3}{4}x = 4$
        $x - \frac{1}{4}y = -1$
    (c) $\frac{1}{2}x + y = 4$
        $\frac{1}{2}x - y = 2$
    (d) $2x - \frac{1}{2}y = 4$
        $\frac{2}{3}x = y - 2$
    (e) $\frac{1}{2}x + \frac{1}{3}y = 5$
        $\frac{1}{3}y - x = -4$
    (f) $\frac{1}{2}a - b = 2$
        $\frac{2}{3}a + b = 5$

10  (a) Find the co-ordinates of the point of intersection for
$$3(x - 1) - 2(y - 1) = 5 \text{ and } 3x - y = 9.$$
    (b) How can you check your answer in (a)?

11  Find the co-ordinates of the point of intersection for each system.
    (a) $2(x - 1) + 3(y - 1) = 7$
        $x - y = -1$
    (b) $\frac{1}{3}x + y = -1$
        $x - 2y = 7$
    (c) $x - 3y = 6$
        $3(x - 2) - 2(y - 3) = 4$
    (d) $4x - y = 5$
        $x - \frac{2}{3}y = -2$

12  What are the co-ordinates of the point that lies on both lines defined by
    (a) $y - x + 2 = 0$
        $x = 2y + 4$
    (b) $3(x - 1) - 2(y + 1) = 4$
        $2x - y = 6$
    (c) $x - \frac{1}{3}y = 1$
        $2x = y + 1$

C 13  (a) Solve for $x$ and $y$ where $x$ and $y$ are given by
$$2^{3(x + 2y) - 2(x - 2y) - y} = 16 \qquad 4^{(2x + y) - (x + 2y)} = 32$$
    (b) Check your answer in (a).

**PSP** Another Strategy: Solving a
System of Equations

Earlier, you learned to solve a system of equations using your graphing skills and the substitution method. Another strategy for solving a system of equations is the **comparison method**. The following simple system of equations is used to illustrate the principles of this method.

$$x + y = 6 \qquad\qquad x - y = 2$$

Any ordered pair, $(x, y)$, that has the property $x + y = 6$ will lie on the line $\ell_1$ defined by

$$\ell_1: x + y = 6, \quad x, y \in R.$$  The symbol, $\ell_1$ is often used to show a line.

From $x + y = 6$, you can write $y = 6 - x$. Thus, the ordered pair can be written as $(x, y) = (x, 6 - x)$ since $y = 6 - x$.

⌐ This point lies on the line $x + y = 6$.

Similarly, any ordered pair $(x, y)$ that has the property $x - y = 2$ will lie on the line $\ell_2$ defined by

$$\ell_2: x - y = 2, \quad x, y \in R.$$

All points of the form $(x, x - 2)$ lie on the line $\ell_1$.

In this case you can write the ordered pair as

$$(x, y) = (x, x - 2). \text{ Since } y = x - 2.$$

This point lies on the line $x - y = 2$.

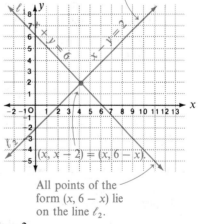

You can use analytic geometry and the co-ordinate plane to illustrate the algebraic steps. This is shown at the right.

To solve the system of equations, you want to find the ordered pair $(x, y)$ that satisfies both equations. Thus, at the point of intersection

$$(x, x - 2) = (x, 6 - x).$$

All points of the form $(x, 6 - x)$ lie on the line $\ell_2$.

*Step 1*

Solve for $x$.

$$x - 2 = 6 - x \longleftarrow \text{ Since the first}$$
$$2x = 8 \qquad\quad \text{components}$$
$$x = 4 \qquad\quad \text{are equal.}$$

*Step 2*

Solve for $y$. Use $x = 4$.

$$x + y = 6$$
$$4 + y = 6 \longleftarrow \text{Use } x = 4.$$
$$y = 2$$

Thus, the solution is given by $x = 4$, $y = 2$ or $(x, y) = (4, 2)$.

The steps of the comparison method are shown in the following example.

**Example**   Solve $x - 2y = 9$, $3y - x = -11$, $x, y \in R$.

**Solution**

$$x - 2y = 9 \qquad ①$$
$$3y - x = -11 \qquad ②$$

Remember: You need to choose which variable to compare.

From equation ①, $x = 2y + 9$   ③
From equation ②, $x = 11 + 3y$   ④
Compare equations ③ and ④.

$$11 + 3y = 2y + 9$$
$$3y - 2y = 9 - 11$$
$$y = -2$$

Substitute $y = -2$ in equation ①.

$$x - 2y = 9$$
$$x - 2(-2) = 9$$
$$x + 4 = 9$$
$$x = 5$$

Record the original equation before you substitute a value for the variable.

Thus, $(x, y) = (5, -2)$.

Remember to check (verify) your answer.
Use $x = 5$, $y = -2$.

L.S. $= x - 2y$          L.S. $= 3y - x$
$\quad = 5 - 2(-2)$          $\quad = 3(-2) - 5$
$\quad = 9$              $\quad = -11$
$\quad =$ R.S. Checks ✓      $\quad =$ R.S. Checks ✓

When you are deciding whether to compare the $x$'s or the $y$'s, look to see if there is a clue in the given equation. For example,

**PSP**

you would compare the $x$'s      you would compare the $y$'s in
in this system                  this system.

$$x - 3y = 8$$                  $$3x - y = 12$$
$$7y + x = -2$$                 $$2x + y = 5$$

## 6.5   Exercise

**A** All variables represent real numbers.

1   Express $x$ in terms of $y$.
(a) $x + 2y = 8$        (b) $x - 3y = 4$        (c) $2y - x = 3$
(d) $3y = 2 - x$        (e) $2x - y = 6$        (f) $3x - 6y = 2$

2   Express $y$ in terms of $x$.
(a) $2x + y = 4$        (b) $y - 2x = 6$        (c) $3x - y = 2$
(d) $2x = y + 4$        (e) $2y - x = 8$        (f) $3x + y - 1 = 0$

3 Use the method of comparison. Solve each system of equations.

(a) $y = x - 1$
$y = 2x - 3$

(b) $x = -2y + 3$
$x = 3y - 7$

(c) $y = x - 1$
$y = 3 - 3x$

(d) $x = 1 - y$
$x = 1 - 2y$

(e) $a = -3 - 2b$
$a = 2b + 1$

(f) $m = 2n - 2$
$m = -3 + 3n$

4 A system is given by the equations $2x - y = 1$ and $x + y = 5$.

(a) Before solving the system, decide which variables are easier to compare.

(b) Solve the system.

5 A system is given by the following equations.

$$2x + y = 8 \text{ and } x - y = 1$$

(a) Write $x$ in terms of $y$ and find the solution.

(b) Then solve again by writing $y$ in terms of $x$.

(c) Which of the above methods do you prefer: (a) or (b)? Why?

B Remember: Before solving a system of equations, plan ahead. Which method will you use?

6 Use the comparison method to solve each of the systems.
• Decide which variables to compare.   • Then solve the system.

(a) $x + y = -1$
$x - y = -3$

(b) $2x + y = 1$
$x - y = 2$

(c) $x + 3y = 3$
$2y - x - 3 = 0$

(d) $3x = y + 11$
$y = x - 5$

(e) $5x - y = -13$
$y - 3x = 9$

(f) $3y + 2 = x$
$x + 2y = 8 - y$

7 Solve.

(a) $x - 2y = -4$
$x + 3y = 6$

(b) $a + b = 0$
$2b - a = 3$

(c) $x - y = 1$
$2x + y = 2$

(d) $m = 2n + 3$
$m + n = 0$

(e) $\dfrac{1}{2}x - y = -2$
$x + 2y = 8$

(f) $3x - 2y = 5$
$2y - x = 1$

8 Solve each system. Use the comparison method.

(a) $2x = 3y + 2$
$2x = 6 + y$

(b) $3 - y = 3x$
$3x = 2y + 3$

(c) $3y = x - 3$
$3y + x = -3$

(d) $3x + 2y = -5$
$2y - x = -1$

(e) $21 - 3y = 5x$
$5x - 4y = 23$

(f) $2x + 16 = 4y$
$4y - 3x = 18$

9 Two lines are given by $2x + y = 5$ and $4x - y = 1$. Find the co-ordinates of the point of intersection.

10   Find the co-ordinates of the point of intersection for each of the following.
     (a)  $x - y = -1$            (b)  $2x - y = 5$            (c)  $x + y - 1 = 0$
          $x + 2y = 5$                 $3x + y = 10$                $2y - x - 5 = 0$

11   What are the co-ordinates of the point that lies on both of the
     following pairs of lines?
     (a)  $y - 3x = -4$           (b)  $3x + y = 7$            (c)  $x + y + 3 = 0$
          $x - y = 2$                  $x - y = 1$                  $x - 2y - 3 = 0$

12   A system is given by the equations $2x - 3y = 4$ and $x + y = 12$.
     (a) Which method, the comparison method or the substitution method,
         is more suitable for solving this system?
     (b) Solve the system of equations.

13   A system is given by the equations $2x - 3y = 1$ and $2x + 4y = -6$.
     (a) Which method, the comparison method or the substitution method,
         is more suitable for solving this system?
     (b) Solve the system of equations.

14   For each of the following systems of equations
     • decide which method, the comparison method or the substitution method,
       is more suitable for solving the system.
     • then solve the system of equations.
     (a)  $x = 3 - 2y$           (b)  $2x - 8 = y$            (c)  $y - x + 1 = 0$
          $x = y + 3$                 $y = 1 - x$                  $x - 2y = 1$

     (d)  $x - 3y = 3$           (e)  $x + \dfrac{1}{2}y = -2$    (f)  $x + \dfrac{1}{3}y = 2$

          $2x - 3y = 6$               $2x - y = -8$                $x - y = -6$
     (g)  $2(x - 1) - 3(y - 1) = 1$   (h)  $x - 3y = -12$
          $3x - y = 7$                     $2(x - 1) - 3(y - 5) = 1$

C 15   The solution of the following system of equations is $(x, y) = (-2, 1)$.
            $px + (9 - q)y = -10$            $(3p + 1)x - (q - 6)y = -21$
       Find the values of $p$ and $q$.

## Problem-Solving

Each of the following has an error. Why do you think the error has been
made?
A: $3x + 5x = 8x^2$   B: $(3x)(5x) = 15x$   C: $5x - 3(2x - 5) = 5x - 6x - 15$

# 6.6 Solving Systems of Equations: Addition-Subtraction Method

Very often, the need to solve a problem or overcome a difficulty results in the development of new skills, strategies, and methods. For example, neither the comparison method nor the substitution method is convenient for solving a system such as $2x + 3y = 48$ and $3x + 2y = 42$.

To develop a method of solving a system of equations, you use your earlier skills in graphing and the properties of equations given in Section 6.2.

| | |
|---|---|
| *Property A* <br> A solution of a system of equations is also a solution of the equation obtained by adding or subtracting the equations of the system. | (2, 3) is a solution of <br> ① $\qquad$ $2x + 3y = 13$ <br> ② $\qquad$ $3x - y = 3$ <br> ① + ② $\qquad$ $5x + 2y = 16$ <br> ① − ② $\qquad$ $-x + 4y = 10$ |

| | |
|---|---|
| *Property B* <br> The solution of an equation is also a solution of the equation obtained by multiplying or dividing the equation by a non-zero number. | (2, 3) is a solution of <br> ① $\qquad$ $2x + 3y = 13$ <br> ② $\qquad$ $3x - y = 3$ <br> $2 \times$ ① $\qquad$ $4x + 6y = 26$ <br> ② $\div 3$ $\qquad$ $x - \dfrac{y}{3} = 1$ |

Based on the above properties, you need only find suitable equations which will allow you to eliminate one of the variables, resulting in one equation in one variable. The **addition-subtraction** method for solving a system of equations is shown in the following example.

**Example 1** Solve $3x + 2y = 4$ and $x - y = 3$.

**Solution**

$$3x + 2y = 4 \qquad ①$$
$$x - y = 3 \qquad ②$$

Multiply ② by 2. $\quad 2x - 2y = 6 \qquad ③$

$$3x + 2y = 4 \qquad ①$$
$$2x - 2y = 6 \qquad ③$$

Add ① and ③. $\quad \overline{5x + \phantom{0} 0 = 10}$

$$x = 2$$

One of the variables is eliminated. Solve the resulting equation.

Use $x = 2$ in the original equation to obtain the value for $y$.

For $x = 2$, $x - y = 3$
$$2 - y = 3$$
$$-y = 1$$
$$y = -1$$

Thus, the solution is $x = 2$, $y = -1$ or $(x, y) = (2, -1)$.

When you solve the system

$$3x + 2y = 4 \quad \text{and} \quad x - y = 3$$

algebraically, you are, in fact, finding an equivalent system of equations whose solution you can more readily obtain. On the graph at the right, each of the systems shown are equivalent, since the pairs of lines pass through the same intersection point. Thus, the systems of equations have the same solution set.

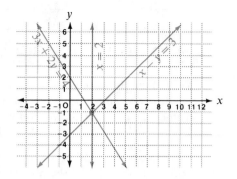

The lines defined by the following equations all pass through the above intersection point. Thus, any of these pairs of equations are equivalent.

A $3x + 2y = 4$    B $3x + 2y = 4$    C $5x = 10$    D $x = 2$
    $x - y = 3$        $2x - 2y = 6$      $x - y = 3$      $x - y = 3$

The original system A was simplified to system D. You can obtain more easily the solution from system D.

**Example 2**    Solve $2x + 3y = 48$
                    $3x + 2y = 42$

**Solution**               $2x + 3y = 48$    ①    First, you need to decide
                  $3x + 2y = 42$    ②    which variable to eliminate.

Multiply equation ① by 3.    ⟵ Do you know why this choice
               $6x + 9y = 144$    ③    was made?

Multiply equation ② by 2.    ⟵ Do you know why this choice
               $6x + 4y = 84$    ④    was made?

Subtract equations ③ and ④ as shown.
               $6x + 9y = 144$
               $6x + 4y = 84$
               $\overline{\phantom{6x+}0 + 5y = 60}$    ③–④
                     $y = 12$    ⑤

Substitute the value of $y$ from ⑤ in the original equation ①.
               $2x + 3y = 48$    ①
             $2x + 3(12) = 48$
              $2x + 36 = 48$
                  $2x = 12$
                    $x = 6$    Since equation ① was used to

Thus, $x = 6$ and $y = 12$.    find $x$, then you should check
                                     your answers in equation ②.

## 6.6 Exercise

**A 1** A system of equations is given by

$$x + y = 12 \quad ① \qquad x - y = 6 \quad ②.$$

(a) Solve the system by finding $x$. Use $① + ②$.

(b) Solve the system by finding $y$. Use $① - ②$.

(c) Why should your answers in (a) and (b) be the same?

**2** A system of equations is given by $\quad x + y = 3 \quad$ and $\quad 2x - y = 3$.

(a) Which variable is easier to eliminate from the system?

(b) Find the solution set.

**3** For each system, decide which variable is more readily eliminated. Then solve the system.

(a) $x + y = 4$
$\quad\; x - 2y = 1$

(b) $x + 2y = 0$
$\quad\; x - y = 3$

(c) $2x + y = 1$
$\quad\; x + y = 2$

(d) $3x - y = 3$
$\quad\; y - 2x = -2$

(e) $3x - 2y = 4$
$\quad\; x - 2y = 4$

(f) $4x + y = 13$
$\quad\; 4x - y = 11$

**4** A system of equations is given by

$$2x + y = -6 \quad ① \qquad x - 5y = 8 \quad ②.$$

(a) Decide which variable you wish to eliminate. Decide by which numbers you will multiply each equation.

(b) Solve the system of equations.

**B** You now have a number of methods of solving systems of equations. Before you solve a system, examine it carefully, and decide which method might be most appropriate.

**PSP**

**5** Solve each system of equations.

(a) $2x + y = 3$
$\quad\; 3x + 2y = 6$

(b) $x - 3y + 7 = 0$
$\quad\; 3x - 2y = -7$

(c) $2a - 3b - 13 = 0$
$\quad\; 3a - b - 9 = 0$

(d) $3a = 2b - 10$
$\quad\; b + 15 = 3a$

(e) $2x + 5y = 8$
$\quad\; 3x - y = 12$

(f) $3x + 21 = 5y$
$\quad\; 2y + 3 = 3x$

(g) $m - 3n = 11$
$\quad\; 2m = 5n + 19$

(h) $6 = 6x - 3y$
$\quad\; 4x - 3y = -2$

(i) $8x - 3y = 6$
$\quad\; 6x + 12y = -24$

(j) $6x = 12 - 3y$
$\quad\; \dfrac{1}{2}y - x = -5$

(k) $\dfrac{1}{2}x - y = 8$
$\quad\; x + \dfrac{1}{3}y = 2$

(l) $5 + y = 4x$
$\quad\; x + 2 = \dfrac{2}{3}y$

6 A system of equations is given by
$$3(x - 1) - 2(y + 2) = 7 \qquad x - 3y = 7.$$
(a) What might be your first step in solving the system?
(b) Solve the system.

7 Two lines are given by
$$2(x - 1) + y = 1 \qquad x - 3y = 5.$$
Find the co-ordinates of the point of intersection.

8 (a) Find the co-ordinates of the point of intersection for
$$2(x - 1) + 3y = -4 \text{ and } x - y = -1.$$
(b) How can you check your answer in (a)?

9 Find the co-ordinates of the intersection point of the graphs defined by each of the following.

(a) $3(x - 1) - 2(y - 2) = 0$
$x + 3y = -4$

(b) $2x - \dfrac{1}{3}y = \dfrac{1}{3}$

$3(x + 1) - 2(y - 3) = 11$

10 Solve.
(a) $0.25a + 0.75b = -0.75$
$0.15a + 0.25b = -0.05$

(b) $0.5x - 0.8y = -1.4$
$0.3x + 0.2y = 0.86$

(c) $1.3m + 2.5n = 0.1$
$4.2m - 6.3n = 14.7$

(d) $1.25p + 3.25q = 5.4$
$2.65p - 1.85q = 0.96$

11 Solve the following systems. Which systems are equivalent?
(a) $3a - b = 4$
$a - 2b = 3$

(b) $3x + y - 1 = 0$
$2x = y - 6$

(c) $a = 6 + 3b$
$3(a - 2) = 4 + 2(b - 3)$

(d) $\dfrac{1}{2}x - y = -3$

$x - \dfrac{2}{3}y = -2$

(e) $a - \dfrac{3}{4}b = -4$

$a + \dfrac{1}{4}b = 0$

(f) $x - \dfrac{1}{3}y = -1$

$\dfrac{2}{3}x - \dfrac{1}{4}y = -1$

12 A forest fire is located at the intersection of the lines of sight defined by
$$2(a - 1) + 3(b - 1) = -7 \text{ and } a = 5b - 1.$$
Find the co-ordinates of the location of the fire.

13 Two ships are to dock at an island located at the intersection point of the lines defined by $y = \dfrac{1}{3}x - 1$ and $x = 2y + 7$.
What are the co-ordinates of the island?

## Applications: Equations for Printing

The total cost of printing tickets, magazines, or programs, is described by the following relation.

$$C = pn + t \longleftarrow t, \text{ cost of setting the type}$$

$C$ is the total cost $\longrightarrow$

$n$, the number of items printed

$p$, the cost for printing each item

For example, if the cost of printing a magazine is 45¢ ($p = 45$) and the typesetting charge is $6.00 ($t = 600$), then the formula is written as

$C = 45n + 600.$

If 100 magazines are printed ($n = 100$), then the total cost is

$C = 45n + 600$
$\phantom{C} = 45(100) + 600$
$\phantom{C} = 4500 + 600$
$\phantom{C} = 5100 \longleftarrow$ The total cost is 5100¢ or $51.00.

For each of the following problems, a system of equations has been provided that helps you attain the answer to the problem.

14  The total cost of printing 40 programs was $26.00. The total cost of printing 20 programs was $17.00. Solve these equations to find the printing cost, $p$, in cents, of each program and the typesetting cost, $t$, in cents.

$\qquad 2600 = 40p + t \qquad\qquad 1700 = 20p + t$

15  To print the tickets the owners of the airline compared these prices.
• The total cost of 50 tickets is $19.00.
• The total cost of 30 tickets is $14.40.
To find the printing cost, $p$, in cents, of each ticket and the typesetting charge, $t$, in cents, these equations were written.

$\qquad 1900 = 50p + t \qquad\qquad 1440 = 30p + t$

(a) Solve the equations.     (b) Find the total cost of printing 100 tickets.

16  To print magazines, the firm obtained the following prices.
• The total cost of printing 100 magazines is $85.00.
• The total cost of printing 200 magazines is $147.00.
To find the cost, $p$, in cents, of printing each magazine, and the typesetting charge, $t$, in cents, these equations were written.

$\qquad 8500 = 100p + t \qquad\qquad 14\,700 = 200p + t$

(a) Solve the equations.     (b) Find the total cost of printing 150 magazines.

## 6.7 **PSP** Strategies for Simplifying Equations

The strategies you learn throughout your study of mathematics are applied over and over. For example, the strategy with equations, that you learned earlier, is now applied to your work with systems of equations. Thus, when you are solving the following equation in one variable, you first simplify the equation by multiplying by the lowest common multiple of 2 and 3, namely 6.

$$\frac{x-3}{2} - \frac{x+4}{3} = -2$$

$$6\left(\frac{x-3}{2}\right) - 6\left(\frac{x+4}{3}\right) = 6(-2) \longleftarrow \text{Remember: You multiply each term of the equation by 6.}$$

$$3(x-3) - 2(x+4) = -12 \longleftarrow \text{The equation is simplified and you continue to solve for } x.$$

The same strategy is applied to your work with solving systems of equations. For example, to solve the following system, you need to simplify equation ① first.

$$\frac{x-3}{2} - \frac{y+3}{4} = -1 \quad ① \qquad\qquad \text{Simplify equation ①.}$$

$$2x + y = 15 \quad ② \qquad\longrightarrow\qquad 4\left(\frac{x-3}{2}\right) - 4\left(\frac{y+3}{4}\right) = 4(-1)$$

Thus the system has been simplified.
$$2(x-3) - (y+3) = -4$$
$$2x - 6 - y - 3 = -4$$

$$2x + y = 15 \qquad ②$$
$$2x - y = \phantom{0}5 \qquad ③ \longleftarrow \qquad\qquad 2x - y = 5 \qquad ③$$

You can now solve the system and obtain the solution using earlier skills.

Another strategy for simplifying your work with equations is to introduce an extra step in your solution that allows you to solve a system more directly.

In the following example, the intermediate step of using $\dfrac{1}{x} = a$ and $\dfrac{1}{y} = b$

helps you to solve the system of equations more directly.

**Example**  Solve $\dfrac{2}{x} + \dfrac{1}{y} = 7$ and $\dfrac{3}{x} + \dfrac{2}{y} = 12$.

**Solution**  Use the substitution step $\dfrac{1}{x} = a$ and $\dfrac{1}{y} = b$ for the original equation.

$$\frac{2}{x} + \frac{1}{y} = 7 \quad ① \qquad\qquad\qquad \frac{3}{x} + \frac{2}{y} = 12 \quad ②$$

$$2\left(\frac{1}{x}\right) + \left(\frac{1}{y}\right) = 7 \qquad\qquad 3\left(\frac{1}{x}\right) + 2\left(\frac{1}{y}\right) = 12$$

$$2a + b = 7 \quad ③ \qquad\qquad\qquad 3a + 2b = 12 \quad ④$$

Then the equations to be solved are

$$2a + b = 7 \qquad ③$$
$$3a + 2b = 12 \qquad ④$$

Multiply equation ③ by 2.

$$4a + 2b = 14 \qquad ⑤$$

Subtract equation ④ from equation ⑤ to obtain

$$a = 2$$

From equation ③ you obtain the value for $b$.

$$2(2) + b = 7$$
$$4 + b = 7$$
$$b = 3$$

To obtain the value for $x$ and $y$ use the substitution step.

Thus, $\dfrac{1}{x} = 2$ or $x = \dfrac{1}{2}$ and $\dfrac{1}{y} = 3$ or $y = \dfrac{1}{3}$.

Thus, $(x, y) = \left(\dfrac{1}{2}, \dfrac{1}{3}\right)$.    The verification is left for you to do.

## 6.7   Exercise

**B** Remember: Plan ahead before you solve a system of equations. Use your    **PSP**
skills in algebra to simplify first.

1    (a) To solve this system of equations, what would you do as your first
step?

$$\frac{3}{4}x + \frac{1}{2}y = 21 \text{ and } \frac{2}{3}x - \frac{1}{6}y = 4$$

(b) Solve the system in (a).

2    (a) To solve this system, what would you do as your first step?

$$\frac{x + 2}{3} - \frac{y - 1}{4} = 1 \text{ and } \frac{x}{2} - \frac{y + 1}{3} = 0$$

(b) Solve the system in (a).

3    (a) What would be your first step in solving this system?

$$\frac{3}{x} - \frac{1}{y} = 9 \qquad \frac{2}{x} + \frac{3}{y} = 13$$

(b) Solve the system of equations in (a).

4   Solve for $x$ and $y$.

(a) $\dfrac{1}{x} + \dfrac{3}{y} = 6$

$\dfrac{2}{x} - \dfrac{1}{y} = 5$

(b) $\dfrac{7}{x} - \dfrac{3}{y} = -1$

$\dfrac{6}{x} + \dfrac{4}{y} = 9$

(c) $\dfrac{1}{x} = \dfrac{2}{y} - 2$

$\dfrac{6}{x} = \dfrac{9}{y} - 11$

5   Solve.

(a) $\dfrac{x-1}{2} + y = -2$

$3x - \dfrac{y+1}{3} = 16$

(b) $\dfrac{x-1}{3} - \dfrac{2(y-2)}{2} = 11$

$2x - y = 16$

(c) $2(2x - 1) - (y - 4) = 11$

$3(1 - x) - 2(y - 3) = -7$

(d) $\dfrac{x}{2} = \dfrac{y}{14}$ and $\dfrac{x}{3} + \dfrac{2y}{7} = \dfrac{7}{3}$.

6   Solve for $x$ and $y$.

$\dfrac{x}{6} - \dfrac{y}{4} = 4 - \dfrac{x}{3} - \dfrac{y}{2}$ and $x - \dfrac{11}{2} = \dfrac{x}{6} - \dfrac{y}{8}$

7   Solve the system of equations.

$\dfrac{2x + 5y}{6} + \dfrac{3x - 8y}{5} = 5$

$\dfrac{3y - x}{3} + \dfrac{x + 4y}{5} = \dfrac{8}{3}$

8   Find the co-ordinates of the point of intersection of the graphs defined by

$\dfrac{x - 2}{5} - \dfrac{y + 3}{6} = -2$

$\dfrac{x - 3}{3} + \dfrac{y - 5}{2} = -3.$

C 9   The ordered pair $(x, y) = (\tfrac{1}{2}, 1)$ is a solution of

$\dfrac{m}{x} + \dfrac{n}{y} = 8$

$\dfrac{n}{x} + \dfrac{m}{y} = 7.$

Find the values of $m$ and $n$.

---

## Math Tip

In solving a problem, often it is helpful to use variables that help you relate what you are given to what you are trying to find. For example, these choices of variables tell you something about the word problem.

$b$, number of boxes          $w$, width of the garden.
$p$, number of points scored   $h$, height of the building.
$d$, distance travelled        $n$, for number.

Now read Section 6.9 and remember this Math Tip.

# Applications: Equations With Literal Coefficients

The steps you use to solve a system of equations that involve *numerical* coefficients extend to the solution of a system that involves *literal* coefficients. Compare the solutions of these two systems.

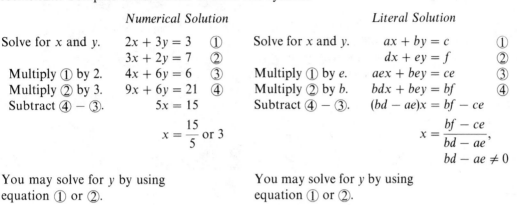

|  Numerical Solution | | Literal Solution | |
|---|---|---|---|
| Solve for $x$ and $y$. | $2x + 3y = 3$ ① | Solve for $x$ and $y$. | $ax + by = c$ ① |
|  | $3x + 2y = 7$ ② |  | $dx + ey = f$ ② |
| Multiply ① by 2. | $4x + 6y = 6$ ③ | Multiply ① by $e$. | $aex + bey = ce$ ③ |
| Multiply ② by 3. | $9x + 6y = 21$ ④ | Multiply ② by $b$. | $bdx + bey = bf$ ④ |
| Subtract ④ − ③. | $5x = 15$ | Subtract ④ − ③. | $(bd - ae)x = bf - ce$ |
|  | $x = \dfrac{15}{5}$ or 3 |  | $x = \dfrac{bf - ce}{bd - ae}$, |
|  |  |  | $bd - ae \neq 0$ |

You may solve for $y$ by using equation ① or ②.

You may solve for $y$ by using equation ① or ②.

---

**10** Compare the solutions of the above systems.

(a) How are the solutions alike?    (b) How are the solutions different?

**11** For the system

$$ax + by = c \quad ① \qquad dx + ey = f \quad ②$$

the value of $x = \dfrac{bf - ce}{bd - ae}$, $bd - ae \neq 0$.

(a) Why do you need to indicate that $bd - ae \neq 0$?

(b) Use the value of $x$ in either equation ① or ② and find the value of $y$.

(c) Use equations ① and ② and solve for $y$ again by using the addition-subtraction method.

(d) Which method, (b) or (c), do you prefer for finding the value of $y$?

**12** Solve for $x$ and $y$.

(a) $x + y = 3a$
$2x + 3y = 8a$

(b) $2x - y = 7m$
$4x + 3y = 9m$

(c) $x + y = a + 2b$
$3x - 2y = 3a - 4b$

(d) $x + y = 2a$
$2x - 3y = 5b - a$

(e) $ax + y = 4$
$x + by = 6$

(f) $bx - y = 3$
$x + y = 6$

## 6.8 Systems and Computers

The computer is a very useful tool which can solve problems that require a great many calculations.

Many problems in real life can be solved by using systems of equations. Often the system of equations used involves many variables and without a computer would take a great deal of time to solve. If a computer is available, a computer program can be written to solve equations quickly, often in only a few seconds. For example, you solved the following system of equations. *A*, *B*, *C*, *D*, *E* and *F*, are constants.

*Data are entered directly into the computer using the keyboard of a typewriter terminal. You may have seen a similar one in a bank or at an airport.*

$$Ax + By = C$$
$$Dx + Ey = F$$

The solution obtained is given by

$$x = \frac{CE - BF}{AE - BD} \quad \text{where } AE - BD \neq 0$$

$$y = \frac{CD - AF}{BD - AE} \quad \text{where } BD - AE \neq 0.$$

To prepare a computer program, first you need to prepare the mathematics. The following program in BASIC provides a solution of the system of equations for the inputs *A*, *B*, *C*, *D*, *E* and *F*.

```
COMPUTER PROGRAM IN BASIC
10 PRINT "SOLVE TWO EQUATIONS IN TWO VARIABLES."
20 INPUT A
21 INPUT B
22 INPUT C
23 INPUT D
24 INPUT E
25 INPUT F
30 IF (B * D) = (A * E), THEN 70
40 LET Y = (C * D − A * F)/(B * D − A * E)
50 LET X = (C * E − B * F)/(A * E − B * D)
60 PRINT X; Y;
70 STOP
80 END
```

For example, if you wish to obtain the solution for the system
$3x + 2y = 11$ and $4x - 3y = 9$, then use the following inputs for the
BASIC computer program and obtain a solution.

$$A = 3, \qquad B = 2, \qquad C = 11, \qquad D = 4, \qquad E = -3, \qquad F = 9$$

Once the computer has been given the above inputs it will print out the
values of $x$ and $y$ almost instantly.

$$X = 3 \qquad\qquad Y = 1$$

## 6.8   Exercise

**B** Be sure to write the system in the form in which the computer is
programmed. Then use the input values for A, B, C, D, E and F.

1   To solve the following systems of equations
   - decide what your first step will be.
   - then use the computer program on the previous page to solve the system.

(a) $a - 15b = 3$
$3b + a = 21$

(b) $41 + 9y = 8x$
$4x = 3 - 3y$

(c) $2x + 5y = 19$
$3x = y + 3$

(d) $8 + 3y = x$
$x + 12 = -7y$

(e) $5x + 2y = 5$
$2x + 3y = 13$

(f) $3a + b = 12$
$2a + 5b = 21$

2   Solve each system of equations. Round your answers to 1 decimal place.

(a) $1.1y - 3.2x = 0$
$2.1x + 5.3y = 11.0$

(b) $4.3x + 5.2y = 7.6$
$3.2x = 6.3 - 4.2y$

(c) $1.9x - 3.3 = 2.8y$
$4.1y + 5.2x - 8.3 = 0$

(d) $2.3(1.1a - 3.2b) = 3.6$
$2.4b + 1.8a = 4.3$

3   Solve each system of equations. Round your answers to 2 decimal places.

(a) $2.35a - 1.86b = -7.25$
$1.86b - 3.25a = -8.19$

(b) $2.69x = 3.85 - 3.76y$
$6.83y + 10.30x + 3.26 = 0$

(c) $0.89x + 2.98y = 1.96$
$3.25(1.11x - 2.31y) = 0.92$

(d) $8.32(1.25 + 0.96y) = 5.82x$
$2(5.65x + 1.85y) = 1.32$

---

## Problem Solving

Often in mathematics, problem posing develops many
new ideas. For example, in the diagram, point P
moves so that $PA + PB = 10$ cm. What do you think
the path of P will be? Try it!

## 6.9 PSP Translating from English to Mathematics

In mathematics, the skills you acquire or the strategies you learn for solving problems can be used in different ways. For example, in your earlier work with equations in one variable, you used the chart of the *Problem-Solving Plan* to help you organize your solution of a problem.

To solve a word problem, you need to introduce the variable and translate the English into mathematics, and then write the equation needed to solve the problem.

**PSP Problem-Solving Plan**

A Ask yourself:
 I What information am I asked to find?
 II What information am I given?
B Decide on a method.
C Do the work.
D Check your work.
E Make a final statement. Answer the original problem.

You may need your skills with per cent.

| Amount invested | Total interest paid ($) |
|---|---|
| $x at 10% | 0.10x |
| $x at 5% and $(100 − x) at 6% | 0.05x + 0.06(100 − x) |
| $x at 5% and $y at 6% | 0.05x + 0.06y |

You may need your skills with money.

| Number of coins | Amount of money (¢) |
|---|---|
| x quarters | 25x |
| x dimes and (10 − x) nickels | 10x + 5(10 − x) |
| x quarters and y dimes | 25x + 10y |

Recognizing which skills you need to solve a particular problem is an important problem-solving skill. The more problems you solve in later sections, the more proficient you will become at recognizing the necessary skills.

## 6.9 Exercise

**A** To solve a problem, an important skill is to translate correctly from English to mathematics.

1 Find the interest, in one year, on each of the following investments.

(a) $200 invested at 10%

(b) $x invested at 8%

(c) $(y + 2) invested at 12%

(d) $2x invested at $8\frac{1}{2}$%

2   Find the amount of interest paid on each of the following investments. (The rate of interest is yearly and the money is invested for a year.)
   (a) $x at 5% and $y at 10%
   (b) $m at 6% and $n at 8%
   (c) $2x at 3% and $(y + 2) at 8%
   (d) $(x − 1) at 10% and $(y + 1) at 12%

3   Find the value, in cents, of each of the following.
   (a) 5 dimes
   (b) $x$ dimes
   (c) $2x$ dimes
   (d) $(y + 2)$ quarters
   (e) $\frac{1}{2}y$ dimes
   (f) $3x$ nickels
   (g) $m$ dimes and $n$ quarters
   (h) $(x + 2)$ quarters and $(y − 1)$ dimes

4   Find the value of each of the following in cents.
   (a) $x$ dimes, $y$ quarters
   (b) $m$ quarters, $n$ dimes
   (c) $n$ nickels, $q$ quarters
   (d) $2x$ dimes, $y$ quarters
   (e) $3m$ nickels, $2n$ dimes
   (f) $2x$ pennies, $3y$ dimes

5   Find the cost of each of the following.
   (a) 10 kg of raisins at $2.59/kg
   (b) $x$ kg of sugar at $1.59/kg
   (c) $x$ kg of dates at $1.86/kg and $y$ kg of dried apricots at $3.89/kg
   (d) $3x$ kg of liquorice at $1.03/kg and $(y + 2)$ kg of peanut brittle at $1.19/kg

6   Find the total distance for each of the following.
   (a) A car travelled for 5 h at 60 km/h.
   (b) A truck travelled for $x$ h at 50 km/h.
   (c) A person walked for 12 h at $x$ km/h.
   (d) A car travelled for $x$ h at 60 km/h and $y$ h at 100 km/h.
   (e) A person ran for 5 h at $x$ km/h and 10 h at $y$ km/h.

   B For each of the following, choose a variable of your own to translate from English into mathematics.

7   Write an equation in two variables for each of the following. The monies are invested for a year in each case.
   (a) The total interest on an amount of money invested at 10% and on another amount invested at 12% is $160.
   (b) The interest on an amount of money invested at 8% exceeds the interest on another amount of money invested at 9% by $10.
   (c) The interest on an amount of money invested at 7.5% is $20 less than the interest on another amount of money invested at 9%.

8    Write an equation in two variables for each of the following.

(a) The total cost of one type of nuts at $1.25/kg and another type at $1.50/kg is $18.75.

(b) The cost of the liquorice at $1.50/kg exceeds the cost of lemon drops at $1.25/kg by $6.25.

(c) Twice the cost of raspberries at $2.75/kg is $1.75 more than the cost of strawberries at $1.25/kg.

9    Write an equation in two variables for each of the following.

(a) A train travelled for $x$ h at 25 km/h and then for $y$ h at 75 km/h and covered a total distance of 275 km.

(b) The distance covered by Fran jogging at $x$ km/h for 5 h is 8 km less than the distance covered by Fran jogging at $y$ km/h for 2 h.

(c) The distance a car travelled in 3 h at $x$ km/h exceeds by 48 km the distance the car travelled in 6 h at $y$ km/h.

10   Write an equation in two variables for each of the following.

(a) The nickels and dimes had a total value of 60 cents.

(b) The value of the nickels exceeded the value of the quarters by 75 cents.

(c) The total value of the quarters and nickels was 75 cents.

11   Write an equation in two variables for each of the following.

(a) The sum of two numbers is 48.        (b) One number exceeds another by 5.

(c) The sum of the width and length of a rectangle equals 96 m.

PSP  12   (a) What are the next two numbers in the pattern?

8, 24, 64, 160, ?, ?

(b) What are the next two letters in the pattern?

F, T, F, T, T, T, T, F, ?, ?

C 13   Write an equation in two variables for each of the following.

(a) When Hilda's age is added to Joya's age the sum is 36 years.

(b) Twice Wilhelm's age is equal to Dietmar's age increased by 4 years.

---

## Calculator Tip

If you need to solve systems of equations frequently, you can find a solution for the system $Ax + By = C$, $Dx + Ey = F$.

Solution

$$x = \frac{CE - BF}{AE - BD}, \quad y = \frac{CD - AF}{BD - AE}$$

Use your calculator to calculate $x$ and $y$ efficiently for the system of equations given by $2.3x + 6.5y = 19.9$, $6.8x - 4.3y = 11.8$.

---

**PSP** Solving Problems: Use a Plan

Although many word problems are different, they all involve the same important steps. The most important step to take before you can actually solve a problem is to answer these two questions accurately and completely.

I │ What information am I asked to find?    II │ What information am I given?

In order to organize the steps of your solution, you need a plan, such as the *Problem-Solving Plan*.    **PSP**

**Example**    Find two numbers such that their sum divided by 4 is equal to 14. The greater number increased by 24 equals three times the smaller number.

**Solution**    Let $m$ represent the greater number and $n$ the smaller number.    Step A

$$\frac{m + n}{4} = 14 \quad \text{①}$$    Step B

$$m + 24 = 3n \quad \text{②}$$

Write equations ① and ② in simplified form.    Step C

$$m + n = 56 \quad \text{③}$$
$$m - 3n = -24 \quad \text{④}$$

Subtract equation ④ from equation ③.

$$n - (-3n) = 56 - (-24)$$
$$n + 3n = 56 + 24$$
$$4n = 80$$
$$n = 20$$

Use $n = 20$ in equation ②.    Step D
*Check* in the original problem.

$$m + 24 = 60$$
$$m = 36$$

Sum of the numbers divided by 4 equals 14.

$$\frac{20 + 36}{4} = 14 \quad \text{Checks} \checkmark$$

Greater number increased by 24

$$36 + 24 = 60$$

is three times the smaller number.

$$3(20) = 60 \quad \text{Checks} \checkmark$$

Thus the required numbers are 20 and 36.    Step E

## 6.10 Exercise

**A** An important skill for solving problems is the ability to translate accurately from English into mathematics.

**PSP**

1   For each of the following
  - choose variables of your own.
  - write an equation.

(a) A number is 8 greater than another number.

(b) The sum of the length and the width of a rectangle equals 48 m.

(c) Twice one number decreased by three times another equals 83.

(d) A number decreased by half of the other equals 33.

2   Translate each of the following. Write an equation.

(a) The total value of the dimes and pennies is $1.86.

(b) The total cost of carrot seeds at 29¢ per package and radish seeds at 36¢ per package is $6.96.

(c) The cost of the lettuce seeds at 38¢ per package is $3.69 more than cost of the pumpkin seeds at 50¢ per package.

3   Write an equation to translate each of the following from English to mathematics.

(a) David's age decreased by 6 years is equal to Zoltan's age.

(b) Five times Jennifer's age added to 3 times Susan's age equals 103 years.

(c) The sum of Jay's age and three times Myra's age is 36 years.

(d) Four years from today Mary's age will be half of Harold's age.

(e) Two years ago, five times Hans' age equalled Monique's age increased by 3 years.

4   Solve each problem. Plan the organization of your solution.

(a) The sum of two numbers is 72. Their difference is 48. Find the numbers.

(b) One number exceeds another by 142. If their sum is 150, find the numbers.

(c) The sum of two numbers is 84. If the difference of the numbers is 12, find the numbers.

5   Read each problem carefully. Then solve.

(a) From the coffee machine, Giorgio collected a total of 76 dimes and quarters. If their total value amounted to $13, how many of each coin were there?

(b) At the raffle, Yosuke won a total of 50 nickels and dimes. If their value was $4.30, how many of each coin were there?

(c) At the concert 191 people attended at a cost of $3.00 per adult and $1.75 per student. If the total receipts were $478.00, how many adults and students attended?

**B** To solve each of the following problems, decide and plan how you are going to organize your solution. Refer to the *Problem-Solving Plan.*

6   Georgette has a total of $155 consisting of $2- and $5-bills. If she has 40 bills in all, how many of each does she have?

7   Two numbers have the following properties:
   • 6 times the first exceeds 3 times the second by 90.
   • their sum is 42.
   Find the numbers.

8   Two persons share a lottery worth $1200. One person received $800 less than 3 times what the other person received. How much did each person receive?

9   During the first part of the season, a baseball team played 35 games. The number of games the team lost was 10 less than $\frac{1}{2}$ of the number they won. How many games have they won so far?

10   In all, 195 sacks were ordered. A sack of wheat costs $6.00 and a sack of oats cost $7.50. If the total cost was $1282.50 then how many sacks of each were bought?

11   A hockey team bought 70 pucks for a total cost of $120. If the pucks used for practice cost $1.50 each and the pucks used for games cost $2.25 each, then how many of each puck did they buy?

12   At the storage site, 7 large tanks and 6 small tanks contained 3300 L of gasoline. If one more large tank and one less small tank were used, there would be 3400 L. How much does each tank hold?

**C** 13   During the week it costs $1.75 for a car wash and $2.25 for a truck wash. On the weekend it costs 25¢ more for each. One week day, $233.75 was collected. If the same number of cars and trucks had been washed on the weekend, then an additional $28.75 would have been collected. How many trucks were washed?

## PSP  Strategy for Solving Problems: Using Charts

To solve a problem, it is important to organize or sort the information given. One strategy that will help you sort the information is to use a chart. The following examples illustrate this. *PSP*

**Example**  Monica invested $1400, one part of it at 7% and the other at 8%. The total interest she received amounted to $104.00. How much was invested at each rate of interest?

**Solution**  Let the amounts invested be represented by $x and $y.

Use a chart to record the given information.

$$x + y = 1400 \quad \text{①}$$
$$0.07x + 0.08y = 104 \quad \text{②}$$

Multiply equation ② by 100.

$$7x + 8y = 10\,400 \quad \text{③}$$

Multiply equation ① by 7.

$$7x + 7y = 9800 \quad \text{④}$$

Subtract ④ from ③

$$y = 600$$

Use the value $y = 600$ in ①.

$$x + 600 = 1400$$
$$x = 800$$

Thus $800 was invested at 7% and $600 was invested at 8%.

| Money invested ($) | Interest rate | Interest received ($) |
|---|---|---|
| $x$ | 7% | $0.07x$ |
| $y$ | 8% | $0.08y$ |

It is left to you to check the answer.

The use of a chart is one strategy to help you organize your work to solve a problem. In the next few sections you will learn other strategies to help you solve problems. *PSP*

## 6.11  Exercise

A 1  Find Debbie's and Klaas' present ages if
- the sum of their present ages is 59 years.
- in 5 years, twice Debbie's age will be equal to Klaas' age.

|  | Present age (in years) | Age in 5 years (in years) |
|---|---|---|
| Debbie | $x$ | $x + 5$ |
| Klaas | $y$ | $y + 5$ |

2　Part of the $2000 prize money was invested at 9% and the remainder at 10%. If the total interest received was $191, how much was invested at each rate?

| Money invested ($) | Interest rate | Interest received ($) |
|---|---|---|
| $x$ | 10% | $0.10x$ |
| $y$ | 9% | $0.09y$ |

3　A chemist mixes a 30% sugar solution and a 40% sugar solution to obtain a 38% solution. If 50 kg of solution was obtained, how much of each type of solution was used?

| | Amount of solution | Amount of sugar |
|---|---|---|
| 30% solution | $x$ | $0.30x$ |
| 40% solution | $y$ | $0.40y$ |
| 38% solution | $(x + y)$ | $0.38(x + y)$ |

B　Use a chart in the following questions to help you organize the information. Refer to the *Problem-Solving Plan* to help you plan your solution.

4　The sum of Janos' age and David's age is 34 years. Five years ago the sum of twice Janos' age and three times David's age was 61 years. What are their present ages?

5　How would you invest $1000 in two types of securities, one earning 6% and the other 8%, so that you will receive twice as much income from the 8% investment as you will from the 6% investment?

6　From the dance receipts, the student council placed part of the $750 in a savings account earning 8% interest and the rest in a chequing account receiving 5% interest. If the total interest received for a year is $46.50, how much was placed in each account?

7　A distribution company in Vancouver sent out 950 brochures. Their cost of mailing in British Columbia was 12¢, while the cost to other places was 16¢. If the total mailing costs were $138.00, how many were mailed in British Columbia?

8　The cost of running a truck is 42¢/km in the city and 33¢/km on the highway. In one month Sam travelled 1200 km and the total cost was $457.02. How many kilometres did he travel in the city and on the highway?

PSP　9　(a) Is it possible to make change from a $20 bill for a $19.45 purchase (including tax) using exactly 9 coins?

(b) If not, then how many coins are needed?

C　10　One alloy of copper, A, contains 60% copper. Another alloy of copper, B, contains 40% copper. If 400 g of 51% copper alloy is obtained when they are melted together, how much of each alloy is used?

# Applications: Making More Profit

When merchandisers or retailers discover that some of their stock isn't being purchased, they think of new ways to "move" that product. In the candy business, a merchandiser may discover that 2 types of bulk candy are not selling at all. The candies may be mixed to offer a new product to the customer. However, in doing so, the amounts to be mixed need to be known.

For example, to increase the sales, a store manager mixed hard candy selling at $1.60/kg and chocolate swirls selling at $2.20/kg. If the new price became $1.75/kg, how much of each candy was used to obtain 50 kg of the new mixture?

|  | Amount of candy (kg) | Cost of candy (¢/kg) | Value of candy (¢) |
|---|---|---|---|
| Hard candy | $x$ | 160 | $160x$ |
| Chocolate swirls | $y$ | 220 | $220y$ |
| New mixture | $x + y$ | 175 | $175(x + y)$ |

11 Use the two equations in the problem above.

$$x + y = 50 \qquad 175(x + y) = 8750$$

(a) How much hard candy was needed?

(b) How much chocolate swirls was needed?

12 Two different brands of coffee beans were not selling so it was decided to mix them. The different brands cost $2.30/kg and $3.20/kg. How much of each brand was used if 150 kg of the resulting mixture was sold at $2.72/kg?

13 To increase sales the red peppers that sold at $3.00/kg and the green peppers selling at $3.80/kg were mixed. If 200 kg were obtained and sold at the new price of $3.34/kg, how many kilograms of each type of pepper were used?

14 A nut mixture contains 20% peanuts by mass and another contains 40%. The two mixtures are combined to obtain 100 kg which contains 36% peanuts by mass. What quantities of each of the original mixtures were used?

15 To make a blend of 2 teas, a manufacturer mixed Orange Pekoe selling at $6.40/kg with Indian Tea selling at $7.20/kg. If 400 kg of the blended tea was sold at $6.72/kg, how much of each type was used?

16 Two nut mixtures were not selling. To increase sales, a retailer mixed one type selling at $2.20/kg with another selling at $2.40/kg. If 100 kg were mixed and sold for $2.28/kg, how much of each type of nut was mixed?

# 6.12 PSP Strategy: Using Diagrams

To solve a problem you can use a chart to help you organize the information and better understand the problem. You can also use a diagram to help you better "picture" or visualize the problem. For example, to solve this problem about motion, use a diagram.

**Example**

The sightseers travelled along the river for 3 h and then travelled in the forest for 6 h. The total length of the trip was 216 km. If they went 12 km/h faster in the forest than along the river, what were the different speeds?

**Solution**

Let the speed along the river be $x$ km/h and in the forest $y$ km/h.

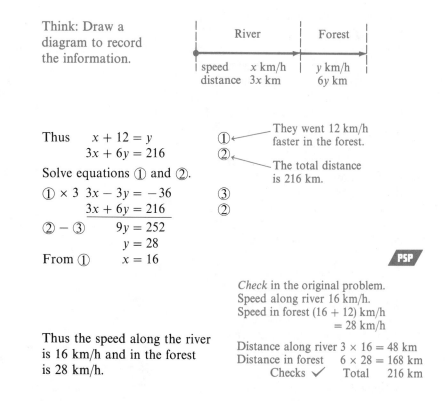

Think: Draw a diagram to record the information.

|  | River | Forest |
|---|---|---|
| speed | $x$ km/h | $y$ km/h |
| distance | $3x$ km | $6y$ km |

Thus     $x + 12 = y$     ① ← They went 12 km/h faster in the forest.
$3x + 6y = 216$     ② ← The total distance is 216 km.

Solve equations ① and ②.

① × 3   $3x - 3y = -36$     ③
$3x + 6y = 216$     ②

② − ③     $9y = 252$
$y = 28$
From ①     $x = 16$

PSP

*Check* in the original problem.
Speed along river 16 km/h.
Speed in forest $(16 + 12)$ km/h
$= 28$ km/h

Thus the speed along the river is 16 km/h and in the forest is 28 km/h.

Distance along river $3 \times 16 = 48$ km
Distance in forest   $6 \times 28 = 168$ km
Checks ✓   Total   216 km

A diagram was used to record the information in the problem. In the following exercise you will see how different problems about motion may be interpreted with the use of diagrams.

# 6.12 Exercise

**A** A diagram is drawn for each of the different problems about motion that follow.
- Use the diagram to help you visualize the problem.
- Write the appropriate equation.  • Solve the problem.  **PSP**

*Problem*                                                    *Diagram*

1   From Acton, Joyce drove her car for
    4 h towards Ballantine and Paul drove
    his motorcycle for 6 h in the opposite
    direction to Caledon. The distance
    between Ballantine and Caledon is
    392 km. If Paul drove 18 km/h slower
    than Joyce, how fast did each go?

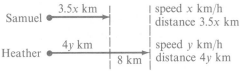

2   Starting from the same point at the same
    time Samuel and Heather rode their
    mini bikes in the same direction. Samuel
    travelled 3 km/h faster than Heather.
    After 3.5 h Samuel stopped for a half-
    hour break, but Heather kept going. At
    the end of the break, Heather was 8 km
    ahead of Samuel. How fast was each going?

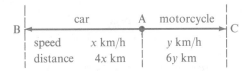

3   Lesley and Marnie live in two different
    cities that are 826 km apart. One day
    they both left at the same time and
    drove towards each other, Lesley going
    18 km/h faster than Marnie. If they met
    after 7 h, how fast was each going?

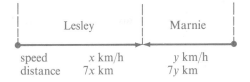

4   Zoltan and Mali are 18 km apart and
    begin to walk at the same time. If they
    walk in the same direction they meet
    after 6 h. If they walk towards each
    other they meet in 2 h. Find their
    speeds.

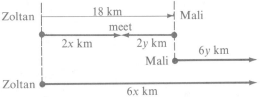
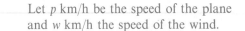

5   A plane flying into the wind takes 4 h
    to make a trip of 960 km. The same
    plane flying with the wind takes only
    3 h to make the same trip. Find the
    speed of the plane and the wind.

Let $p$ km/h be the speed of the plane
and $w$ km/h the speed of the wind.

With the wind                   Against the wind
Speed $(p + w)$ km/h            Speed $(p - w)$ km/h
Distance $3(p + w)$ km          Distance $4(p - w)$ km

B For each of the following problems draw a diagram to help you visualize the problem. All speeds dealt with in the following questions are constant speeds.

6   Two ships start towards each other at the same time from two islands that are 264 km apart. One ship travels 4 km/h faster than the other. If they meet in 6 h, how fast is each ship travelling?

7   A taxi left Gatineau and drove towards Bearcroft which was 380 km away. At the same time another taxi left Bearcroft and drove towards Gatineau but at a speed 5 km/h faster. If the two taxis met 4 h later, what was the speed of each taxi?

8   From Vancouver International Airport a Piper Cub took off 2 h before a jet, which accidentally flew on the same course. The jet travelled 190 km/h faster than the other plane. If there was a near collision 3 h later, how far had the planes travelled?

9   A hovercraft travels over flat land at 40 km/h and over rough water at 10 km/h. If a total distance of 185 km took 5.75 h partly over land and over water, then how many kilometres were travelled over

(a) land?                                (b) water?

10  During a recent trip Jackie travelled 62 km. Part of it was on a congested highway as shown in the photograph. The total trip took 2 h, of which 1.25 h were spend in congestion. Find her speed on the congested highway if she travelled 40 km/h faster on the highway that was not congested.

11  Two trucks left Winnipeg, one going east on the Trans Canada Highway and the other west. The truck going east drove 8 km/h faster since it was partly downhill. At the end of 5 h, they discover over their CB radios that they are 460 km apart. How fast is each truck travelling?

12  A survey crew took a trip up the river and back in 10 h. Going upstream they paddled at 4 km/h, but downstream they travelled at 12 km/h. How far upstream did the crew go?

13  A jet travelled with the wind for 2 h and returned in 2 h 10 min. If the total trip is 2080 km, find

(a) the speed of the jet.                (b) the speed of the wind.

# PSP Solving Problems: Making Decisions

The more you practise a skill, the better you will be at that skill. Similarly, in mathematics, the more problems you solve, the better you will become at solving problems. This means you will become better at making decisions about which skills are needed to solve a problem you have not seen before. To solve a problem, you must be able to answer these two questions:

I What am I asked to find?

II What information am I given (in the original problem)?

The more problems you solve the better you will become at solving problems.

| **PSP** | **Problem-Solving Plan** |

A Ask yourself:
  I What information am I asked to find?
  II What information am I given?

Read the problem carefully. Be sure you understand what it is you are to find. Then introduce the variables.

B Decide on a method.

Translate from English to mathematics and write the equations.

C Do the work. Solve the equations.

D Check your work.
Check answers in the *original* problem.

E Make a final statement. Answer the problem. Write a final statement.

## 6.13 Exercise

**B** The following problems are not given in any special order. It is important, when solving problems, to be able to decide which skills you need to solve the problem.

1 To analyze the solution, two chemists spent 58 h in all making tests. One of the chemists spent 6 h more than the other. How many hours did each spend?

2 On a quiz Mati scored 14 more marks than Anna. If the total of their marks was 178, how many marks did each person get on the test?

3 Find Michael's and Lesley's present ages,

  • if the sum of twice Michael's age and Lesley's age is 74.

  • if 3 years ago Lesley's age was 3 times Michael's age.

4 The Province stocked a lake with 9000 pike and perch. If there had been twice as many pike and three times as many perch used, the total number of fish placed would have been 23 500. How many of each fish were placed in the lake?

5  At a major conference there were 48 more chemists than physicists. If there was a total of 424 chemists and physicists, how many was there of each?

6  The average of two numbers is 44, their difference is 12. Find the numbers.

7  A mailing house in Fredericton processed 1200 advertisements. The cost of mailing them in New Brunswick was 10¢ each, but out-of-province mailings cost 14¢ each. If the total postage budget was $152, how many were mailed in each of New Brunswick and out-of-province?

8  Linda and Dave won a recent Provincial Lottery amounting to $10 000. They shared the amount of the win according to how much each paid for the ticket. Thus, Linda received $1100 less than twice what Dave received. How much did each receive?

9  At the fair $540 was collected in $2- and $5-bills. If the number of bills had been reversed, then $720 would have been collected. How many bills of each type were there?

10  During one time, the total value of dimes and pennies produced at the mint was $147.30. If the number of dimes and pennies produced had been reversed, then the value would have been $638.43. How many dimes and pennies were produced?

*At the Winnipeg Mint, metal blanks are softened and cleansed before the design is struck. Then the coins are inspected, bagged, and shipped to many parts of Canada.*

11  The trip up the Amazon River in dugouts and back to the mouth of the Amazon took 12 h. Going upstream, the dugouts travelled at 5 km/h, but downstream they travelled 10 km/h faster. How far upstream did they go?

C  12  A teacher treated a class to hot dogs and hamburgers. If every member of the class had only hot dogs at 75¢ each, the cost would be $17.25. However, if the boys had hot dogs and the girls, hamburgers at 90¢ each, the cost would be $19.35. How many boys are in the class? How many girls are there?

# 6.14 PSP Problem-Solving: Extraneous Information

Often, you need to assemble the information needed to solve a problem, and at the same time, decide upon the method that is to be used to solve the problem. An important strategy for solving problems is the ability to recognize information that is not needed. Information that is not needed is called **extraneous information**. The following problem contains extraneous information.

**Example**

(a) What information in the following problem is not needed in order to solve it?

(b) Solve the problem.

The concentration of Brand A of antifreeze is 25% by mass while Brand B has a concentration of 50%. Brand A also contains 10% rust inhibitor. If a total of 50 kg were mixed from the two brands to obtain a concentration of 42%, how much of each type was used?

**Solution**

(a) The information that is not needed to solve the problem is the statement "Brand A also contains 10% rust inhibitor".

(b) Let the amounts used be $x$ kg of Brand A, $y$ kg of Brand B.

Think

$$x + y = 50 \quad ①$$
$$0.25x + 0.50y = 21 \quad ②$$
$100 \times ② \longrightarrow \quad 25x + 50y = 2100 \quad ③$
$25 \times ① \longrightarrow \quad 25x + 25y = 1250 \quad ④$
$③ - ④ \longrightarrow \quad 25y = 850$
$$y = 34 \quad ⑤$$

|  | Amount used (kg) | Amount of antifreeze (kg) |
|---|---|---|
| Brand A | $x$ | 25% of $x$ |
| Brand B | $y$ | 50% of $y$ |
| Mixture | 50 | 42% of 50 = 21 |

From equation ⑤ use $y = 34$ in equation ①.
$$x + 34 = 50$$
$$x = 16$$

Thus, 16 kg of the 25% solution and 34 kg of the 50% solution were used.

---

## 6.14 Exercise

**B** Remember: Plan the steps of your solution. Refer to the *Problem-Solving Plan*.

1  At the Pollution Studies Conference, there were 168 more engineers than chemists. However, there were 268 physicists. If there were a total of 1134 engineers and chemists, how many of each were there?

2  At the Sportsarama event, 500 people attended, some paying $3.50 and some $2.75 for their tickets. The total receipts collected from the event was $1510. This is $609 more than last year's event. How many people paid $3.50 for their tickets?

3  Each spring the Conservation Authority places 10 000 bass and perch into the lake. About 3000 of them do not grow to be larger than 5 cm. If there had been three times as many bass and twice as many perch, the total number of fish placed would have been 22 000. How many of each fish were placed in the lake?

4  Find two numbers so that their sum divided by 4 is 12. The first number, if doubled and increased by 24, is equal to twice the other. When 1 is added to each number they become prime numbers. Find the numbers.

5  For next year John bought a total of 470 sacks consisting of corn seed at $8.00 per sack and clover seed at $12.00 per sack. For each 250 ha 112 sacks of corn seed are needed. If the total cost was $4260, how many sacks of clover seed were bought?

6  From the soft drink machine Marie collected 75 coins consisting of only quarters and dimes. You may also deposit nickels and 50-cent pieces in the machine. If the total amount collected was $13.50, how many of each coin were collected?

7  At the candy shop, two types of candy are mixed.
   • Red Barons selling at $3.60/kg
   • Bon Bons selling at $4.60/kg
   Last week the Red Barons were selling for 30¢ more per kilogram and the Bon Bons were 59¢ less per kilogram. If 100 kg were mixed and sold for $4.40/kg, then how many kilograms of each type of candy were used?

8  In the laboratory only 40% and 60% alcohol solutions were available. For a special experiment the alcohol must have a concentration of 45%. For a previous experiment, the concentration was 52%. If 200 kg of the solution is needed, how many kilograms of each solution should be mixed?

9  A prop-jet plane when flying into the wind takes 4 h to complete a trip of 960 km. A twin jet would take 3 h 20 min. Flying with the wind the prop-jet takes only 3 h to make the same trip, but the twin jet only 2 h 30 min. Find the speed of the prop-jet. What is the speed of the wind?

PSP  10  Numbers often have unusual properties. For example, 407 has the property that
$$4^3 + 0^3 + 7^3 = 407.$$
Find another number less than 1000 that has the same property.

## Practice and Problems: Review

1 Decide which method to use to solve each system and then solve.

(a) $3x + y = 12$
$2x + 5y = 21$

(b) $m = 3 + 15n$
$3n + m = 21$

(c) $2a + 7 = b$
$b = -3a - 8$

2 Solve and verify. $3(x + 2y) = 48$ and $\dfrac{1}{4}(x - 3y) = \dfrac{1}{2}x - 5$

3 A ship travels on the path defined by $2x - 3y = 12$. Another ship travels on the path defined by $y = 5x - 17$. What are the co-ordinates of the point where the paths cross?

4 Most famous people have hired a writer for jokes or one-liners. The cost of 8 jokes and 6 one-liners is $610.00. The cost of 6 jokes and 8 one-liners is $510. What does a joke and a one-liner cost?

5 Johnson rented a motorcycle and went at 40 km/h on the Prairie and at 10 km/h along the rivers. If it took 5.75 h to travel 185 km on the trip, how many kilometres did he drive along the rivers?

6 Sam bought 5 boxes of chocolates and 3 bags of candies for $12.05. If the cost of boxes and bags were reversed, the cost would have been $11.07. How much

(a) does a box of chocolates cost?    (b) would 12 bags of candies cost?

## Practice Test

1 Solve (a) $3x + y = 5$
$x - 2y = 11$

(b) $3x - 2y = -8$
$y - 7 = 3x$

(c) $a - 3b = -2$
$2b + a = 8$

2 Solve and verify. $2x + 3y + 17 = 0$ and $x - 2y = 9$

3 S. S. Alberta is on a course defined by $3(x - 1) - 2(y + 1) = -14$. S. S. Quebec is on a course defined by $3x - y = -6$. At what point do their paths cross?

4 Two numbers have these properties. Find the numbers.
• The sum of the two numbers is 84.
• 3 times the greater exceeds twice the smaller by 62.

5 Sweeny has a total of $580 consisting of $5-bills and $10-bills. If he has 76 bills in all, how many of each does he have?

6 Kelly invested her savings of $4800, part at 9% and the rest at 10%. At the end of the year the interest from the 9% investment was $43 less than the interest from the 10% investment. How much was invested at each rate?

# 7 Nature of Mathematics: Inequations and Variation

Regions, systems of linear inequations, linear programming, using graphs, direct variation, inverse variation, partial variation, solving problems, applications, strategies and problem-solving

## Introduction

Strategies and skills, based on the use of graphs, provide researchers an important method of studying scientific phenomena. The study of variation often provides a framework, within which the scientific researcher can use the principles of mathematics to report on the scientific findings. Mathematics can show relationships between and among phenomena that at first glance seem unrelated. For example, these phenomena have similar characteristics.

▶ the relationship between the stretch of a spring and the amount of pull applied to the spring
▶ the relationship between the amount of fuel consumed on a trip and the distance travelled
▶ the relationship between the diameter of a circle and its corresponding circumference

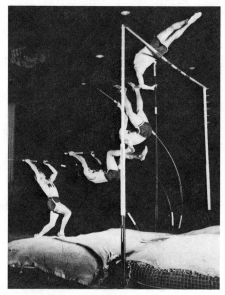

The photo to the right captures the step-by-step movements of an athelete preparing for the pole vault event. Photography, along with skills with mathematics, can be used to analyze the movements of an athlete, so that his or her performance can be improved. By applying these skills to different situations you learn that similarities exist. It is in these similarities that patterns occur and new relationships and properties are discovered. In this chapter, your skills with variation and inequations are combined with your earlier skills in algebra to learn new strategies for solving problems. Remember to record them in your chart for *Problem-Solving Plan* **PSP**

# 7.1 Systems of Linear Inequations: Regions

To help you learn mathematics,

- look for similarities and differences in the new skills and concepts you learn related to what you have learned earlier.
- examine carefully how the skills and concepts you learn are extended to develop more useful mathematics.

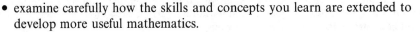

Earlier, you developed these skills.
The graph of a linear equation such as

$$y = x + 2$$

separates the Cartesian plane into 3 regions.

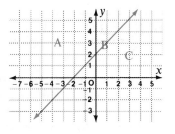

A: points that are above the line.
B: points that are on the line.
C: points that are below the line.

- Points on the line satisfy the equation
    $$y = x + 2.$$
- Points above the line satisfy the inequation
    $$y > x + 2.$$
- Points below the line satisfy the inequation
    $$y < x + 2.$$

## System of Linear Inequations
You can now extend these skills to draw the graph of a system of linear inequations.

The graph below shows all $(x, y)$ that satisfy

$$2x - y \geq 4.$$

The graph below shows all $(x, y)$ that satisfy

$$x + y \geq 1.$$

All $(x, y)$ that satisfy both inequations

$$2x - y \geq 4 \text{ and } x + y \geq 1$$

are shown by the intersection of regions A and B.

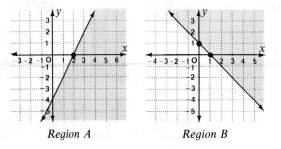

*Region A*          *Region B*

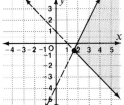

You need to apply your skills in solving a system of equations in order to be able to draw the graph of a system of inequations. In the following example, the region is defined by a system of 3 inequations.

**Example**   Draw the region given by $y \geq x - 4$, $2x + y \geq 4$, and $y < 6$.

**Solution**   Think: Sketch each region. Mark the boundary of the region with a solid or broken line. Mark the vertices of the region. Then shade the region to show the graph of the system of linear inequations.

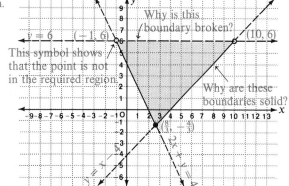

To find the solution of the system of linear inequations $y \geq x - 4$, $2x + y \geq 4$, and $y < 6$ means to find all $(x, y)$ that satisfy all of the inequations. To show the solution, draw the region as shown in the previous example.

## 7.1   Exercise

**A** Remember: You need to know the equations of the boundaries of a region before you can draw that region.

1   Which of the following equations or inequations describes the region as shown?

A   $-3x + 2y = 6$     D   $-3x + 2y < 6$
B   $-3x + 2y > 6$     E   $-3x + 2y \geq 6$
C   $-3x + 2y \leq 6$

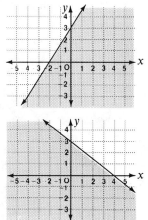

2   A region is shown. Which of the following points satisfy

$$3x + 4y \leq 12?$$

(a) $(1, 1)$        (b) $(1, 3)$

(c) $(6, -2)$       (d) $(7, -2)$

3   A region defined by

$$3x - 4y \leqq 12$$

is drawn. Which of the following points may be used to check the accuracy of the region that has been shaded?

A(1, 1)   B(−1, −6)   C(0, 0)

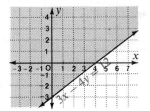

4   For each region, write the inequation that defines it.

(a)            (b)            (c)

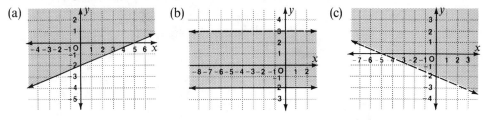

5   In each of the following, the equations show the lines that indicate the boundaries of the region. Write the system of inequations that define the region.

(a)            (b)            (c)

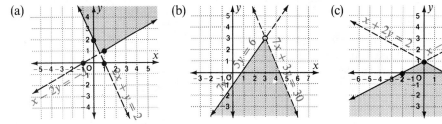

6   The quadrants of the co-ordinate plane are shown.

(a) Write the equation of the $x$-axis.

(b) Write the equation of the $y$-axis.

(c) Write the system of inequations that show each quadrant.

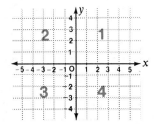

7   For each region, write the system of inequations.

(a)            (b)            (c)            (d)

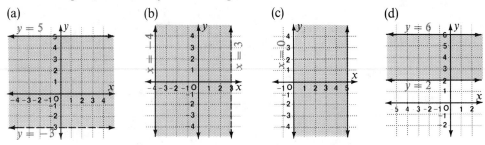

**B** For each region that you draw, how can you check the accuracy of your work?

8   Draw the region given by each system of inequations.
  (a) $x + 2y \le 4$ and $x - y \ge 1$.
  (b) $2x - y \le 3$ and $x + y \ge 3$.
  (c) $y + 2x \ge 4$ and $3x - y < 6$.
  (d) $2x - y < 8$ and $x - y \ge 3$.
  (e) $x > y - 1$ and $3y - x < 1$.

9   For each region,
  • first find the equation of the boundary,
  • then find the system of inequations.

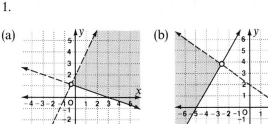

10  Solve each system of inequations.
  (a) $x + y > 9$ and $x - y \le 3$.
  (b) $3x - y \le -2$ and $x - y \ge -6$.
  (c) $3x - y < 4$ and $x - 2y > 3$.
  (d) $2x - 3y < -12$ and $2x + 3y \ge 0$.

11  For each graph, the given equations represent the boundaries. Write the system of inequations that give the region.

  (a) 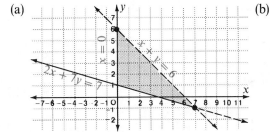   (b)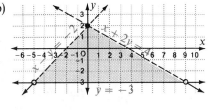

12  Draw the graph given by each system of inequations.
  (a) $x + y < 4$, $x \le 3$, $y < 2$
  (b) $y - x \le 4$, $y - 3x \ge 0$, $x + y > 1$
  (c) $2x - y \le -2$, $x + y > 2$, $x \ge 0$
  (d) $x - y < 1$, $2x + 3y > 6$, $x > 0$
  (e) $2x - 3y \ge 6$, $x \ge 0$, $y \ge 0$
  (f) $y - x > 1$, $x < 0$, $y < 0$

13  Solve each system of inequations.
  (a) $x \ge 0$, $y \ge 0$, $2x - 3y \le 6$
  (b) $x + y \ge 6$, $x - y \le 4$, $y \ge 2$
  (c) $x \le 3$, $y < 2$, $x + y < 4$
  (d) $2x - 3y > 0$, $x - 6y \le -5$, $x > 2$

**C** 14  Draw the graph of each of these regions.
  (a) $y \ge 3x^2$, $x + y \ge 1$
  (b) $y < \frac{1}{2}x^2$, $x - y \le 2$
  (c) $y < -2x^2$, $y \ge -3$
  (d) $y \ge -\frac{1}{2}x^2$, $y \le -0.5$

# 7.2 Applying a Linear System of Inequations

The strategy of solving a system of inequations can now be applied to the solution of a business problem.

A profit, $P$, may be represented by the equation

$$P = 2x + 3y \text{ where } P \text{ is a parameter.}$$

profit on $x$ items
at \$2 profit per item ⎯⎯ profit on $y$ items at \$3 profit per item

As the profit, $P$, takes on different values, a family of lines occurs on the plane. You can apply your skills in drawing a region defined by a system of inequations to find the maximum value of the profit, $P$, under certain conditions.

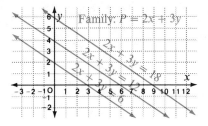

**Example 1**   Find the maximum value of $P$ given by $P = 2x + 3y$ in the region defined by $x \geq 0$, $y \geq 0$, $4x + y \leq 28$, $x + 3y \leq 18$.

A system of equations, such as this one, is often referred to as the **constraints** of the problem.

**Solution**   Draw the region defined by the system.

Think: Draw one member of the family given by $P = 2x + 3y$ in the region.

As the family of lines given by $P = 2x + 3y$ moves upwards across the region, the value of $P$ increases. Thus, at vertex M the value of $P$ is a maximum (the greatest value). To find the co-ordinates of M, solve the equations.

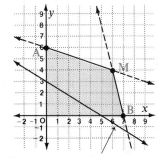

$$
\begin{array}{lll}
& x + 3y = 18 & \text{①} \\
& 4x + y = 28 & \text{②} \\
4 \times \text{①} & 4x + 12y = 72 & \text{③} \\
\text{③} - \text{②} & 11y = 44 & \\
& y = 4 & \\
\text{From ①} & x = 6 &
\end{array}
$$

The equation, with parameter $P$, has the slope as shown.

Thus, the co-ordinates of M are (6, 4). The maximum value of $P$ is given by

$$
\begin{aligned}
P &= 2x + 3y \\
&= 2(6) + 3(4) \\
&= 24
\end{aligned}
$$

For the above example, you can test the values of $P$ at the other vertices.

The value of $P$ at the point A(0, 6) is given by

$$P = 2x + 3y$$
$$= 2(0) + 3(6)$$
$$= 18$$

The value of $P$ at the point B(7, 0) is given by

$$P = 2x + 3y$$
$$= 2(7) + 3(0)$$
$$= 14$$

Thus, the maximum value *does* occur at M since 24 is greater than either 18 or 14.

It is possible for the equation of the profit to be different for the same constraints (the same region). For example, use $P = 2x + 7y$. For this profit, the maximum occurs at the vertex A.

Profit at A(0, 6).

$$P = 2x + 7y$$
$$= 2(0) + 7(6)$$
$$= 0 + 42$$
$$= 42$$
$$\uparrow$$

Maximum value occurs at A.

Profit at M(6, 4).

$$P = 2x + 7y$$
$$= 2(6) + 7(4)$$
$$= 12 + 28$$
$$= 40$$

Profit at B(7, 0).

$$P = 2x + 7y$$
$$= 2(7) + 7(0)$$
$$= 14 + 0$$
$$= 14$$

You can use the same strategy to find the minimum value (the least value) of a problem.

## 7.2 Exercise

A The questions of this exercise develop essential skills for solving business problems.

1 Find the maximum value of $P$ if

$$P = x + y$$

over the region as shown.

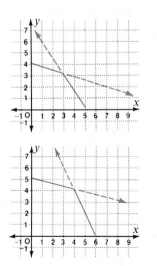

2 The profit $P$, of making two types of dishes is given by

$$P = 2x + 4y.$$

Find the maximum profit for the given region.

3    The expenses, $E$, for manufacturing two
     types of dog food are given by

$$E = 3x + 6y.$$

     Find the minimum value of $E$.

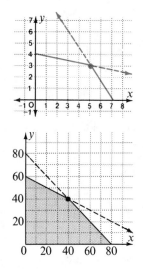

4    The profit $P$ is given by

$$P = 3x + 10y.$$

     Find the maximum profit if the constraints
     are shown by this region.

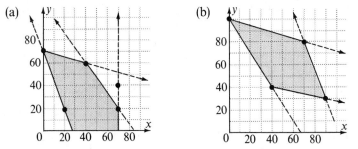

5    Find the minimum value of $P = 3x + 4y$ for each region.

     (a)                           (b)

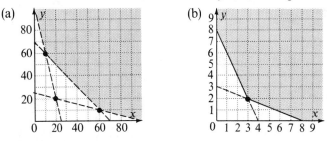

**B**  Read each problem carefully. Are you asked to find a minimum or a
       maximum value?

6    Find the minimum and maximum value for $P = x + y$ over each region.

     (a)                           (b)

7    (a)  Draw the region given by $x \geq 0$, $y \geq 0$, $x + 19 \geq 3y$, $3x + 2y \leq 31$.
     (b)  Name the co-ordinates of the vertices of the region in (a).
     (c)  For the region, find
          (i)  the maximum value of $P$, given by $P = 2x + 4y$.
          (ii) the maximum value of $R$, given by $R = 3y + x$.

8 (a) Draw the region given by the system of inequations $x \geq 0$, $y \geq 0$,
$5x + 4y \geq 32$, $x + 2y \geq 10$.

(b) Name the co-ordinates of the vertices of the region given in (a).

(c) For the region, find
(i) the minimum value of $P$, given by $P = 3x + 2y$.
(ii) the minimum value of $S$, given by $S = 3y + 2x$.

9 (a) A region is given by $x \geq 0$, $y \geq 0$, $x + y \leq 5$, $x + 2y \leq 8$.
Find the maximum value of $P$ if $P = 2x + 3y$.

(b) Find the minimum value of $P$ given by

$$P = 3x + 4y$$

for the region given by

$$x \geq 0, \ y \geq 0, \ 2x + y \geq 8, \ x + 3y \geq 9, \ x + y \geq 7.$$

10 The constraints for manufacturing two types of hockey skates are given by the following region.

$$x \geq 0, \ y \geq 0, \ x + 4y \leq 41, \ y \geq 2x - 10, \ 7x + 64 \geq 11y.$$

Find the maximum value of $Q$ over the region if $Q = 3x + 5y$.

11 The constraints for making basketballs and soccer balls are given by the region

$$x \geq 0, \ y \geq 0, \ 2x + y \leq 260, \ x + 5y \leq 400.$$

Find the minimum value of the expenses, $E$, given by $E = 5x + 4y$ over the above region.

---

## Problem-Solving  PSP

Evariste Galois (1811–1832) developed solutions to problems that had not been solved for two thousand years. For example, he used algebra to prove that it is impossible to trisect an angle using only a ruler and compasses. Would you believe that although he was one of the world's most brilliant mathematicians he had difficulty with some of his studies in mathematics? By the time he was 17 Galois had invented new ideas in mathematics, but unfortunately he was killed in a duel on May 30, 1832. Some problems, although stated in simple terms have never been proved, such as the following,

▶ Every even number greater than 2 can be written as the sum of exactly two primes (e.g. $16 = 3 + 13$).
▶ The equation $x^n + y^n = z^n$ where $n$ is an integer greater than 2, has no solutions that are positive integers.

# 7.3  Applications: Linear Programming

The skills you have learned for graphing regions defined by systems of inequations may be used to solve many problems in industry. For example, manufacturers are interested in maximizing profits and minimizing expenses.

Sports Unlimited manufactures soft and hard baseballs. It makes $3.00 and $2.00 profit respectively on each type of ball. Thus, the profit, $P$, in dollars, is given by $P = 3x + 2y$ where $x$ is the number of soft balls and $y$ is the number of hard balls. However, there are certain manufacturing conditions at the plant that impose restrictions on the number of soft and hard baseballs that can be manufactured. These restrictions are referred to as the **constraints** of the business problem. To find the maximum value, $P$, the company needs to satisfy these restrictions.

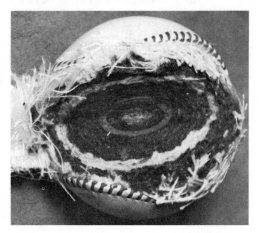

**Example**  The Sports Unlimited firm manufactures soft and hard baseballs. Each hard ball requires 1 min on the stitching machine and 3 min on the ball-covering machine. Each soft ball requires 2 min on the stitching machine and 2 min on the ball-covering machine. The stitching machine is only available for 100 min each day, while the ball-covering machine is available for 180 min each day. The profit on a hard ball is $2 and on a soft ball is $3. How many hard balls and soft balls should be manufactured each day to make a maximum profit?

PSP

**Solution**  Let $x$ represent the number of hard balls.
Thus, $x \geq 0$.
Let $y$ represent the number of soft balls.
Thus, $y \geq 0$.

Think: Use a chart to sort the information.

|       | Number of balls | Stitching time (min) | Covering time (min) | Profit ($) |
|-------|-----------------|----------------------|---------------------|------------|
| hard  | $x$             | $x$                  | $3x$                | $2x$       |
| soft  | $y$             | $2y$                 | $2y$                | $3y$       |

PSP  Use the given information in the problem to construct the inequations.

$x + 2y \leq 100$

$3x + 2y \leq 180$

$2x + 3y = P$

To solve the problem draw the region given by $x \geq 0$, $y \geq 0$, $x + 2y \leq 100$ and $3x + 2y \leq 180$.

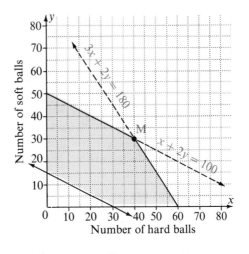

From the graph, the maximum value of $P = 2x + 3y$ occurs at the point M. The co-ordinates of M are found as follows.

$$3x + 2y = 180 \quad \text{①}$$
$$x + 2y = 100 \quad \text{②}$$
$$\text{①} - \text{②} \qquad 2x = 80$$
$$x = 40 \quad \text{③}$$

From ① $\quad 3(40) + 2y = 180$
$$2y = 60$$
$$y = 30$$

Thus to make the maximum profit, 40 hard balls and 30 softballs should be manufactured per day.

The previous graphical method of drawing a region defined by a system of inequations and solving a problem based on certain constraints is referred to as **linear programming**. The problems you will be asked to solve will involve only two variables, and may be solved using a graphical approach. More difficult problems involving more than two variables are solved in business with the help of computers.

## 7.3 Exercise

B Remember: You can use a chart to help you to organize the given information.

1 The Pro Shop makes golf hats and visors. Each golf hat requires 4 min on the cutting machine and 3 min on the stitching machine. Each visor requires 3 min on the cutting machine and 1 min on the stitching machine. The cutting machine is available 2 h/d while the stitching machine is only available 1 h/d. If the profit on a golf hat is $1.10 and the profit on a visor is $0.60, calculate how many of each should be made to realize a maximum profit.

PSP

(a) Copy and complete the chart.

(b) Use the information in the chart. Draw the region.

(c) Solve the problem.

| | Number of each | Cutting time (min) | Stitching time (min) | Profit ($) |
|---|---|---|---|---|
| golf hats | $x$ | $4x$ | ? | $1.10x$ |
| visors | $y$ | ? | $y$ | ? |
| total | | ? | ? | ? |

2   A sports firm makes basketballs and soccer balls. Two machines are used
    to make the balls and the time required on each machine is shown.

| | Time on Machine A | Time on Machine B |
|---|---|---|
| Basketball | 1 min | 1 min |
| Soccer Ball | 1 min | 2 min |

Each day Machine A is available for only 110 min to manufacture them
while Machine B is available for 140 min. If the profit on a basketball
is 90¢ and on a soccer ball it is $1.30, calculate how many of each ball
should be made to realize a maximum profit. What information is not needed?

3   To manufacture cushions and pillows, a firm uses two machines I and II.
    The time required on each machine is shown.

| | Machine I | Machine II |
|---|---|---|
| Pillows | 2 min | 4 min |
| Cushions | 9 min | 7 min |

Machine I is available for 9 h/d and Machine II for 10 h 40 min/d. If the
profit made on a cushion is $3.20 and on a pillow it is $1.20, then find
how many cushions and pillows should be made to make the maximum
profit. What information is not needed?

4   A firm manufactures 2-bulb bedroom lamps and 4-bulb living room
    lamps. Each day they get a consignment of 480 bulbs and 180 shades.
    Determine how many of each lamp they should manufacture to yield a
    maximum profit if their profit on a 2-bulb lamp is $20 and on a 4-bulb
    lamp is $35. What is the maximum profit?

5   A firm manufactures bicycles and tricycles making a profit of $50 on each
    bicycle and $30 on each tricycle. Find the maximum profit that may be
    made based on the following conditions.

    A: The total number of frames made cannot exceed 80 per month.

    B: It takes 2 h to assemble a bicycle but only 1 h to assemble a tricycle.
       The assembly machine is available for only 100 h each month.

6   Two employees, Janet and Sam, make hockey sticks and goalie sticks.
    Janet can make 3 hockey sticks and 3 goalie sticks/h, while Sam can
    make 4 goalie sticks and 1 hockey stick/h. At least 12 hockey sticks and
    30 goalie sticks must be made each day. If Janet earns $7/h and Sam
    earns $6/h, then

    (a) how long should each person spend making hockey sticks and making
        goalie sticks to minimize the cost?

    (b) how many goalie sticks and hockey sticks may be made by them at
        the minimal labour cost?

Linear programming can also be used to solve problems in different types of business and related problems. Solve the following problems.

7   It is recommended that cattle be supplemented with 19 g of iron and 12 g of riboflavin in their diet. Two feeds are available which contain both nutrients in different amounts as shown.

| Feed | Iron | Riboflavin |
|------|------|------------|
| Husky | 5% | 2% |
| Vibrant | 2% | 3% |

Husky Feed sells for $25/kg and Vibrant Feed sells for $32/kg.

(a) How many kilograms of each feed are required to feed 100 cattle as economically as possible?

(b) What is the cost of these quantities in (a)?

8   To produce top quality fruit, a fruit farmer throughout each growing season needs to use at least 7.3 kg of nutrient A and 4.7 kg of nutrient B for each fruit tree. Two suppliers provide the nutrients but the amounts of A and B vary in each kilogram of each brand they provide, as shown in the chart.

| Supplier | Amount of nutrient A | Amount of nutrient B | Cost per kilogram |
|----------|----------------------|----------------------|-------------------|
| Erunam Brand | 40% | 60% | $2.40 |
| Goodwin Brand | 90% | 10% | $3.00 |

(a) How many kilograms of each brand from each supplier is required in order to provide the required amount of nutrients A and B for each tree at a minimum cost?

(b) What is the minimum cost to provide the nutrients for each tree?

## Computer Tip

The square root function is useful for solving problems about the horizon distance. The distance $d$, in metres, to the horizon from a building with height $h$, in metres, above sea level is given by the formula. $d = \sqrt{2rh}$   $r$ is the radius of the earth, in kilometres

▶ Use an efficient procedure on a calculator to solve this problem. How far is the horizon from a building 86.8 m high? The diameter of the earth is 12 759.0 km. (You will need a telescope to see the actual horizon).

▶ Write a computer program to find the distance $d$.

## 7.4 Using Graphs: Direct Variation

You can use mathematics to relate phenomena that otherwise appear to be unrelated.

A Data are collected to show the relation between the cost of syrup and the amount purchased. The data are then graphed as shown.

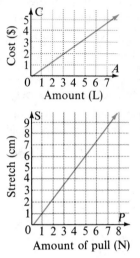

B Data are collected in answer to the question: "How is the stretch of a spring related to the amount of pull on the spring?"

Corresponding values of the variables are chosen from each graph to do each calculation.

A: Syrup $\dfrac{\text{cost in dollars}}{\text{amount of litres}} = \dfrac{C}{A}$

$$\frac{1.36}{2} = 0.68$$

$$\frac{2.04}{3} = 0.68$$

$$\frac{4.08}{6} = 0.68$$

Based on the calculations, note the constant value. Thus, write the equation $\dfrac{C}{A} = \text{constant}$

B: Stretch $\dfrac{\text{amount of stretch}}{\text{amount of pull}} = \dfrac{S}{P}$

$$\frac{2.4}{2} = 1.2$$

$$\frac{7.2}{6} = 1.2$$

$$\frac{9.6}{8} = 1.2$$

Based on the calculations $\dfrac{S}{P} = \text{constant.}$

If $x$ and $y$ are used as variables, then, for the two examples, the phenomena are related by a **direct variation**.

$y$ varies directly as $x$　　or　　$y$ varies as $x$.

$$\frac{y}{x} = k \qquad\qquad y = kx$$

$k$ is a constant, often called the **constant of variation**.

Thus if $x$ increases then $y$ increases and conversely as $x$ decreases, $y$ decreases.

Each of the phenomena on the previous page are examples of direct variation and you would write,

A: The cost in dollars of syrup *varies directly* with the amount purchased.

B: The amount of stretch of the spring (in centimetres) *varies directly* with the amount of pull (in Newtons).

Often, you need to obtain a table of values in order to draw the graph of a direct variation.

For example, fuel consumption is expressed as litres used to travel 100 km. A compact car has an average fuel consumption of 8 L/100 km.

Construct a table of values based on the fuel consumption.

| fuel (L) | 8 | 16 | 24 | 4 |
|---|---|---|---|---|
| distance (km) | 100 | 200 | 300 | 50 |

Use the data in the table of values to draw the graph. The graph is a straight line. The fuel consumption, f, in litres, varies directly with the distance travelled, $d$, in kilometres.

$$f \propto d \qquad f = kd$$

$k$ is the **constant of variation**.

From the graph, $\dfrac{f}{d} = \dfrac{8}{100}$

$$= 0.08$$

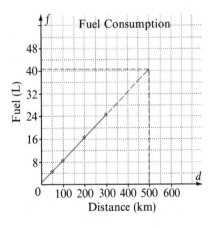

Thus, the constant of variation is 0.08.
The slope of the graph is 0.08.

 Be sure to learn the meaning of words in mathematics.

- Reading the graph for values not given is called **interpolation**. For example, 150 km was not a value used in the table of values used to plot the graph. Thus, the corresponding value of 12 L is obtained by interpolation.

- Extending the graph to predict values beyond those plotted is called **extrapolation**. For example, the distance travelled for 40 L extends beyond the graph. Thus, the value of 500 km is obtained by extrapolation.

## 7.4 Exercise

**A** Review the meaning of *direct variation* and *constant of variation*.

1 Write an equation to express each of the following relationships.
   (a) The distance travelled varies directly with the time (if the speed is constant).
   (b) The force of gravitation between the earth and a body on its surface varies directly with the mass of the body.
   (c) The area of a rectangle, when the base is fixed, varies directly with its height.
   (d) The total cost of gasoline varies directly with the number of litres purchased.
   (e) The area of a triangle, when the height is fixed, varies directly with its base.

Use the graph at the right to answer Questions 2 to 4.

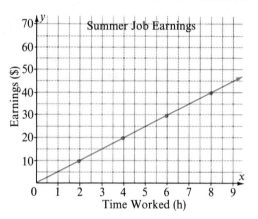

2 What are the earnings for each amount of time?
   (a) 1 h      (b) 6 h      (c) 8.5 h

3 What amount of time is needed to earn each of these amounts?
   (a) $20.00      (b) $45.00      (c) $35.00

4 (a) Write an equation to express the direct variation.
   (b) What is the value of the constant of variation?

5 (a) Jennifer purchased cookies that cost $3.15/kg. Write an equation to show the variation.
   (b) Complete the table of values needed to construct a graph.

| mass (kg) | 1 | 2 | 3 | 4 | 5 | 6 | 7 | 8 |
|-----------|---|---|---|---|---|---|---|---|
| cost ($)  | ? | ? | ? | ? | ? | ? | ? | ? |

   (c) Use the graph to find the cost of 4.5 kg. Which process did you use, interpolation or extrapolation, to find this value?
   (d) Use the graph to find how many kilograms you can buy for $30.00. Did you use interpolation or extrapolation to find this value?

B When you draw a graph, choose appropriate variables to label the axes.

6   The cost of parking a car downtown is $1.50/h.
    (a) Construct a table of values based on this relationship.
    (b) Draw a graph to show the relationship.
    (c) What is the constant of variation?

7   Lea grows and sells peas for $1.50/kg with a 5-kg limit per customer.
    (a) Construct a table of values for cost and mass.
    (b) Draw a graph to show that cost varies directly with mass.
    (c) What is the cost of (i) 3.0 kg? (ii) 5.0 kg? (iv) 0.5 kg?

8   Based on collected data, the amount of garbage, G, in tonnes, produced
    in Canada varies directly with the number of people, N, who produce the
    garbage.
    (a) If 20 t of garbage are produced by 100 people each year, write an
        equation relating G and N.
    (b) Draw the graph of the relationship in (a).
    (c) The population of Charny is 5300. How much garbage is produced in
        one year?
    (d) The amount of garbage produced in Gravenhurst is 36 490 t. Estimate
        the population of Gravenhurst.

9   Michelle is a cross-country skier and travels, on average, 7.5 km/h.
    (a) Construct a table of values.
    (b) Draw a graph to show the relationship.
    (c) What is the value of the constant of variation?
    (d) Create a problem based on the graph. What is the answer to your
        problem?

10  The diameter and corresponding circumference of various circular objects
    were measured to the nearest tenth of a centimetre. The data are recorded
    in a table.

| diameter (cm) | 9.0 | 12.5 | 20.0 | 25.0 |
|---|---|---|---|---|
| circumference (cm) | 28.3 | 39.3 | 62.8 | 78.5 |

    (a) Use the table of values to draw a graph.
    (b) Does the circumference vary directly with the diameter?
    (c) What is the value of the constant of variation?
    (d) Create a problem based on the graph. What is the answer to your
        problem?

## 7.5 **PSP** Direct Variation: Problem-Solving

You can use the graphs of direct variation to solve a problem. You can also use the graphs to develop skills for solving equations about direct variation.

The stretch of a spring, $S$, varies directly with the pull, $P$.

$$S \propto P \qquad S = kP \qquad \frac{S}{P} = k$$

$k$ is the constant of variation

Choose an ordered pair, such as $(4, 5)$, from the graph in order to calculate $k$, the constant of variation.

$$\frac{S}{P} = k \quad \text{or} \quad k = \frac{S}{P}$$

$$= \frac{5}{4}$$

$$= 1.25$$

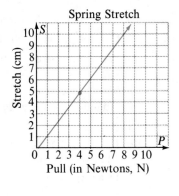

Spring Stretch

**Example 1**   $y$ varies directly as $x$. When $x = 14$ $y = 28$. Find $y$ when $x = 42$.

**Solution**   Use $\dfrac{y}{x} = k$, $k$ a constant

Then $\dfrac{28}{14} = k$.

$2 = k$ or $k = 2$ ⟵ The constant of variation is 2.

Use $\dfrac{y}{x} = 2$. If $x = 42$, then

$$\frac{y}{42} = 2$$

$$y = 84$$

From the graph, $(S_1, P_1)$ and $(S_2, P_2)$ are ordered pairs of the direct variation. Thus,

$$\frac{S_1}{P_1} = k \quad \text{and} \quad \frac{S_2}{P_2} = k \quad \text{means} \quad \frac{S_1}{P_1} = \frac{S_2}{P_2}.$$

The proportion $\dfrac{S_1}{P_1} = \dfrac{S_2}{P_2}$ can also be used to solve problems about direct variation.

**Example 2**  A direct variation is given by the proportion $\dfrac{x_1}{y_1} = \dfrac{x_2}{y_2}$.

Find $x_1$ when $y_1 = 8$, $x_2 = 24$ and $y_2 = 64$.

**Solution**  $\dfrac{x_1}{y_1} = \dfrac{x_2}{y_2}$   Think: Record the given information.  **PSP**

$x_1 = ?$, $y_1 = 8$, $x_2 = 24$, $y_2 = 64$

$\dfrac{x_1}{8} = \dfrac{24}{64}$

$x_1 = \dfrac{(8)(24)}{64}$

$= 3$

You can use the methods shown in the previous examples to solve a problem about direct variation.

- *Method 1:* Use a constant of variation.   **PSP**
- *Method 2:* Use a proportion.

**Example 3**  The volume of a gas kept at constant pressure varies directly as the temperature. If the temperature of 800 cm$^3$ of a gas at 200° C is reduced to 150° C, find the resulting volume.

**Solution**  Let $V$ represent the volume of gas in cubic centimetres and $T$ represent the temperature in degrees Celsius.

*Method 1:* Find the constant of variation.

$$V \propto T$$
$$V = kT$$
$$800 = k(200)$$
$$4 = k \text{ or } k = 4$$

Use   $V = kT$, $k = 4$, $T = 150$
$$V = 4(150)$$
$$= 600$$

*Method 2:* Use a proportion. Since $V \propto T$, write a proportion

$$\dfrac{V_1}{T_1} = \dfrac{V_2}{T_2} \qquad V_1 = 800, \ T_1 = 200,$$
$$V_2 = ?, \ T_2 = 150$$

$$\dfrac{800}{200} = \dfrac{V_2}{150}$$

$$\dfrac{150(800)}{200} = V_2$$

$$\text{or } V_2 = 600$$

Thus, when the temperature is reduced to 150°C, the volume is 600 cm$^3$.

## 7.5 Exercise

**A** Remember: A direct variation $y \propto x$ may be shown by the proportion $\dfrac{y_1}{x_1} = \dfrac{y_2}{x_2}$.

1 Find the constant of variation if
   (a) $m$ varies directly as $n$ and $m = 28$ when $n = 14$.
   (b) $p$ varies directly as $q$ and $p = 36$ when $q = 3$.
   (c) $b$ varies directly as $c^2$ and $b = 64$ when $c = 4$.
   (d) $m$ is directly proportional to $n^2$ and $m = 36$ when $n = 9$.
   (e) $s \propto t^2$ and $s = 18$ when $t = 3$.

2 (a) If $m$ varies directly as $n$, write an equation to express the direct variation.
   (b) If $m = 120$ when $n = 24$, find $m$ when $n = 8$.

3 (a) If $x$ is directly proportional to $y$, write an equation to express the direct variation.
   (b) If $x = 25$, when $y = 16$, find $y$ when $x = 100$.

4 (a) If $p$ varies directly as $q^2$, write an equation to express the direct variation.
   (b) If $p = 4$ when $q = 5$, find $p$ when $q = 8$.

5 If $y \propto x$, find the missing values for each direct variation.
   (a) $x_1 = 4$, $y_1 = 10$, $x_2 = 20$, $y_2 = ?$      (b) $x_1 = 5$, $y_1 = 25$, $x_2 = ?$, $y_2 = 40$
   (c) $x_1 = ?$, $y_1 = 8$, $x_2 = 24$, $y_2 = 64$      (d) $x_1 = 7.2$, $y_1 = ?$, $x_2 = 3.6$, $y_2 = 1.8$

6 If $m \propto n$ and $m = \dfrac{4}{5}$ when $n = \dfrac{2}{3}$, find

   (a) $m$ when $n = \dfrac{4}{9}$.      (b) $n$ when $m = \dfrac{16}{25}$.

**B** Remember: To solve a problem, record the given information accurately. **PSP** Refer to the *Problem-Solving Plan* to organize your solution.

7 The mass of a substance varies directly with its volume.
   (a) Write an equation to express the direct variation.
   (b) When the mass is 300.0 g the volume is 240.0 cm$^3$. Find the mass when the volume is 384.0 cm$^3$.

8    The amount of stretch of a spring is directly proportional to the mass added.

(a) If the spring stretched 28.0 cm when 8.0 g was added, how much will the spring stretch when 28.0 g is added?

(b) What mass was added if the spring stretched 42.0 cm?

9    A compact car travelling for 6.0 h consumed 120.0 L of gasoline.

(a) How much gas will the car consume if it is driven for 24.0 h?

(b) What assumption do you make in finding your answer in (a)?

10   The distance a plane flies varies directly with the mass of fuel the plane carries. If a plane can fly 250.0 km with 600.0 kg of fuel, how far will it fly with 900.0 kg of fuel?

11   The annual interest earned on a savings account varies directly with the amount of the deposit. If Michelle earns $34.00 on a deposit of $600.00, how much will she earn on a deposit of $800.00?

12   The cost of parking fees in a downtown car lot varies directly with the length of time parked. If Roberto paid $10.50 for 6 h, what is the charge for 2h?

13   The mass of an alloy varies directly with its volume. If 4.36 g of the alloy has a volume of 2.25 $cm^3$, what is the volume of 9.85 g of the alloy?

PSP  14   At a rodeo, the total number of eyes for contestants and animals is 96. If there are 168 legs, how many contestants are there?

C 15   The distance that a body falls from rest varies directly as the square of the time of falling. A certain body fell 83.0 m in 3.0 s.

(a) How far would it fall in 15.0 s?     (b) How long would it take to fall 1.0 km?

16   The mass of a metal sphere varies directly as the cube of its diameter. A sphere with a diameter of 6.0 cm has a mass of 81.0 g. Find the mass of a sphere that has a diameter 4.0 cm.

---

## Math Tip

It is important to clearly understand the vocabulary of mathematics when solving problems. *You cannot solve problems if you don't know what the clues are.*

▶ Make a list of all the words you have learned in this chapter.
▶ Provide a simple example to illustrate the meaning of each word.
▶ Review your list of Problem-Solving Strategies. Refer to your PSP chart. Place any new strategies you have acquired in this chapter and previous ones in your list.

## 7.6 Using Graphs: Inverse Variation

By drawing graphs for tables of values, you can explore other ways in which variables are related. For example, the time required to empty a tank was measured at different pumping rates. The results were recorded and a graph was drawn as shown at the right.

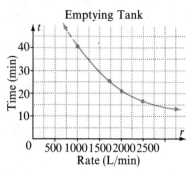

Emptying Tank

| rate (L/min) | 2500 | 2000 | 1600 | 1000 |
|---|---|---|---|---|
| time (min) | 16 | 20 | 25 | 40 |

You can make these observations from the graph.

• When the rate increases, the time decreases.
• When the rate decreases, the time increases.

If $t$ represents the time and $r$ represents the rate, then you can say

$t$ varies inversely with $r$    $t \propto \dfrac{1}{r}$    $t = k\left(\dfrac{1}{r}\right)$ or $t = \dfrac{k}{r}$

constant of variation

Choose a pair of values, say (2500, 16), from the graph to find the constant of variation.

$t = k\left(\dfrac{1}{r}\right)$    $16 = \dfrac{k}{2500}$    Thus, $k = (16)(2500)$
$= 40\ 000$

From the graph,

• by interpolation, when the time is 30 min, the rate is about 1300 L/min.
• by extrapolation, when the rate is 5000 L/min, the time is about 8 min.

When you are learning mathematics, always look for similarities and differences.

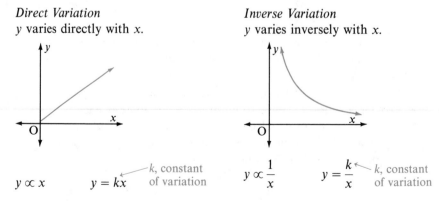

*Direct Variation*
$y$ varies directly with $x$.

$y \propto x$    $y = kx$    $k$, constant of variation

*Inverse Variation*
$y$ varies inversely with $x$.

$y \propto \dfrac{1}{x}$    $y = \dfrac{k}{x}$    $k$, constant of variation

# 7.6 Exercise

**A** Construct a table of values in order to draw a graph.

1 Write an equation to express each of the following relationships.
   (a) The wavelength, $w$, varies inversely with the frequency, $f$.
   (b) The time, $t$, required to travel a fixed distance varies inversely with the speed, $s$.
   (c) The selling price, $S$, of a used car varies inversely with its age, $A$.

---

Refer to the graph at the right when answering Questions 2 to 4.

2 What is the distance for each noise level?
   (a) 30 dB   (b) 70 dB   (c) 15 dB

3 What is the noise level for each distance?
   (a) 40 m   (b) 90 m   (c) 25 m

4 (a) Write an equation to express the inverse variation.
   (b) What is the value of the constant of variation?

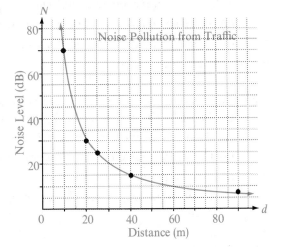

5 Refer to the graph at the right. The tanning power is represented by $P$, and the distance by $D$.
   (a) What is the tanning power 1 m from the sun lamp?
   (b) What distance has a tanning power of 40 units?
   (c) What is the value of the constant of variation?

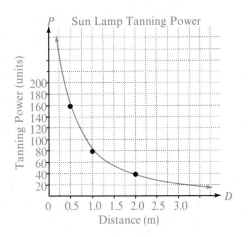

**B** To draw a graph, choose appropriate variables to name the axes.

6  Data for the area of a rectangle are recorded.

| length (cm) | 100.0 | 50.0 | 25.0 | 20.0 | 10.0 | 5.0 | 4.0 | 2.0 | 1.0 |
|---|---|---|---|---|---|---|---|---|---|
| width (cm) | 1.0 | 2.0 | 4.0 | 5.0 | 10.0 | 20.0 | 25.0 | 50.0 | 100.0 |

(a) Draw a graph to show the data. Is the variation shown direct or inverse?

(b) Use the graph. If the length is 2.5 cm, what is the width?

(c) What is the value of the constant of variation?

7  The frequency of the sound made on a guitar string varies inversely with the length when the string tension is kept constant. The frequency is 373.0 Hz when the length is 60.0 cm.

(a) Write an equation relating frequency, $f$, and length, $l$.

(b) Construct a table of values for length from 50.0 cm to 92.0 cm.

(c) Draw a graph.

8  The electrical current, in amperes (A), varies inversely with the resistance in ohms ($\Omega$). The current is 0.3 A when the resistance is 480.0 $\Omega$.

(a) Write an equation relating current, $I$, and resistance, $R$.

(b) Construct a table of values for resistances from 200.0 $\Omega$ to 600.0 $\Omega$.

(c) Draw a graph.

(d) Create a problem based on your graph. What is the answer to your problem?

9  The value of a mid-size car varies inversely with the age of the car. The value of a mid-size car, after 4 years, is $1600.

(a) Write an equation relating the value, $V$, and the age, $A$.

(b) Construct a table of values for ages from 2 years to 6 years.

(c) Draw a graph.

(d) Create a problem based on your graph. What is the answer to your problem ?

**C** 10  The time required to fill a tank varies inversely with the square of the diameter of the hose used. It takes 6.0 min to fill a tank with a hose 2.0 cm in diameter.

(a) Write an equation relating time, $t$, and diameter, $d$.

(b) Construct a table of values for diameters from 1.0 cm to 8.0 cm.

(c) Draw a graph.

# 7.7 Inverse Variation: Applications

You can use a graph of inverse variation to solve a problem and to develop skills for solving equations involving inverse variation. The time, $t$, required to travel 100 km varies inversely with the speed, $v$.

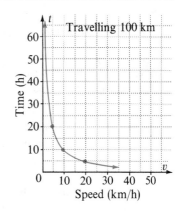

$$t \propto \frac{1}{v} \qquad t = \frac{k}{v} \qquad tv = k$$

$k$ is the constant of variation.

Choose an ordered pair, say (20, 5), from the graph to calculate $k$, the constant of variation.

$$t = \frac{k}{v} \text{ or } k = tv$$
$$= (5)(20)$$
$$= 100$$

The equation $t_1 v_1 = t_2 v_2$ can also be used to solve problems about inverse variation. The equation is obtained as follows.

$(v_1, t_1)$ and $(v_2, t_2)$ are ordered pairs of the inverse variation. Thus,

$$\left. \begin{array}{ll} t_1 = \dfrac{k}{v_1} \text{ and } & t_2 = \dfrac{k}{v_2} \\ \text{or } t_1 v_1 = k & \text{or } t_2 v_2 = k \end{array} \right\} \text{Thus, } t_1 v_1 = t_2 v_2.$$

**Example 1**    $p$ varies inversely with $r$. When $r = 25$, $p = 16$. Find $p$ when $r = 20$.

**Solution**    *Method 1:* Calculate the constant of variation. $p \propto \dfrac{1}{r}$

$$p = \frac{k}{r}$$

$$16 = \frac{k}{25}$$

$$(16)(25) = k \text{ or } k = 400$$

$$p = \frac{k}{r}$$

$$p = \frac{400}{20}$$

$$p = 20$$

*Method 2:* Use the proportion $p_1 r_1 = p_2 r_2$.

$$p \propto \frac{1}{r}$$

$$p_1 = 16, r_1 = 25,$$
$$p_2 = ?, r_2 = 20$$

$$p_1 r_1 = p_2 r_2$$
$$(16)(25) = p_2(20)$$

$$\frac{(16)(25)}{(20)} = p_2$$

$$20 = p_2$$

Thus, $p$ is 20 when $r$ is 20.

You can use the methods shown in the previous examples to solve problems about inverse variation.

- *Method 1:* Calculate the constant of variation.
- *Method 2:* Use the proportion which expresses the inverse variation.

Variation plays an important role in the study of many sciences. The questions in the exercise will illustrate some of those scientific principles. The next example illustrates an important law in chemistry.

**Example 2**  In chemistry, Boyle's law states that if the temperature of a gas is constant, then the volume of the gas is inversely proportional to the pressure. If the volume of the gas is 40 L when the pressure is 6 units, calculate how much pressure should be used to compress the gas to 30 L.

**Solution**  Let $V$ represent the volume of gas and let $P$ represent the pressure.

*Method 1:* Calculate the constant of variation.

$$V \propto \frac{1}{P} \qquad V = 40, P = 6$$

$$V = \frac{k}{P}, \quad k, \text{ constant of variation}$$

$$40 = \frac{k}{6}$$

$$k = 240$$

Use $V = \dfrac{240}{P}$ where $V = 30$

$$30 = \frac{240}{P}$$

$$P = \frac{240}{30} \text{ or } P = 8.$$

*Method 2:* Use the proportion $P_1 V_1 = P_2 V_2$.

$$P_1 = ?, V_1 = 30,$$
$$P_2 = 6, V_2 = 40$$

$$P_1 V_1 = P_2 V_2$$
$$P_1(30) = (6)(40)$$

$$P_1 = \frac{(6)(40)}{30}$$

$$= 8$$

Thus, a pressure of 8 units is needed to compress the volume to 30 L.

## 7.7    Exercise

A   1   Write an equation to express each of the following.

(a) When the amount of work done is constant, the amount of force, $F$, required to do the work is inversely proportional to the distance, $s$, through which the force acts.

(b) The value, $V$, of a car is inversely proportional to the age, $A$, of the car.

2   If $D$ varies inversely as $T$ and $D = 48$ when $T = 64$, find
    (a) the constant of variation.    (b) $D$ when $T = 24$.    (c) $T$ when $D = 16$.

3   (a) If $m$ varies inversely as $n$, write an equation to express the inverse
        variation.
    (b) If $m = 75$ when $n = 36$, find $m$ when $n = 50$.

4   Find the missing values for each inverse variation.
    (a) $x_1 = 3$, $y_1 = ?$, $x_2 = 8$, $y_2 = 12$    (b) $a_1 = 25$, $b_1 = 16$, $a_2 = ?$, $b_2 = 100$

B 5   The time required to travel a fixed distance varies inversely as the speed.
    (a) Write the equation to express the inverse variation.
    (b) When the speed is 60.0 km/h, the time required is 3.0 h. How much
        time is required when the speed is 90.0 km/h?

6   The value of a car varies inversely with the age of the car. The value of
    a car was \$3200.00 after 1.25 years.
    (a) Find the value of the car in 6.00 years (to the nearest dollar).
    (b) How long will it take the car to be worth \$1500.00?
    (c) What assumption(s) do you make in finding your answer in (b)?

7   The time required to cook a roast varies inversely with the oven
    temperature. If a roast takes 3.0 h at 160.0° C to cook, how long would it
    take to cook the same roast at 190.0° C?

8   When the tension on a piano wire is kept constant, the number of
    vibrations per second varies inversely as its length. A wire, 1.25 m long,
    vibrates at 512.00 vibrations per second. How long should a wire be
    made to sound the musical note, concert A (435.00 vibrations per second)?

9   If the area of a triangle is constant, then the base varies inversely as the height.
    (a) If the height is 36.0 cm when the base is 40.0 cm, find the base when
        the height is 15.0 cm.
    (b) Find the height when the base is 48.0 cm.

10   Air temperature, in degrees Celsius, varies inversely with the height, in
    metres, above sea level. The air temperature is 4.0° C at 400.0 m above
    sea level. What is the temperature at 250.0 m above sea level?

C 11   (a) $A$ is inversely proportional to $M$. If $M$ is doubled, find the change in $A$.
    (b) $A$ is inversely proportional to $D$. If $A$ is doubled, find the change in $D$.

## 7.8   Extending Strategies: Variation

You must be able to answer clearly these two questions before you can solve any problem.

A: What am I asked to find? (What don't I know?)
B: What information is given in the problem? (What do I know?)

Once you have answered questions A and B you can plan your solution. For example, compare these variations:

- The mass, $M$, of a rod varies directly with its length, $L$.

  $M = kL$

- The value, $V$, of a diamond varies directly with the square of its mass, $M$.

  $V = kM^2$

- The time of swing, $T$, of a pendulum varies directly with the square root of its length, $L$.

  $T = k\sqrt{L}$

Each of these variations is a direct variation, but each equation has a different form. The following example shows how you can extend any strategies you have already learned in the previous sections to solve any problem involving a direct variation.

**Example**    The number of bacteria in a culture varies directly with the square of the time the bacteria have been growing. A culture is estimated to have 1200 bacteria after 4 min. If it continues to grow under the same conditions, how long will it take to have 30 000 bacteria?

**Solution**    Let $M$ represent the number of bacteria and $T$ the time in minutes

$$M \propto T^2 \text{ or } M = kT^2 \text{ where } k \text{ is the constant of variation.}$$

*Method 1:* Find the constant of variation.

$M = kT^2, M = 1200, T = 4$
$1200 = k(4)^2$

$\dfrac{1200}{(4)^2} = k \text{ or } k = 75$

The variation equation is given by $M = 75T^2$
Use $M = 30\,000, T = ?$
$30\,000 = 75T^2$
$400 = T^2$
$20 = T \ (T \text{ is positive.})$

*Method 2:* Use the proportion for the variation.

$\dfrac{M_1}{T_1^2} = \dfrac{M_2}{T_2^2}$    $M_1 = 1200, T_1 = 4,$
$M_2 = 30\,000, T_2 = ?$

$\dfrac{1200}{(4)^2} = \dfrac{30\,000}{T_2^2}$

$T_2^2 = \dfrac{30\,000(4)^2}{1200}$

$= 400$
$T_2 = 20 \ (T \text{ is positive.})$

Thus, there will be 30 000 bacteria after 20 min.

## 7.8 Exercise

**A** Remember: Record the given information before you do any calculations.

1 Write an equation to express each variation.

(a) The distance, $D$, a car travels upon braking on a wet surface varies directly with the square of its speed, $s$, at the time of braking.

(b) The amount of heat, $I$, from a camp fire varies inversely with the square of the distance, $d$, from the camp fire.

(c) The distance, $d$, an object falls from a height varies directly with the square of the time, $t$, the object has been falling.

(d) The force of gravity, $F$, between the sun and the earth is inversely proportional to the square of the distance, $r$, between them.

(e) The power, $P$, of a current varies directly with the square of the current, $I$.

(f) The cost, $C$, of operating a power boat varies directly with the cube of the speed, $S$, of the boat.

2 (a) If $y$ varies directly with $x^2$, find the constant of variation if $y = 288$ and $x = 24$.

(b) If $R$ varies inversely with the square of $s$, find the constant of variation if $R = 24$ when $s = 15$.

3 (a) $S$ is said to be directly proportional to the square of $T$. Find $T$ when $S = 800$, if you know that $T = 30$ when $S = 200$.

(b) A variation is given by $PQ^2 = k$ where $k$ is a constant. If $P = 3$ when $Q = 36$, then find $P$ when $Q = 9$.

4 A variation is given by "$t$ varies directly with $q^2$."

(a) Write the variation equation to express the relationship.

(b) If $t = 81$ when $q = 18$, then find $t$ when $q = 90$.

5 (a) If $P$ varies inversely with $V^2$, then write an equation for the inverse variation.

(b) If $P = 16$ when $V = 10$, find $P$ when $V = 4$.

**B** 6 As a vehicle moves, the resistance to its movement by the air varies directly with its speed.

(a) Write a proportion to express this variation.

(b) For a car travelling at 40 km/h, the resistance is 8 units. Find the resistance when the speed of the car is 10 km/h.

7   The volume of a cylinder varies inversely with the square of its radius.
    (a) Find the constant of variation if a cylinder of radius 3.0 cm holds 49.5 L.
    (b) If a cylinder holds 137.5 L, find its radius.

8   The resistance of air to a moving object varies directly as the square of
    the velocity of the object. If the air resistance is 50.0 units when the
    velocity is 15.0 km/h, find the resistance when the velocity is 30.0 km/h.

9   The pull, $P$, between a magnet and a piece of metal varies inversely as
    the square of the distance between them, $d$. If the pull is 8.0 units when
    the distance is 4.0 cm, find the pull when the distance is increased by 4.0 cm.

10  The distance a hockey puck travels on ice varies directly with the square
    of the speed of the puck. A puck, moving at a speed of 4.0 m/s, travels
    220.0 m before stopping. How fast is a puck moving, if it travels 495.0 m
    before stopping?

11  The exposure time required for a photograph is inversely proportional
    to the square of the diameter of the camera lens. If the diameter of
    the lens is 2.0 cm, the exposure time is $\frac{1}{100}$ s. Find the diameter of the
    lens if the exposure time is $\frac{1}{625}$ s.

12  The number of bacteria in a culture is directly proportional to the square
    of the time the bacteria have been growing. A culture contains 900 bacteria
    after growing for 15 min. How long will it take for the culture to contain
    3000 bacteria?

13  The illumination provided by a light varies inversely with the square
    of the distance from the lamp. Jessica is sitting 3.0 m from the lamp. How
    close should she sit to receive twice as much light?

14  The time of the swing of a pendulum varies directly as the square root
    of its length. A pendulum that is 1.0 m in length swings once every 2.0 s.
    Find the time of swing of a pendulum that is 72.0 cm in length. (Express
    your answer to 1 decimal place.)

15  The amount of material required to cover a ball is directly proportional to
    the square of the radius of the ball. A ball with a radius of 15.0 cm requires
    2826.0 cm². What is the radius of the ball that requires 803.8 cm² of material?

C 16  If you shine a spotlight at an object, the intensity of illumination varies
    inversely with the square of the distance from the object, Michael stood
    4.0 m from a fence and registered a reading of 4.0 units. How far from the
    fence must Michael stand in order to double the reading of the intensity?

# 7.9 Using Graphs: Partial Variation

The total cost, $C$, of catering a banquet depends partly on a fixed cost, $F$, and partly on a variable cost, $V$.

$$C = F + V$$

Such a variation is called a **partial variation**.

The cost of a banquet at Julians Banquet Hall is $450 for the facilities (fixed cost) and $15 for each meal served (variable cost). The cost, $C$, in dollars, is given by

$$C = 450 + 15n$$

fixed cost     variable cost, where $n$ is the number of meals served

*Fixed costs might include rental of facilities, cleaning staff, music, decorations. Variable costs might include number of meals served, and number of serving staff.*

A table of values is constructed to draw a graph of the partial variation.

| Number of people | 50 | 75 | 100 | 200 | 250 |
|---|---|---|---|---|---|
| Cost ($) | 1200 | 1575 | 1950 | 3450 | 4200 |

The graph does not pass through the origin. By interpolation, the cost of a banquet for 225 people is about $3800. The number of meals served for a banquet costing $2400 is 130.

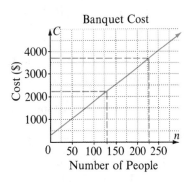

Banquet Cost

## 7.9 Exercise

**B 1** The cost of a 30.0-cm pizza with cheese and tomato sauce is $6.00. It costs $0.75 for each additional topping.

(a) Write an equation to show the partial variation.

(b) Construct a table of values for up to 8 additional toppings.

(c) Draw a graph of the partial variation.

2   The cost of a long-distance call between Eckville and Darwin is 72¢ for the first minute and 61¢ for each additional minute.

(a) Write an equation to show the partial variation.

(b) Construct a table of values for up to 20 min.

(c) Draw a graph of the partial variation.

3   The cost of having furniture or an appliance delivered from a retailer is $25.00 if within a 50-km radius of its location and 50¢ for each additional kilometre.

(a) Write an equation to show this partial variation.

(b) Construct a table of values for up to 200 additional kilometres.

(c) Draw a graph of the partial variation.

(d) On which customer is the retailer making the most profit?
      (i) One 5 km away    (ii) One 50 km away   (iii) One 100 km away

4   The daily cost of renting a car from Ace Rental is $22.00 plus 5¢/km driven. The daily cost of renting a car from Brights Rental is $35.00 plus 2¢/km driven.

(a) Write an equation to show each partial variation.

(b) Construct a table of values for each company for up to 750 km.

(c) Draw a graph for each partial variation on the same set of axes.

(d) After how many kilometres is the cost the same for both companies?

C 5   Refer to your answer in Question 4 above. Write conclusions about renting a car if the planned distance to be travelled is
   • greater than        • less than
   the number of kilometres identified in part (d) of Question 4.

## Problem-Solving  PSP

To solve some problems, you often cannot find a direct method, so you make an estimate and then guess and check. For example, numbers have intrigued people and in developing strategies to solve problems, often much mathematics has subsequently been created. The number 153 has a strange property. $153 = 1^3 + 5^3 + 3^3$.

▶ What other numbers have the same property? To solve the problem you could guess and check. One of the answers is 407.

▶ Use a calculator to estimate another answer and then check.

▶ You could spend a lifetime checking numbers. Write a computer program in BASIC to check all the numbers to 1000 that have the same property.

# 7.10 PSP Partial Variation: Problem-Solving

There are many situations in which the strategy of partial variation is needed in order to solve the problem.

- The total expenses of a basketball tournament are partly constant and partly vary with the number of players participating in the tournament.
- The total cost of placing an advertisement in the newspaper depends partly on a fixed cost and partly varies with the number of words in the advertisement.
- The total amount earned by a person may depend on a fixed part and a part that varies with the amount of sales.

The payment made to a sales manager is related to partial variation, as shown in the following example.

**Example 1**   Jennifer, a sales manager, receives a fixed salary of $3500 per month plus a variable amount calculated as $\frac{1}{2}\%$ commission on the amount of the sales of her staff. Find her total December income if the December sales were $525 000?

**Solution**   Let $I$, in dollars, represent Jennifer's total December income. Then the amount of income, in dollars, can be represented by

$$I = 3500 + 0.005A$$

$\uparrow$ fixed amount, a salary of $3500            $\uparrow$ variable amount based on $\frac{1}{2}\%$ commission

Use $A = 525\ 000$. Then

$$I = 3500 + 0.005(525\ 000)$$
$$= 3500 + 2625$$
$$= 6125$$

Thus, Jennifer's total December income was $6125.

To solve some problems involving partial variation, you need to apply your skills in solving systems of equations, as shown in the following example.

**Example 2**   The cost of renting a car for the day depends on a fixed cost and a variable cost. Sam's cost for renting a car for the day and driving 250 km is $39.50. The cost of renting the same car for a day and driving 425 km is $44.75. Find the cost of renting the same car for a day and driving 550 km.

**Solution**  Let $f$ be the fixed cost and $h$ the variable cost.

$$39.50 = f + 250h \quad \text{①}$$
$$44.75 = f + 425h \quad \text{②}$$

Use the given information to construct the equations.

Subtract equation ① from ②.

$$5.25 = 0 + 175h$$

$$\frac{5.25}{175} = h \text{ or } h = 0.03$$

Use $h = 0.03$ in ①.

$$39.50 = f + 250(0.03)$$
$$39.50 = f + 7.50$$
$$f = 32$$

Thus, the equation expressing the cost $C$, in dollars, is

$$C = 32 + 0.03n \quad \text{where } n \text{ is the number of kilometres}$$

Use $n = 550$.

$$C = 32 + 0.03(550)$$
$$= 32 + 16.50$$
$$= 48.50$$

Thus, the cost of renting the car and driving 550 km is $48.50.

## 7.10 Exercise

**A** Review your skills in solving a system of linear equations.

1  A partial variation is given by $B = 18 + 6n$. Find B for
   (a) $n = 12$     (b) $n = 25$     (c) $n = 36$     (d) $n = 50$

2  A partial variation is given by $W = 150 + 20p$. Find $p$ for
   (a) $W = 390$     (b) $W = 790$     (c) $W = 490$     (d) $W = 1330$

3  A partial variation is given by $D = L + sb$. Use the following information to solve for $L$ and $s$.
   • If $b = 8$, then $D = 200$.     • If $b = 5$, then $D = 140$.

4  The total cost, $T$, in dollars, of publishing a school magazine depends on a fixed cost $800 and a variable cost of 40¢ per copy. Thus,
   $$T = 800 + 0.40n \quad \text{where } n \text{ is the number of copies produced.}$$
   1000 copies are produced.
   (a) What is the total cost, $T$?
   (b) What should one copy sell for so that production costs are *just covered*? Express your answer to the nearest cent.

5    The total cost, $T$, in dollars, of printing advertisement brochures consists
     of a fixed cost $K$ and a cost that varies with the number, $n$, of copies
     printed.
     (a) Explain why $T = K + pn$, where $p$ is the constant of variation,
         expresses this partial variation.
     (b) Find $T$ if $K = 400$ (in dollars), $p = 20$ (in cents) and $n = 300$.

   B For each problem, be sure to write the equation that expresses the
     partial variation.

6    For publishing a newsletter, the total cost $T$ in dollars is given by
           $T = S + kn,$    where $k$ is the constant of variation
                            $n$ is the number of copies
                            $S$ is the fixed cost
                            $T$ is the total cost
     (a) Find the value of the constant of variation, $k$, if the fixed cost, $S$, is
         $160, the total cost, $T$, is $205, and 150 copies are printed.
     (b) Find $T$ if 350 copies are printed.

7    The cost of printing handbills is partly constant and partly varies directly
     as the number printed. To print 20 copies, the total cost would be $47.80
     and the variable cost would be $41.80. Find the cost of printing
     1000 copies.

8    The cost of taking a class to a beach party is partly constant and partly
     varies inversely as the number of students. If 12 students are taken, then
     it costs each student $4. If 30 students were to go it would cost each
     student $1.20.
     (a) What would it cost to take 60 students?
     (b) What costs would be included as part of the constant cost?

9    The expenses of playing in a basketball tournament in another city is
     partly constant and partly varies directly with the number of players that
     go. If 10 players were to go, they would each have to pay $14. However,
     if 20 players were to go, then each player would need to pay $10.25.
     What would it cost each player if 40 players were to go?

 C 10  The value of a piece of machinery is partly constant and partly varies
     inversely as the age, in years, of the machine. The value of a machine is
     $200 after 4 years, but after 8 years it is worth $150.
     (a) Calculate the value of the machine after 10 years.
     (b) How long will it take the machine to be worth $120?

## Practice and Problems: Review

1   Find the minimum value of $C = 6x + 7y$ if $4x + 3y \geq 30$, $x + 3y \geq 12$, $x$ and $y$ positive.

2   A partial variation is given by $y = b + mx$. Find $m$ and $b$ if $y = 30$ when $x = 12$ and $y = 34$ when $x = 14$.

3   An inverse variation is given by $M$ varies inversely as $K$. When $M = 90$, then $K = 55$. Find the constant of variation, and find $M$ when $K = 40$.

4   The cost of a person-to-person phone call to the Arctic is $3.50 for the first 3 minutes plus $0.65 for each additional minute.

   (a) Find the cost for an 8 minute phone call to the Arctic.

   (b) The charge for a call is $11.30. How many minutes was the call?

5   Burlington Runners repairs sports shoes, particularly tennis and jogging shoes. Two operations are required on each shoe and the times required on each operation are shown. If two people repair these shoes, one person performing each operation and each working 8 h/d, and if the profits on tennis and jogging shoes are $3 and $5 respectively, how many pairs of each shoe should be repaired daily to maximize the profits?

|         | Strip  | Re-sew |
|---------|--------|--------|
| Tennis  | 16 min | 12 min |
| Jogging | 8 min  | 16 min |

## Practice Test

1   Draw the region defined by each system of inequations.

   (a)   $2x - y \geq 3$, $x + y \leq 3$       (b)   $y - x \leq 4$, $y - 3x \geq 0$, $x + y > 1$

2   Find the maximum value of $P = 50x + 30y$ subject to the conditions $x \geq 0$, $y \geq 0$, $x + y \leq 80$, $2x + y \leq 100$.

3   The mass of a substance varies directly as its volume.

   (a) Write an equation to express the direct variation.

   (b) When the mass is 125 g, the volume is 100 cm$^3$. Find the mass when the volume is 160 cm$^3$.

4   (a) $p$ varies inversely as $q$. Write an equation to express the inverse variation.

   (b) If $p = 86$, when $q = 38$, find $p$ when $q = 20$.

5   The electrical resistance in a wire is directly proportional to its length. A copper wire is 15.0 cm in length and has a resistance of 4.5 $\Omega$ (ohms). Find the resistance of 2.0 cm of this wire. What length would you need to use to obtain a resistance of 12.0 $\Omega$?

# 8 Methods of Geometry: Problem-Solving

Language of deductive geometry, congruence, postulates, side-side-side, side-angle-side, angle-side-angle, hypotenuse-side, properties, writing proofs, proving theorems, strategies and problem-solving

## Introduction

The language of geometry has evolved in the same way as any other language that is thousands of years old. That is, with each stage of evolution, an attempt is made to make the meanings and symbols clearer to understand. In your study of geometry, you will continue a process that has been used and studied for thousands of years - the use of logical reasoning to prove geometric facts, given in the form of deductions. The diagram at the right will help you to understand the nature of solving a problem.

> I — What you know.
>
> To go from I to II, or II to I, use your mathematical skills and strategies. The more of them you know and remember, the better are your chances of success in solving a problem.
>
> II — What you want to know.

The history of mathematics is an exciting display of the achievements of many minds that have developed a language of mathematics, skills, and strategies in their attempt to solve problems. About two thousand years ago, Euclid, a Greek mathematician, wrote thirteen books called *The Elements*, a compilation of the various facts already known about deductive geometry. This body of facts, taken as a whole, is often referred to today as Euclidean Geometry. The study of Euclidean Geometry is not unlike your study of mathematics, as shown below.

Study of Euclidean Geometry                    Study of Mathematics

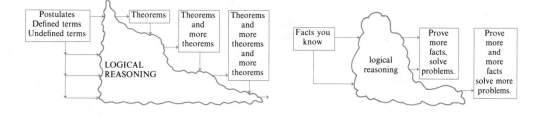

# 8.1 PSP Thinking Strategies for Mathematics

The ability to connect the answers to these two important questions is an important strategy for solving a mathematical problem, or any other type of problem.

| A: What am I given? | to find | B: What I want to know. |

The diagram at the right illustrates a process that can be followed to solve a problem. Each of you may use your skills and strategies in different ways. Often two *different* persons may obtain two *different* solutions to the *same* problem. However, by learning different strategies for solving a problem, you can better apply them when you are confronted with a new problem. The following are some types of thinking available to you for learning new facts.

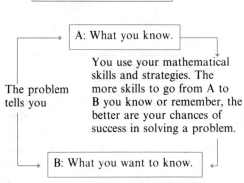

A: What you know.

You use your mathematical skills and strategies. The more skills to go from A to B you know or remember, the better are your chances of success in solving a problem.

The problem tells you

B: What you want to know.

## Patterned Thinking

You can use a pattern to suggest a solution to a problem such as:   PSP

What is the last digit of the value of $2^{100}$?

You do not have to calculate $2^{100}$ in order to answer the problem. That would take a long time. However, by thinking of a simpler problem, you can find the last digit, as shown below.

| 2 is the last digit of the value of these powers. | 4 is the last digit of the value of these powers. | 8 is the last digit of the value of these powers. | 6 is the last digit of the value of these powers. |
|---|---|---|---|
| $2^1 = 2$ | $2^2 = 4$ | $2^3 = 8$ | $2^4 = 16$ |
| $2^5 = 32$ | $2^6 = 64$ | $2^7 = 128$ | $2^8 = 256$ |
| 2 | 4 | 8 | 6 |

Now all you have to do is to determine into which column $2^{100}$ can be placed. $2^{100}$ belongs in the last column. Thus,

The last digit of the value of $2^{100}$ is 6.

You can use patterned thinking to solve some problems in algebra and in geometry.

## Inductive Thinking

You can learn new facts through experimentation. For example, while exploring the triangles in your previous work in geometry, you might have noticed that by measuring the angles and finding their sum, the sum is 180° (approximately). By trying other triangles, you find again that the sum of the angles is approximately 180°. Thus you might make the general statement.

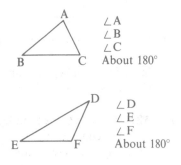

The sum of the measures of the angles of any triangle seems to be 180°.

When you make a general statement from a number of particular examples, you are thinking *inductively*. The inductive method has been used by all of you at some time or another to learn new facts. (You used the inductive method to learn that a hot stove hurts when you touch it.) The scientist depends on the inductive method to learn new things from experiments.

## Deductive Thinking

The nature of deductive thinking is best described by using a number of examples. Suppose you accept the truth of the following general statement.

General Statement: Rattlesnakes are dangerous.

Then, if you happen to meet a rattlesnake (named Ben), in the desert, you will come to a particular conclusion.

Ben is a rattlesnake. Therefore Ben is dangerous.

By using your powers of thought you have deduced that Ben, the rattlesnake in the desert, is dangerous. This form of thinking is called *deductive thinking.*

Deductive thinking is used many times in mathematics. You have already shown inductively that the following general statement is true.

The sum of the measures of the angles of a triangle is 180°.

You can use this proven statement (fact) to deduce new information about figures in geometry. Thus, when you happen to meet a particular triangle, you can write

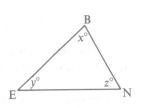

$$\angle B + \angle E + \angle N = 180°$$
$$x° + y° + z° = 180°$$

Thus, when you use facts to prove more statements, you are *thinking deductively.* You will meet many examples of deductive thinking in subsequent chapters.

# 8.1 Exercise

**A** Review the meaning of *patterned, inductive* and *deductive thinking.*

Identify which type of thinking each of the following is an example of. Give reasons for your answer.

1 After a number of examples, the class concluded that vertically opposite angles are equal.

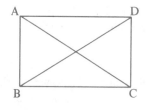

$x, y$ indicate vertically opposite angles when two line segments intersect.

2 All cows are animals. Mirabel is a cow, so Mirabel is an animal.

3 The class found the sum of even numbers. They concluded that the sum of any number of even numbers is always even.

4 Chocolate becomes smooth when heated. If Sam heats the chocolate, it will become smooth.

**B** Decide which type of reasoning was used in each of the following.

5 The diagonals of a rectangle bisect each other. In the diagram ABCD is a rectangle. Thus $\overline{BD}$ and $\overline{AC}$ bisect each other.

6 The class found that in the triangles it drew that $\overline{DE} = 2\overline{BC}$.

These symbols mean $\overline{AC} = \overline{CE}$.

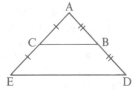

7 The team scored a touchdown during each game of the season. Thus they will score a touchdown in the last game of the season.

8 Any tomato juice will stain a carpet. Jennifer spilled tomato juice on the carpet. What did Jennifer deduce?

9 To qualify in the race you must run 100.0 m in less than 11.5 s. Joanne qualified in the race. Thus, Joanne ran 100.0 m in less than 11.5 s.

10 In any parallelogram, the opposite angles are equal.

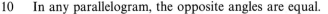

Heather drew a parallelogram EFGH.
Thus she knew that $\angle F = \angle H$.

11 On a hot day the swimming pool is open. Monday will be a hot day.
Thus the pool will be open.

12 When the toaster is plugged in at the same time as the hairdryer, the fuse
is blown. If Lori plugs in the hairdryer and the toaster, the fuse will blow.

13 The first 4 triangular numbers are shown.

    1        3        6        10

Use patterned thinking to find the 5th and 6th triangular number.

14 If two people shake hands, this is counted as 1 handshake. The diagram shows
the number of handshakes. Each diagonal is a handshake.

| 2 people | 3 people | 4 people |
|---|---|---|
| 1 handshake | 3 handshakes | 6 handshakes |

(a) Use patterned thinking to find how many handshakes in all there will
be for 5 people.

(b) Find a pattern in your answers in (a) to find how many handshakes
there will be in all for 25 people.

## Problem-Solving

To solve this problem you must be
organized. You must choose all the
possibilities. How many triangles
are in the diagram?

## 8.2 The Language of Deductive Geometry

You have already used logical reasoning many times to arrive at certain conclusions, without really being aware of its importance as a method of thinking. For example

| A General statement | and | B Particular statement | $\longrightarrow$ | C Conclusion |
|---|---|---|---|---|

$$\left(\begin{array}{l}\text{During a game, 5}\\\text{persons are used on}\\\text{the basketball team.}\end{array}\right) \quad \text{and} \quad \left(\begin{array}{l}\text{Westend College is}\\\text{playing basketball.}\end{array}\right) \longrightarrow \left(\begin{array}{l}\text{Thus Westend uses}\\\text{5 persons on the}\\\text{basketball team.}\end{array}\right)$$

$$\left(\begin{array}{l}\text{All isosceles triangles}\\\text{have two equal sides.}\end{array}\right) \quad \text{and} \quad (\triangle ABC \text{ is isosceles.}) \longrightarrow \left(\begin{array}{l}\text{Thus two sides of}\\\triangle ABC \text{ are equal.}\end{array}\right)$$

Everyday, you use deductive thinking to *deduce* new information. The above method of deductive thinking involves the following steps.

*Step A*
Based on your earlier knowledge (your experience, what you have learned, etc.) you accept certain general statements to be true.

*Step B*
Then you are confronted with a particular case that is related to the general statement in Step A.

*Step C*
Then you are able to deduce a conclusion, based on Steps A and B.

You will use this method to *deduce* the properties of geometric figures and many geometric relationships. To develop your work in geometry in an organized way, think as Euclid did. He organized the material in his books in a logical way. Euclid and his followers then used their logical reasoning to expand their knowledge of geometry. The diagram shown below demonstrates the plan followed in developing skills in geometry.

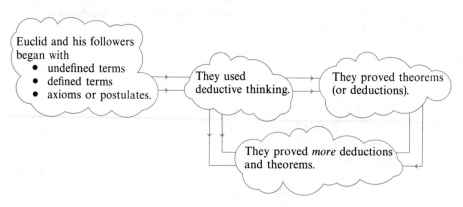

There is a special vocabulary that you need to learn in order to study deductive geometry. It is most important that there is a general agreement on the meanings of the vocabulary of geometry. The meaning of each word below is very precise.

**Undefined Terms:** Not all words can be defined. Some must be accepted as true. Such terms are called *undefined terms*. These undefined terms are basic to your study of geometry: point, line, plane.

**Axioms or Postulates:** In your endeavours, whether it be in business or as a member of a club, there are certain working agreements or assumptions that are made and accepted as true. (Very often these assumptions or agreements are called "the ground rules".) The assumptions you make in geometry are called *axioms* or *postulates*. They are the "ground rules" in the study of geometry. A few axioms or postulates made by Euclid are as follows:

- A line contains at least two points.
- For every two different points, there is exactly one straight line that contains them.
- If three sides of one triangle are respectively congruent to three sides of another triangle, the triangles are congruent.
- If parallel lines are cut by a transversal, corresponding angles are congruent.

**Definition:** This is an agreement, which has been established, about the meaning of a word or a group of words. The following is an example of a definition:

> An isosceles triangle is a triangle with two equal sides.
>
> A good definition is *reversible*. In this case you can reverse the order to read "A triangle with two equal sides is isosceles."

A good definition uses the simplest words, or is written in words that have already been defined. You will develop skills for writing definitions in the following exercise.

**Deductions:** Statements to be proved or questions to be answered are called *deductions*.

**Theorems:** Some proven statements are so important that they can be used to prove more statements or to find the answer to more questions. Important proven statements are called *theorems*. The following are two examples of theorems:

*Theorem:* The sum of the measures of the angles of a triangle is 180.

*Theorem:* The angles opposite the equal sides of a triangle are equal.

In this section and others, you will trace some of the thinking and some of the methods of proof that Euclid and his followers contributed to mathematics.

## 8.2 Exercise

**B** Throughout this exercise, make a list of the vocabulary of geometry so that you may have them for later reference.

**PSP**

1  Write a definition for each of the diagrams shown.

(a) line segment AB, $\overline{AB}$

A•————•B

A, B are **end points**

(b) ray AB, $\overrightarrow{AB}$

A•————————•→ B

(c) angle ABC, $\angle ABC$

**vertex** of the angle.

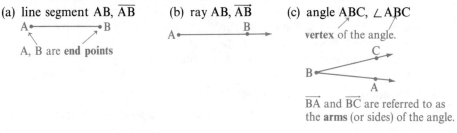

$\overrightarrow{BA}$ and $\overrightarrow{BC}$ are referred to as the **arms** (or sides) of the angle.

2  $\overrightarrow{BA}$ and $\overrightarrow{BC}$ are opposite rays. Write a definition for opposite rays.

←————•————•————•————→
C        B        A

3  Certain points have special properties. A diagram illustrates the property. Write a definition for each of the following.

(a) Midpoint of a segment:
A is the midpoint of BC.

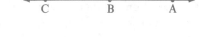

These symbols show $\overline{AB}$ and $\overline{AC}$ have equal lengths.

(b) Collinear points:  A, B, C, and D are collinear.

(c) Coplanar points:  A, B, C, and D are coplanar.

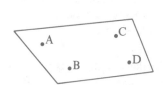

4  Write a definition for each of the following words. Use the diagrams to help you.

(a) Bisector of a segment: in each diagram, a bisector of $\overline{AB}$ is shown.

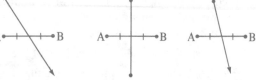

(b) Perpendicular bisector of a line segment. In each diagram a perpendicular bisector of $\overline{AB}$ is shown.

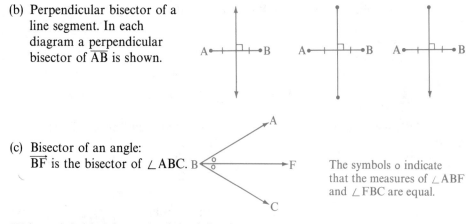

(c) Bisector of an angle:
$\overrightarrow{BF}$ is the bisector of $\angle ABC$.

The symbols o indicate that the measures of $\angle ABF$ and $\angle FBC$ are equal.

5 Write a definition for each of the following

(a) Congruent line segments: $\overline{AB}$ and $\overline{CD}$ are congruent.

(b) Congruent angles: $\angle ABC$ and $\angle DEF$ are congruent.

A

46°

B     C

D

46°

E     F

6 Angles are classified according to their measures. Write a definition for each angle.

|     | Name of angle | Measure of the angle, $x°$ |
|-----|---------------|----------------------------|
| (a) | acute         | $0° < x° < 90°$            |
| (b) | right         | $90°$                      |
| (c) | obtuse        | $90° < x° < 180°$          |
| (d) | straight      | $180°$                     |
| (e) | reflex        | $180° < x° < 360°$         |

7 Write a definition for each of the following types of angles. Diagrams illustrate the types of angles.

(a) Adjacent angles $\angle BAC$ and $\angle CAD$ are adjacent angles.

(b) Complementary angles ∠BAC and ∠CAD are complementary angles.

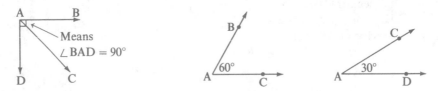

(c) Supplementary angles ∠BAC and ∠CAD are supplementary angles.

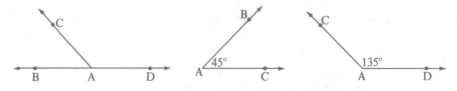

8   The word *polygon* is derived from the Greek words meaning *many angles*.

| These are examples of convex polygons. | These are examples of concave polygons. | These are not polygons. |

(a) Use the above illustrations to help you write the definition of a polygon.

(b) Once the meaning of the word *polygon* has been defined it can be used in other definitions. Write a definition for each of these special polygons.

| Name of special polygon | Number of sides |
| --- | --- |
| triangle | 3 |
| quadrilateral | 4 |
| pentagon | 5 |
| hexagon | 6 |
| septagon | 7 |
| octagon | 8 |

(c) You can use adjectives with the word *polygon* to define other types of polygons. Write a definition for each of the following.

equilateral polygon       equiangular polygon       regular polygon

9   Once the meaning of the word triangle has been defined, it can be used, along with adjectives, to define special triangles. Write a definition for each.

(a) Acute       (b) Equiangular    (c) Right       (d) Obtuse
    triangle          triangle         triangle      triangle

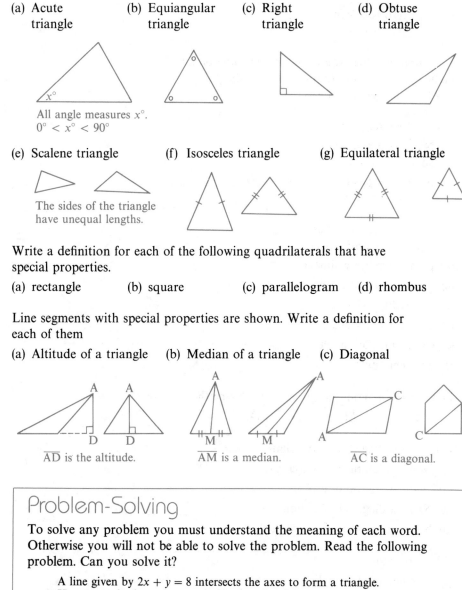

All angle measures $x°$.
$0° < x° < 90°$

(e) Scalene triangle      (f) Isosceles triangle      (g) Equilateral triangle

The sides of the triangle have unequal lengths.

10   Write a definition for each of the following quadrilaterals that have special properties.

(a) rectangle        (b) square        (c) parallelogram    (d) rhombus

11   Line segments with special properties are shown. Write a definition for each of them

(a) Altitude of a triangle    (b) Median of a triangle    (c) Diagonal

$\overline{AD}$ is the altitude.        $\overline{AM}$ is a median.        $\overline{AC}$ is a diagonal.

## Problem-Solving

To solve any problem you must understand the meaning of each word. Otherwise you will not be able to solve the problem. Read the following problem. Can you solve it?

> A line given by $2x + y = 8$ intersects the axes to form a triangle. How many lattice points are inside the triangle?

To solve the problem, you need to know the meaning of **lattice points.** Lattice points on the co-ordinate plane are those that have integral co-ordinates. $(3, 4)$, $(-2, 0)$ and $(-3, -4)$ are examples of lattice points. Now solve the problem.

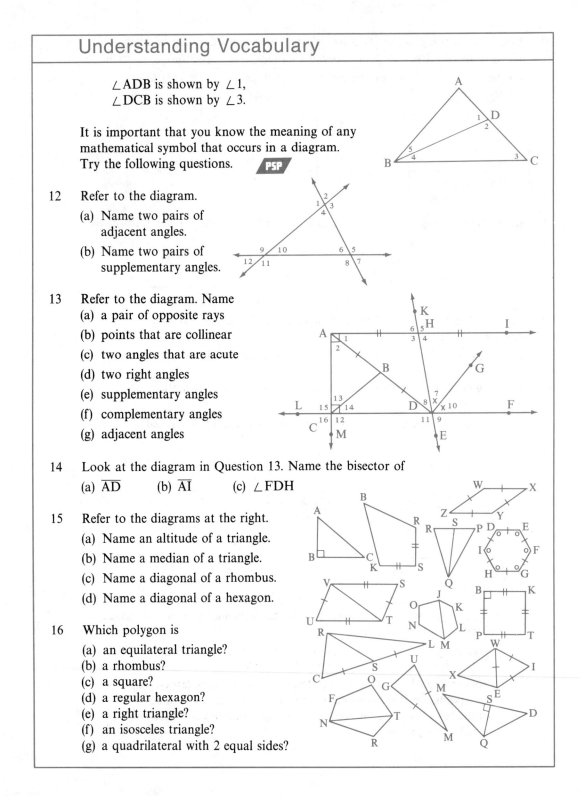

∠ADB is shown by ∠1,
∠DCB is shown by ∠3.

It is important that you know the meaning of any
mathematical symbol that occurs in a diagram.
Try the following questions. **PSP**

12  Refer to the diagram.

(a) Name two pairs of
adjacent angles.

(b) Name two pairs of
supplementary angles.

13  Refer to the diagram. Name

(a) a pair of opposite rays

(b) points that are collinear

(c) two angles that are acute

(d) two right angles

(e) supplementary angles

(f) complementary angles

(g) adjacent angles

14  Look at the diagram in Question 13. Name the bisector of

(a) $\overline{AD}$      (b) $\overline{AI}$      (c) ∠FDH

15  Refer to the diagrams at the right.

(a) Name an altitude of a triangle.

(b) Name a median of a triangle.

(c) Name a diagonal of a rhombus.

(d) Name a diagonal of a hexagon.

16  Which polygon is

(a) an equilateral triangle?

(b) a rhombus?

(c) a square?

(d) a regular hexagon?

(e) a right triangle?

(f) an isosceles triangle?

(g) a quadrilateral with 2 equal sides?

## 8.3 **PSP** Writing Proofs

Certain postulates are used when working with numbers $a$, $b$, $c$, and $d$.

*Addition Postulate:* If $a = b$ and $c = d$, then $a + c = b + d$.

*Subtraction Postulate:* If $a = b$ and $c = d$, then $a - c = b - d$.

*Multiplication Postulate:* If $a = b$, then $ac = bc$.

*Division Postulate:* If $a = b$, then $\dfrac{a}{c} = \dfrac{b}{c}$, $(c \neq 0)$.

You also use postulates such as the following in your study of geometry.

*Postulate:* There is exactly one straight line through any two points. The postulate above seems obvious, but it can be used to prove ideas or deductions that are not so obvious. The process used to do this is called **deductive thinking**. It uses accepted facts to arrive at a **conclusion**.

Example 1 demonstrates the process of deductive thinking. In it, certain facts and *logical reasoning* are combined to *reach a conclusion* or *prove a statement*.

**Example 1**   Prove that if two angles are equal their complements are equal.

Draw a diagram to help you understand the deduction.

**Solution**   Given: $\angle ABC = \angle PQR$
$\angle DBC = 90°$
$\angle SQR = 90°$

Required to prove:
$\angle DBA = \angle SQP$

Proof:

| Statements | Reasons |
|---|---|
| $\angle DBC = \angle SQR$ | given |
| $\angle ABC = \angle PQR$ | given |
| Thus, | |
| $\angle DBC - \angle ABC = \angle SQR - \angle PQR$ | subtraction postulate |
| $\angle DBA = \angle SQP$ | substitution postulate |

Write a concluding statement of your deduction.

Thus, if two angles are equal then their complements are equal.

Give a reason for each line of your proof.

Because the deduction you proved in Example 1 is considered important enough to be used in the proof of other deductions, it is called a **theorem**.

> **Complementary Angle Theorem (CAT):** If two angles are equal, then their complements are equal.

Example 2 combines theorems and algebraic skills to deduce other facts.

**Example 2**  $\angle BCD$ and $\angle GFH$ are equal complements of $\angle ACB$ and $\angle EFG$ respectively. Find $x$.

**Solution**

| Statements | Reasons | |
|---|---|---|
| Since $\angle BCD = \angle GFH$ | given | |
| then $\angle ACB = \angle EFG$ | CAT | Give the reason for |
| Thus, $2x - 3 = x + 2$ | | writing $\angle ACB = \angle EFG$. |
| $x = 5$ | | |

Whenever you record a proof, give reasons for each step. These reasons may be one of the following.
- definitions or postulates
- given information in the original problem
- theorems

You will develop important theorems throughout the following exercise. As a result, you will begin to develop an understanding of the nature of deductive proof.

# 8.3  Exercise

**A** Throughout this exercise, write **AB** for $\overline{AB}$ to simplify your work.

1  A proof is given for the following deduction.

Prove that if two angles are equal, then their supplements are equal.

Give the missing reasons, (a), (b), (c), and (d), in the following proof.

Given: $\angle SQP = \angle DBA$
$\angle RQP = \angle CBA = 180°$

Required to prove: $\angle SQR = \angle DBC$

Proof:

| Statements | Reasons |
|---|---|
| From the diagrams | |
| $\angle RQP = \angle CBA$ | (a) |
| $\angle SQP = \angle DBA$ | (b) |
| $\angle RQP - \angle SQP = \angle CBA - \angle DBA$ | (c) |
| $\angle SQR = \angle DBC$ | (d) |

The deduction proved in Question 1 is called the Supplementary Angle Theorem (SAT).

> **Supplementary Angle Theorem (SAT):** If two angles are equal, then their supplements are equal.

2 Find $p$ and $q$ in each of the following. Give reasons for your answers, (SAT or CAT).

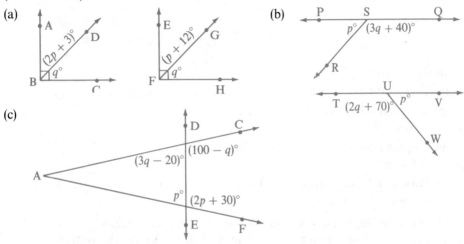

(c)

B Remember: Give a reason for each line of your proof.

3 Write a proof for each of the following.

(a) Given:  AG $\perp$ CB
$\qquad\qquad$ $\angle$ EGC $= \angle$ FGB
$\qquad$ Required to prove:
$\qquad\qquad$ $\angle$ AGE $= \angle$ AGF

(b) Given: $\triangle$ ABC
$\qquad\qquad$ $\angle$ DBH $= \angle$ ECG
$\qquad$ Required to prove:
$\qquad\qquad$ $\angle$ ABC $= \angle$ ACB

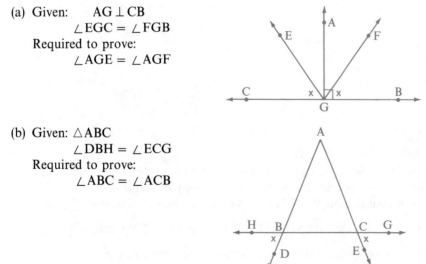

(c) Given: $\angle BDC = \angle GFE$
Required to prove:
$\angle ADB = \angle HFG$

(d) Given: $AB \perp BD$, $CB \perp BE$
Required to prove:
$\angle ABC = \angle DBE$

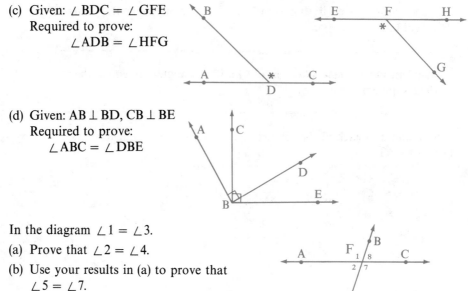

4 In the diagram $\angle 1 = \angle 3$.

(a) Prove that $\angle 2 = \angle 4$.

(b) Use your results in (a) to prove that $\angle 5 = \angle 7$.

(c) Use your results in (b) to prove that $\angle 6 = \angle 8$.

(d) How could you prove your result in (c) in a different way?

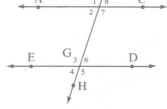

5 For the following diagrams, name the equal angles. Give reasons for your answers. Now you may use the symbols SAT and CAT to refer to the theorems.

(a)                              (b)

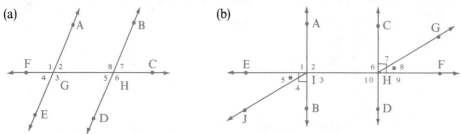

Earlier, you used inductive thinking to make observations about geometric properties. For example, you made the following observation for angles formed by intersecting lines:

If two lines intersect, then the vertically opposite angles are equal.

By measurement, you observed, $\angle AOC = \angle DOB$.

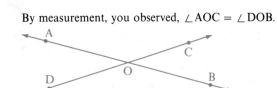

Now you can use the work you have completed in geometry, to prove that your observation is true. Not all deductions that are proven are called theorems. If a deduction is important enough to be used to prove other deductions it is called a **theorem**.

6 Write a proof for the following.

Given: AB and CD are intersecting lines.
Required to prove: $\angle DOA = \angle BOC$ and
$\qquad \angle AOC = \angle DOB$

The result of Question 6 is referred to as the Vertically Opposite Angles Theorem (VOAT).

> **Vertically Opposite Angles Theorem (VOAT):** If two lines intersect, then the vertically opposite angles are equal.

7 For each diagram, find $x$ and $y$. Give reasons for your answers.

(a)

(b)

(c) $AB \perp BC$

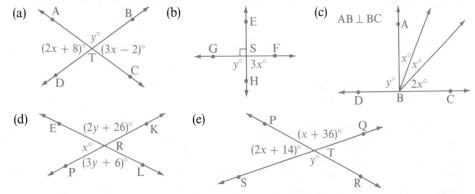

(d)

(e)

8 Illustrate each of the following theorems by an example of your own.

(a) Complementary Angles Theorem (CAT).
(b) Supplementary Angles Theorem (SAT).
(c) Vertically Opposite Angles Theorem (VOAT).

## 8.4 Writing Congruences

In the photograph, the tailor is cutting out parts for jeans. The parts are the same shape and size and for this reason are said to be **congruent**.

Congruence is a concept that permeates our everyday world. Replacement parts for bicycles are congruent. Bottles of the same brand are congruent. Footballs used in professional football are congruent. Mass produced items such as stamps are congruent.

If two figures are congruent, then they are congruent in all respects, whether you are working in 2 dimensions or 3 dimensions. However, all figures in this chapter will be in 2 dimensions (on the plane). You can use the following to simplify your work.

If two line segments are congruent, then their lengths are equal.

$$\overline{AB} \cong \overline{CD} \qquad \longrightarrow \qquad AB = CD$$

$\overline{AB}$ is congruent to $\overline{CD}$.        The lengths of AB and CD are equal.

Throughout, use AB = CD, since if AB = CD then you know that $\overline{AB}$ *is congruent to* $\overline{CD}$.

In a similar way, use $\angle ABC = \angle DEF$ throughout your work since

$$\angle ABC = \angle DEF \qquad \longrightarrow \qquad \angle ABC \cong \angle DEF$$

The measures of $\angle ABC$    $\longrightarrow$    $\angle ABC$ is congruent to $\angle DEF$.
and $\angle DEF$ are equal.

The two triangles drawn on the grid are congruent. For $\triangle ABC$ and $\triangle DEF$ the following corresponding parts are congruent and thus their corresponding measures are equal.

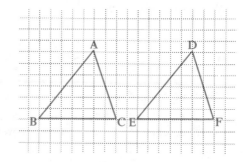

$$\angle A = \angle D \qquad AB = DE$$
$$\angle B = \angle E \qquad BC = EF$$
$$\angle C = \angle F \qquad CA = FD$$

Since △ABC and △DEF are congruent, you use symbols to write a congruence statement in a particular way.

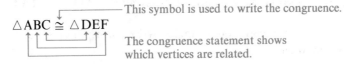

In general, two figures are said to be congruent if the measures of their corresponding parts are equal. The congruence statement shows which sides and angles are related. Thus,

$$\triangle ABC \cong \triangle DEF \qquad \triangle ABC \cong \triangle DEF$$
$$AB = DE \qquad\qquad \angle C = \angle F$$

For this reason, when you work with congruence statements, it is important and essential that you match corresponding vertices when congruent triangles are given.

**Example**   In the diagram, △PQR ≅ △PQS
Name the pairs of equal sides and angles.

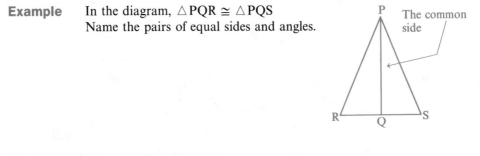

**Solution**   Since △PQR ≅ △PQS
then     RQ = SQ        ∠RPQ = ∠SPQ
         RP = SP        ∠PQR = ∠PQS
         QP = QP        ∠PRQ = ∠PSQ

To show which corresponding parts are equal, use symbols on the sides and the angles as shown.

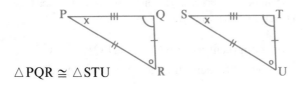

△PQR ≅ △STU

## 8.4 Exercise

**A** Be sure you know the meaning of the symbol △ABC ≅ △DEF.

1   For each pair of congruent triangles, write corresponding pairs of equal sides and angles.

(a)  △ABC ≅ △PQR          (b)  △EFG ≅ △RST

(c)  △XYZ ≅ △STU          (d)  △BCD ≅ △QRS

2   If △PQR ≅ △ABC which of the following are true?

(a)  PQ = AB   (b)  ∠P = ∠B   (c)  ∠R = ∠C          (d)  QR = BC

(e)  RQ = BC   (f)  ∠Q = ∠B   (g)  ∠QRP = ∠BAC   (h)  ∠PQR = ∠ABC

3   The triangles shown in each diagram are congruent. For each pair of triangles,
   • write an appropriate congruence statement.
   • name the pairs of equal corresponding angles and sides.

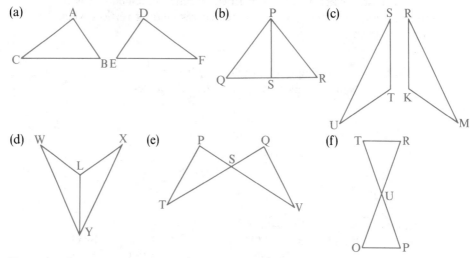

4   Two triangles are congruent as shown.     △ABC ≅ △DEF

   Which of the following are true?

(a)  △BCA ≅ △EFD          (b)  △BAC ≅ △EFD          (c)  △CBA ≅ △FED

(d)  △CAB ≅ △FDE          (e)  △DFE ≅ △ABC          (f)  △EDF ≅ △BAC

**B** To write a congruence statement, you need to identify clearly, the corresponding parts of the triangle.

5   Two triangles are congruent as shown.     △PQR ≅ △EFG

   Write the congruence statement in as many other ways as you can.

6   Write the 6 facts that must be true if △MNP ≅ △QRS.

7   (a) Refer to the diagrams. Which pairs of triangles are congruent? Give
       reasons for your answer.

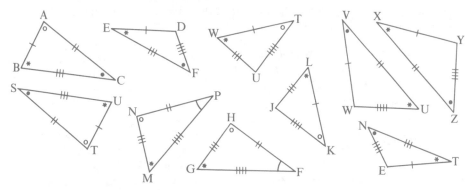

   (b) Write the appropriate congruence statement for your answers in (a).

8   (a) Write a congruence statement for each of the following pairs of
       congruent triangles.

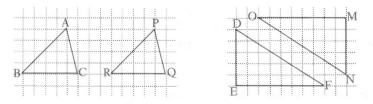

   (b) Write the congruence statement in as many ways as you can.

9   The vertices of two triangles are given.
       △ABC    A(−1, −1)    B(4, −1)    C(2, 1)
       △DEF    D(−1, −2)    E(4, −2)    F(1, 0)
   (a) Plot the triangles.    (b) Which sides are equal?    (c) Which angles are equal?
   (d) If the two triangles are congruent, write the appropriate congruence
       relation.

C 10   Points are given on the co-ordinate plane.
       A(0, 0)       B(2, 3)      C(0, 5)      D(−5, 0)     E(−1, 0)    F(−3, 3)
       G(−1, −2)     H(6, −2)     I(2, 0)      L(7, −2)     M(9, 0)     N(12, −2)
       P(−3, 2)      Q(1, 2)      R(−1, 5)     S(−3, −2)    T(−1, 2)    U(−3, 5)
   (a) Which pairs of triangles from this list are congruent?
       △ABC, △DEF, △GHI, △LMN, △PQR, △STU
   (b) Write congruence relations for pairs of congruent triangles in (a) above.

# 8.5 Congruence Postulate: Side-Side-Side

In mathematics, the question "What if . . . ?" is often asked. The answer to this question often results in the pursuit of the answer to many ideas in mathematics. For example:

If two triangles are congruent then you know all 6 corresponding parts have equal measures.

$$\triangle ABC \cong \triangle DEF$$

| | |
|---|---|
| AB = DE | $\angle A = \angle D$ |
| BC = EF | $\angle B = \angle E$ |
| AC = DF | $\angle C = \angle F$ |

What if only some of the corresponding parts have equal measures? Will the triangles be congruent?

Under what conditions will triangles be congruent if only certain corresponding parts have equal measures?

If you were to construct, as an experiment, a number of triangles with the measures shown in the diagram, you would find that all the triangles constructed would have the same angle measures. Thus it seems that congruent triangles can be constructed if the measures of only three sides are given. This observation leads to the following congruence postulate.

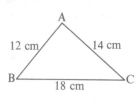

**Congruence Postulate: Side-Side-Side** If three sides of a triangle are respectively equal to three sides of another triangle, then the triangles are congruent.

Remember that a postulate in geometry is a statement that is accepted without proof.

Use the symbol SSS to refer to this postulate.

In $\triangle ABC$ and $\triangle DEF$,

since AB = DE ⎫
    BC = EF ⎬ —— The corresponding
    AC = DF ⎭     sides are equal.
then $\triangle ABC \cong \triangle DEF$   (SSS Postulate)

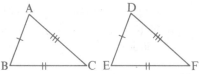

Write the reason why the two triangles are congruent.

Once you know that the two triangles are congruent you can write other facts about the triangles. For example, since $\triangle ABC \cong \triangle DEF$ then $\angle A = \angle D$, $\angle B = \angle E$, and $\angle C = \angle F$. You can use your postulates and your earlier work to prove other statements in geometry.

**Example 1**  Show that $\angle Q = \angle S$.

**Solution**  Given: $\triangle TQR$, $\triangle TSR$,
$\qquad\qquad TQ = TS$, $QR = SR$

Required to prove: $\angle Q = \angle S$

Proof:

| Statements | Reasons |
|---|---|
| In $\triangle TQR$ and $\triangle TSR$ | |
| $TQ = TS$ | given |
| $QR = SR$ | given |
| $TR = TR$ | common side |
| Thus $\triangle TQR \cong \triangle TSR$ | SSS Postulate |
| Thus $\angle Q = \angle S$ | |

Remember to justify each step of your proof.

In the next example, you need to remember the properties of a rhombus. Remember: A rhombus is a quadrilateral with all sides equal.

**Example 2**  For the rhombus ABCD show that $\angle A = \angle C$.

**Solution**  Given: rhombus ABCD

Required to prove: $\angle A = \angle C$

It is useful to mark known information on the diagram. →

Proof:  Join DB

| Statements | Reasons |
|---|---|
| In $\triangle DAB$, $\triangle DCB$ | |
| $DA = DC$ | rhombus definition |
| $AB = CB$ | rhombus definition |
| $DB = DB$ | common side |
| Thus $\triangle DAB \cong \triangle DCB$ | SSS Postulate |
| Thus $\angle A = \angle C$ | Why? |

## 8.5 Exercise

**A** 1  Two triangles are given as shown.
(a) Why are they congruent?
(b) Write the congruence statement.

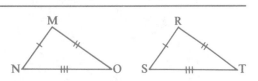

2 (a) Which pairs of triangles are congruent?

(b) Write the congruence statement for the pairs of congruent triangles.

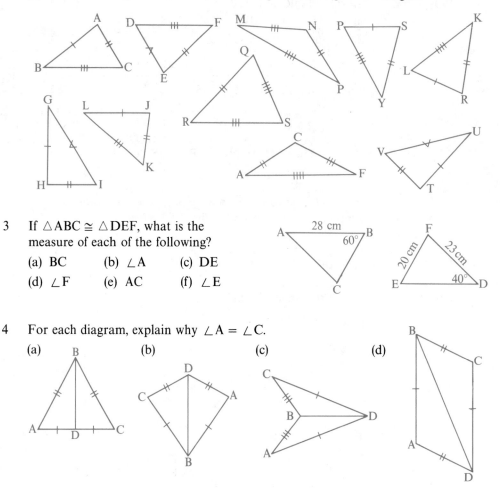

3 If △ABC ≅ △DEF, what is the measure of each of the following?

(a) BC     (b) ∠A     (c) DE

(d) ∠F     (e) AC     (f) ∠E

4 For each diagram, explain why ∠A = ∠C.

(a)     (b)     (c)     (d)

5 If you wish to prove each of the following pairs of triangles congruent using the SSS Postulate, what additional information would you need to know for each pair of triangles?

(a)     (b)

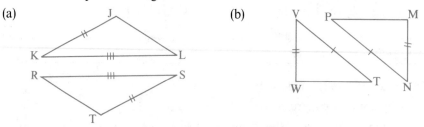

**B** Remember: Give reasons for each step of your proof.

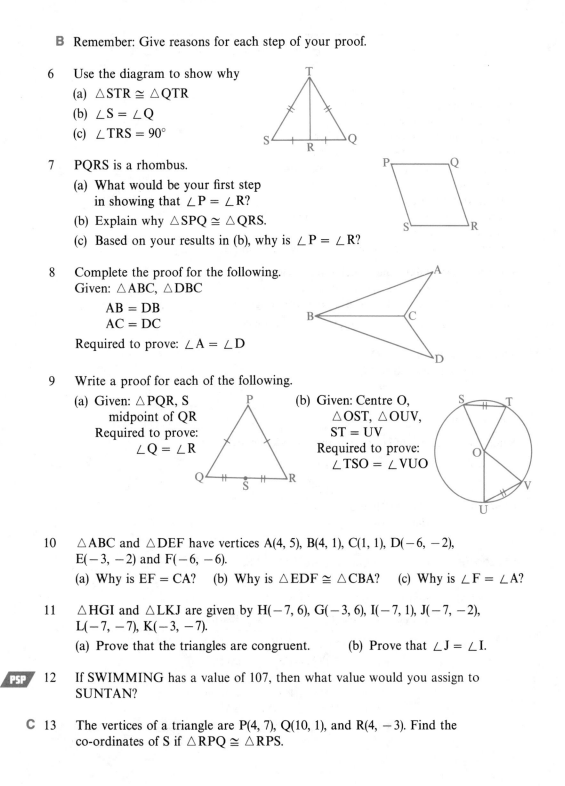

6　Use the diagram to show why
   (a) $\triangle STR \cong \triangle QTR$
   (b) $\angle S = \angle Q$
   (c) $\angle TRS = 90°$

7　PQRS is a rhombus.
   (a) What would be your first step
      in showing that $\angle P = \angle R$?
   (b) Explain why $\triangle SPQ \cong \triangle QRS$.
   (c) Based on your results in (b), why is $\angle P = \angle R$?

8　Complete the proof for the following.
   Given: $\triangle ABC$, $\triangle DBC$

$$AB = DB$$
$$AC = DC$$

   Required to prove: $\angle A = \angle D$

9　Write a proof for each of the following.
   (a) Given: $\triangle PQR$, S          (b) Given: Centre O,
       midpoint of QR              $\triangle OST$, $\triangle OUV$,
       Required to prove:           ST = UV
          $\angle Q = \angle R$            Required to prove:
                             $\angle TSO = \angle VUO$

10　$\triangle ABC$ and $\triangle DEF$ have vertices A(4, 5), B(4, 1), C(1, 1), D(−6, −2),
   E(−3, −2) and F(−6, −6).
   (a) Why is EF = CA?   (b) Why is $\triangle EDF \cong \triangle CBA$?   (c) Why is $\angle F = \angle A$?

11　$\triangle HGI$ and $\triangle LKJ$ are given by H(−7, 6), G(−3, 6), I(−7, 1), J(−7, −2),
   L(−7, −7), K(−3, −7).
   (a) Prove that the triangles are congruent.   (b) Prove that $\angle J = \angle I$.

**PSP**　12　If SWIMMING has a value of 107, then what value would you assign to
   SUNTAN?

**C**　13　The vertices of a triangle are P(4, 7), Q(10, 1), and R(4, −3). Find the
   co-ordinates of S if $\triangle RPQ \cong \triangle RPS$.

# 8.6 Congruence Postulate: Side-Angle-Side

In the previous section, you saw that for two triangles to be congruent, it is sufficient that three sides be correspondingly equal. Certain other sets of three facts about two triangles are sufficient to show that they are congruent. For example, as an experiment, if you were to draw a triangle based on the information given at the right, you would *all* draw congruent triangles.

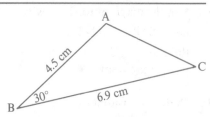

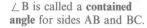

∠B is called a **contained angle** for sides AB and BC.

The experiment would suggest the following postulate.

**Congruence Postulate: Side-Angle-Side** If two sides and the contained angle of a triangle are respectively equal to two sides and the contained angle of another triangle, the triangles are congruent.

> Use SAS as a symbol to refer to this postulate.

Thus in △ABC and △PQR
  if you know AB = PQ
          ∠B = ∠Q
          BC = QR
then you know △ABC ≅ △PQR.

Since the triangles are congruent then you know other facts.

∠A = ∠P          AC = PR          ∠C = ∠R

**Example 1**   Use the diagram to show that ∠Q = ∠S.

**Solution**   Given: △PQR, △PSR, PQ = PS,
          ∠QPR = ∠SPR

Required to prove: ∠Q = ∠S

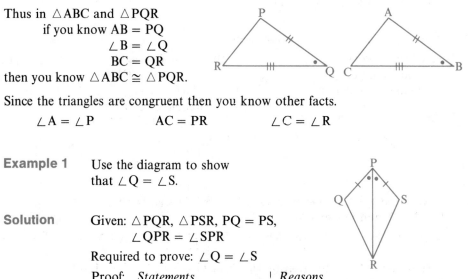

Proof:

| Statements | Reasons |
|---|---|
| In △PQR and △PSR | |
| PQ = PS | given |
| ∠QPR = ∠SPR | given |
| PR = PR | common side |
| Thus △PQR ≅ △PSR | SAS |
| Thus    ∠Q = ∠S | Since the triangles are congruent, the corresponding parts are congruent. |

You have already proved the theorem that you need to complete Example 2.

**Vertically Opposite Angle Theorem (VOAT)**
If two lines intersect, then the vertically opposite angles are equal.

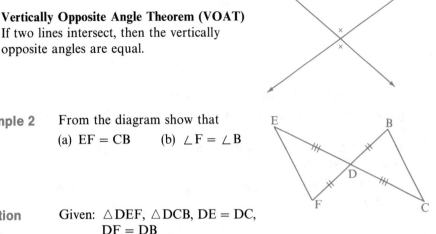

**Example 2**    From the diagram show that
(a) EF = CB        (b) ∠F = ∠B

**Solution**    Given:  △DEF, △DCB, DE = DC,
DF = DB

Required to prove:
(a) EF = CB        (b) ∠F = ∠B

Proof:

| Statements | Reasons |
|---|---|
| In △DEF and △DCB | |
| DE = DC | given |
| ∠EDF = ∠CDB | vertically opposite angles |
| DF = DB | given |
| Thus △DEF ≅ △DCB | SAS |
| Thus (a) EF = CB | Since the triangles are congruent, |
| (b) ∠F = ∠B | corresponding parts have equal measures. |

# 8.6    Exercise

**A** In order that you can use your methods in geometry to solve advanced problems first you need to practise your skills.

1    Two triangles are given as shown.
(a) Why are they congruent?
(b) Write the congruence relation.
(c) What other facts do you know about the two triangles?

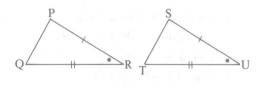

2  Refer to the triangles.

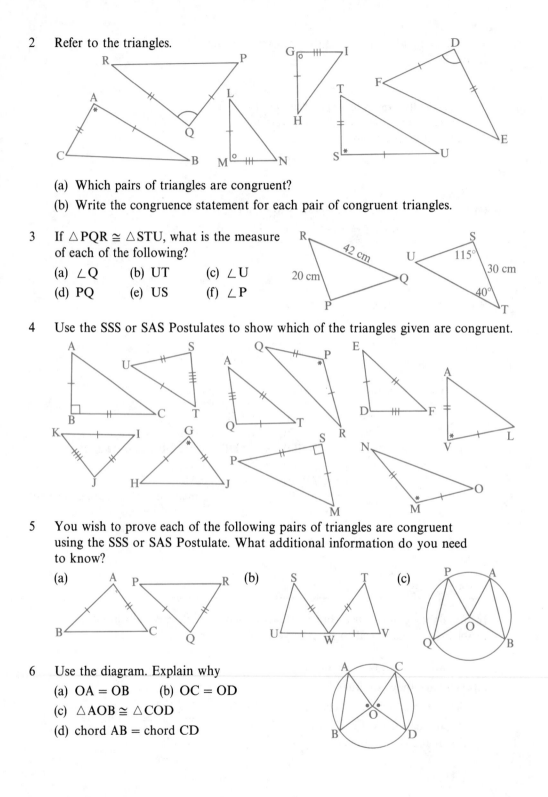

(a) Which pairs of triangles are congruent?

(b) Write the congruence statement for each pair of congruent triangles.

3  If $\triangle PQR \cong \triangle STU$, what is the measure of each of the following?

(a) $\angle Q$     (b) UT     (c) $\angle U$

(d) PQ     (e) US     (f) $\angle P$

4  Use the SSS or SAS Postulates to show which of the triangles given are congruent.

5  You wish to prove each of the following pairs of triangles are congruent using the SSS or SAS Postulate. What additional information do you need to know?

(a)     (b)     (c)

6  Use the diagram. Explain why

(a) OA = OB     (b) OC = OD

(c) $\triangle AOB \cong \triangle COD$

(d) chord AB = chord CD

Remember: Give a reason for each step of your proof.

7 Why does $\angle A = \angle C$ in each of the following diagrams? You may use SSS or SAS.

(a)　　　　　　　　(b)　　　　　　(c)　　　　　　(d)

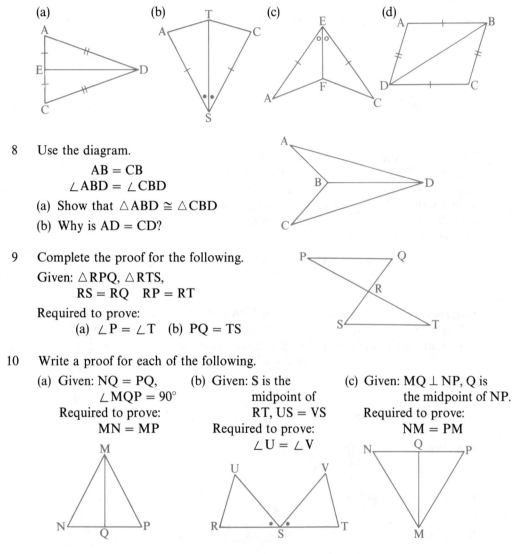

8 Use the diagram.

$$AB = CB$$
$$\angle ABD = \angle CBD$$

(a) Show that $\triangle ABD \cong \triangle CBD$

(b) Why is $AD = CD$?

9 Complete the proof for the following.

Given: $\triangle RPQ$, $\triangle RTS$,
　　　　$RS = RQ$　$RP = RT$

Required to prove:
　　(a) $\angle P = \angle T$　(b) $PQ = TS$

10 Write a proof for each of the following.

(a) Given: $NQ = PQ$,　(b) Given: S is the　(c) Given: $MQ \perp NP$, Q is
　　　　$\angle MQP = 90°$　　　midpoint of　　　　　the midpoint of NP.
　Required to prove:　　　$RT$, $US = VS$　　Required to prove:
　　　　$MN = MP$　　Required to prove:　　　$NM = PM$
　　　　　　　　　　$\angle U = \angle V$

11 (a) $\triangle ABC$ is an isosceles triangle with $AB = AC$. AF bisects $\angle BAC$ and meets BC at F. Show that $\angle B = \angle C$.

(b) In (a) you have proven an important property about isosceles triangles. Write this property in the form of a theorem. You may refer to this result as the Isosceles Triangle Theorem (ITT).

# 8.7 Congruence Postulate: Angle-Side-Angle

In the previous section, you used two important postulates to prove geometric facts.

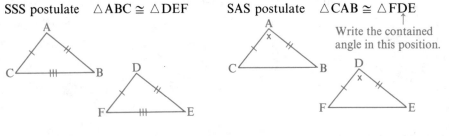

SSS postulate   △ABC ≅ △DEF        SAS postulate   △CAB ≅ △FDE

Write the contained angle in this position.

There is one other set of conditions that allows you to obtain congruent triangles. If all of you were to construct triangles with the information given on the right, you would obtain congruent triangles. The results of this experiment suggest the following postulate.

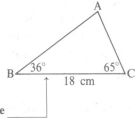

BC is the **contained side** for angles B and C.

**Congruence Postulate: Angle-Side-Angle** If two angles and the contained side of a triangle are respectively equal to two angles and the contained side of another triangle, then the triangles are congruent.

Use ASA as the symbol to refer to this postulate.
Note that S represents the contained side.

Thus, based on the ASA Postulate, the triangles that follow are congruent.

If you know         ∠Q = ∠B
                    QR = BC
                    ∠R = ∠C
then you know   △PQR ≅ △ABC

If you know

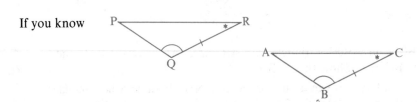

then you know △PQR ≅ △ABC

**Example 1**   Use the diagram to prove that
RS = TU.

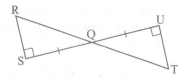

**Solution**   Given: △SQR, △UQT, SQ = UQ, ∠S = ∠U = 90°
Required to prove: RS = TU

Proof:

| Statements | Reasons |
|---|---|
| In △SQR and △UQT | |
| ∠S = ∠U | both given 90° |
| SQ = UQ | given |
| ∠SQR = ∠UQT | vertically opposite angles |
| Thus △SQR ≅ △UQT | ASA Postulate |
| Thus     RS = TU | congruent triangles |

You can also state the ASA Postulate in the following form.

*ASA Postulate:* If any two angles and a side of one triangle are respectively equal to two angles and a corresponding side of another triangle, then the triangles are congruent.

Thus

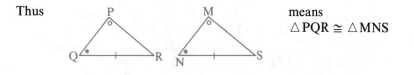

means
△PQR ≅ △MNS

When you study geometric ideas you need to examine carefully any diagrams. Often, a sketch of the given information will suggest the strategy you can use to prove the deduction. Sometimes a diagram contains more than one pair of corresponding triangles. You need to decide which pair of triangles you need to prove the deduction.   **PSP**

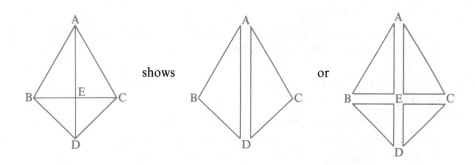

shows                or

Sometimes you may need more than one pair of corresponding triangles to prove deductions. In the following example, two pairs of overlapping triangles are used.

**Example 2**   Prove that in the diagram
RP ⊥ ST.

**Solution**   Given: △RST and △PST,
∠RTS = ∠PTS,
∠RST = ∠PST

Required to prove: RP ⊥ ST

Proof:

| Statements | Reasons |
|---|---|
| In △RST and △PST | |
| ∠RST = ∠PST | given |
| ST = ST | common side |
| ∠RTS = ∠PTS | given |
| Thus △RST ≅ △PST | ASA Postulate |
| Thus RT = PT | congruent triangles |

Think: Now I need to refer to another pair of corresponding triangles.

| In △QTR and △QTP | |
|---|---|
| RT = PT | proven |
| ∠RTQ = ∠PTQ | given |
| QT = QT | common side |
| Thus △QTR ≅ △QTP | SAS Postulate |
| ∠RQT = ∠PQT | congruent triangles |
| RQP is a straight line | given |

Thus ∠RQT + ∠PQT = 180°
But ∠RQT = ∠PQT
Thus ∠RQT = 90° and RP ⊥ ST.

# 8.7   Exercise

**A** Remember: In order to use SSS, SAS, and ASA, you need to be able to recognize the given facts in the diagram.

1   Two triangles are given as shown.
   (a) Why are they congruent?
   (b) Write the congruence statement.
   (c) What other facts do you know about the two triangles?

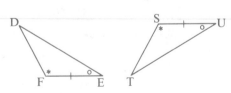

2   (a) Why are the given triangles congruent?
    (b) Write the congruence statement.
    (c) What other facts do you know about
        the two triangles?

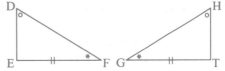

3   (a) Which pairs of triangles are congruent? Give reasons why.
    (b) Write the congruence statements.

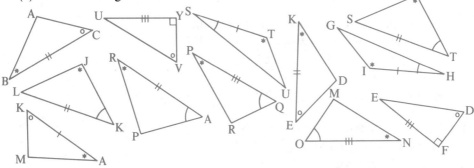

4   For each diagram, give reasons why ∠A = ∠B.
    (a)   (b)   (c)   (d)

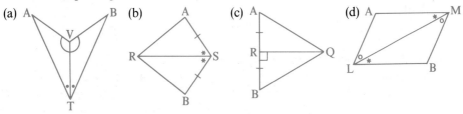

5   You wish to prove each of the following pairs of triangles is congruent
    using one of SSS, ASA, or SAS. What additional information do you need
    to know in each case? Justify your answer. Note: There may be more than
    one answer for each pair of triangles.

    (a)   (b)   (c)

    (d)   (e)   (f)

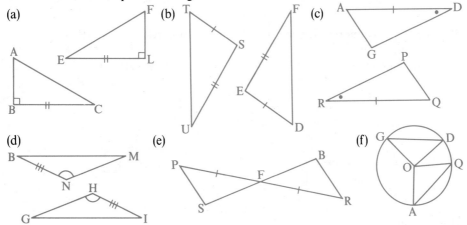

**B**  Remember: Give a reason for each step of your proof.

6   Use the diagram. Prove that
    (a) △DEF ≅ △DEG
    (b) ∠F = ∠G
    (c) △DFG is an isosceles triangle.

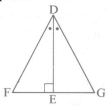

7   Use the diagram. PQST is a parallelogram in which ∠PQT = ∠STQ and ∠SQT = ∠PTQ.
    (a) To show that ∠S = ∠P, what would be your first step?
    (b) Explain why △TQS ≅ △QTP.   (c) Why is ∠S = ∠P?

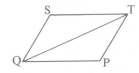

8   Complete the proof for the following.
    Given: Quadrilateral PQRS,
        PR bisects ∠P,
        ∠S = ∠Q
    Required to prove:
        PS = PQ

9   Write a complete proof for each of the following.
    (a) Prove that
        AB = AC.

    (b) SQ = TR, PS = PT, and ∠PST = ∠PTS. Prove that △PQR is isosceles.

10  (a) Use the information shown in the diagram to prove that ST ⊥ UV.

    (b) ∠ABC = ∠DCB and ∠A = ∠D. Prove AB = DC.

    (c) If SP ⊥ PQ and QR = PS, prove that ∠S = ∠R.

    (d) Prove that ∠D = ∠E.

# Problem-Solving: Proving Constructions

In your earlier work in geometry, you have used various constructions *without having proved them*. The following questions prove the validity of these constructions.

11 The construction diagram shown was drawn to bisect ∠DAC.

Construction: Bisect an angle.

(a) Why is AD = AC?

(b) Why is DB = CB?

(c) Prove that ∠DAB = ∠CAB.

12 Use the diagram drawn to construct an angle equal to the given angle DAE. Prove that ∠A = ∠B.

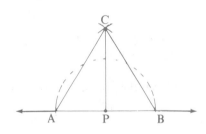

13 The construction diagram was used to construct a perpendicular to a point on a line. Prove that ∠APC = ∠BPC.

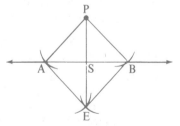

14 The construction diagram was used to construct a perpendicular to a line from a point outside the line. Prove that PS ⊥ AB.

15 The construction diagram was used to construct the right bisector of a line segment. Prove that CD is the right bisector of AB.

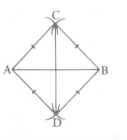

## 8.8 Congruence Postulate: Hypotenuse-Side

Each time you learn a geometric fact, you can combine it with the other facts you know to prove further deductions.

Do you know what each of these mean?

SSS Postulate   SAS Postulate   ASA Postulate

Another congruence postulate is shown.

**Congruence Postulate: Hypotenuse-Side** If the hypotenuse and one side of a right triangle are respectively equal to the hypotenuse and the corresponding side of another right triangle, then the triangles are congruent. ⌐HS is the symbol used to refer to this postulate.

For example, these two triangles are congruent because of the HS postulate.

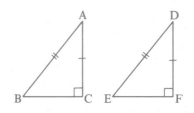

$\triangle ABC$ and $\triangle DEF$ are right triangles. If AB = DE and AC = DF, then $\triangle ABC \cong \triangle DEF$

By using your postulates and the theorems you develop, you can deduce other facts in geometry.

**Example**   From the diagram, prove that
$\angle EDC = \angle BAC$.

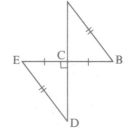

**Solution**   Given: $\triangle ABC$ and $\triangle DEC$,
ED = BA, EC = BC,
$\angle ECD = 90°$

Required to prove: $\angle EDC = \angle BAC$.

Proof:   From the diagram AD and EB intersect at C.
Thus, $\angle ECD = \angle ACB$
Since $\angle ECD = 90°$, then $\angle ACB = 90°$
Thus $\triangle ECD$ and $\triangle ACB$ are right triangles.

| Statements | Reasons |
|---|---|
| In $\triangle ECD$ and $\triangle BCA$   EC = BC | given |
| DE = AB | given |
| $\angle ECD = \angle BCA$ | both 90° |
| Then $\triangle ECD \cong \triangle BCA$ | Hs postulate |
| Thus $\angle EDC = \angle BAC$ | congruent triangles |

## 8.8 Exercise

**A** Review the meaning of each of these postulates: SSS, SAS, ASA, HS.

1   Two triangles are given as shown.
    (a) Why are they congruent?
    (b) Write the congruence statement.
    (c) What other facts do you know about
        the two triangles?

2   (a) Which of the following pairs of triangles are congruent? Give reasons
        for your answer.
    (b) Write the congruence statements.

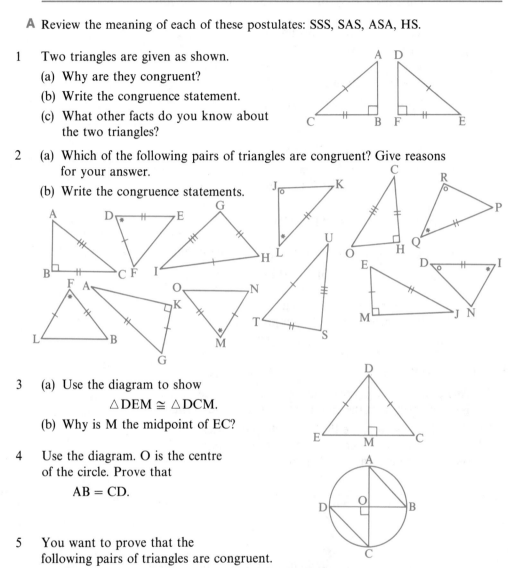

3   (a) Use the diagram to show
            △DEM ≅ △DCM.
    (b) Why is M the midpoint of EC?

4   Use the diagram. O is the centre
    of the circle. Prove that
        AB = CD.

5   You want to prove that the
    following pairs of triangles are congruent.
    • What additional information do you need to know?
    • Give reasons for your answer.

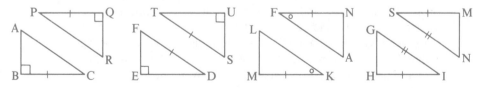

**B** Remember: Examine carefully each diagram to make sure you notice all the given information. Also, make sure the information you notice is *correct*.

6   Complete the proof for the following.

Given: △PQR and △PSR
    so that PQ = PS and
    ∠PQR = ∠PSR = 90°

Required to prove: RP bisects ∠QPS.

7   Complete the proof for the following.

Given: △ABE and △CBD so that
    ∠A = ∠C = 90° and EB = DB.

Required to prove:
    (a) ∠E = ∠D   (b) AE = CD

8   In △PQS, E is a point on QS. EP bisects ∠QPS. If PQ = PS prove that
    (a) ∠Q = ∠S.              (b) E is the midpoint of QS.

9   Quadrilateral PQRS is drawn so that PS ⊥ SR, QR ⊥ SR, and
    PS = QR. If QS meets RP at T then prove that
    (a) ST = RT              (b) PT = QT.

**C** 10   The Perpendicular Bisector Theorem (PBT) states:

Any point on the perpendicular bisector of a line segment
is equidistant from the end points of the line segment.

Use the diagram to prove the Perpendicular Bisector
Theorem. Copy the diagram and be sure to mark the
known information on your diagram.

Remember: Now you can refer to the PBT in any of
the proofs you write.

---

## Math Tip

There are several important skills you need to have when
you are solving geometric problems or proving geometric
deductions. First, you must be able to remember all the geometric
properties, postulates and theorems. Secondly, it is important for
you to be able to decide which skills you need to solve the problem.
And finally you must be able to use the skills you need in the right
order. For this reason a summary of what you know is essential.
Use a diagram to help you remember the given information.

## PSP Proving Deductions in Geometry

The skills and strategies you acquire throughout your study of mathematics can often be applied in more than one branch of mathematics. For example, the ability to translate English into mathematics is an essential skill that can be used in more than one branch of mathematics.

| PSP | Problem-Solving Plan |
| --- | --- |

A Ask yourself:
   I What information am I asked to find?
   II What information am I given?
B Decide on a method.
   Translate from English to mathematics.
   Draw a diagram. Record the information.
C Do the work. Write the proof.
D Check your work.
   Justify each step of your proof.
E Make a final statement.
   Answer the problem. Write a final statement.

Compare the following.

*Algebra*
In algebra, you translate the word problem into symbols. You arrange these symbols to form an equation (or inequation).

*Geometry*
In geometry, you translate the word problem into diagrams. A diagram is used to help you to prove geometric facts.

In the following example, no diagram is given. The first step is to **PSP** translate the deduction and in order to do so, a diagram is drawn. Then, the information given in the original problem is recorded on the diagram.

**Example 1**    In $\triangle ABC$, $AB = AC$. If the bisector of $\angle A$ meets BC at F, show that $AF \perp BC$.

**Solution**    Given: $\triangle ABC$ with
         $AB = AC$,
         $\angle BAF = \angle CAF$

Required to prove:
         $AF \perp BC$

AF is the bisector of $\angle A$.
Mark the facts on the diagram.

Mark
$AB = AC$.

Proof:

| Statements | Reasons |
| --- | --- |
| In $\triangle ABF$ and $\triangle ACF$ | |
| $\qquad AB = AC$ | given |
| $\qquad \angle BAF = \angle CAF$ | bisected angle |
| $\qquad AF = AF$ | common side |
| Thus $\qquad \triangle ABF \cong \triangle ACF$ | SAS |
| $\qquad \angle AFB = \angle AFC$ | Why? |
| Since $\angle AFB + \angle AFC = 180°$, | $\angle BFC$ is a straight angle. |
| then $\qquad \angle AFB = 90°$ | Why? |
| Thus $\qquad AF \perp BC$ | Why? |

In Example 1 you constructed a diagram to help you visualize the problem that you needed to solve. As you translated the problem you marked the given information onto the diagram. In Example 2, you need to not only draw a diagram to help you but also choose labels for the diagram.

**Example 2**    Prove that in any rectangle the diagonals bisect each other.

Choose letters to name the rectangle and diagonals.

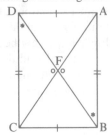

**Solution**    Given: rectangle ABCD such that
AB = DC, BC = AD.
The diagonals AC and DB intersect at F.

Required to prove: AF = CF,
DF = BF

Proof:

| Statements | Reasons |
|---|---|
| In △ABD and △CDB | |
| AB = CD | given |
| ∠A = ∠C | both 90° |
| AD = CB | given |
| Then △ABD ≅ △CDB | SAS |
| Thus ∠ABD = ∠CDB | congruent triangles |
| ∠ADB = ∠CBD | congruent triangles |
| In △DFC and △BFA | |
| DC = BA | given |
| ∠CDF = ∠ABF | proved |
| ∠DFC = ∠BFA | VOAT |
| Then △DFC ≅ △BFA | ASA |
| Thus, ∠DCF = ∠BAF | congruent triangles |
| Thus,   DF = BF and | corresponding sides |
| AF = CF | of congruent triangles |

Remember: The symbol VOAT means vertically opposite angles theorem.

Conclusion: The diagonals of any rectangle bisect each other.

A special vocabulary is developed for each branch of mathematics. For example, in the process of constructing diagrams, you are often asked to produce line segments. For example note how the instructions differ for producing the line segments in different directions.

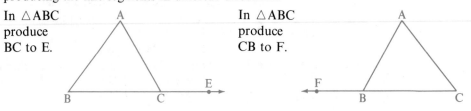

In △ABC produce BC to E.

In △ABC produce CB to F.

**B** Remember: When you are proving deductions, you need to translate the given information into a diagram. Use the *Problem-Solving Plan* to help you organize your work.

1   Line segments AB and CD bisect each other at E. Prove AC = BD.

2   In △PQR, PQ = PR. If PS bisects ∠P and meets QR at S, prove PS ⊥ QR.

3   In quadrilateral RABT, BT = BA and ∠TBR = ∠ABR. Prove ∠T = ∠A.

4   △PQR ≅ △SAB. If E is the midpoint of PQ and F is the midpoint of SA, prove that △PER ≅ △SFB.

5   A quadrilateral RSVP is drawn so that ∠RSP = ∠VPS and ∠RPS = ∠VSP. Prove that the opposite sides of the quadrilateral are equal.

6   In △PQM, T is the midpoint of QM. The segment PT is produced to S so that PT = TS. Prove that QP = MS.

7   In quadrilateral EFGH, GE bisects ∠HGF. If HG = FG prove EH = EF.

8   Two circles with centres O and P intersect at A and B. Prove that PO is the right bisector of AB.

9   In a quadrilateral PSTA, B is the midpoint of ST. If PB = AB and ∠SBP = ∠TBA then prove that ∠S = ∠T.

10   In △STV, ST = SV. A point P is found on ST and Q on SV so that ∠PVS = ∠QTS. Prove that TQ = VP.

11   The line segments BR and QS bisect each other, meeting at T. V is a point on BQ. If VT produced meets SR at W then prove that TW = TV.

12   Prove that in an equilateral triangle, the bisector of any angle, when produced, bisects a side of the triangle.

13   Prove that in any rhombus the diagonals bisect each other at right angles.

**C** 14   In quadrilateral KLMN, MN = ML and LK = NK.
   (a) Sketch the information on a diagram.
   (b) Use the diagram to decide what other facts may be true. Then write a proof of the fact that you have noticed in the diagram.

# Practice and Problems: Review

1  For quadrilateral ABCD
   $\angle DAB = \angle BCD$.

   (a) To show that
   $\angle ADB = \angle CBD$,
   what would be
   your first step?

   (b) Show why $\triangle DAB \cong \triangle BCD$.

2  In the diagram
   $\angle ABC = \angle ACB$.

   Prove that
   $\angle DBA = \angle DCA$.

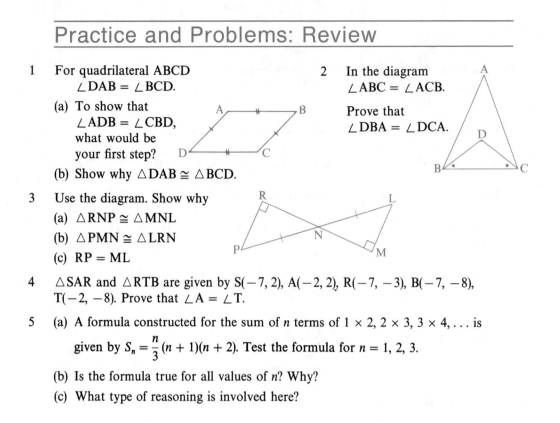

3  Use the diagram. Show why
   (a)  $\triangle RNP \cong \triangle MNL$
   (b)  $\triangle PMN \cong \triangle LRN$
   (c)  $RP = ML$

4  $\triangle SAR$ and $\triangle RTB$ are given by $S(-7, 2)$, $A(-2, 2)$, $R(-7, -3)$, $B(-7, -8)$, $T(-2, -8)$. Prove that $\angle A = \angle T$.

5  (a) A formula constructed for the sum of $n$ terms of $1 \times 2, 2 \times 3, 3 \times 4, \ldots$ is
   given by $S_n = \dfrac{n}{3}(n + 1)(n + 2)$. Test the formula for $n = 1, 2, 3$.

   (b) Is the formula true for all values of $n$? Why?

   (c) What type of reasoning is involved here?

# Practice Test

1  Two triangles are congruent as shown. $\triangle PQR \cong \triangle EFG$. Write the congruence
   relation in as many other ways as you can.

2  In the diagram, give
   reasons why
   (a)  $\angle GEF = \angle GFE$
   (b)  $\angle DEG = \angle DFG$
   (c)  $GS \perp EF$

3  Use the diagram. $DE \perp EH$
   $GH \perp EH$. If $DH = GE$
   prove $\angle D = \angle G$.

4  $\triangle DEF$ is given by $D(2, 4)$, $E(8, 4)$, $F(6, 10)$.
   Find the co-ordinates of G if $\triangle DEF \cong \triangle DEG$.

5  In $\triangle PQR$, M is the midpoint of PQ. If $MR = MQ$
   (a) prove $\angle MPR = \angle MRP$.   (b) prove $\angle PRQ = 90°$.

6  Prove that the diagonals in a square are right bisectors of each other.

# 9 *Proving Properties: Concepts and Skills*

Using converses, parallel lines and properties, angle sum of a triangle, method of indirect proof, proving deductions, proving properties, proof of the Pythagorean Theorem, converse of the Pythagorean Theorem, proving theorems, strategies and problem solving

## Introduction

The development of geometry, as well as mathematics, has often been based on asking useful questions such as: "What if . . . ?", or "Why?" or on making a conjecture. Often, mathematics is invented in the process of answering these questions. Often, the method, skill, or strategy you develop for a particular topic can be extended and applied to solving other problems.

The process of solving deductions follows a plan. This plan is illustrated below.

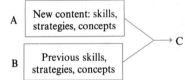

To prove a deduction, you need a plan not only to obtain a solution, but also to leave a record of your solution so that others can trace the steps you used in obtaining your answer. The *Problem-Solving Plan* **PSP** you have been using also provides a framework to solve problems in geometry. The skills and strategies you have learned in the previous chapter and those in this chapter help you to complete the steps in your *Problem-Solving Plan.*

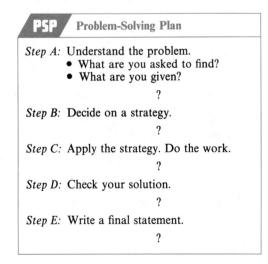

# 9.1 Converses in Mathematics

Throughout your study of mathematics, certain terms occur that are used in different branches of mathematics. For example, **if-then statements**, such as the following, are often referred to in the language of mathematics.

If $a$, $b$ are even, then $a + b$ is even.

This is called the **hypothesis**.
It states what is given.

This is called the **conclusion**.
It states what follows or what is asked to be proven.

An **if-then** statement is also called a **conditional statement**. Each of the following statements are conditional statements, occurring in different ways.

A: If $x + 3 = 7$, then $x = 4$.

B: If $y$ is positive, then $-y$ is negative.

C: If a polygon is a square, then it is also a rectangle.

D: If $y > 10$, then $y > 3$.

A conditional statement in general, is shown by the form.

If $p$, then $q$.

Hypothesis —————↑     ↑——— Conclusion

You could write the **converse** of the statement above by interchanging the $p$ and $q$.

| | |
|---|---|
| *Statement* | *Converse of the statement* |
| If $q$, then $p$. | If $p$, then $q$. |

The converses of statements A, B, C, D above are shown as follows.

A* If $x = 4$, then $x + 3 = 7$.

B* If $-y$ is negative, then $y$ is positive.

C* If a polygon is a rectangle, then it is also a square.

D* If $y > 3$, then $y > 10$.

The converse statements C* and D* illustrate that the converse of a conditional statement *need not be true*.

You have already proved this theorem.

> *Isosceles Triangle Theorem (ITT):* If two sides of a triangle are equal, then the angles opposite these sides are equal.

The converse of the above theorem is given as:

> If two angles of a triangle are equal, then the sides opposite these angles are equal.

Example 1 proves that, in this case, the converse of the theorem is also true.

**Example**    Prove that if two angles of a triangle are equal, then the sides opposite the angles are equal.

**Solution**    Given: $\triangle ABC$, with $\angle B = \angle C$.

Required to prove: $AB = AC$.

Construction: Bisect $\angle A$ to meet BC at D.

Proof:

| Statements | Reasons |
|---|---|
| In $\triangle ABD$ and $\triangle ACD$ | |
| $\angle BAD = \angle CAD$ | constructed |
| $AD = AD$ | common side |
| $\angle B = \angle C$ | given |
| Thus $\triangle ABD \cong \triangle ACD$ | ASA |
| Thus $\quad AB = AC$ | congruent triangles |

{Which is what you wanted to prove.

If the converse of a theorem is true it can be combined with the theorem into one statement called a **biconditional statement**. For example, the Isosceles Triangle Theorem and its converse are combined. The result is the following biconditional statement.

> In any triangle, the two sides of a triangle are equal **if and only if** the angles opposite these sides are equal.

You will study many statements with **if and only if**.     $\leftarrow$ You can write *iff* for *if and only if*.

## 9.1    Exercise

**A** Remember: The converse of a true statement is not necessarily true.

1    Write the converse of each of the following.

(a) If $y > 12$, then $y > 2$.          (b) If $4x + 1 = 9$, then $x = 2$.

(c) If an equilateral triangle has sides of 2 cm, then the perimeter is 6 cm.

(d) If $x + y = 6$, then $x = 6 - y$.

(e) If two angles have a sum of $90°$, then they are complementary angles.

(f) If $x$ and $y$ are odd, then $x - y$ is even.

(g) If $x$ and $y$ are even, then $x + y$ is even.

(h) If $m$ is an odd integer, then $5m$ is odd.      (i) If $x = 3$, then $x^2 = 9$.

(j) If $a$ and $b$ are both negative, then $ab$ is positive.

(k) If triangles are congruent, then they are equal in area.

2  Refer to the converses you wrote in Question 1.
   (a) Which of those converses are true (T)? Give reasons for your answer.
   (b) Which are false (F)? Give reasons for your answer.

3  Write each of the following in an *if-then* form.
   (a) The angles of a rectangle are right angles.
   (b) An equilateral triangle has 3 equal sides.
   (c) Every positive number has two square roots.
   (d) The sum of 2 even integers is even.   (e) A square is also a rectangle.
   (f) A rhombus is a quadrilateral with equal sides.
   (g) Squares that have equal perimeters have equal areas.

4  Refer to your answers in Question 3.
   (a) Write the converse of each of your answers.
   (b) Write your answers in (a) in a sentence using *if and only if*.


B  You use your earlier skills in geometry to prove whether or not the
   converse of a geometric statement is true.

5  Refer to the following geometric fact.
        If a point is on the perpendicular bisector of a line segment, then
        it is equidistant from the end points of the line segment.
   (a) Write the converse of this statement.
   (b) Show whether or not the converse is true.

6  Use the following statement.
        If a triangle is equilateral, then each angle is 60°.
   (a) Write the converse of the statement.
   (b) Show whether or not the converse is true.

7  In the diagram ∠TAB = ∠TBA.          8  Use the diagram.
   Prove that T lies on the                 Prove that AE = BE.
   perpendicular bisector of AB.

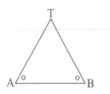

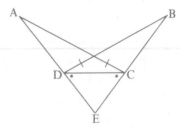

9    Use the diagram.
     Prove that PS lies on the
     perpendicular bisector of DE.

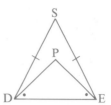

10   Refer to the statement:

     If the diagonals of a quadrilateral
     bisect each other, then the
     quadrilateral is a parallelogram.

     (a)  Prove that the statement is true.

     (b)  Write the converse of the statement in (a). Show whether or not the
          converse is true.

     (c)  Use the *if and only if* form to combine the results in (a) and (b).

For each of the following deductions.
• translate the given information into a diagram.
• write a complete proof.

11   In △PQR, QR is produced to T and RQ is produced to S so that
     ∠PRT = ∠PQS. Prove that PQ = PR.

12   In △PQR, PQ is produced to S and PR is produced to T so that
     ∠RQS = ∠QRT. Prove that △PQR is isosceles.

13   In △ABC, D is the midpoint of AC. If BD = DC, then prove that ∠B is
     a right angle.

14   △PQR is equilateral and A, B, C are
     the midpoints of the sides. Prove that
     △ABC is an equilateral triangle.

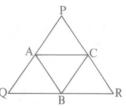

15   In △STU, ∠T = ∠U. A point P is found in the interior of △STU so
     that ∠PTU = ∠PUT. Prove that PS is the bisector of ∠TSU.

16   In an isosceles triangle the vertical and base
     angles are defined as shown. Prove that if a
     triangle is isosceles, then the median drawn from the
     vertical angle to the other side is also an altitude.

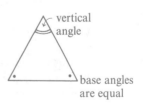

C 17  Refer to your results in Questions 11 to 16.

     (a)  Write a converse for each of the results you have proven.

     (b)  Show whether or not each converse is true.

## 9.2 Working With Parallel Lines: Vocabulary

The structure of the geometry that you have dealt with so far may be shown by this familiar diagram.

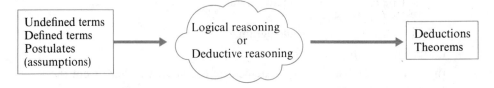

In order to be successful at proving deductions, you must understand **PSP** clearly the meaning of the words used.

Certain terms, which are defined below, are used to study parallel lines.

**Parallel lines** lie in the same plane and do not intersect.

Associated with parallel lines is a very specific vocabulary.

A **transversal** is a line that intersects 2 or more lines in the plane (in more than 1 point). TR is a transversal of AB and ED.

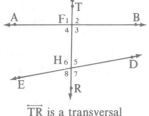

$\overrightarrow{TR}$ is a transversal

When a transversal intersects two or more lines certain pairs of angles are named as follows.

**Corresponding Angles** From the diagram above $\angle 1$ and $\angle 6$ are a pair of corresponding angles. $\angle 3$ and $\angle 7$ are another pair of corresponding angles. The diagrams show pairs of corresponding angles.

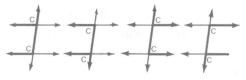

**Alternate Angles** From the diagram above $\angle 4$ and $\angle 5$ are a pair of alternate angles. These diagrams show pairs of alternate angles.

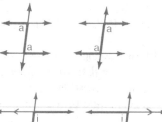

**Interior Angles on the Same Side of the Transversal** From the diagram above $\angle 3$ and $\angle 5$ are a pair of interior angles on the same side of the transversal. These diagrams show pairs of interior angles.

# 9.2 Exercise

**A** List the meanings of the new words you have learned in this section.

1 Examples of parallel lines or line segments can be found all around you. Do you recognize the photo at the right?
List four other examples of parallel lines or line segments.

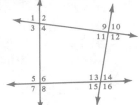

2 Use the diagram at the right. List pairs of
   (a) corresponding angles.
   (b) alternate angles.
   (c) interior angles on the same side of the transversal.

3 Use the diagram in Question 2. List angles that are
   (a) supplementary.        (b) vertically opposite.

**B** 4 Write a definition for each of the following pairs of angles.
   (a) alternate    (b) corresponding    (c) interior angles on same side of transversal

5 For each diagram, name a transversal and write pairs of angles that are
   • alternate    • corresponding    • interior angles on same side of transversal

(a)                    (b)                    (c)

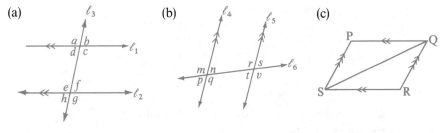

6 Use the diagram.
   Name pairs of
   angles that are
   (a) equal.
   (b) supplementary.

7 Use the diagram.
   Name pairs of
   angles that are
   (a) equal.
   (b) supplementary.

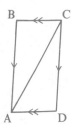

# 9.3 Parallel Lines and Their Properties

From your earlier work on exploring parallel lines it seemed that, for parallel lines, the alternate angles were equal. As well, it appeared that corresponding angles were also equal. For this reason the parallel postulate is used.

> *Parallel Postulate:* If two parallel lines are cut by a transversal then the corresponding angles are equal.

Example 1 shows how you can use your earlier theorems and the parallel postulate above to develop new useful theorems in geometry.

**Example 1**   Prove that if two parallel lines are cut by a transversal, then the alternate angles are equal.

**Solution**   Given: EF is a transversal, AB ∥ CD

Required to prove: Alternate angles are equal, that is $\angle AGH = \angle GHD$.

Proof: From the diagram, since AB ∥ CD then corresponding angles are equal.

| Statements | Reasons |
|---|---|
| Thus, $\angle EGB = \angle GHD$ | Parallel Postulate |
| Since AB and EF are intersecting lines, | |
| then $\angle EGB = \angle AGH$ | VOAT |
| Since $\angle EGB = \angle GHD$ | |
| and $\angle EGB = \angle AGH$ | Which is what you |
| then $\angle AGH = \angle GHD$ | wanted to prove. |

You can use the diagram in Example 1 to help you prove the following property about parallel lines.

> If a transversal intersects two parallel lines, then the interior angles on the same side of the transversal are supplementary.

That is, from the above diagram

$$\angle GHD + \angle HGB = 180°$$

and also $\angle AGH + \angle CHG = 180°$

The previous results are combined into the following theorem called the *Parallel Lines Theorem.* It is referred to as *PLT*.

*Parallel Lines Theorem (PLT):* If a transversal intersects two parallel lines then
- the corresponding angles are equal (accepted as a postulate).
- the alternate angles are equal.
- the interior angles on the same side of the transversal are supplementary.

Use a diagram to help you remember important theorems.

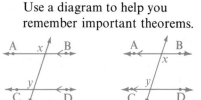

If $AB \parallel CD$ then $x = y$

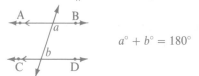

$a° + b° = 180°$

Now, the PLT and earlier theorems can be combined to prove more **deductions**.

**Example 2**  Use the information in the diagram to prove that $\triangle TRS \cong \triangle TQP$.

**Solution**  Given: $PQ \parallel RS$ and $\triangle TRS$, $\triangle TQP$ so that $PT = ST$

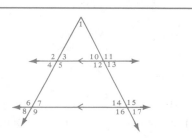

Required to prove: $\triangle TRS \cong \triangle TQP$

Proof:

| Statements | Reasons |
|---|---|
| Since $PQ \parallel RS$ and $RQ$ is a transversal, then $\angle PQT = \angle TRS$ | PLT |
| Since $PQ \parallel RS$ and $PS$ is a transversal, then $\angle QPT = \angle TSR$ | PLT |
| In $\triangle TRS$ and $\triangle TQP$ $\angle PQT = \angle SRT$ | proved |
| $PT = ST$ | given |
| $\angle QPT = \angle RST$ | proved |
| Thus $\triangle TRS \cong \triangle TQP$ | ASA |

# 9.3  Exercise

**A** Review the geometric facts of PLT.

1  Use the diagram. Write all the pairs of angles that are equal. Give reasons for your answers.

2  (a) Use the diagram to prove that
$$\angle ABG + \angle EGB = 180°.$$
   (b) Express the result in (a) in words.

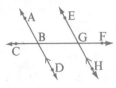

3  Refer to the diagram.
   (a) List what information you know
      from the diagram.
   (b) Use the diagram to prove that
$$\angle PSR = \angle VUW.$$

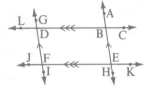

4  (a) List the information you know
      from the diagram.
   (b) Prove that
$$\angle ABC = \angle DFE.$$

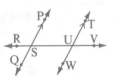

5  Read deductions A, B, and C.

A  Use a diagram.
   Prove that
   $\angle AGH = \angle GHC.$

B  Use the diagram
   to prove that
   alternate angles
   are equal.

C  Prove that if a
   transversal intersects
   two parallel lines,
   the alternate angles
   are equal.

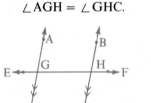

   (a) How are deductions A, B, and C related? How do they differ?
   (b) Prove deduction A.
   (c) Use the diagram in deduction B to prove deduction C.

B  Remember to justify each step of the following proofs.

6  Use the diagram to prove that
$$\angle P = \angle R.$$

7  Use the diagram to prove that
$$\angle A = \angle C.$$

$\angle A$ and $\angle C$ are
opposite angles.

8  (a) How are Questions 6 and 7 related? How are they different?
   (b) Write the results of Questions 6 and 7 in the form of a theorem.

9 Use the diagram to show that
(a) $\angle BAC + \angle B + \angle C = 180°$
(b) Write the result for (a) in words.

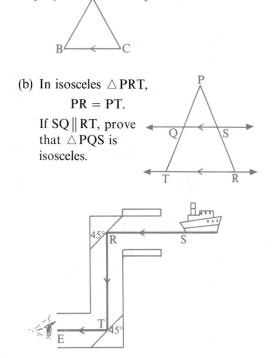

10 (a) Prove that PS bisects $\angle APQ$.

(b) In isosceles $\triangle PRT$, PR = PT.
If $SQ \parallel RT$, prove that $\triangle PQS$ is isosceles.

11 When a beam of light strikes a mirror, it is reflected so that the angles shown are equal.

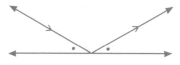

The mirrors used in a periscope are placed as shown. Prove $RS \parallel ET$.

12 (a) $\triangle ABC$ is isosceles so that AB = AC. PS is drawn parallel to BC meeting AB and AC at Q and T respectively. Prove that BQ = CT.
(b) In quadrilateral PQRS, $PQ \parallel SR$. If the diagonal QS bisects $\angle PSR$, prove that PS = PQ.

13 A rhombus is a quadrilateral with all sides equal. Prove that, in any rhombus, the opposite angles are equal.

## Problem-Solving

Three married couples enter a room. The women sit at a round table. The husbands sit so that A: the women and men alternate around the table
B: no husband or wife is beside each other

- In order that condition A and B be satisfied, there is only one way to show the arrangement. What is it?
- How many ways are possible if 4 couples enter the room and condition A and B must be satisfied?

# Problem-Solving: Finding Measures

The properties about parallel lines and about triangles are used with your problem solving strategies to find missing measures as shown by the following.

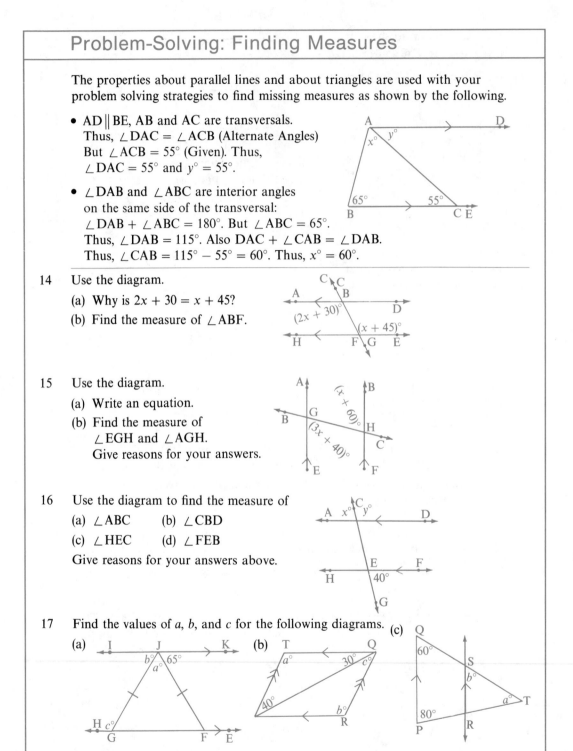

- AD ∥ BE, AB and AC are transversals.
  Thus, ∠DAC = ∠ACB (Alternate Angles)
  But ∠ACB = 55° (Given). Thus,
  ∠DAC = 55° and $y° = 55°$.

- ∠DAB and ∠ABC are interior angles
  on the same side of the transversal:
  ∠DAB + ∠ABC = 180°. But ∠ABC = 65°.
  Thus, ∠DAB = 115°. Also DAC + ∠CAB = ∠DAB.
  Thus, ∠CAB = 115° − 55° = 60°. Thus, $x° = 60°$.

14 Use the diagram.

(a) Why is $2x + 30 = x + 45$?

(b) Find the measure of ∠ABF.

15 Use the diagram.

(a) Write an equation.

(b) Find the measure of
∠EGH and ∠AGH.
Give reasons for your answers.

16 Use the diagram to find the measure of

(a) ∠ABC    (b) ∠CBD

(c) ∠HEC    (d) ∠FEB

Give reasons for your answers above.

17 Find the values of $a$, $b$, and $c$ for the following diagrams.

(a)

(b)

(c)

# 9.4 PSP Problem-Solving: Angle Sum of a Triangle

Mathematicians often obtain useful ideas from their inductive work. They 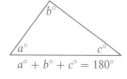 use their results to make conjectures (intelligent guesses). Once they make the conjectures, they use logical methods, such as inductive thinking, to prove the conjectures. For example, you made the following conjecture based on your earlier work:

> *Conjecture:* In any triangle, the sum of the measures of the angles is 180°.

You can use your skills in deductive thinking to prove this conjecture.
This is done in Example 1.

$$a^\circ + b^\circ + c^\circ = 180^\circ$$

**Example 1** Prove that the sum of the measures of the angles of a triangle is 180°.

"The sum of the angles" is another way of saying "the sum of the measures of the angles".

**Solution**

Given: $\triangle$ ABC with DF drawn parallel to BC through A.

Required to prove:
$$\angle BAC + \angle B + \angle C = 180^\circ$$

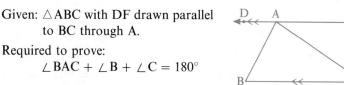

Proof:

| Statements | Reasons |
|---|---|
| From the diagram, DF ‖ BC. | |
| Thus $\angle DAB = \angle B$ | PLT ⟵ Remember: |
| $\angle FAC = \angle C$ | PLT ⟵ PLT is the |
| since $\angle DAF$ is a straight angle, | given    Parallel Lines Theorem. |
| $\angle DAB + \angle BAC + \angle CAF = 180^\circ$ | |
| Thus, $\angle B + \angle BAC + \angle C = 180^\circ$ | angle substitution |

Thus, you proved an important theorem in Example 1.

**Angle Sum of a Triangle Theorem (ASTT)** The sum of the measures of the angles of a triangle is 180°.

You can use your theorems in geometry and skills in algebra to calculate the measures of angles.

**Example 2**   Use the diagram.
Find the measures of $\angle A$, $\angle B$, $\angle C$.

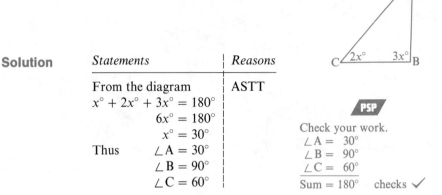

**Solution**

| Statements | Reasons |
|---|---|
| From the diagram | ASTT |
| $x° + 2x° + 3x° = 180°$ | |
| $6x° = 180°$ | |
| $x° = 30°$ | |
| Thus $\qquad \angle A = 30°$ | |
| $\angle B = 90°$ | |
| $\angle C = 60°$ | |

**PSP**

Check your work.
$\angle A = \phantom{0}30°$
$\angle B = \phantom{0}90°$
$\underline{\angle C = \phantom{0}60°}$
Sum $= 180°$   checks ✓

Based on ASTT, you can find the sum of
the angles of other polygons. For example,
for a quadrilateral, draw a diagonal AC
as shown.

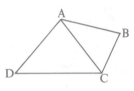

From the diagram,
in $\triangle ACD$, $\angle ACD + \angle CAD + \angle CDA = 180°$ ←——————— These facts have been
in $\triangle ACB$, $\angle ACB + \angle CAB + \angle CBA = 180°$ ←——————— accepted for a triangle.
$(\angle ACD + \angle ACB) + (\angle CAD + \angle CAB) + \angle CDA + \angle CBA = 360°$
$\qquad \angle C \qquad + \qquad \angle A \qquad + \angle D + \angle B = 360°$

Thus, you have *deduced* that the sum of the angles of a quadrilateral is
360°.

The following angle postulates can be used to obtain results such as the
one above.

*Addition Postulate*

$\angle ABC = \angle PQR$
$\underline{\angle CBD = \angle RQS}$
$\angle ABC + \angle CBD = \angle PQR + \angle RQS$
Thus $\qquad \angle ABD = \angle PQS$

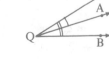

*Subtraction Postulate*

$\angle PSV = \angle RQB$
$\underline{\angle PST = \angle RQA}$
$\angle PSV - \angle PST = \angle RQB - \angle RQA$
$\angle TSV = \angle AQB$

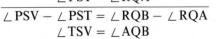

## 9.4 Exercise

**A** Throughout this exercise, give reasons for the answers you give.

1   Explain why
    (a) $x° = 60°$
    (b) $y° = 40°$
    (c) $\angle DAB + \angle BAC + \angle CAE = 180°$

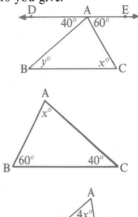

2   Use the diagram.
    (a) Why can you write $x° + 60° + 40° = 180°$?
    (b) Find $x$.

3   Use the diagram.
    (a) Explain why $2x° + 3x° + 4x° = 180°$.
    (b) Find the measure of $\angle A$.

4   For each triangle, find the missing measures. Justify your answers.
    (a)     (b)     (c)     (d)     (e)

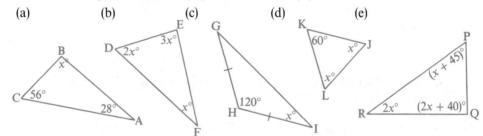

5   (a) Two angles of a triangle are $36°$ and $75°$. Find the measure of the
        third angle.
    (b) Show that the measure of each angle in an equilateral triangle is $60°$.

**B** Remember: You need to use your skills with equations to find the missing
measures.

6   Find the value of $x$ for each of the following.
    (a)                                 (b)

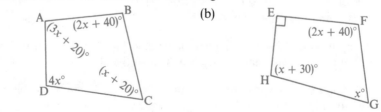

7  Find the values of *a*, *b*, and *c* for the following diagrams.

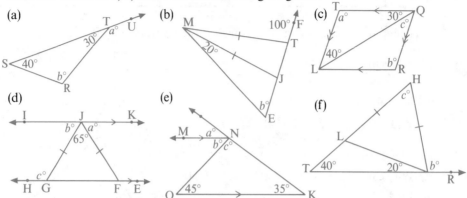

(a)

(b)

(c)

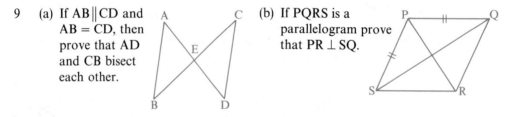

(d)

(e)

(f)

8  (a) In △PQR, ∠P is 20° more than ∠R and ∠Q is 20° more than ∠P.
     Find the measures of the angles.

   (b) In △PQR, ∠P is three times the size of ∠Q and ∠R is twice the size
       of ∠P. Find the measures of the angles.

9  (a) If AB∥CD and
       AB = CD, then
       prove that AD
       and CB bisect
       each other.

   (b) If PQRS is a
       parallelogram prove
       that PR ⊥ SQ.

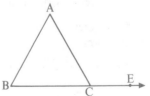

10  In △SQP, TR∥QP and T and R are points on SQ and SP respectively.
    If SQ = SP, prove △STR is isosceles.

11  A transversal EF intersects AB and CD at G and H respectively. The
    bisectors of a pair of interior angles meet at K. If AB∥CD prove ∠GKH = 90°.

12  In the diagram, ∠ACE is an exterior angle of △ABC. ∠A and ∠B are
    called the related interior and opposite angles.

    (a) In △ABC, prove that ∠A + ∠B = ∠ACE.

    (b) Write your result in (a) in words.

    (c) Prove that in any triangle the exterior angle
        of a triangle is equal to the sum of the related
        interior and opposite angles.

13  Prove that in an equilateral triangle, the median (line drawn from vertex
    to midpoint of opposite side) to any side is also the altitude.

14  A chapter of a book begins on a page numbered 322. If 366 more digits
    are used to number the rest of the pages in the chapter, on what page
    does the chapter end?

## 9.5 PSP Converse Statements: Parallel Lines

When you studied parallel lines, you learned that

**A** If a transversal intersects two parallel lines, then the corresponding angles are equal.

**B** If a transversal intersects two parallel lines, then the alternate angles are equal.

**C** If a transversal intersects two parallel lines, then the interior angles on the same side of the transversal are supplementary.

You can summarize the information above visually as shown.

If $AB \parallel CD$ then

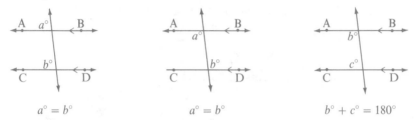

The converses of the above statements are written below.

**A\*** If a transversal intersects two lines and the corresponding angles are equal, then the lines are parallel.

**B\*** If a transversal intersects two lines and the alternate angles are equal, then the lines are parallel.

**C\*** If a transversal intersects two lines and the interior angles on the same side of the transversal are supplementary, then the lines are parallel.

You have already seen that the converse of a true statement is not necessarily true. One strategy for proving deductions is to use the given information directly. Another strategy for proving deductions is used to prove the converse of the statement above. This strategy is called the **method of indirect proof** or **proof by contradiction**. PSP

### The Method of Indirect Proof

The *method of indirect proof* is based on the simple fact that a given piece of information is one of the following: it is true, or it is not true. The basis of indirect proof is to choose one of the alternatives and if the alternative leads to a contradiction of a known fact or theorem, then the other alternative must be true. In order to use the method of indirect proof to prove Example 1, you make use of the known fact that: *In any triangle, an exterior angle is equal to the sum of the related interior and opposite angles.*

**Example 1**    If a transversal intersects two lines and the alternate angles are equal, then the lines are parallel.

**Solution**    Given: Transversal CD intersects
        AB and EF so that
        $\angle$ AHG = $\angle$ HGF.

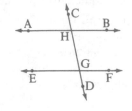

Required to prove: AB $\parallel$ EF

Proof: Either AB $\parallel$ EF or AB $\nparallel$ EF. $\left\{\begin{array}{l}\text{There are only} \\ \text{two possibilities.}\end{array}\right.$

Assume AB $\nparallel$ EF.
Then AB and EF intersect at some
point P as shown in the diagram.

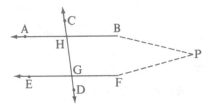

In $\triangle$GPH, $\angle$CHP is an exterior angle.
Then $\angle$CHP = $\angle$HGP + $\angle$HPG.
But this contradicts what was given, namely,
$\angle$CHP = $\angle$HGF. Thus assuming AB $\nparallel$ EF leads to a
contradiction. Thus, AB $\nparallel$ EF is not true. Since one of
AB $\parallel$ EF or AB $\nparallel$ EF must be true and since AB $\nparallel$ EF is
not true, then AB $\parallel$ EF must be true.

Once the converses for parallel lines have been proved, then you can
prove lines are parallel based on the following.

If $m° = n°$, then AB $\parallel$ CD.   If $x° = y°$, then AB $\parallel$ CD.   If $a° + b° = 180°$, then
                                                                 AB $\parallel$ CD.

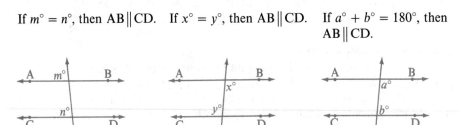

The results above are now included as part of the Parallel Lines Theorem (PLT),
which is used in the following example.

**Example 2**　In quadrilateral PQRS, PQ = RQ and RP bisects ∠QRS. Prove that RS ∥ QP.

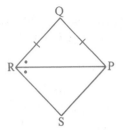

**Solution**　Given: Quadrilateral PQRS with PQ = RQ and ∠QRP = ∠SRP.

Required to prove: RS ∥ QP

Proof:

| Statements | | Reasons |
|---|---|---|
| In △RQP, QR = QP | | given |
| Thus ∠QRP = ∠QPR | | ITT |
| and ∠QRP = ∠SRP | | given |
| Thus ∠QPR = ∠SRP | | |
| Since PR is a transversal that intersects RS and QP so that ∠QPR = ∠SRP | | equal alternate angles |
| then RS ∥ QP | | PLT |

**PSP**

The method of indirect proof is a useful strategy in problem-solving. It allows you to prove facts that otherwise might be difficult or even impossible to prove.

# 9.5　Exercise

**B** Review the method of indirect proof. Remember that the method of indirect proof can be used to prove facts in geometry as well as in algebra.

1　Use the method of indirect proof to prove that only one perpendicular can be drawn from P to the line segment AB.

2　Use the method of indirect proof to prove that the product of two even numbers is even.

3　Use the method of indirect proof to prove each of the following statements.

(a) Only two equal line segments can be drawn at one time from any point P to AB.

(b) If $a < 0$, then $\dfrac{1}{a} < 0$.

(c) If $a, b > 0$, then $\dfrac{a}{b} > 0$.

(d) A triangle has at most one altitude drawn from a vertex to the opposite side or opposite side produced, of the triangle.

(e) If $a > b$ and $b > c$, then $a > c$.     (f) If $\ell_1 \| \ell_2$ and $\ell_2 \| \ell_3$, then $\ell_1 \| \ell_3$.

(g) Any triangle has at most one obtuse angle.

4   For the diagram

$$\angle AGH = \angle GHD.$$

Use the indirect method of proof, to prove $AB \| CD$.

5   In the diagram
    $a \neq b$.

Prove that

$$GH \! \not\| FE.$$

6   (a) Write the converse of this statement:

   If a transversal intersects two parallel lines, then the alternate angles are equal.

   (b) Use the method of indirect proof to prove that the converse in (a) is true.

7   (a) Write the converse of this statement:

   If a transversal intersects two parallel lines, then the interior angles on the same side of the transversal are supplementary.

   (b) Use the method of indirect proof to prove that the converse in (a) is true.

8   Use the method of indirect proof to prove the following:

   If two lines are perpendicular to the same line, then the two lines are parallel.

9   Use the method of indirect proof. Prove that the equal angles in an isosceles triangle are acute.

C 10   In $\triangle ABC$, line segments AD and BE are drawn.

   (a) Use the method of indirect proof to prove that AD and BE cannot bisect each other.

   (b) Write up your conclusion in (a) as a theorem.

The Parallel Lines Theorem can be used to prove many deductions in geometry. Prove each of the following deductions. Remember to justify each step of your proof.

11　Which lines in each of the following diagrams may be proven parallel? Give reasons for your answers.

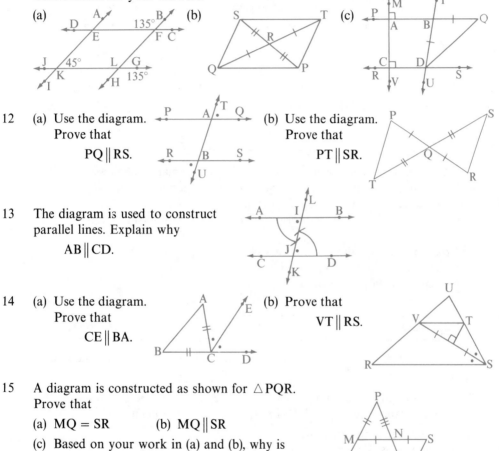

(a)　(b)　(c)

12　(a) Use the diagram. Prove that

$$PQ \parallel RS.$$

(b) Use the diagram. Prove that

$$PT \parallel SR.$$

13　The diagram is used to construct parallel lines. Explain why

$$AB \parallel CD.$$

14　(a) Use the diagram. Prove that

$$CE \parallel BA.$$

(b) Prove that

$$VT \parallel RS.$$

15　A diagram is constructed as shown for $\triangle PQR$. Prove that

(a) $MQ = SR$　　(b) $MQ \parallel SR$

(c) Based on your work in (a) and (b), why is MSRQ a parallelogram?

(d) Explain why $MN = \dfrac{1}{2} QR$, and $MN \parallel QR$.

16　Explain how you would use the construction in the previous question to prove that:

In any triangle, the line joining the midpoints of two sides of a triangle is parallel to the third side and equal to one half of it.

## 9.6 Proving Properties: Quadrilaterals

Most of the theorems that have been developed so far can be used to prove properties of quadrilaterals. Remember: A **quadrilateral** is a polygon with 4 sides.

The following diagrams show the properties of special quadrilaterals.

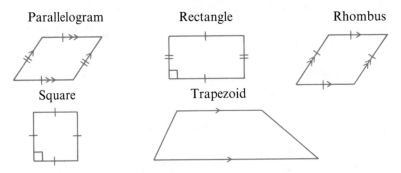

Parallelogram    Rectangle    Rhombus

Square    Trapezoid

The definitions of these special quadrilaterals are summarized below.
- A trapezoid (or trapezium) is a quadrilateral with a pair of opposite sides that are parallel and a pair that are not parallel.
- A parallelogram is a quadrilateral with both pairs of opposite sides parallel.
- A rhombus is a quadrilateral with all sides equal.
- A rectangle is a parallelogram with a right angle.
- A square is a rhombus with a right angle.

## 9.6 Exercise

**B** Some of the deductions that you prove about the properties of quadrilaterals are listed as part of a theorem.

1    The following properties of a parallelogram are known as the Properties of Parallelograms Theorem (PPT). Prove each of the following.

(a) In a parallelogram prove that
- the opposite sides are equal.    • the opposite angles are equal.

(b) In a parallelogram, prove that the diagonals bisect each other.

(c) If both pairs of opposite sides of a quadrilateral are equal then the quadrilateral is a parallelogram.

(d) If one pair of opposite sides of a quadrilateral is equal and parallel, then the quadrilateral is a parallelogram.

(e) If the diagonals of a quadrilateral bisect each other then the quadrilateral is a parallelogram.

2   These properties relate to a rhombus.

(a) Use the definition of a rhombus to prove that any rhombus is a parallelogram.

(b) Prove that the opposite angles of a rhombus are equal.

(c) Prove that the diagonals of a rhombus are perpendicular bisectors of each other.

(d) Prove that if the diagonals of a quadrilateral are perpendicular bisectors of each other, then the quadrilateral is a rhombus.

3   These properties relate to a rectangle.

(a) Prove that if a quadrilateral has a right angle and opposite sides are equal then the quadrilateral is a rectangle.

(b) Prove that the diagonals of a rectangle are equal.

4   In the diagram, QT = TS and BT = TM. Prove that $\angle XSM = \angle MQY$.

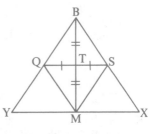

5   The line segment QX in the parallelogram CQTX bisects $\angle CQT$. Prove that CQTX is a rhombus.

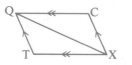

6   In the diagram RP = RQ. If RS bisects $\angle PRT$ (RS ≠ PQ) then prove quadrilateral PQRS is a trapezoid.

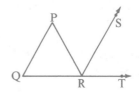

7   In quadrilateral ABCD, AC ⊥ DB. If the midpoints of BD and AC are coincident with the intersection point of AC and BD, prove that ABCD is a rhombus.

8   The midpoints of the sides of a square ABCD are P, Q, R, and S in turn. Prove that quadrilateral PQRS is a rhombus.

9   ECAF is a parallelogram in which B is the midpoint of FE and S is the midpoint of AC. Prove that BASE is a parallelogram.

# 9.7  **PSP** Proving the Pythagorean Theorem

In your earlier work in mathematics, you explored the properties of a right triangle using inductive thinking. These properties are summarized as follows.

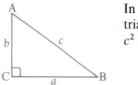

In right triangle ABC
$$c^2 = a^2 + b^2$$

In words, the Pythagorean Theorem states: In a right triangle the square of the hypotenuse equals the sum of the squares of the other two sides.

These results have been accepted as true without their having been proved. In this section, the Pythagorean Theorem will be proved. In mathematics there is often more than one way of proving a fact. Since Pythagoras' time, over 400 different proofs have been supplied for the Pythagorean Theorem. In the exercise that follows you will develop some of the different proofs of the Pythagorean Theorem.

## 9.7  Exercise

**A** Any new facts that you learn should be listed in your summary of geometric facts which you began earlier in the year.

Questions 1 to 6 are based on the following diagram.

The diagram was constructed by a mathematician to prove the Pythagorean Theorem. A square CDEF is constructed. Points M and N are chosen and the sides are marked as shown.

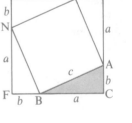

1 (a) Prove that $\triangle ACB \cong \triangle MDA$

(b) Use your result in (a) to show why $\angle BAM = 90°$

2 Prove each of the following.

(a) $\triangle BFN \cong \triangle NEM$       (b) $\angle BNM = 90°$

(c) $\angle AMN = 90°$       (d) $\angle ABN = 90°$

3 Use the results in Questions 1 and 2. Explain why the quadrilateral AMNB is a square.

4 (a) Find the area of $\triangle ACB$.

(b) Why are the areas of $\triangle ACB$, $\triangle BFN$, $\triangle NEM$, $\triangle MDA$ equal?

5 (a) Explain why you can write the following.

Area of CDEF = Area of BAMN + $\triangle$ACB + $\triangle$BFN + $\triangle$NEM + $\triangle$MDA

The symbol "$\triangle$ACB" is often used to represent "the area of $\triangle$ACB".

(b) Simplify $(a + b)^2 = c^2 + \dfrac{1}{2}ab + \dfrac{1}{2}ab + \dfrac{1}{2}ab + \dfrac{1}{2}ab.$

(c) How are (a) and (b) related?

(d) Based on your answer in (b), why is $c^2 = a^2 + b^2$?

6 Use your answers in Questions 1 to 5 to write the complete proof for the Pythagorean Theorem:

> In a right triangle the square of the hypotenuse is equal to the sum of the squares of the other two sides.

7 Another proof of the Pythagorean Theorem is given by the following diagram. This diagram allows us to write the shortest known proof of the theorem.

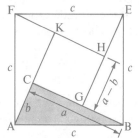

$$EG = FH = AK = BC = a$$
$$AC = FK = EH = BG = b$$

(a) Why are $\triangle$'s EHF, FKA, ACB, BGE congruent?

(b) Explain why the quadrilateral KHGC is a square.

(c) Why is area square ABEF = area square CGHK + $\triangle$ACB + $\triangle$BGE + $\triangle$EHF + $\triangle$FKA?

(d) Simplify $c^2 = (a - b)^2 + \dfrac{1}{2}ab + \dfrac{1}{2}ab + \dfrac{1}{2}ab + \dfrac{1}{2}ab.$

(e) How are (c) and (d) related?

(f) Use the information in (a) to (e) above to write the shortest proof known for the Pythagorean Theorem.

**B** Review your skills in finding square roots.

8 Find the length of the missing sides to one decimal place.

(a)

(b)

(c)

(d)

(e)

9   Find the length of the diagonal of a rectangle with sides 12.0 cm, 16.0 cm.

10  In isosceles △ABC,
    (a) explain why CE = EB.
    (b) Find the length of AE to 1 decimal place.

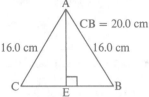

11  For the rhombus
           AC = 14.0 cm, DB = 10.0 cm.
    Calculate the length of the sides.

12  The radius of the circle with centre O is 12.0 cm. If the altitude OB is 6.0 cm, find the length of the chord AC.

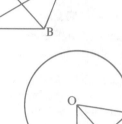

13  Find the distance between each pair of points. You may express your answer as a radical.
    (a) A(6, 3), B(1, 2)                    (b) C(−1, −1), D(8, 11)
    (c) P(1, 3), Q(−3, −1)                  (d) R(6, −4), S(8, 3)

14  Show that the quadrilateral with vertices P(1, 3), Q(4, 1), R(2, −2), and S(−1, 0) is a rhombus.

15  △PQR is given by P(−1, 3), Q(4, 7), and R(−5, −2). Classify what type it is: scalene, isosceles, or equilateral. Give reasons for your answer.

## Problem Solving

A question often posed in mathematics that leads to new developments begins, "What if . . . ?"
In particular: What if a semi-circle is drawn on each side of a right triangle?
- Is this statement true: The area of the semi-circle drawn on the hypotenuse is equal to the sum of the areas of the semi-circles drawn on the other two sides?
- Can you draw any other figures and obtain a true statement?

## 9.8 The Converse of the Pythagorean Theorem

The converse of the Pythagorean Theorem is given by:

> If the square on one side of a triangle is equal to the sum of the squares on the other two sides, then the angle opposite the longest side is a right angle.

You have seen that the converse of a theorem may or may not be true. Thus, you need to prove the above converse.

**Example**  Prove the converse of the Pythagorean Theorem (PT).

**Solution**  Given: $\triangle ABC$ so that $a^2 + b^2 = c^2$

Required to prove: $\angle C = 90°$

Proof: To prove the converse, construct $\triangle DEF$ as shown.

| Statements | Reasons |
|---|---|
| In $\triangle DFE$, $\angle F = 90°$ | constructed |
| thus $\quad f^2 = a^2 + b^2$ | Pythagorean Theorem |
| But $\quad a^2 + b^2 = c^2$ | given |
| Thus $\quad f^2 = a^2 + b^2$ | |
| $\quad\quad\quad = c^2$ | |
| $\quad\quad\quad f = c$ | since $f$, $c$, are positive |
| Thus $\quad ED = BA$ | |
| In $\triangle ABC$, $\triangle DEF$ | |
| $\quad\quad BC = EF$ | constructed |
| $\quad\quad AC = DF$ | constructed |
| $\quad\quad AB = DE$ | proved |
| Thus $\quad \triangle ABC \cong \triangle DEF$ | SSS |
| and $\quad \angle C = \angle F$ | congruent triangles |
| $\quad\quad\quad = 90°$ | |

## 9.8 Exercise

**A**  Use the symbol PT to refer to the Pythagorean Theorem and its converse.

1  Which of the following triangles are right triangles? (Diagrams are not drawn to scale.)

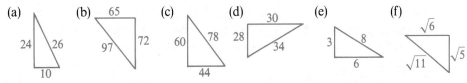

2   The numbers shown represent the sides of triangles. Which triangles are right triangles?

(a) 36, 36, 72        (b) 30, 40, 50        (c) 120, 119, 169        (d) 90, 56, 106

3   (a) Use the diagram. Prove that $\angle P = 90°$.     (b) Use the diagram. Prove that $AB \perp CB$.

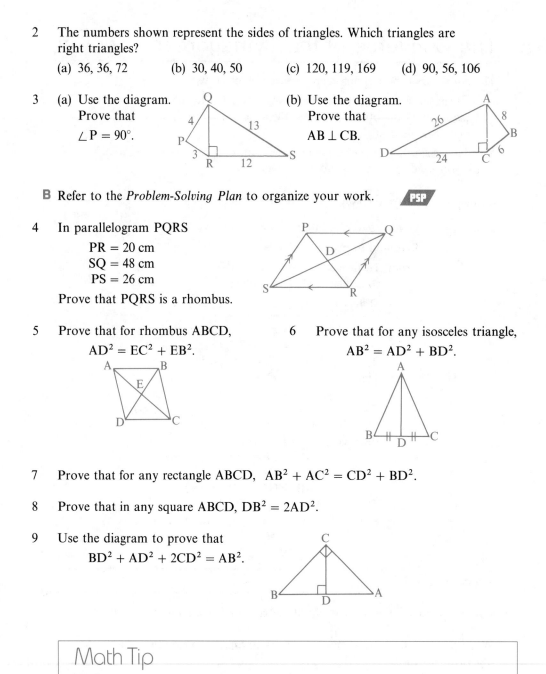

B   Refer to the *Problem-Solving Plan* to organize your work.        **PSP**

4   In parallelogram PQRS

$PR = 20$ cm
$SQ = 48$ cm
$PS = 26$ cm

Prove that PQRS is a rhombus.

5   Prove that for rhombus ABCD,
$AD^2 = EC^2 + EB^2$.

6   Prove that for any isosceles triangle,
$AB^2 = AD^2 + BD^2$.

7   Prove that for any rectangle ABCD,   $AB^2 + AC^2 = CD^2 + BD^2$.

8   Prove that in any square ABCD, $DB^2 = 2AD^2$.

9   Use the diagram to prove that
$BD^2 + AD^2 + 2CD^2 = AB^2$.

## Math Tip

To solve problems you must understand the meaning of each mathematical word. Make a list of all the new words you met in this chapter. Use an example to illustrate the meaning of each word.

## Practice and Problems: Review

1    In △MNP, ∠M is twice the size of ∠N and ∠P is 30° more than twice the size of ∠N. Find the measures of the angles.

2    In the diagram, AB‖CD and AE = ED. Prove that AB = CD.

3    Use the diagram. If PQRS is a parallelogram, prove that △HSR ≅ △GQP.

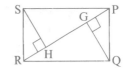

4    In △ABC, D and E are found on AB and AC respectively so that AD = AE and DB = EC. Prove ∠EBC = ∠DCB.

5    In △PQR, the midpoint M is found for PR. If PM = QM, prove ∠PQR is right.

6    Use the indirect method of proof to prove that the bisector of the vertical angle of an isosceles triangle bisects the base.

## Practice Test

1    Two angles of a triangle are 100° and 40°. What type of triangle is it?

2    Find the missing measures.

(a)                         (b)

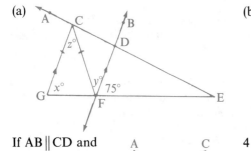

3    If AB‖CD and AB = CD, then prove that AD and CB bisect each other.

4    If PQRS is a parallelogram prove that PR ⊥ SQ.

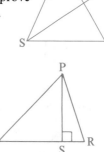

5    In △ABD, ∠A = ∠D. If AD is produced to C so that ∠DBC = ∠DCB, then prove that BA = DC.

6    △PQR is scalene. Use the method of indirect proof to prove that PS is not the median.

# Cumulative Review (5 to 8)

1   (a) Write the equation of the family of lines that passes through the point $(2, -3)$.

(b) Find the equation of the member in (a) with slope $\dfrac{2}{3}$.

(c) Find the $x$-intercept of the line in (b).

2   (a) The lines $x + 2y = 3$ and $3x - y = mx + 4$ are parallel. Find the value of $m$.

(b) The point $\left(\dfrac{1}{2}, -1\right)$ is on the line given by $2x - ky = 1$. Find the value of $k$.

3   For each system, decide which variable may be more easily eliminated. Then solve the system.

(a) $x + 4y = 6$
    $2x - y = 3$

(b) $2x - y = 6$
    $3x + y = 9$

(c) $3m - 2n = -4$
    $m - 3n = -6$

4   Solve for $m$ and $n$ and verify. $\dfrac{m-1}{2} - \dfrac{n+1}{3} = -1$ and $m + n = 3$

5   Two lines are defined by the equations $3x - y = 14$ and $2x + y = 6$. Find the co-ordinates of the point of intersection.

6   For the concert, 420 tickets were sold. Orchestra seats sold at $6.00 and balcony seats at $4.00. If the total receipts were $1920.00, how many of each type of seat were sold?

7   John decided to invest his savings of $3300, part at 8% and the rest at 10%. At the end of the year he noticed that the interest from the 8% investment was $84 more than the interest from the 10% investment. How much was invested at each rate?

8   Draw the graph of each region defined by the system of inequations.

(a) $x > y - 1,\ 3y - x \le 1$

(b) $y \ge 2x + 2,\ x - 2 > -y,\ x \ge 0$

9   A partial variation is given by $T = k + pn$. Find $k$ and $p$ if $T = 100$ when $n = 20$ and $T = 160$ when $n = 40$.

10  In $\triangle ABC$, $AB = AC$. If $CB$ is produced to $F$ and $BC$ is produced to $G$, prove that $\angle ACG = \angle ABF$.

11  In $\triangle PQR$, $QR$ is produced to $T$ so that $QR = RT$ and $RQ$ is produced to $S$ so that $SQ = QR$. If $PQ = PR$, then prove that $PS = PT$.

# 10 Applications in Three Dimensions

Calculating surface area, using models, nets, developing formulas, solving problems, calculating volume, using principles, using estimates, projections for sketching figures, applications, strategies and problem solving

## Introduction

So far, you have seen that the study of mathematics and the process of studying and learning mathematics take on many aspects. For example, you have seen that

- Mathematics can be used to study the many applications around you.

- The main purpose of mathematics is to solve problems.

- Patterns play an important role in the study of mathematics. Often, they suggest strategies for solving problems or developing skills.

- Often, a skill or strategy in mathematics is developed to solve a particular problem. This skill then extends to the solution of problems that were not originally intended.

- The development of mathematics has often been furthered by the question: What if . . . ?

- Technology, such as calculators and computers, can be used to reduce the need for tedious calculations to solve certain problems.

In this chapter you will once again meet some of these aspects in mathematics along with some other ones. In particular, the calculator can play an important role in solving problems. For example, in which section can you use these calculator steps?

$$\boxed{C} \; 2.38 \; \boxed{y^x} \; 3 \; \boxed{=} \; \boxed{\times} \; \boxed{\pi} \; \boxed{\times} \; 4 \; \boxed{\div} \; 3 \; \boxed{=} \quad \text{output} \atop ?$$

What problem do these calculator steps solve?

**PSP** Problem-Solving: Using Diagrams

As you learn more and more concepts and strategies in mathematics, you will begin to realize that one strategy can be more useful than another in solving a problem. Also sometimes you need to combine strategies in order to solve a problem. However, you must always read the problem carefully and be able to answer these two questions:

A: What am I asked to find?
B: What information am I given?

Being able to visualize a problem sometimes helps you to solve the problem. For example, the surface area of a box is the total area of all the faces of that box. Use the diagrams below to help you plan how to calculate the surface area of a rectangular prism.

You call this shape the net of the rectangular prism.

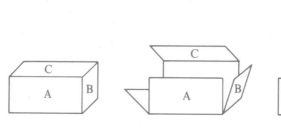

Thus, to calculate the surface area of a rectangular prism you need only calculate the area of 3 different rectangles, A, B, and C.

**Example 1**    Calculate the surface area of the square-based pyramid.

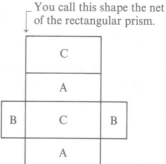

2.1 m

**Solution**    Think of a net to plan the calculations.

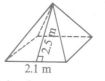

height of triangle

Surface area = 4 × area of triangular face + area of square base
        = 4 × [$\frac{1}{2}$ × 2.1 × 2.5] m² + (2.1)² m²
        = 10.5 m² + 4.41 m²
        = 14.91 m²

The surface area is 14.9 m².

Visualizing a net of a cylinder also helps you to plan a method for finding the surface area of cylinders.

**Example 2**   Calculate the surface area of the cylinder. Round your answer to the nearest square centimetre.

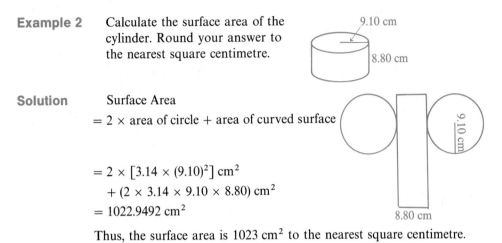

**Solution**   Surface Area

$= 2 \times$ area of circle $+$ area of curved surface

$= 2 \times [3.14 \times (9.10)^2] \text{ cm}^2$
$+ (2 \times 3.14 \times 9.10 \times 8.80) \text{ cm}^2$
$= 1022.9492 \text{ cm}^2$

Thus, the surface area is $1023 \text{ cm}^2$ to the nearest square centimetre.

## 10.1   Exercise

**A** Use a net to help you plan the calculations of surface areas.

1   A rectangular prism is shown.
   (a) Sketch a net of the prism and show the measures.
   (b) Calculate the surface area.

2   Calculate the surface area of each rectangular prism.

   (a) 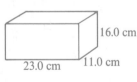   (b) 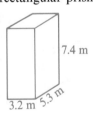   (c)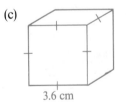

3   Find the surface area of each rectangular prism.

|     | Length  | Width    | Height   |
|-----|---------|----------|----------|
| (a) | 14.1 cm | 6.2 cm   | 4.5 cm   |
| (b) | 21.0 cm | 15.5 cm  | 27.5 cm  |
| (c) | 5.5 m   | 3.7 m    | 1.5 m    |
| (d) | 7.9 cm  | 5.4 cm   | 7.0 cm   |

4   A square-based pyramid is shown.

    (a) Sketch a net of the pyramid and show the measures.

    (b) Calculate the surface area of the pyramid.

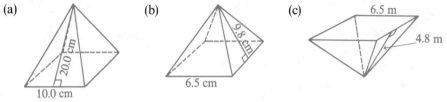

5   Calculate the surface area of each square-based pyramid.

    (a)              (b)             (c)

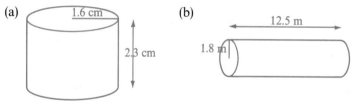

6   (a) Sketch the net of this cylinder and show the measures.

    (b) Calculate the surface area of the cylinder.

7   Calculate the surface area of each cylinder.

    (a)                   (b)

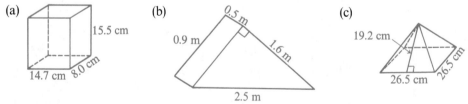

Remember to use estimation to check the reasonableness of your results. **PSP**
Use $\pi \doteq 3.14$.

8   Calculate the surface area of each of the following solids.

    (a)              (b)             (c)

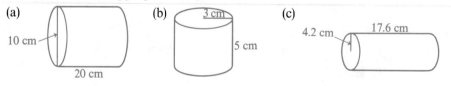

9   Find the surface area of each cylinder. Use a calculator. Express your final answer in the appropriate form.

    (a)              (b)             (c)

(d)

6.7 cm

2.6 cm

(e)

17.3 cm

24.9 cm

(f)

2.84 m

4.35 m

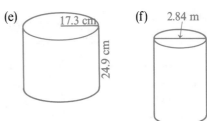

10  (a) Calculate the area of glass needed to
        construct the aquarium.

    (b) If the glass used costs $58.95/m², what
        is the cost of this aquarium?

11  A tin is 12.5 cm high and has a diameter of
    8.0 cm. Calculate the area of the label that
    needs to be used if the overlap is 0.5 cm.

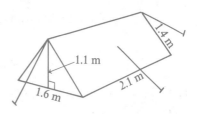

40.0 cm

50.0 cm

34.0 cm

12  10% extra material for the overlap of the edges is needed to construct each
    tissue box. Calculate the amount of paper needed to construct each one.

(a)

15.2 cm

12.5 cm

20.2 cm

(b)

24.8 cm

7.2 cm

10.6 cm

13  The tent shown in the diagram has a
    sewn-in ground sheet. Find the amount of
    material used to make the tent if 0.3 m²
    of extra material is added for the seams.

1.1 m

1.4 m

2.1 m

1.6 m

14  Sealed oil drums are often used to support a floating dock. The outside
    of an oil drum is to be painted with 2 coats of underwater paint. The
    diameter of the drum is 0.6 m and its height is 1.2 m.

    (a) Calculate the surface area.

    (b) Twelve drums are used to make a floating dock at a marina. How
        many litres of paint are needed if 1 L covers 6.5 m²?

C 15  You are given 150 cm² of tin.    PSP

    (a) Design a cube and a cylinder so that they have the same surface area.

    (b) What are the dimensions of the shapes you have constructed?

## 10.2 **PSP** Strategy: Developing a Formula

You can use your skills with nets to find the surface area of other shapes. You can also use a net to help you to develop a formula for the surface area of a cone.

r, radius of the cone.
h, height of the cone.
s, slant height of the cone.

The length of arc AB is the same measure as the circumference of the base circle where

$$C = 2\pi r$$

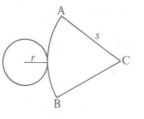

The curved surface is formed from a sector of a circle with radius s, where s is the slant height of the cone.

Since the curved surface is a fraction of a circle, you can find the area of a sector of the circle.

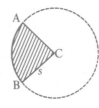

The shaded area is a sector of the circle.

To find the area of the sector use the fact that the ratio of the length of an arc compared to the circumference is the same as the ratio of the area of the sector compared to the area of the full circle as follows.

$$\frac{\text{area of sector}}{\text{area of circle}} = \frac{\text{arc AB}}{\text{circumference of circle}}$$

$$\frac{\text{area of sector}}{\pi s^2} = \frac{2\pi r}{2\pi s}$$

$$\text{area of sector} = \frac{2\pi r}{2\pi s} \times \pi s^2$$

$$= \pi r s$$

Thus the surface area of the cone, S, is given by the formula

$$S = \underset{\substack{\uparrow \\ \text{area of} \\ \text{base circle}}}{\pi r^2} + \underset{\substack{\text{area of} \\ \text{curved surface}}}{\pi r s}$$

You combined a number of skills in order to develop a formula for the surface area of a cone. **PSP**

A similar procedure, but at a more advanced level of mathematics, was used to develop a formula for the surface area of a sphere.

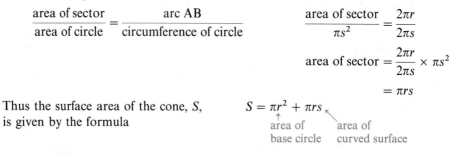

The surface area of a sphere is given by the formula

$$S = 4\pi r^2, \text{ where } r \text{ is the radius of the sphere.}$$

**Example**

A spherical gas storage tank has a diameter of 8.6 m. Calculate its surface area. (Use $\pi \doteq 3.14$.)

*A spherical shape is the most efficient use of material to make a tank.*

**Solution**

Surface area, $S$, of a sphere is given by

$$S = 4\pi r^2$$
$$\doteq 4 \times 3.14 \times (4.3)^2$$
$$= 232.2344$$

Thus, the surface area is 230 m².    Rounded to 2 significant digits.

## 10.2 Exercise

**A** Use $\pi \doteq 3.14$. Remember to round your answers according to the accuracy of the measures given in the questions.

1. (a) What do the variables of each of these formulas represent?
       (i) Surface Area, $S$, of a cone     (ii) Surface Area, $S$, of a sphere
   $$S = \pi r^2 + \pi rs \qquad\qquad S = 4\pi r^2$$
   (b) Sketch a diagram to show what measures each variable represents.

2. The cone has a radius of 8.0 cm and a slant height of 17.0 cm.
   (a) Find the area of the base.
   (b) Find the area of the curved surface.
   (c) What is the surface area?

   17.0 cm
   8.0 cm

3. Find the surface area of each of the following cones.

   (a)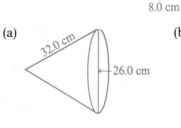
   32.0 cm   26.0 cm

   (b)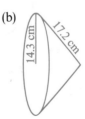
   14.3 cm   17.2 cm

4. Calculate the area of each cone.
   (a) radius = 3.6 cm, slant height = 12.5 cm
   (b) diameter = 11.8 cm, slant height = 11.3 cm

5   Find the surface area of each sphere.

(a) 7 cm   (b) 3.9 cm   (c) 15.2 cm

6   Calculate the surface area of a sphere with

(a) a diameter of 12.6 cm   (b) a radius of 8.2 m   (c) a diameter of 4.62 cm

**B** Check each of your answers to see if it is reasonable.   **PSP**

7   The curved surface of a cone is called the **lateral surface**. Calculate the lateral surface area if the slant height is 8.5 cm, and the radius of the base is 5.2 cm.

lateral surface

8   (a) The area of the lateral surface of a cone is 32.64 cm². If the slant height is 2.81 cm, find the radius.

(b) The area of the lateral surface of a cone is 184.82 cm². If the radius is 6.75 cm, find the slant height.

9   (a) The slant height of a cone is 18.10 cm. Calculate the area of the lateral surface if the radius is 7.23 cm.

(b) By how much does the area of the lateral surface increase if the radius is increased by 1.00 cm?

10   A stereo speaker is shown.

(a) Find the approximate area of material used to make the speaker.

(b) What assumption do you make in (a)?

24.6 cm   14.4 cm

11   The radius of a volleyball is 15.2 cm. By how much does the surface area of the volleyball increase if you inflate the ball so that the radius increases by 2.0 cm?

12   (a) The slant height of a cone is doubled. By what percentage is the lateral surface changed?

(b) If the radius of a cone is doubled, what change occurs in its area?

(c) If the radius of a cylinder is doubled, how does the curved surface change? How does the area of its base change?

(d) If the radius of a sphere is doubled, by what percentage is its surface area increased?

# 10.3 Principles of Volume

To be a good problem-solver, you need to learn various principles in mathematics. These principles occur over and over, even in advanced mathematics.

For example, the volume of a solid is the amount of space it occupies. Volume is measured in cubic units. To develop a formula to calculate the volume of a rectangular prism, you can think of the layers shown.

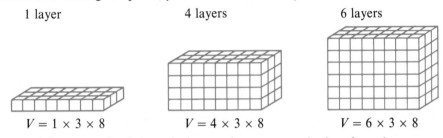

1 layer    4 layers    6 layers

$V = 1 \times 3 \times 8$    $V = 4 \times 3 \times 8$    $V = 6 \times 3 \times 8$

Once you have examined numerical examples, you can obtain a formula for the volume.

Volume = length × width × height        $V = l \times w \times h$

By rearranging your calculations in a different way, you can develop a different strategy for calculating volume.

**PSP**

$V = l \underbrace{\times w \times h}$

$B$, where $B$ is the area of the base of the prism

$V = B \times h$

You can extend this strategy to calculate the volume of *any prism*, or *cylinder* using the area of the base and height. To calculate the volume of a prism or cylinder you use

$V = B \times h.$

area of base    height

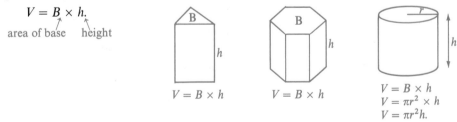

$V = B \times h$        $V = B \times h$

$V = B \times h$
$V = \pi r^2 \times h$
$V = \pi r^2 h.$

**Example**    An expensive paper weight, in the shape of a triangular prism, is made of pure gold.

(a) Calculate the volume of the paper weight, to 1 decimal place.

(b) Calculate its value, if gold is worth $180.00/cm³.

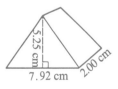

5.25 cm

7.92 cm

2.00 cm

**Solution**   (a) Use the formula   $V = B \times h$
$$= (\tfrac{1}{2} \times 7.92 \times 5.25) \times 2.00$$
$$\underbrace{\phantom{(\tfrac{1}{2} \times 7.92 \times 5.25)}}_{\text{area of base}}$$
$$= 41.58$$

The volume of the paper weight is 41.6 cm³ to 1 decimal place.

(b) Gold is valued at $180.00/cm³.
Thus 1 cm³ of gold is valued at $180.00.
Thus 41.6 cm³ of gold is valued at 41.6 × $180.00 or $7488.00.
Thus the value of the paper weight is $7488.00.

> Did you know that the highest price ever paid for a paper weight was $143 000? (And it was only made of glass!)

## 10.3   Exercise

**A** Round off the answer to each of the following questions to 1 decimal place.

1  (a) Calculate the area of the base.
   (b) Calculate the volume.

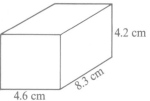

4.2 cm
8.3 cm
4.6 cm

2  Calculate the volume of each prism.

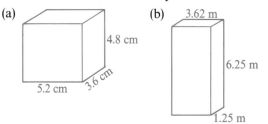

(a)  4.8 cm
5.2 cm  3.6 cm

(b)  3.62 m
6.25 m
1.25 m

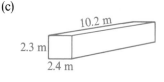

(c)  10.2 m
2.3 m
2.4 m

3  (a) Calculate the area of the base of the prism.
   (b) Calculate the volume of the prism.

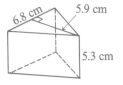

6.8 cm   5.9 cm
5.3 cm

4  (a) Calculate the area of the base of the cylinder.
   (b) Calculate the volume of the cylinder.

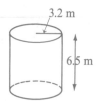

3.2 m
6.5 m

5   Find each volume.

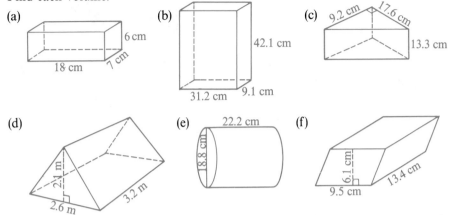

(a) 6 cm, 18 cm, 7 cm

(b) 42.1 cm, 31.2 cm, 9.1 cm

(c) 9.2 cm, 17.6 cm, 13.3 cm

(d) 2.1 m, 2.6 m, 3.2 m

(e) 22.2 cm, 18.8 cm

(f) 6.1 cm, 9.5 cm, 13.4 cm

**B** After you do each calculation, check whether your answers are reasonable.  **PSP**

6   Calculate each volume. You may need to take more than one step.

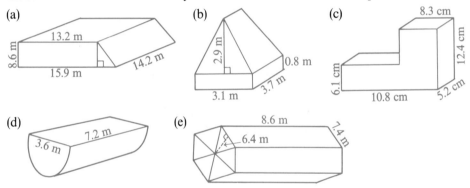

(a) 13.2 m, 8.6 m, 15.9 m, 14.2 m

(b) 2.9 m, 3.1 m, 0.8 m, 3.7 m

(c) 8.3 cm, 12.4 cm, 6.1 cm, 10.8 cm, 5.2 cm

(d) 7.2 m, 3.6 m

(e) 8.6 m, 6.4 m, 7.4 m

7   Oak is used as a veneer for dining room furniture. An oak tree is cut into
    a rectangular solid with dimensions 12.2 m by 1.5 m by 1.1 m.

    (a) Calculate the volume of the oak.

    (b) Oak has a value of $169.80/m$^3$. Calculate the value of this block of oak.

8   Pat has two cartons, one with dimensions 20.0 cm by 15.0 cm by 12.0 cm
    and the other with dimensions 15.0 cm by 12.0 cm by 10.0 cm.

    (a) If the contents of the smaller carton are poured into the larger carton,
        how much space is still available in the larger carton?

    (b) How many times could the contents of the smaller carton be poured
        into the larger carton?

9   A car engine has 6 cylinders each with a diameter of 6.9 cm and a height
    of 7.8 cm. The capacity of the engine is the total volume of the cylinders.
    Calculate the engine capacity.

10    The dimensions of three cans are shown.

(a) Estimate which can you think holds the most.

(b) Calculate the volume of each can.

(c) Compare your answers in (a) and (b). How close were you?

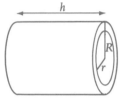

11    Find a formula for the volume of the material used to construct the concrete pipe.

Write a BASIC program to calculate the volume of any pipe. Use your program to find the volume of a pipe for which $R = 1.3$ m, $r = 1.1$ m and $h = 10.6$ m.

12    An aquarium is 58.6 cm long, 25.3 cm wide and 19.5 cm deep.

(a) Calculate how many litres of water the tank will hold when full. (Remember: $1 \text{ cm}^3 = 1 \text{ mL}$)

(b) The tank above is filled so that the water is 3.8 cm from the top. Calculate how much water is in the tank.

(c) When water freezes, it expands and its volume increases by about 10%. If the aquarium from part (b) is left outside on a sub-zero day, what volume of ice is obtained?

(d) The mass of $1 \text{ cm}^3$ (1 ml) of water is 1 g. The mass of the glass is 3.65 kg. Calculate the total mass of the aquarium.

13    The haulage part of the transport truck is shown.

Calculate the volume of the haulage part of the truck.

C 14   (a) Refer to the previous question. How many boxes that measure 0.8 m × 0.5 m × 0.5 m could you pack into the truck?

(b) How much space in (a) is not used?

# 10.4

**PSP**

## Problem-Solving Strategy: Trying Formulas

Very often, the question "What if . . . ?" results in the development of significant mathematics. For example, what if you wanted to develop the formula for the volume of a cone? Think of the cone as made up of layers of cylinders, each with a smaller radius, as shown in the diagram. Follow the steps in the exercise.

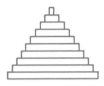

## 10.4 Exercise

**B** Notice that the greater the number of cylinders in the stack, the closer the volume of the cone is approached.

1   Use a base radius of 5.0 cm and each cylindrical layer of height 0.5 cm. The radius of each successive cylinder decreases by 0.5 cm, with the smallest radius 0.5 cm.

   *Step 1:* Calculate the total volume of the stack of cylinders.

   *Step 2:* Calculate the volume of a cylinder with the same base and height equal to the height of the stack in Step 1.

   *Step 3:* Compare your answers in (a) and (b). Do you notice any particular result?

2   Repeat the steps of Question 1 for the following cylinders. Use a base radius of 2.0 cm and a height of 0.1 cm for each cylinder. Decrease the radius of successive cylinders by 0.2 cm.

3   (a) Repeat the steps in Question 1 for different radii and heights for the cylinders in the stack. Remember that the successive layers of cylinders must diminish to a cylinder of a small radius to represent the tip of the cone.

   (b) Write a program in BASIC to improve the accuracy of your results in (a). Repeat the steps of Question 1.

4   (a) Based on your results in Questions 1 to 3, write a formula that you think gives the volume of a cone with radius $r$ and height $h$.

   (b) Design a physical experiment to test the reliability of your formula.

**C** 5   Use the strategy illustrated in Questions 1 to 4 to investigate a formula for the volume of a square-based pyramid. What is the shape of each successive layer? Based on your findings, propose a formula for finding the volume of a square-based pyramid.   **PSP**

## 10.5 Applications: Cones and Spheres

In the previous section you explored a formula to find the volume of a cone. Formulas to find volume are developed using skills in mathematics.

- The formula for the volume, $V$, of a cone is given by

$$V = \frac{1}{3}\pi r^2 h \qquad \begin{array}{l}\text{where } r \text{ is the radius,}\\ \quad h \text{ is the height.}\end{array}$$

- The formula for the volume, $V$, of a sphere is given by

$$V = \frac{4}{3}\pi r^3 \qquad \text{where } r \text{ is the radius.}$$

To calculate the volume of some shapes, you need to use both formulas as shown in the following example.

**PSP**

**Example**  A water marker is used to show where rocks occur in a channel. The dimensions are shown in the diagram. Calculate its volume to two decimal places.

1.23 m   0.59 m

**Solution**  *Step 1:* Calculate the volume of the cone.

$$V = \frac{1}{3}\pi r^2 h \qquad h = 1.23, r = 0.59$$

$$\doteq \frac{1}{3}(3.14)(0.59)^2(1.23) \qquad \begin{array}{l}\text{Remember: you can input the value}\\ \text{of } \pi \text{ directly on a calculator.}\\ \text{Use the key marked } \boxed{\pi}\end{array}$$

$$= 0.4481 \text{ (in cubic metres)}$$

*Step 2:* Calculate the volume of the base (a hemisphere).

$$\frac{1}{2}V = \frac{1}{2}\left(\frac{4}{3}\pi r^3\right) \qquad r = 0.59$$

$$\doteq \frac{1}{2} \times \frac{4}{3}(3.14)(0.59)^3 \qquad \begin{array}{l}\text{Think of an efficient procedure for}\\ \text{doing the calculation on a calculator.}\end{array}$$

Output

$$\boxed{c}\,4\,\boxed{\times}\,\boxed{\pi}\,\boxed{\times}\,.59\,\boxed{y^x}\,3\,\boxed{\div}\,6\,\boxed{=} \qquad ?$$

$$= 0.4299 \text{ (in cubic metres)}$$

The total volume is 0.88 m³, expressed to 2 decimal places.

$0.4481 + 0.4299 = 0.878$
Round to 2 decimal places, namely 0.88.

## 10.5   Exercise

**A** Remember: Check whether your answer is reasonable. **PSP**
Estimate each answer.

1   (a) Record the formula used to calculate
       the volume of a sphere.
    (b) Calculate the volume of the sphere.

2   Find the volume of each sphere.

(a)   (b) 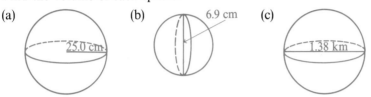 (c)

3   Find the volume of a sphere with each radius.
    (a) 10.0 cm        (b) 35.0 cm        (c) 9.6 cm        (d) 4.69 m

4   Find the volume of a sphere with each diameter.
    (a) 28.0 cm        (b) 10.2 m        (c) 12.6 mm        (d) 8.36 m

5   (a) Find the volume of a sphere with diameter 12.8 cm. Use $\pi \doteq 3.14$.
    (b) Find the volume of the sphere in (a) using the $\boxed{\pi}$ key on your
        calculator for the value of $\pi$ in the calculation.
    (c) How do your results in (a) and (b) differ?

6   (a) Record the formula used to calculate
       the volume of a cone.
    (b) Calculate the volume of the cone.

7   Find the volume of each cone.

(a)   (b)   (c)

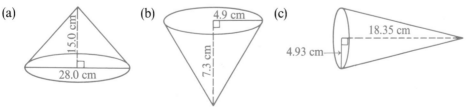

8  (a) Find the volume of a cone with height 6.85 cm and with radius 1.69 cm. Use $\pi \doteq 3.14$.

(b) Find the volume of the cone in (a) using the $\boxed{\pi}$ key on your calculator for the value of $\pi$ in the calculation.

(c) How do your results in (a) and (b) differ?

**B** Be sure to make a final statement to complete your solution.

9  (a) Calculate the volume of the baseball.

(b) How much material is needed to cover the baseball?

3.6 cm

10  (a) A tennis ball used in international competition has a diameter of 6.8 cm. Calculate the circumference of one tennis ball. What is its volume?

(b) A North American hardball has a diameter of 7.4 cm. Calculate its circumference. What is its volume?

(c) Which ball has the greater maximum cross-sectional area? By how much is it greater?

11  Bearings are used to make wheels roll. A bearing has a diameter of 0.95 cm.

(a) Calculate the volume of 100 bearings.

(b) The density of a bearing is 6.8 g/cm$^3$. Calculate the mass of 100 bearings.

12  A billiard ball has a diameter of 5.3 cm. Calculate the mass of 9 balls made of ivory, if ivory has a density of 2.1 g/cm$^3$.

13  The thickness of an orange peel is 0.47 cm. If the diameter of an unpeeled orange is 7.8 cm, what fraction of the orange is peel?

14  How much more does the hemispherical tank hold than the conical tank?

2.4 m                2.4 m

2.4 m

15 Potash is stored in a conical pile. Calculate the volume of the pile, if the height is 7.83 m and its radius is 17.62 m.

16 Ice cream is sold in a cylindrical container with a height of 15.0 cm and a radius of 8.0 cm.

(a) If a scoop of ice cream is a sphere about 5.0 cm in diameter, calculate the number of scoops from a box.

(b) What assumption do you make in finding your answer in (a)?

17 A tornado is a narrow funnel shaped cloud similar to a cone. The diameter of the tornado is 92 m and its height is 960 m. Calculate the volume of the funnel of the tornado.

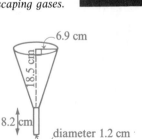

*Tornadoes occur very quickly and unexpectedly. They usually result in much destruction. Trees are uprooted. Damage to houses often leads to disastrous fires fed by escaping gases.*

C 18 How much liquid can the funnel hold when it is full?

6.9 cm

18.5 cm

8.2 cm

diameter 1.2 cm

## 10.6 **PSP** Making Decisions: Using Formulas

To solve a problem, you have to organise your solution so that another person can follow the steps to arrive at the same answer. Before you solve a problem, you should ask yourself two important questions:

 I What information am I asked to find?

 II What information am I given?

When you learn formulas in mathematics, examine
▶ how they are alike
▶ how they differ.

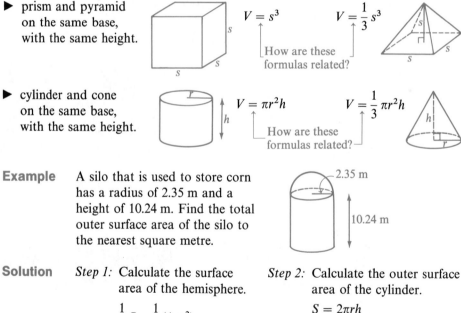

| **PSP** Problem-Solving Plan |
|---|
| *Step A* Do I understand the problem?<br> I. What information am I asked to find?<br> II. What information am I given?<br>*Step B* Decide on a method. (Which formula do I use?)<br>*Step C* Find the answer. (Do the calculations.)<br>*Step D* Check my answer in the *original* problem.<br>*Step E* Write a final statement to answer the question. |

For example, the volumes of these shapes are related.

▶ prism and pyramid on the same base, with the same height.

$$V = s^3 \qquad V = \frac{1}{3}s^3$$

How are these formulas related?

▶ cylinder and cone on the same base, with the same height.

$$V = \pi r^2 h \qquad V = \frac{1}{3}\pi r^2 h$$

How are these formulas related?

**Example** A silo that is used to store corn has a radius of 2.35 m and a height of 10.24 m. Find the total outer surface area of the silo to the nearest square metre.

2.35 m

10.24 m

**Solution**  *Step 1:* Calculate the surface area of the hemisphere.

$$\frac{1}{2}S = \frac{1}{2}(4\pi r^2)$$

$$= \frac{1}{2} \times 4(3.14)(2.35)^2$$

$$= 34.68 \text{ (to 2 decimal places)}$$

*Step 2:* Calculate the outer surface area of the cylinder.

$$S = 2\pi rh$$
$$= 2(3.14)(2.35)(10.24)$$
$$= 151.12 \text{ (to 2 decimal places)}$$

The outer surface area of the silo is 186 m², to the nearest metre.

## 10.6 Exercise

**A** Review the various formulas to find surface area and volume. What measures do the variables in each formula represent?

1 Write the formula that you would use to calculate the surface area of each of the following.

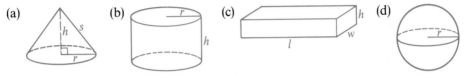

(a)  (b)  (c)  (d)

2 Write the formula that you would use to calculate the volume of each shape in the previous question.

3 Calculate the volume of each of the following.

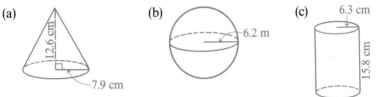

(a)  (b)  (c)

4 Find the surface area of each shape.

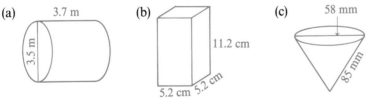

(a)  (b)  (c)

5 (a) Predict which container holds the most.

(b) Arrange the containers in order from the one that holds the most to the one that holds the least.

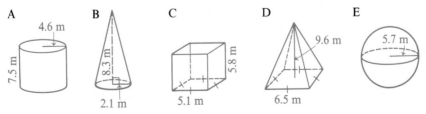

A  B  C  D  E

**B 6** Find each volume.

(a)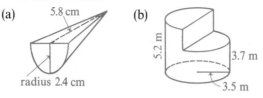
5.8 cm

radius 2.4 cm

(b)
5.2 m

3.7 m

3.5 m

7   A rectangular pool has dimensions 10.6 m long, 6.2 m wide and 2.1 m deep.

(a) The water level is 22.5 cm below the edge of the pool. Calculate the volume of water in the pool.

(b) Each day it costs 3.29¢/m³ to maintain the pool. Calculate the total cost of maintaining the pool from May 24 to September 18.

8   The cylindrical container is full of liquid plastic.

(a) Calculate the volume of liquid plastic.

(b) Billiard balls, with a diameter of 5.7 cm, are made from the plastic. How many can be made from one container of liquid plastic?

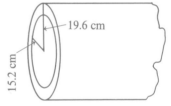
0.8 m

1.2 m

9   A concrete drainage pipe has an inner radius of 15.2 cm and an outer radius of 19.6 cm.

(a) Calculate the number of litres of water that a pipe 6.0 m in length can hold.

(b) If the material used to make the pipe has a mass of 12.6 g/cm³ find the mass of the pipe in (a).

19.6 cm

15.2 cm

10   For each of the following ▶ guess what you think the final result will be ▶ then show what actual result occurs.   **PSP**

(a) A cylinder has the radius cut in half and the height doubled. What change occurs to the volume?

(b) A cone has the radius cut in half and the height doubled. What change occurs to the volume?

**PSP** 11   (a) Gail paid a $72.00 invoice using a $100 bill. Is it possible for her to receive exactly 11 bills as her change?

(b) If not, then how many bills need to be used?

**C 12**   (a) What are the dimensions of the greatest cube that can be placed inside a sphere with radius 15.0 cm?

(b) Calculate the surface area of the cube.

(c) How many times greater is the surface area of the sphere than that of the cube?

# 10.7 Projections: Sketching Figures

The three diagrams show 3 views of a shape. Can you tell, based on these 3 photos, what the shape looks like?

Front view        End View

Top View

A 3-dimensional shape may appear different, depending on how you look at it. These 3 views are used to provide a clear picture of a 3-dimensional object. Each view is a **projection** of one of the surfaces: front, top, end.

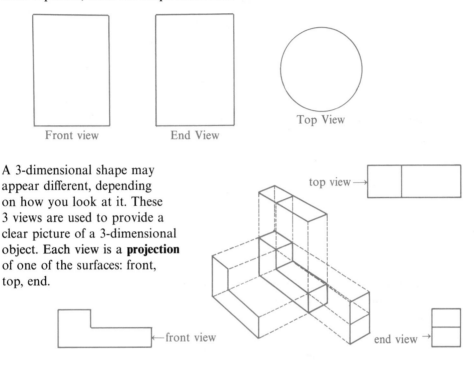

top view →

←front view        end view →

The shape shown by the three diagrams at the beginning is, as you probably guessed, a cylinder.

# 10.7 Exercise

**B** Review the meaning of a front, end and top view.

1   The front, end, and top views are shown for various solids. Draw the solid that best fits the views.

(a)        (b)

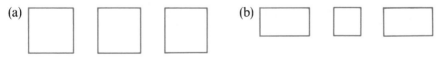

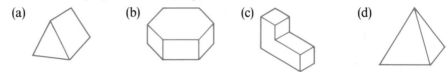

2  Use 3 views: project the front, top, and end, to describe each solid.

(a)      (b)      (c)      (d)

3  Sketch 3 views: front, top and end to describe each of the following.

(a)      (b)      (c)

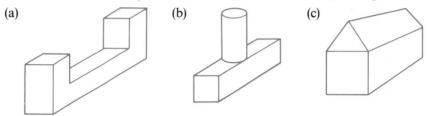

4  The end, front and top views are shown for various shapes. Use these views to predict the shape of the 3-dimensional object.

(a)

(b)      (c)

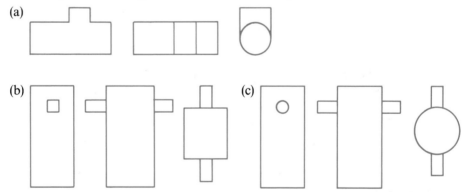

5  A concrete pillar has the shape shown.

(a) Draw a front, side and top view. Include dimensions on each view.

(b) Calculate the volume of the pillar.

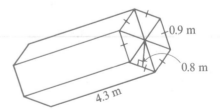

0.9 m

0.8 m

4.3 m

6 A swimming pool is shown.

(a) Draw a front, top and side view. Include the dimensions on each view.

(b) Calculate the volume of water that the pool can hold.

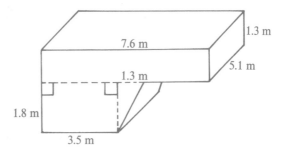

7 To draw a cube to appear from different views you can draw lines as shown to create the effect of 3 dimensions.

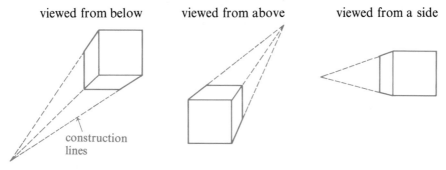

viewed from below    viewed from above    viewed from a side

construction lines

Draw each shape to appear as viewed from the 3 points of view shown above.

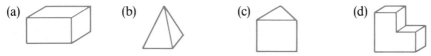

(a)    (b)    (c)    (d)

8 You can use special techniques to draw objects that appear 3-dimensional as follows.

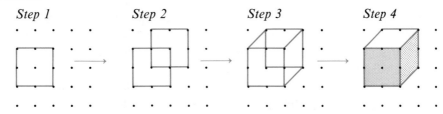

Step 1    Step 2    Step 3    Step 4

(a) Use the above procedure. Create 3-dimensional figures of your own.

(b) For each figure you create, draw a front, top and end view.

C 9 A side view of a pillar is shown.

(a) Draw 4 possible top views that the pillar may have.

(b) Sketch possible shapes that have this side view.

# Practice and Problems: Review

1   (a)  The base of a rectangular glass aquarium measures 62.0 cm by 130.0 cm. The aquarium is 40.0 cm high. Find the amount of glass needed to construct it.

(b)  The height of the water in the aquarium is 39.5 cm. A cylindrical container, with diameter 9.5 cm and height 20.5 cm was used to fill the aquarium. How many full containers were used?

(c)  List any assumptions you make to arrive at your answer in (a) and (b).

2   The funnel has the shape of a cone. The diameter of the cone is 80.0 cm and its height is 180.0 cm. Find the surface area of the funnel. Hint: Use the Pythagorean Property to find slant height.

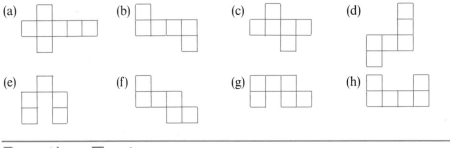

3   Predict which nets can be folded to make a cube. Use a net to check your prediction.

(a)    (b)    (c)    (d)

(e)    (f)    (g)    (h)

# Practice Test

1   Sketch a net for each of the following. Then calculate the surface area and volume.

(a)  cylinder, radius 4.8 m, height 6.9 m

(b)  rectangular prism, 4.3 cm by 6.8 cm by 12.8 cm.

(c)  sphere, diameter 8.25 cm     (d) cone, diameter 12.8 cm, slant height 16.5 cm

2   Oil drips from a full cylindrical tank that measures 1.20 m in diameter and is 1.50 m high. A rectangular tank measuring 0.80 m by 1.20 m and 0.60 m deep catches the oil.

(a)  If the oil level in the cylinder drops 0.35 m, how much will it rise in the rectangular tank?

(b)  If the oil drips at the rate of 0.09 $m^3$/h, how long will it take for the rectangular tank to fill?

3   (a)  The radius of Mars is approximately 3390 km. Find the surface area of Mars.

(b)  The diameter of Earth is 1.89 times that of Mars. Find the surface area of Earth.

(c)  Predict how many times greater the surface area of Earth is than the surface area of Mars. How can you verify your prediction?

4   Sketch 3 views: front, top and end to describe the solid.

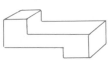

# *11* *Interpreting Data: Statistics and Probability*

Concepts and skills for statistics, types of samples, frequency distributions and histograms, mean, median, and mode, grouping data, interpreting dispersion and deviation, box and whisker diagrams, scatter diagrams, solving problems, concepts, and skills for probability, sample spaces, applications, strategies, and problem-solving

## Introduction

Making sense of all the information you are bombarded with is an important study in such fields as commerce, science, sports, space studies, medicine, and manufacturing. Often, it is necessary to interpret information intelligently and make decisions. The various pieces of information are referred to as **data**. When you work with and analyze data you are working with **statistics**. Statistics is a branch of mathematics which involves

A: collecting data

B: organizing and analyzing the data

C: interpreting and making inferences, predictions and decisions about
   data, problem-solving.

*The accumulation of various types of data from competitive sports allows us to better interpret and understand the preparation for competition.*

*The constant improvement in traffic and transportation is in no small part due to the analysis of data, resulting in improved efficiency, energy savings and a high degree of safety for the travellor.*

## 11.1 Concepts of Statistics

The concepts of statistics are used in many fields.

- How can a manufacturer predict for which product there will be an increase in demand?
- How does a coach determine a winning combination of the team players?
- How does a fast-food company determine the best location for a new restaurant?

*Mandatory seatbelt legislation has reduced the number of traffic deaths.*

Statistics is a branch of mathematics that involves the process of these steps.

| Steps of Statistics |
| --- |
| A: collecting data<br>B: organizing and analyzing data<br>C: using the data to make predictions, inferences, and decisions |

Different methods of collecting data are used.

- Personal interviews, either door to door or at a shopping centre<br>Polls conducted by telephone<br>Questionnaires
- Experiments designed to collect data<br>Measurements taken to check the quality of products
- Data from past records

The steps involved in statistics are illustrated by the following example.

A manufacturer of cassette tapes wishes to check the quality of the tapes before they are shipped to the retail outlets.

*Step A* Cassette tapes are mass produced by the millions. Each cassette tape cannot be checked individually for quality or defects. To do so would be called taking a **census**, a time-consuming and costly procedure. Instead a sample of the cassette tapes is chosen. In order that a proper decision will be reached

- the sample should be *representative* of the complete shipment.
- the sample should be selected at random. (A **random sample** means each member of the sample had an equal chance of being selected.)

The total number of tapes is referred to as the **population** and the tapes selected at random are called a **sample** from the population.

*Step B* Once you have collected the sample, you then carry out experiments on the sample and record the results. You may draw a chart or graph to help you analyze the information you obtain from the sample. Whenever a sample is used, there is always some degree of uncertainty about the information obtained from the results. Certain techniques can be used to choose a sample that is representative of the population.

*Step C* Using the information you obtain from the sample you can then decide what percentage of the tapes in the sample meet the required standards. Then, a decision can be made about all the tapes (the population) based on the sample studied. In general, once you analyze the data obtained from the sample, you can interpret the nature of the entire population. Again, various techniques are used to express the reliability of your predictions.

The above example illustrates the steps involved in studying statistics, namely: using the basic skills of statistics to make inferences about a population based on a random sample from that population.

## 11.1   Exercise

**A** Review the meaning of these words about statistics: *sample, population, census.*

1   In order to determine the most popular comic strips, a company made a telephone survey.
   (a) What are some advantages of making a telephone survey to collect data?
   (b) What are some disadvantages of this method?
   (c) Suggest other ways of determining the most popular comic strip.

2   In order to determine the most popular songs, a questionnaire was sent to a number of teenagers.
   (a) What are some advantages of using a questionnaire to collect data?
   (b) What are some disadvantages of this method?
   (c) Suggest other ways of collecting data to predict the most popular songs for teenagers.

3   Experiments were conducted to collect information about the effectiveness of thermostats.
   (a) What are some advantages of using experiments to collect data?
   (b) What are some disadvantages of this method?

4   Often it is not possible, nor desirable, to use a sample from a population
    to make a decision. Sometimes it is better to use all of the population to
    make the decision (take a census).

    For each of the following, decide whether to use a sample or to take a
    census to make a decision.

    (a) testing the air system in submarines

    (b) determining the popularity of a particular magazine

    (c) determining the quality of the picture tubes in a shipment of TV sets

    (d) determining the quality of a number of parachutes

    (e) deciding on the effectiveness of a new type of headache pill

    (f) predicting the number of young people who will get married next
        year

    (g) determining the chemical composition of a good cooking oil for
        chicken

    (h) checking the quality of the pistons in the engine of a car

    (i) determining the number of potential buyers of a brand of TV set

    (j) determining the attendance at a football game

    (k) determining the amount of oil in a new well discovery

5   List other ways of collecting data.

    (a) What are any advantages of each method?

    (b) What are any disadvantages of each method?

  B Make a final statement in answering problems.

6   To test the quality of a type of television converter, a sample of 200
    was chosen randomly from different lots. From the sample it was found
    that 2 were defective.

    (a) How many converters of a shipment of 1000 converters, would you
        predict to be defective? Give reasons why.

    (b) Do you think the above sample is representative? Why or why not?

7   Which of the following methods would you use to obtain data, upon
    which you would predict the outcome of an election for mayor?

    A: 100 persons interviewed in a specific neighbourhood.
    B: 100 telephone calls to different parts of the city.
    C: 100 completed questionnaires from a survey distributed across the city.
    D: 100 phone calls to children living in the city.

8   A school board received a shipment of 10 000 compasses to sell to students.

A: First, 10 sets were randomly selected and no compasses were found to be defective.

B: Then, 100 sets were randomly selected and 1 compass was found to be defective.

C: Then, 1000 sets were randomly selected and 9 compasses were found to be defective.

(a) Based on A, would you be accurate in saying that none of the compasses in the shipment was defective. Why or why not?

(b) Which of the following statements is likely to be more representative of the population? Give reasons for your answer.
$S_1$: 1% are defective.          $S_2$: 0.9% are defective.

(c) In the total shipment of 10 000 compasses, how many would you estimate to be defective? Give reasons for your answer.

9   You are a manufacturer of running shoes.

(a) Create a questionnaire to be used to collect data to help you determine which colour of running shoe to manufacture.

(b) In your questionnaire in (a), include any other questions that will help you make decisions about the manufacture of your running shoes.

10  Paper cups are tossed to determine the percentage of cups that fall in these positions.

Experiments A, B, and C are completed and the data are recorded.

(a) From which experiment would you choose data to predict how many cups will land up if 500 are tossed—A, B, or C?

| Experiment | Cups tossed | Cups land up | Cups land sideways |
|---|---|---|---|
| A | 10 | 3 | 7 |
| B | 100 | 36 | 64 |
| C | 1000 | 351 | 649 |

(b) Calculate the percentage of cups that will land sideways for Experiments A, B, and C.

11  The data of Experiments A, B, and C are combined.

| | Cups tossed | Cups land up | Cups land sideways |
|---|---|---|---|
| D | 1110 | 390 | 720 |

(a) Give reasons why a conclusion based on the data for D is probably more reliable than a conclusion based on the data from Experiments A, B, or C.

(b) List any assumption that you make in your answer in (a).

## 11.2 Types of Samples

A manufacturer often selects a sample of the product to test whether the quality of the product is acceptable. A sample is selected because it would be uneconomical, both with respect to time and money, to test the entire population. The sample, however, has to be representative of the population which, in this case, is the entire batch of manufactured goods. Thus, the manufacturer takes a **random sample**. However random sampling is not always the best indicator of a population. There are other types of specialized sampling that may be used to obtain data to solve a problem.

*TV Audience research by Nielsen takes a sample (about 0.002%) of households—city, town, farm, etc. One source of their data is an audimeter. It records the channels, times, and lengths of time the sets are switched on. The data are "picked up" by a computer (by special telephone line). The results are then applied to the whole country.*

### Clustered Sampling

A manufacturer of farm equipment wants to decide whether to spend its advertising budget on magazine, A, B, or C. The manufacturer should not survey just *any* citizen to determine which magazine is preferred, but rather it should survey farmers to see which magazine, A, B, or C they read. Thus, the manufacturer will take a *clustered sample* of only farmers. When a sample is taken from a particular segment of a population, it is said to be *clustered*. The following is a poor example of clustered sampling.

> To determine whether a city official would be elected, voters in polling station A were surveyed. Of these voters, 75% said they would vote for the city official.

Would you accept the statement that the city official will be elected? Probably not, since the sample does not provide information about all the other polling stations and is therefore not a very useful statement.

### Stratified Sampling

To determine the popularity of 3 Canadian political leaders, you could choose a sample from Canadians.

- If 1000 people across Canada are polled, and the sample is random it is possible that the same number of people is chosen from each province. This sample might give misleading results, since the number of voters in each province *differs* greatly.

- To ensure that the sample is a better representative of the population, the population of Canada is divided into provinces.

The number of people from each province polled is *in the same proportion* as the population of each province.

When you divide a population into *strata* or *classes*, and if the number of people you poll from each stratum (or province) is in the same proportion as the number in each stratum, then you are taking a **stratified sample**.

**Destructive Sampling**
To test the quality of orange juice, cartons are chosen at random from the production line and tested. Once these cartons of orange juice are opened they are destroyed. This type of sampling is said to be *destructive* since the sample cannot be reintroduced into the population after testing. In destructive sampling, the entire population cannot be used.

A most important skill is the ability to design a sampling technique which will allow you to obtain the best possible sample. Later, you will learn additional types of sampling.

## 11.2 Exercise

**A** Review the meaning of *random, clustered, stratified,* and *destructive sampling.*

1  The quality of batteries is tested by first randomly choosing a battery from the production line, and then performing tests on it in the laboratory. After the tests, the battery cannot be sold to the consumer.
   (a) What type of sample is obtained?
   (b) What are some advantages of the above method?
   (c) What are some disadvantages of the above method?

2  A rental chain wants to determine the suitability of a suburban plaza for a new shop. A team of interviewers conducts a poll at the plaza. It collects data to help head office make a decision.
   (a) What type of sample is obtained?
   (b) What are some advantages of the above approach?

**B** Your choice of sample will determine the reliability of your results.

3  In a school, the number of students in Grade 9 is 300, in Grade 10 is 200, in Grade 11 is 150, and in Grade 12 is 100. A sample of 100 students is used to determine which of 3 formats for the yearbook should be used. How many of the 100 opinions should be
   (a) Grade 9s?                    (b) Grade 11s?
   (c) What type of sample is the sample above?

4 British Columbia has approximately 11.3% of the Canadian population.
   (a) If a cross-Canada poll of 2000 people is to be conducted, how many will be chosen from British Columbia?
   (b) What type of sample have you used?
   (c) What type of sample would you use to create a new type of ski for the Canadian Rockies?

5 Decide whether destructive (D) or non-destructive (ND) sampling is required to find an answer for each of the following.
   (a) the accuracy of calculators    (b) the mass of cereals    (c) the quality of wine
   (d) the outcome of an election    (e) the crunch factor of a batch of crackers
   (f) the quality of gold charms for bracelets    (g) the brilliance of firecrackers

6 Clustered sampling is used to collect each of the following samples. Which samples are good (G) and which samples are bad (B)? Justify your answer.
   (a) going to a high school to determine the most popular song
   (b) asking only senior students about the format for graduation
   (c) asking doctors about the value of a new medical procedure
   (d) asking compact car owners about energy conservation policy

7 In each example, indicate whether a stratified sample should or should not be used. Give reasons for your answers.
   (a) The director of a camp is to decide whether any funds should be spent on improving the swimming facilities.
   (b) A shipment of 10 000 ball point pens is to be checked for defects.
   (c) At a club, an opinion poll is to be conducted on the exercise facilities.
   (d) A nation is to hold a general plebiscite to decide an issue. A sample of 1000 is chosen to predict the outcome.
   (e) There are 750 women and 250 men in an organization. A sample of 20 is to be taken to determine the type of social night to be planned.

8 Choose one of these terms
        random, destructive, clustered, non-destructive, stratified
   as a description of the type of sample needed to obtain information for each of the following.
   (a) the amount of dues payable by plumbers of a trade union
   (b) the effervescence of soda pop      (c) the preference of fast-food
   (d) the preferred brand of diapers     (e) the sweetness of oranges
   (f) the best brand of tractor          (g) the attendance of a particular movie

# 11.3 Frequency Distributions and Histograms

Data given in an unorganized manner cannot be used to detect any patterns or to help make a decision. For example, people on a busy street were stopped at random and asked the following question:

> When you go on holiday, what is your preferred mode of transport: plane (P), car (C), bus (B), or train (T)?

The following is a record of the responses of the first 20 people stopped.

B  C  C  T  B  C  C  B  T  B  P  C  T  T  P  P  T  T  C  C

Each mode of transport is referred to as an **outcome**.

The collected information or raw data are unorganized and, as a result, no pattern is seen. Learning to organize data in such a way as to show patterns is an important part of the study of **descriptive statistics**.

The data can be recorded in a table that shows the frequency of each outcome. The total number of times each outcome is chosen is called the **frequency** of that outcome. Since 4 people gave the bus as their preferred mode of transport, then the frequency for the bus is 4. The table is referred to as a **frequency distribution table**.

| Outcome | Tally | Frequency |
|---------|-------|-----------|
| Bus | \|\|\|\| | 4 |
| Car | ⊮\|\| | 7 |
| Plane | \|\|\| | 3 |
| Train | ⊮\| | 6 |

Each mark represents one response.

When a large array of numbers is given, the data are grouped first and then recorded in a frequency table. For example, during a basketball season, the points scored for 25 games were recorded as shown, (50 scores in all). In its present form, it is difficult to tell how the scores were distributed.

```
35  68  44  79  41  21  70   8  49  51  19  81  36  63  82  61  30  25  16  38
32  91  51  71  33  90  54  85  44  79  62  23  57  59  46  64  43  93  78  12
42  95  73   6  52  63  54  37  55  58
```

The scores range from 6 to 95. To interpret the data in a useful way the outcomes are compressed into a convenient number of distinct classes, (often called **class intervals**).

*Step 1:* Calculate the **range**. This is the difference between the greatest and least value in the sample. The range is $95 - 6 = 89$.

*Step 2:* Decide on the number of classes, usually 10 classes will represent the data. To approximate the width of each class, divide the range by 10.

Width (approximate): $\dfrac{89}{10} = 8.9$

*Step 3:* Use the number from Step 2 to determine the width of each class. Usually the number is rounded to a multiple of 5. (8.9 rounded to 10)

The smallest and greatest numbers in each class are called the **class limits**. The number of observations in each class is called the **frequency** of that class as shown in the diagram.

| Class | Class Limits | Frequency | Class | Class Limits | Frequency |
|-------|--------------|-----------|-------|--------------|-----------|
| 1 | 1–10 | 2 | 6 | 51–60 | 9 |
| 2 | 11–20 | 3 | 7 | 61–70 | 7 |
| 3 | 21–30 | 4 | 8 | 71–80 | 5 |
| 4 | 31–40 | 6 | 9 | 81–90 | 4 |
| 5 | 41–50 | 7 | 10 | 91–100 | 3 |

### Discrete Data

For the basketball scores, there is a countable number of outcomes. In this case, the results are referred to as **discrete data**. The graph drawn for the data is a **bar graph**. For discrete data, none of the class limits between one class and the next is the same. Thus there is only one possible place in the graph for each data.

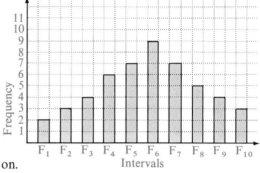

You can denote the class frequency of class 1 as $f_1$, of class 2 as $f_2$, and so on.

Thus, $f_3 = 4$    $f_4 = 6$    $f_5 = 7$.

The bar graph is a useful way of organizing data to show any patterns the data may have.

**PSP**

- Which class contains the most scores?
- Which class contains least scores?
- Which classes together contain half of the total number of scores?

### Continuous Data

Often data are obtained from measurements. The data shown represent heights of students in centimetres.

| | | | | | | | | | |
|---|---|---|---|---|---|---|---|---|---|
| 162.3 | 175.0 | 173.5 | 172.0 | 163.0 | 174.5 | 162.1 | 155.5 | 159.6 | 185.1 |
| 174.7 | 152.6 | 161.9 | 167.5 | 159.0 | 164.6 | 165.1 | 158.5 | 167.0 | 157.8 |
| 164.0 | 167.5 | 153.2 | 182.4 | 165.5 | 162.2 | 182.7 | 158.3 | 177.5 | 176.2 |
| 179.5 | 167.5 | 160.5 | 171.8 | 160.0 | 161.1 | 168.0 | 152.9 | 169.6 | 166.7 |
| 164.5 | 169.4 | 174.0 | 175.5 | 157.5 | 166.0 | 156.0 | 168.9 | 177.0 | 168.0 |

Data obtained by measurement are said to be **continuous data**. For this reason, the data are divided into classes with class limits as shown. The upper limit of a class does not include that value, but the lower limit of the class does include that value. Thus a class limit of 150–155 means values between 150 and 155 are included. A value of 150 may also be included, but a value of 155 is not included.

The table at the right represents the frequency distribution for the data of the heights of students.

| Class | Class Limits | Tally | Frequency |
|---|---|---|---|
| 1 | 150–155 | ||| | 3 |
| 2 | 155–160 | ⅃ℋⅢ | 8 |
| 3 | 160–165 | ℋℋⅠ | 11 |
| 4 | 165–170 | ℋℋⅡ | 12 |
| 5 | 170–175 | ℋⅡ | 7 |
| 6 | 175–180 | ℋⅠ | 6 |
| 7 | 180–185 ← | || | 2 |
| 8 | 185–190 | | | 1 |

Value of 185 included ⌐    ⌐ Value of 185 not included

To show how the frequencies are distributed in a graphical form, a **histogram** is used. There are no spaces between bars. The areas of the bars are proportional to the frequencies of the classes. The height of each bar in the graph is determined by the class frequency—which is marked along the vertical axis. The **class limits** separate one class from another.

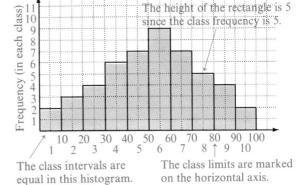

The height of the rectangle is 5 since the class frequency is 5.

The class intervals are equal in this histogram.

The class limits are marked on the horizontal axis.

## 11.3 Exercise

**A**   Questions 1 to 5 are based on the following information.
The test results for 33 students are shown in the following histogram.

1   (a) What are the classes?

    (b) What are the class limits?

2   (a) What is the vaue of $f_2$, $f_5$?

    (b) Calculate the ratios, $\dfrac{\text{area D}}{\text{area E}}$ and $\dfrac{f_4}{f_5}$.
    What do you notice about your answers?

3   (a) In which class did most marks occur?

    (b) In which three classes do the least number of marks occur? Why?

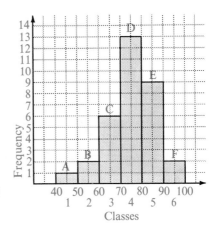

Classes

4  (a) Based on the results shown in the histogram, how would you describe this exam?

   (b) What are the advantages of using a histogram to show numerical data?

5  For an ordinary bar graph you may rearrange the bars as shown.

   Explain why you may not rearrange the bars A, B, C, D, E, F in the histogram at the beginning of this exercise?

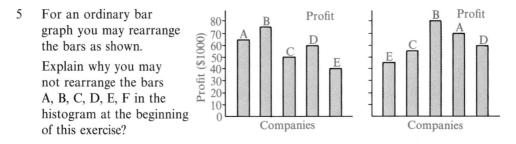

B  Questions 6 to 11 are based on the following information. In a group of 44 people, the following pulses were obtained during a period of 1 min.

```
66  61  79  71  53  86  81  73  84  87  76  72  76  71  67
64  67  83  71  68  81  92  86  56  62  67  77  90  91  72
79  76  82  93  78  62  76  76  56  82  96  88  73  67
```

6  (a) Why is it difficult to make observations about the above data in its present form?

   (b) Rearrange the data from smallest to greatest.

7  (a) Use your answer in Question 6 to make a frequency distribution for the data.

   (b) Decide on class intervals for the data and construct a histogram. (The horizontal axis need not start at 0.)

8  Based on your histogram, answer these questions.

   (a) In which of your classes does the most common pulse occur?

   (b) In which of your classes do 75% of the pulses occur?

9  What percentage of the people have a pulse over 90?

10 (a) If you record the pulse for 1000 people, how many would you expect to have a pulse in the interval 75–80? Give reasons for your answer.

   (b) What assumptions do you make in obtaining your answer?

11 (a) Create a problem based on your histogram of Question 7.

   (b) Solve the problem in (a).

Questions 12 to 14 are based on the following numerical data. The lengths, in centimetres, of perch (a fish) in a lake were measured from a batch of 35 fish.

19.2  22.9  26.1  18.9  21.3  23.5  25.1  22.3  19.6  17.8  17.9  21.9
30.1  23.2  25.0  24.3  16.3  22.0  24.5  28.1  21.6  22.5  25.2  23.1
26.2  18.6  26.3  28.2  20.3  24.8  22.8  26.2  25.6  24.6  24.7

12   Decide on class intervals and construct a histogram.

13   (a) Which class has the greatest frequency?

   (b) How long is the longest fish? The shortest fish?

   (c) Based on your graph, what three classes contain most of the fish?

14   (a) Create a problem based on your histogram in Question 12.

   (b) Solve the problem in (a).

---

Questions 15 to 19 are based on the following information.
The following grades (out of 100) were obtained by a science section.

26  53  63  70  73  43  82  92  32  64  73  75  35  56  63
46  56  64  87  23  67  67  40  52  51  28  55  76  43

15   (a) Construct a histogram for the data.

   (b) Based on your graph, which class has the greatest frequency?

16   Use the histogram.

   (a) Estimate what per cent of the section received first class honours (80 marks or better).

   (b) Use the data. Calculate what per cent received a failing mark (less than 50 marks).

17   For the same science course, the marks awarded for another science section are shown.

66  57  62  54  14  84  41  68  45  74  89  61  59  54  43
34  67  70  37  45  31  64  65  76  50  70  43  65  53

   Construct a histogram for these data.

18   (a) Compare the histograms for each science section. How are they different? How are they the same?

   (b) Create a problem based on the graphs. Solve the problem you have created.

C 19   Refer to the graphs in the previous question.

   (a) What explanation might you have to account for the differences in the histograms?

   (b) What information do the differences indicate to the science instructor?

## Applications: Stem-and-Leaf Plots

Another method of organizing data is to use a stem-and-leaf plot such as the one following. A stem-and-leaf plot has the advantage that the original data are a part of the diagram.

The data shown in the table represent the number of students enrolled in Driver Education courses at 30 different locations.

| 21 | 47 | 65 | 34 | 38 | 37 | 48 | 53 | 31 | 37 |
|----|----|----|----|----|----|----|----|----|----|
| 29 | 56 | 24 | 34 | 29 | 22 | 43 | 73 | 56 | 49 |
| 55 | 43 | 54 | 48 | 62 | 66 | 40 | 45 | 42 | 71 |

| Stem | Leaves |   |   |   |   |   |   |   |   |   |
|------|--------|---|---|---|---|---|---|---|---|---|
| 1 |   |   |   |   |   |   |   |   |   |   |
| 2 | 1 | 9 | 2 | 9 | 4 |   |   |   |   |   |
| 3 | 4 | 1 | 7 | 4 | 8 | 7 |   |   |   | ← |
| 4 | 8 | 9 | 7 | 0 | 3 | 3 | 2 | 8 | 5 |   |
| 5 | 3 | 6 | 5 | 4 | 6 |   |   |   |   |   |
| 6 | 2 | 6 | 5 |   |   |   |   |   |   |   |
| 7 | 1 | 3 |   |   |   |   |   |   |   |   |

Tens      Ones

This part of the diagram represents the data

34   31   37   34   38   37

From the diagram,
- The range of the data is $73 - 21 = 52$.
- The data seem to cluster about one part of the diagram.
- Most of the classes had 40 or more enrolled students at the location. The least number enrolled was 21; the greatest number enrolled was 73.

---

20   The stem-and-leaf diagram shown represents the number of shots on goal taken in 35 hockey games by the Weyburn Greyhounds.

| 1 | 9 | 6 | 9 | 5 | 5 | 7 |   |   |   |   |   |
|---|---|---|---|---|---|---|---|---|---|---|---|
| 2 | 3 | 1 | 8 | 5 | 4 | 0 | 8 | 6 | 4 |   |   |
| 3 | 0 | 3 | 1 | 1 | 0 | 2 | 4 | 3 | 3 | 2 | 8 |
| 4 | 2 | 0 | 9 | 8 | 3 | 1 | 2 |   |   |   |   |
| 5 | 3 | 1 |   |   |   |   |   |   |   |   |   |

(a) During how many games was the number of shots on goal
(i) 19?   (ii) 53?   (iii) 33?   (iv) 59?

(b) During how many games was the number of shots on goal (i) 29 or less?   (ii) 50 or more?   (iii) over 45?   (iv) under 35?

21   These data were obtained from an experiment which measured the time in minutes it took students to complete a timed physical activity test.

| 19.9 | 15.3 | 25.2 | 25.1 | 21.1 | 17.2 | 24.4 | 20.2 | 19.1 | 17.7 | 18.5 | 21.3 | 19.8 |
|------|------|------|------|------|------|------|------|------|------|------|------|------|
| 25.1 | 15.2 | 23.9 | 25.5 | 26.8 | 19.4 | 20.0 | 21.7 | 23.9 | 23.9 | 14.1 | 21.0 |      |
| 23.3 | 24.4 | 13.5 | 13.1 | 18.8 | 26.4 | 15.2 | 21.4 | 19.3 | 27.3 | 17.4 | 21.2 | 14.0 |
| 23.9 | 18.8 | 21.2 | 20.7 | 22.4 | 19.2 | 17.9 | 19.5 | 11.2 | 17.1 | 17.5 | 21.3 |      |

(a) Construct a stem-and-leaf plot for the data.

(b) A score of 22.0 or more is poor. What percentage of the results are poor?

(c) A score of less than 18.0 is excellent. What percentage of the results are excellent?

(d) If the sample is representative of a population, what percentage would you expect to obtain a score of 18.0 or greater?

(e) Construct a histogram for the data. How are the histogram and the stem-and-leaf plot alike? How are they different?

# 11.4 Interpreting Mean, Median, and Mode

You have used frequency distribution tables and histograms to detect any patterns that might occur in data you have collected. For example, histograms are drawn for two sets of data. The outcomes appear to be clustered or "centred" around a value that is distinct for each histogram.

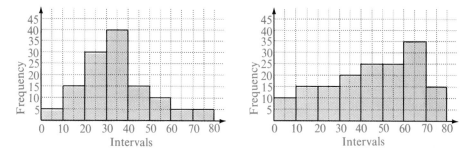

Calculations of the mean, the median, and the mode give you further information about a frequency distribution by helping you locate the "centre" of the data.

## Mean
The heights, in centimetres, of 9 persons are shown.

$$167 \quad 170 \quad 179 \quad 163 \quad 172 \quad 163 \quad 176 \quad 174 \quad 175$$

To calculate the mean (arithmetic mean) you find the average.
The arithmetic mean includes all the data and is obtained as shown.

$$\frac{167 + 170 + 179 + 163 + 172 + 163 + 176 + 174 + 175}{9} = \frac{1539}{9}$$
$$= 171$$

Thus you may say that the mean (average height) is 171 cm. The value of the mean need not be a member of the set of data. For example, not one of the 9 persons has a height of 171 cm.

## Median
The data show an odd number of heights. To find the median of the heights, arrange them from smallest to greatest. The median is the middle number.

$$163 \quad 163 \quad 167 \quad 170 \quad 172 \quad 174 \quad 175 \quad 176 \quad 179$$

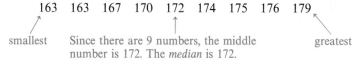

smallest        Since there are 9 numbers, the middle            greatest
                number is 172. The *median* is 172.

Thus, the median height is 172 cm.

The median is not influenced by the value of the greatest and smallest values. For example, if the greatest value were 190 cm instead of 179 cm, the median would still be 172 cm. However, the value of the mean would increase.

If there were only 8 numbers, then the median would be the average of the 2 middle numbers.

163   167   170   172   174   175   176   179

smallest                middle numbers                greatest

$$\text{The median is } \frac{172 + 174}{2} \text{ or } 173.$$

**Mode**

The mode of the above data is the number which occurs most frequently. Since 163 occurs most frequently (twice) the mode is 163. Again, if the greatest value were to increase, or if the smallest value were to decrease, the mode would not be affected. The mode does not take into consideration any of the other values. A set of data can have more than 1 mode, and it can also have no mode.

The values of the mean, the median and the mode indicate the centre of the data shown in the frequency distribution. Thus, they are often referred to as the **measures of central tendency**.

## 11.4   Exercise

**A** Round your answers to 1 decimal place where necessary.

1   Find the mean, the median, and the mode for each set of data.
   (a) 6, 9, 8, 12, 8, 14, 9, 11, 13        (b) 62, 58, 60, 52, 68, 73, 69, 64
   (c) 6, 12, 9, 2, 0, 4, 8, 6, 5, 8, 6     (d) 11.5, 12.6, 13.2, 4.6, 7.8, 12.1, 11.9, 11.5

2   (a) If the mean for a set of data is 41, is 41 one of the data? Use an example to illustrate your answer.
   (b) If the mode for a set of data is 60, is 60 one of the data? Use an example to illustrate your answer.
   (c) If the median for a set of data is 60.5, is 60.5 one of the data? Use an example to illustrate your answer.

3   A set of data is given by   3   7   8   6   5   $y$   4   3   2   1   9
   The modes of the data are 3 and 8. What is the value of $y$?

4   The measurements shown are in centimetres.
   13.8   14.6   12.6   11.9   13.2   16.2   15.3   12.3   13.2   $k$   14.1   16.2   18.3
   (a) The mean of the data is 14.2 cm (to 1 decimal place). Predict whether $k$ is greater than or less than the mean value.
   (b) Calculate the value of $k$.

5   A missing value in a set of data is shown by s.

6.8   5.7   7.2   4.2   9.1   5.5   7.8   s   8.3   4.1

(a) The median of the data is 7.0. Estimate the value of s.

(b) The mean of the data is 6.8 (to 1 decimal place). Calculate the value of s.

6   The masses, in kilograms, of members on the basketball team, rounded to the nearest kilogram, are shown.

72   76   71   70   72   67   65   73   81   79   78   72   83

(a) Find the median, mean, and mode of the masses.

(b) Is the median greater than or less than the mean?

(c) Is the mode greater than or less than the mean?

7   These data represent the lengths of humerous bones, in centimetres.

22.3   24.5   26.3   27.4   23.2   25.4   28.0
29.5   22.3   30.9   30.7   27.4   29.6   22.3

(a) Calculate the mean, median and mode.

(b) Which of your answers in (a) best represents the data?

8   The hourly rates of a restaurant staff are listed.

$9.50   $4.60   $6.25   $4.80   $7.80   $9.75
$5.15   $5.15   $5.15   $5.30   $15.10   $5.65

(a) Calculate the mean, median, and mode of the hourly rates.

(b) Which of your answers in (a) best represents the data? Give reasons for your answer.

9   During the weekend, Walkers Incorporated sold shoes of the following sizes.

10   10   7   9   11   10   8   7   9   8   12

The owner said that the average size of shoe sold was 10. Which measure is the manager referring to: the mean, median, or mode? Give reasons for your answer.

**B** To do work with statistics, you have to clearly understand the meanings of *mean, mode, median*. Review their meanings.

10   (a) Find the mean and the median for each set of data.

M:   10,   12,   14,   16,   18,   98,   99,   100,   120
N:   10,   12,   14,   16,   94,   96,   98,   100,   120

(b) Which is more representative of the centre of the data in M, the mean or the median?

(c) Which is more representative of the centre of the data in N, the mean or the median?

11 Various salespersons were asked this question: "Is the length of your coffee break less than the average, more than the average, or average?"

(a) Explain why the *mean* cannot be found.

(b) Explain what additional information would be needed in order to calculate the mean.

(c) Why should the mode best represent the data?

12 The monthly rainfall, in millimetres, for a region is shown.

| J | F | M | A | M | J | J | A | S | O | N | D |
|---|---|---|---|---|---|---|---|---|---|---|---|
| 68 | 72 | 61 | 48 | 24 | 0 | 0 | 26 | 50 | 62 | 64 | 65 |

(a) Find the mean, the median, and the mode for the data.

(b) Why is the mode misleading about the data?

(c) Which of your answers in (a) best represents the data? Give reasons why.

13 The salaries paid in one division of a manufacturing company are shown.

(a) Find the mean, median, and mode of the salaries.

(b) Which measure seems to best describe the average salary?

(c) Which of your answers in (a) would present misleading information?

| Position (number of people) | Salary |
|---|---|
| Manager (1) | $55 000 |
| Assist. Manager (1) | $47 000 |
| Floor Manager (3) | $38 000 |
| Machine Operator (10) | $32 000 |
| Machine Maintenance (3) | $32 000 |
| Asst. Machine Operator (6) | $26 000 |
| Floor Maintenance (2) | $23 000 |

14 Based on collected data, a sports magazine issued the statement:

**The average hockey player uses stainless steel blades.**

(a) Which of the following measures of central tendency was probably used to predict the above conclusion?
   A: mean          B: median          C: mode.
   Give reasons for your choice.

(b) Why did you not choose the other measures for your answer in (a)?

15 Explain which of the following statements or predictions are based on the mean, the mode, or the median.

(a) The average salary of part-time help is $92.50 per week.

(b) Most part-time help receive $5.90/h.          (c) 20% of the tires are defective.

(d) Weekends in the summertime is when most boating accidents occur.

(e) The favourite T.V. program is MIFF.

(f) The most popular type of dancing in the 1940's was ballroom dancing.

# Applications: The Weighted Mean

The price of the same carton of orange juice over four weeks changed as shown.

Week 1: 65¢      Week 2: 60¢      Week 3: 56¢      Week 4: 63¢

During that time Marc purchased the following number of cartons.

6 at 65¢      12 at 60¢      24 at 56¢      8 at 63¢

To find the average selling price, you calculate the arithmetic mean.

$$\text{Arithmetic mean price} = \frac{65\text{¢} + 60\text{¢} + 56\text{¢} + 63\text{¢}}{4}$$

$$= 61\text{¢}$$

The average price is 61¢

However, Marc bought different quantities at these different prices. To find the average price of his purchases you would need to calculate the **weighted mean**. The weighted mean is given by the calculation,

$$\text{weighted mean price} = \frac{6(65\text{¢}) + 12(60\text{¢}) + 24(56\text{¢}) + 8(63\text{¢})}{50}$$

$$= \frac{2958}{50} \quad \text{total number of cartons}$$

$$= 59.16$$

Marc's average price for the orange juice was 59.2¢

---

16   During October, Melanie purchases gasoline at different prices.

36 L at 43.2¢      42 L at 45.7¢
28 L at 39.1¢      38 L at 41.6¢

(a) Calculate the average price per litre of the gasoline.

(b) Calculate the average cost per litre of Melanie's gas purchases.

17   Investment rates vary depending on the way you invest. Freddie invested $250 at 9.5% in a term deposit, $520 in a savings account at 6.2%, $1030 in a savings bond at 8.9%.

Calculate the weighted mean per $100 of the investment rate of Freddie's investments.

18   During the year Michael paid the following amounts for car washes.

12 at $6.50      21 at $2.25      33 at $3.75

(a) Calculate the average price of the car wash charges.

(b) Calculate the average price Michael paid for car washes.

# 11.5 Statistics for Grouped Data

To display data, you often group the data and use a histogram to show the frequency distribution. When data are grouped, you can estimate the mean or median from the displayed data. To do so, you assume that the data in each interval are distributed uniformly. The midpoint of the interval is used to calculate the mean, as shown in the following example.

**Example**  Data are collected to determine the life of stored light bulbs.

(a) From the data, what is the average life of the light bulbs?

(b) What is the median of the data?

 **PSP**  Refer to your *Problem-Solving Plan.*

| Interval (hours) | Frequency |
|---|---|
| 0–5 | 3 |
| 5–10 | 8 |
| 10–15 | 13 |
| 15–20 | 20 |
| 20–25 | 9 |
| 25–30 | 2 |

**Solution**  *Step 1:* Complete the table

| $i$ | Interval | $x_i$ Midpoint | $f_i$ Frequency | $x_i \times f_i$ |
|---|---|---|---|---|
| 1 | 0–5 | 2.5 | 3 | 7.5 |
| 2 | 5–10 | 7.5 | 8 | 60.0 |
| 3 | 10–15 | 12.5 | 13 | 162.5 |
| 4 | 15–20 | 17.5 | 20 | 350.0 |
| 5 | 20–25 | 22.5 | 9 | 202.5 |
| 6 | 25–30 | 27.5 | 2 | 55.0 |
|  | Total | | 55 | 837.5 |

The score 2.5 occurred 3 times for a total of 7.5. The mean is calculated as if each light bulb in the interval has the same time of 2.5 h.

2.5 h is the midpoint of the interval

*Step 2:* Do the calculation. The mean is given by the calculation,

$$\frac{837.5}{55} = 15.2 \text{ (to 1 decimal place)}$$

(a) Based on the calculations, the average, or mean life, of each light bulb is 15.2 h.

(b) 55 light bulbs were tested. The median occurs in the interval 15–20. Thus the median life of the light bulbs is estimated between 15 h and 20 h.

## 11.5 Exercise

**B** Round your answers, when necessary, to 1 decimal place. Remember to use an efficient method on your calculator.

1 Data are displayed in a stem-and-leaf plot.

(a) From the display, estimate the mean value. Then calculate the mean value. How do your answers compare?

(b) From the display, estimate the median. What is the median?

| | | | |
|---|---|---|---|
| 23 | 4 | | |
| 24 | 3 | 8 | |
| 25 | 1 | 9 | 2 |
| 26 | 4 | 1 | |
| 27 | 3 | | |
| 28 | 8 | | |

2 Use the data given in the table.

| Interval | 0–5 | 5–10 | 10–15 | 15–20 | 20–25 | 25–30 | 30–35 | 35–40 | 40–45 | 45–50 |
|---|---|---|---|---|---|---|---|---|---|---|
| Frequency | 2 | 4 | 6 | 9 | 15 | 12 | 10 | 8 | 3 | 1 |

(a) Estimate the mean and the median of the data.

(b) What is the mean and median of the data?

(c) How do your answers in (a) and (b) compare?

3 Find the mean and median for each frequency distribution.

Check whether your answer is reasonable.

(a)

| Class Intervals | Frequency |
|---|---|
| 0–10 | 2 |
| 10–20 | 3 |
| 20–30 | 8 |
| 30–40 | 12 |
| 40–50 | 6 |
| 50–60 | 1 |

(b)

| Class Intervals | Frequency |
|---|---|
| 5.0–7.5 | 2 |
| 7.5–10.0 | 5 |
| 10.0–12.5 | 7 |
| 12.5–15.0 | 11 |
| 15.0–17.5 | 13 |
| 17.5–20.0 | 4 |

4 For each histogram,
(i) estimate the mean and the median.
(ii) Then calculate the mean and the median.

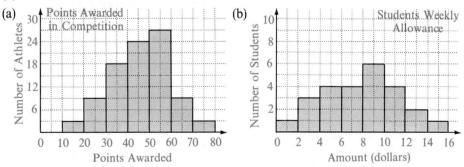

5   People were randomly chosen to answer the question, "At what age did you first fly on a jet?" The answers are shown in the display.

21  39  25  27  20  34  29  23  26  31  25  39  19  34  28  34  26
35  26  36  38  24  37  28  24  22  28  22  26  39  34  27  20  25
35  37  27  29  25  32  23  26  32  40  31  30  31  18  27  22  31
22  27  25  28  33  21  30  17  27  26  41  42  31  23  37  29  36
45  30  30  30  32  33  24  30  21  29  37  43  33  27  25  24  33

(a) Construct a histogram for the data.

(b) Estimate the mean and the median from your histogram.

(c) Calculate the mean of the actual data.

(d) Calculate the mean from your histogram.

(e) How do your answers in (c) and (d) compare?

(f) Can you use your calculations to make a statement? What statement will you make regarding your poll?

6   The time, in minutes, it took marathon runners to cover 1 km were recorded as follows.

4.6  3.9  4.1  5.3  4.5  3.5  5.5  5.1  3.4  3.6  4.7  4.7  3.8  5.2  5.2  3.3  3.5
3.9  3.6  4.5  4.3  3.7  3.8  5.1  5.5  4.3  3.7  4.9  5.5  3.3  3.8  4.3  5.6  4.0
4.2  3.6  5.4  5.5  3.8  3.8  4.2  4.3  5.1  3.7  3.9  4.6  4.2  3.4  3.2  3.2

(a) Construct a stem-and-leaf plot for the data.

(b) From your display, what is the mean, median, and mode?

7   Refer to the data in Question 6.

(a) Construct a histogram of the data.

(b) From your display, what is the mean, median, and mode?

(c) How do your answers in (b) compare to those in Question 6(b)?

C 8   Refer to the data in Question 6.

(a) Choose 10 values at random from the data. Calculate the mean, $m_1$, of these values.

(b) Choose another 10 values at random from the data. Calculate the mean, $m_2$, of these values.

(c) Calculate the mean value, $m = \dfrac{m_1 + m_2}{2}$.

(d) How does your value in (c) compare to the mean value of all the data?

(e) Suggest a method of obtaining a better estimate of the mean of a sample.

# 11.6 Interpreting Data: Dispersion and Deviation

Often, data from such fields as medicine, economics and sports are collected and analyzed. The results are then used to make a better decision about an operation, a purchase or a player. Thus, analyzing data helps you make better decisions.

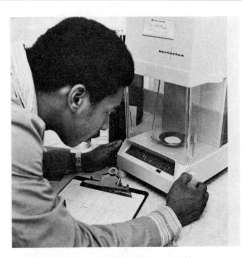

- You have already used the mean, median, and mode of a sample to give some information about how the data are *clustered*.

- The *range* and *deviation* of a sample will give you information about how the data are *dispersed*.

Two sets of data may have the same mean and median, but how they are dispersed can vary significantly. For example, Samples A and B have the same mean and median, but are dispersed quite differently.

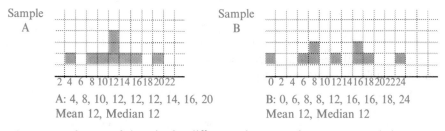

Sample A

2 4 6 8 10 12 14 16 18 20 22

A: 4, 8, 10, 12, 12, 12, 14, 16, 20
Mean 12, Median 12

Sample B

0 2 4 6 8 10 12 14 16 18 20 22 24

B: 0, 6, 8, 8, 12, 16, 16, 18, 24
Mean 12, Median 12

The **range** of a set of data is the difference between the greatest and the smallest data obtained.

A: range = 16                           B: range = 24

Samples C and D have the same range but they are clustered quite differently.

Sample C

0 2 4 6 8 10 12 14 16 18 20

Sample D

0 2 4 6 8 10 12 14 16 18 20 22

The following example shows how you can calculate values which can be used to demonstrate how the data are dispersed. The following data represent the percentage, $S$, of passes completed by two quarterbacks in 8 games.

| Jackson | 27% | 76% | 90% | 6% | Wirkowski | 66% | 52% | 51% | 60% |
|---------|-----|-----|-----|-----|-----------|-----|-----|-----|-----|
|         | 36% | 63% | 52% | 66% |           | 43% | 6%  | 90% | 48% |

The following calculations give results which seem similar for the quarterbacks.

Jackson:  mean $= \dfrac{416}{8} \doteq 52$   Wirkowski:  mean $= \dfrac{416}{8} \doteq 52$

range $= 84$   range $= 84$

However, the data for Jackson seem to deviate more from the mean than do the data for Wirkowski. To analyze the data further, you can calculate how much each percentage, $S$, deviates from the mean, $m$. Thus, you can calculate the **deviation**, $|S - m|$, for each $S$.

Jackson

| Percentage S | Deviation from the mean, m | |
|---|---|---|
| | $S - m$ | $|S - m|$ |
| 90 | $90 - 52 = \quad 38$ | 38 |
| 76 | $76 - 52 = \quad 24$ | 24 |
| 66 | $66 - 52 = \quad 14$ | 14 |
| 63 | $63 - 52 = \quad 11$ | 11 |
| 52 | $52 - 52 = \quad 0$ | 0 |
| 36 | $36 - 52 = -16$ | 16 |
| 27 | $27 - 52 = -25$ | 25 |
| 6 | $6 - 52 = -46$ | 46 |

total $= 174$

Wirkowski

| Percentage S | Deviation from the mean, m | |
|---|---|---|
| | $S - m$ | $|S - m|$ |
| 90 | $90 - 52 = \quad 38$ | 38 |
| 66 | $66 - 52 = \quad 14$ | 14 |
| 60 | $60 - 52 = \quad 8$ | 8 |
| 52 | $52 - 52 = \quad 0$ | 0 |
| 51 | $51 - 52 = -1$ | 1 |
| 48 | $48 - 52 = -4$ | 4 |
| 43 | $43 - 52 = -9$ | 9 |
| 6 | $6 - 52 = -46$ | 46 |

total $= 122$

Once you have calculated the deviation from the mean for all the data, you can calculate the **mean deviation** for the data.

Jackson   Wirkowski

mean deviation $= \dfrac{174}{8}$   mean deviation $= \dfrac{122}{8}$

$\doteq 21.8$   $\doteq 15.3$

You can use a diagram to express the result visually.

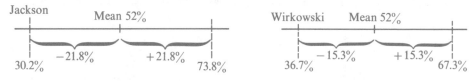

You can see from the diagrams and the data

- Jackson's percentage is more likely to occur between 30.2% and 73.8%
- Wirkowski's percentage is more likely to occur between 36.7% and 67.3%

Thus, in a crucial game, the coach should probably use the more consistent Wirkowski if the game plan call for lots of passing. The analysis of the data has helped the coach make a potentially better decision.

# 11.6 Exercise

**A** Use a calculator where needed. Round your answers to 1 decimal place.

1 Calculate the range and mean of each of the following.
   (a) 14, 8, 16, 20, 6, 8, 26, 16, 12         (b) 27, 6, 6, 30, 27, 15, 27, 30
   (c) 13.8, 20.7, 41.4, 11.5, 16.1, 18.4, 6.9
   (d) 7.50, 6.25, 3.75, 8.75, 2.50, 1.25, 3.75, 6.25, 5.00

2 The accuracy of a person in 10 trials is given by these data.
   76%  43%  60%  75%  83%  54%  48%  52%  72%  79%
   (a) Calculate the mean of the data.
   (b) What is the range?         (c) Calculate the mean deviation.

3 The daily heights, in centimetres, of plants after 2 weeks of growth are
   3.7  2.3  6.6  7.6  4.9  5.3  6.4  2.9  5.8  4.4  5.4  6.9  6.1  7.4
   (a) What is the mean, median, and mode of the data?
   (b) What is the range of the data?       (c) Calculate the mean deviation.

4 Use the data given in each stem-leaf diagram. Calculate
   (i) the mean          (ii) the mean deviation for each set of data.

(a)

| 1 | 0 | | | | |
|---|---|---|---|---|---|
| 2 | 1 | 2 | | | |
| 3 | 1 | 3 | | | |
| 4 | 4 | 2 | | | |
| 5 | 5 | 6 | 7 | | |
| 6 | 1 | 8 | 9 | 3 | 2 |
| 7 | 1 | 3 | 6 | | |
| 8 | 1 | 2 | | | |
| 9 | 3 | | | | |
| 10 | 5 | | | | |

(b)

| 10 | 3 | | | | | |
|----|---|---|---|---|---|---|
| 11 | 6 | 7 | | | | |
| 12 | 2 | 5 | 3 | | | |
| 13 | 4 | 2 | 5 | | | |
| 14 | 1 | 8 | 7 | 6 | 5 | |
| 15 | 1 | 3 | 2 | 1 | 5 | 2 |
| 16 | 4 | 2 | 3 | 1 | | |
| 17 | 3 | 2 | 4 | | | |
| 18 | 2 | 3 | | | | |
| 19 | 6 | | | | | |

**B** Review the meaning of *mean* and *mean deviation*.

5 A machine, packaging candy in 90-g packages, is thought to be faulty. A sample of 10 packages is randomly selected and the actual masses, in grams, are
   86  91  89  88  92  90  93  90  90  91
   (a) Calculate the mean deviation.
   (b) If the mean deviation exceeds 1.5 g, the batch of packages is rejected. What decision needs to be made?

6   The numbers of hours worked by students on a part-time basis are listed below.

   14   8   16   8   14   18   8   5   15   12   18   5   4   12   8

   (a) Find the range. Is the range a useful representative of these data?

   (b) Calculate the mean.          (c) Calculate the mean deviation.

   (d) Does the difference between the mean and the mean deviation exceed 1.5 h?

7   The number of points scored
    by two players is shown.

| Kevin | 25 | 11 | 38 | 12 | 30 | 36 | 29 | 16 |
|-------|----|----|----|----|----|----|----|----|
| Paul  | 38 | 30 | 25 | 23 | 27 | 22 | 20 | 11 |

   (a) Calculate the mean and the
       mean deviation for each player.

   (b) Based on your calculations, which player would you use in a crucial
       situation, in which you must score points?

8   Inspector 2-3C used 10 samples to determine the number of defective
    bottles in a large order. The numbers of defective bottles are

    52   46   78   5   42   50   37   43   39   35

   (a) Calculate the mean deviation for the data.

   (b) Use your calculation in (a). Estimate the number of defective bottles
       the inspector might expect in the next sample that is chosen.

9   At the same company, inspector 1-2B used an identical set of samples as
    inspector 2-3C and obtained the following numbers of defective bottles.

    58   21   42   60   62   48   5   78   51   28

   (a) Calculate the mean deviation for the data.

   (b) Use your calculation in (a). Estimate the number of defective bottles
       inspector 1-2B would expect in the next sample that is chosen.

C 10   Compare the work of the inspectors 2-3C and 1-2B in the previous
       questions. Based on the data and your calculations, which inspector
       appears to be more reliable?

## Problem-Solving   PSP

Often to solve a problem you need to think of the problem from different
points of view. Solve the following problem.

Make a copy of the nine points as shown. Draw
at most 4 line segments to pass through each and
all of the points once and only once. Once you
start to draw the line segments you cannot lift
your pen off the diagram. Hint: The line segments
do not have to end at one of the given points.

# 11.7 Data: Box and Whisker Diagrams

You have learned different techniques for displaying data. You can use the displayed data to calculate values such as

- mean, median, mode, range, mean deviation. Often the form of the displayed data allows you to analyze them and, as a result, to make useful predictions or to solve a problem. The **box and whisker diagram** is another useful way of displaying data.

*Data collected over long periods of time allow experts to predict the possible occurrence of earthquakes.*

The number of points scored by the North Shore Barons in a 24-game season is listed.

| 40 | 71 | 49 | 34 | 36 | 82 | 87 | 56 |
| 33 | 52 | 44 | 62 | 57 | 78 | 42 | 85 |
| 63 | 38 | 58 | 38 | 65 | 35 | 46 | 59 |

To construct a box and whisker diagram, do the following steps.

*Step 1:* Find the median of the data. List the data from smallest to greatest.

33  34  35  36  38  38  40  42  44  46  49  52
56  57  58  59  62  63  65  71  78  82  85  87

There are 24 games. Median A is the average of the two middle scores.

$$\text{Median A} = \frac{52 + 56}{2}$$

$$= 54$$

*Step 2:* Determine the median of the bottom and top half of the scores.

*Bottom Half:* 33  34  35  36  38  38    *Top Half:* 56  57  58  59  62  63
40  42  44  46  49  52        65  71  78  82  85  87

$$\text{Median B} = \frac{38 + 40}{2} \qquad\qquad \text{Median C} = \frac{63 + 65}{2}$$

$$= 39 \qquad\qquad\qquad\qquad = 64$$

*Step 3:* Construct the box and whisker diagram. Plot the data on the number line. Indicate the values A, B, and C on the diagram. Draw a box around the central half of the data (between Median B and Median C). Draw a whisker from the box to show the range.

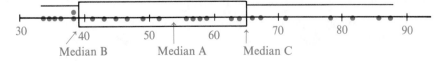

Once the box and whisker diagram is constructed, you can interpret the data visually. Based on the data for the North Shore Barons,

- a likely number of points scored is between 39 and 64 points. Thus the range of the score you might expect in a game is between 39 and 64 points.

- A score less than 39 is not their normal score. This score would represent a bad game for the North Shore Barons.

- A score above 64 is also not their normal score. This score would represent a great game for the North Shore Barons.

## 11.7  Exercise

**B** Review the steps needed to construct a box and whisker diagram.

1   Refer to the box and whisker diagram.  **PSP**  Place this strategy in your chart.

(a) What is the median of the lower half of the data?

(b) What is the median of the upper half of the data?

(c) Based on the diagram, what values could be considered
   (i) typical?                      (ii) not typical?

2   Interpret the data shown in each box and whisker diagram.

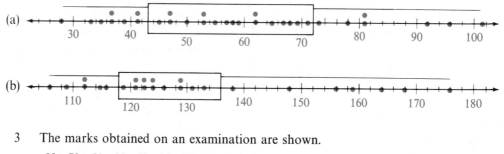

3   The marks obtained on an examination are shown.

88   73   64   44   52   34   27   41   55   63   92   46   59   65   74
100   55   62   71   75   61   84   97   39   94   69   88   82   63

(a) Construct a box and whisker diagram for the data.

(b) What is a "typical" mark on the exam?

(c) What is the range of the high marks on the exams?

(d) What is the range of the low marks on the exam?

4   Earthquakes occur frequently on the Pacific coast of North America. The magnitude of an earthquake is measured on the Richter Scale. The Richter numbers for 30 earthquakes are recorded below.

4.1  1.0  2.1  7.6  2.2  2.4  2.0  6.5  1.4  2.8  1.1  8.3  4.0  2.2  5.0
4.2  1.1  1.9  2.0  1.3  5.2  2.1  1.5  3.2  1.2  2.3  3.4  1.4  3.0  1.2

(a) Construct a box and whisker diagram for the Richter numbers.

(b) Based on your diagram in (a), estimate the mean value of the Richter numbers.

(c) Use the data to calculate the mean value of the Richter numbers. How does your answer compare to that in (b)?

(d) If an earthquake were to occur, in what range would you expect the Richter number to occur?

(e) What is the range of the low Richter numbers?   the high Richter numbers?

5   Box and whisker diagrams can be used to compare sets of data. These diagrams display data to compare the distance needed to stop, on different road surfaces and under similar conditions.

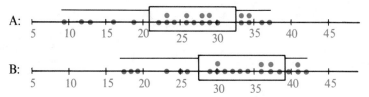

A:                                                          Distance, in metres, needed to stop on a dry concrete surface.
   5    10   15   20   25   30   35   40   45

B:                                                          Distance, in metres, needed to stop on a dry asphalt surface.
   5    10   15   20   25   30   35   40   45

(a) Qn which type of road surface is the stopping distance less?

(b) What is the least stopping distance recorded for each diagram?

(c) What is the greatest stopping distance recorded for each diagram?

(d) By how much do the medians of the lower half of the data of each diagram differ?

6   An experiment compares the time required to run 100 m by 25 athletes.

*Experiment A* (time in seconds)

| Relax 2 minutes. Take no deep breaths. Then run. | | | | |
|---|---|---|---|---|
| 12.80 | 12.64 | 12.03 | 12.50 | 12.19 |
| 13.27 | 12.35 | 12.67 | 12.66 | 12.37 |
| 12.65 | 12.05 | 12.51 | 12.48 | 12.01 |
| 12.95 | 12.52 | 10.96 | 12.63 | 12.46 |
| 12.93 | 11.73 | 12.16 | 12.51 | 12.34 |

*Experiment B*

| Relax 2 minutes. Take 10 deep breaths. Then run. | | | | |
|---|---|---|---|---|
| 11.80 | 12.18 | 12.04 | 11.88 | 11.89 |
| 11.90 | 10.43 | 11.78 | 11.45 | 11.77 |
| 11.43 | 11.60 | 12.03 | 11.91 | 12.62 |
| 12.32 | 12.06 | 12.02 | 11.47 | 12.04 |
| 11.57 | 11.71 | 11.16 | 12.29 | 11.89 |

(a) Construct a box and whisker diagram for each set of data.

(b) Compare the results in (a). What observations do you make?

C 7  (a) Create a question based on the diagrams in Question 6(a).

(b) Write a solution for your question in (a).

# 11.8  Applications: Using Scatter Diagrams

In working through the *Steps of Statistics*, you have displayed data, and you have used various techniques to analyze the data. The analysis you do helps you interpret the data in a useful way. For example, in economics and business, graphs based on data help you to forecast and make predictions.

Data based on advertising are recorded in a chart. The dollar amounts have been rounded to the nearest dollar.

| Store | A | B | C | D | E | F | G | H | I |
|---|---|---|---|---|---|---|---|---|---|
| Dollars spent on advertising | 30 | 15 | 17 | 7 | 32 | 9 | 23 | 26 | 36 |
| Dollars earned by the region each day | 4640 | 1740 | 3250 | 880 | 5570 | 2090 | 3360 | 4990 | 5680 |

The data *may* be related but no pattern is obvious with the data given as they are in the chart. You can analyze the data by recording them as ordered pairs and drawing a graph.

The ordered pairs are shown as

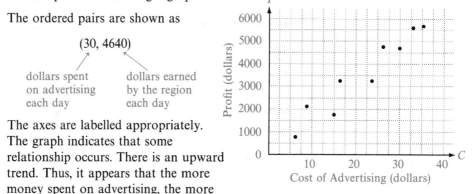

(30, 4640)

dollars spent on advertising each day — dollars earned by the region each day

The axes are labelled appropriately. The graph indicates that some relationship occurs. There is an upward trend. Thus, it appears that the more money spent on advertising, the more profit. A graph such as this one is called a **scatter diagram** or a **scatter plot**, since the points on the graph do not fall exactly on the line.

You can obtain a straight line that reasonably approximates the data. To do so you could estimate the position of the line so that the points lie near or on the line and it visually displays the relationship. This line is called **the line of best fit**.

In the following steps you use the medians of the horizontal and vertical co-ordinates to sketch this line.

*Step 1:* Find the median of the horizontal co-ordinates.

7  9  15  17  23  26  30  32  36
↑
median

Find the median of the vertical co-ordinates.

880  1740  2090  3250  3360  4640  4990  5570  5680
↑
median

The median point has co-ordinates (23, 3360).

*Step 2:* Find the median for the data given by the lower half of graph.

(7, 880)     (9, 2090)     (15, 1740)     (17, 3250)

Median of horizontal co-ordinates     $\dfrac{9 + 15}{2} = 12$

Median of vertical co-ordinates     $\dfrac{2090 + 1740}{2} = 1915$

The lower median point has co-ordinates     (12, 1915).

*Step 3:* Find the median for the data given by the upper half of the graph.

(26, 4990)     (30, 4640)     (32, 5570)     (36, 5680)

Median of horizontal co-ordinates     $\dfrac{30 + 32}{2} = 31$

Median of vertical co-ordinates     $\dfrac{4990 + 5570}{2} = 5280$

The upper median point has co-ordinates     (31, 5280).

*Step 4:* Sketch the straight line that best approximates the 3 median points in *Step 1*, *Step 2*, and *Step 3*.

The method described in *Steps 1 to 4* above is often referred to as the **median averaging method**.

From the sketch of the graph, you can obtain an equation that approximates the data.

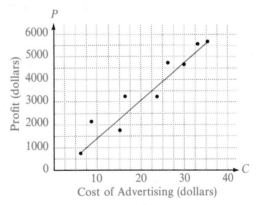

A: Calculate the slope: Choose 2 points that are representative of the data. From the diagram choose $P(7, 880)$ and $Q(36, 5680)$.

$$\text{Slope} = \dfrac{5680 - 880}{36 - 7}$$

$= 166$ (to the nearest whole number)

The equation is of the form $P = 166C + b$.

B: Find the *y*-intercept. Use $(C, P) = (23, 3360)$

$$P = 166C + b$$
$$3360 = 166(23) + b$$
$$b = -458$$

Thus, one equation of the line that approximates the data is
$$P = 166C - 458.$$

In an actual business problem, computers are used along with specialized formulas, to obtain the best line of fit.

# 11.8 Exercise

**A** Review the meaning of *scatter diagram* or *scatter plot*. Unless otherwise stated, round your answers to 1 decimal place, when necessary. Questions 1 to 8 are based on the scatter plot on the previous page.

1  Estimate the corresponding profit for each cost of advertising.
   (a) $19.00          (b) $28.00          (c) $34.00          (d) $12.00

2  Estimate the corresponding cost of advertising for each profit.
   (a) $1400           (b) $4950           (c) $2675           (d) $3760

3  Use the equation that relates the profit $P$ and cost of advertising $C$.
   $$P = 166C - 458$$
   Complete each of the following.
   (a) (35, ?)          (b) (?, 2530)          (c) (5, ?)          (d) (?, 1534)

4  (a) Use the graph. Estimate the corresponding value of the profit, $P$, for $C = 0$.
   (b) Interpret your answer in (a).
   (c) Did you make any assumptions to obtain your answer in (b)?      **PSP**

5  (a) Use the equation. When $C = 0$, what is the corresponding value of the profit $P$.
   (b) Interpret your answer in (a).
   (c) Did you make any assumptions to obtain your answer in (b)?

6  (a) Use the graph. When $P = 0$, estimate the corresponding value of $C$.
   (b) Use the equation. When $P = 0$, what is the corresponding value of $C$?
   (c) Interpret your answers in (a) and (b).
   (d) List any assumption(s) you made to obtain your answer in (c).

7  (a) Use the graph. For $C = 60$, estimate the value of $P$.
   (b) Interpret your answer in (a).
   (c) List any assumptions you make to obtain your answer in (b).

8  (a) Use the equation. For $C = 75$, estimate the value of $P$.
   (b) Interpret your answer in (a).
   (c) List any assumption(s) you made to obtain your answer in (b).

**B** When you interpret a scatter plot, be sure to list any assumptions you made to obtain your answers.

9 Use the data.

| $p$ | 46.0 | 17.3 | 32.2 | 5.8 | 55.2 | 20.7 | 33.4 | 41.4 | 49.5 | 56.4 |
|---|---|---|---|---|---|---|---|---|---|---|
| $q$ | 32.6 | 16.7 | 18.6 | 7.4 | 34.4 | 9.3 | 25.1 | 28.8 | 27.9 | 39.1 |

(a) Construct a scatter plot of the data. Record the data as ordered pairs $(p, q)$.

(b) Sketch a line of best fit. What is the slope of the line? Find an equation of the line of best fit. Use the median averaging method.

(c) Use your results. Estimate the missing entries for each of the following.

     A(28.9, ?)    B(?, 34.6)    C(43.8, ?)    D(?, 76.3)

(d) List any assumptions you made to obtain your answers in (d).

10 The coach of the Red Wings recorded the number of points a player scored and the corresponding amount of time the player was in the game. The results are recorded in the following table.

| Player Sweater No. | 1 | 2 | 4 | 6 | 9 | 11 | 27 | 50 | 66 | 99 | 100 |
|---|---|---|---|---|---|---|---|---|---|---|---|
| Amount of playing time, in minutes | 118 | 51 | 168 | 186 | 99 | 69 | 140 | 87 | 160 | 19 | 149 |
| Number of points scored | 39 | 12 | 59 | 58 | 34 | 26 | 40 | 24 | 41 | 11 | 53 |

(a) Construct a scatter plot for the data.

(b) Sketch a line that best fits the data on your scatter plot in (a).

(c) Choose 2 appropriate points. Calculate the slope of the line in (b).

(d) Use the median averaging method to sketch a line that fits the data. Calculate the slope of the line. How does your answer compare to that in (c)?

11 Refer to the graph in the previous question.

(a) Describe any relationship or trend shown in the graph.

(b) Obtain an equation that relates the *amount of playing time*, in minutes, and the *number of points scored*.

(c) Use your answer in (b) to complete the following table.

| Player | Sybil | Teresa | Ginger | Hesper | Libby |
|---|---|---|---|---|---|
| Playing Time | 135 | ? | 30 | ? | 170 |
| Points scored | ? | 26 | ? | 42 | ? |

12 (a) Refer to your results in Questions 10 and 11. Create a problem based on your results.

(b) Write a solution to your problem in (a).

## PSP Problem-Solving: Interpretation

The study of statistics plays an important role in the making of predictions. Skills in statistics are used in any area in which decisions, based on given information, need to be made. **Inferential statistics** is the study of that branch of statistics which deals with the making of decisions about a population based on random samples of that population.

*By collecting data, and interpreting the climatic conditions, weather forecasters are able to forecast a tornado warning*

For example, a sample of 100 light bulbs is randomly drawn from a shipment of 10 000 light bulbs. From this sample, the mean life of a light bulb is calculated to be 55.3 h. Based on this sample, you might ask,

"What is the mean life of a light bulb for the entire shipment of light bulbs?"

You cannot answer this question precisely, but you could infer that, based on your sample, the mean life of a bulb in the entire population (10 000 light bulbs) is probably 55.3 h.

Interpreting your results is an essential part of inferential statistics. In the following exercise, you will investigate predictions and inferences based on collected data.

## 11.9 Exercise

**B** Review the various methods you have learned for working with data.   **PSP**

1   Two dice were rolled 144 times and the sums of the numbers obtained were recorded as follows.

| Sum | 2 | 3 | 4 | 5 | 6 | 7 | 8 | 9 | 10 | 11 | 12 |
|-----|---|---|---|---|---|---|---|---|----|----|----|
| Frequency | 5 | 8 | 12 | 17 | 22 | 23 | 20 | 16 | 11 | 8 | 2 |

The sum of 4 turned up 12 times in the 144 tosses of the dice.

Based on the above sample, if the dice were rolled 1000 times, estimate how many times a sum of

(a) 5 would turn up.     (b) 7 would turn up.     (c) 11 would turn up.

2   To make predictions about the spending habits of vacationers, 56 people were asked what was the average amount of money they spent each day while on vacation. These data, in dollars, were collected.

| 98 | 72 | 52 | 91 | 48 | 51 | 64 | 83 | 69 | 61 | 61 | 55 | 56 | 87 |
|----|----|----|----|----|----|----|----|----|----|----|----|----|----|
| 82 | 86 | 77 | 58 | 65 | 64 | 73 | 92 | 92 | 59 | 96 | 77 | 88 | 67 |
| 86 | 77 | 67 | 73 | 66 | 85 | 71 | 61 | 42 | 91 | 68 | 69 | 56 | 63 |
| 81 | 57 | 74 | 76 | 73 | 66 | 84 | 77 | 76 | 73 | 58 | 62 | 61 | 68 |

(a) Calculate the mean, the median, and the mode for the data.

(b) Use the data in (a) to predict what the histogram might look like for the values in the chart.

(c) Construct the histogram. How does your constructed histogram compare to the one predicted in (b)?

(d) In order to make decisions about the spending habits of vacationers for the next year, predict how many people will spend more than
A: $60 each day          B: $80 each day

(e) If you were going on a vacation, based on the above results, how much money would you expect, on the average, to spend in a week?

3   Based on collected data, a sports magazine issued the following statement.

*The average football player uses Brand X helmet.*

On which of the following characteristics of data was the statement based?

A: mean                     B: median                  C: mode.

Give reasons for your answer.

---

Questions 4 to 7 are based on the following information. A sample of 25 men and 25 women was chosen and these measurements were made.

*Female*

Measure of foot (cm)

| 23.5 | 24.6 | 22.9 | 22.3 | 25.5 |
|------|------|------|------|------|
| 25.1 | 25.3 | 26.1 | 25.8 | 24.3 |
| 23.7 | 24.1 | 24.0 | 22.1 | 25.2 |
| 25.9 | 24.8 | 22.4 | 28.3 | 16.8 |
| 23.3 | 26.3 | 24.9 | 26.0 | 22.6 |

Measure of hand span (cm)

| 17.2 | 18.5 | 16.9 | 16.1 | 19.5 |
|------|------|------|------|------|
| 19.0 | 19.1 | 20.6 | 19.8 | 17.9 |
| 16.9 | 17.6 | 17.8 | 15.8 | 19.3 |
| 20.2 | 18.3 | 15.9 | 26.2 | 23.1 |
| 17.1 | 20.8 | 18.9 | 20.7 | 16.3 |

*Male*

Measure of foot (cm)

| 27.7 | 28.5 | 28.1 | 27.2 | 27.9 |
|------|------|------|------|------|
| 28.9 | 26.0 | 28.3 | 30.2 | 29.3 |
| 29.1 | 27.5 | 28.0 | 27.3 | 26.9 |
| 30.1 | 29.9 | 25.3 | 28.7 | 29.0 |
| 25.1 | 26.3 | 29.5 | 29.7 | 29.4 |

Measure of hand span (cm)

| 20.8 | 21.1 | 21.0 | 20.2 | 20.6 |
|------|------|------|------|------|
| 22.0 | 19.9 | 21.3 | 23.5 | 22.1 |
| 22.3 | 20.5 | 20.5 | 20.4 | 20.3 |
| 23.3 | 23.0 | 19.6 | 21.6 | 22.4 |
| 19.8 | 20.1 | 22.8 | 22.7 | 22.5 |

4   (a) Construct a histogram for the data of female foot measures.

(b) What percentage of the females have a foot measure less than 24.0 cm?

(c) Based on the data for the sample, what is the mean length of the female foot measure?

(d) Based on the results of the sample, what percentage of the females in the corresponding population would you expect to have a foot measure less than 23.5 cm?

5 (a) Construct a stem-and-leaf plot for the data of male hand spans.

(b) Estimate the mean length of the male hand span. Then calculate the mean. How do your estimated value and calculated value of the mean compare?

(c) Based on the results of the sample, what percentage of the males in the corresponding population have a hand span of 20.5 cm or greater?

6 (a) Construct a scatter plot to show all the data. Use the ordered pairs

$$(?, ?)$$

measure of hand span    measure of foot

Distinguish on your scatter plot the data for women and for men.

(b) Based on the scatter plot, is there any trend in the women's data?

(c) Based on the scatter plot, is there any trend in the men's data?

(d) Compare the data for the men and women on your scatter plot. What general observations can you make?

7 Refer to the data for male and female foot and hand span measures.

(a) Create a problem based on the data.

(b) Write a solution for the problem in (a).

8 (a) Fill a box with a different number of red, green, and blue chips, to total 100 in all.

(b) Have someone take a random sample of 10 chips. Use this sample to predict the percentage of red, green and blue chips in the box. Return the chips to the box.

(c) Repeat step (b) for another 10 chips and again predict the percentage of red, green, and blue chips.

(d) Have the person repeat step (b) until a reasonable prediction can be made about the number of red, green, and blue chips in the box.

9 A thumbtack can land in one of 2 ways, ⋏ or ⊥. Devise an experiment to decide whether the following statement is reasonable.

"When a thumbtack is dropped it will more likely land with its point down".

# 11.10 Probability: Skills and Concepts

Many of the answers you obtain to questions often involve uncertainty.
The answers are often only *probably true*.

- There is a 75% chance of rain tomorrow.
- Based on the advance polls, the plebiscite will probably take place.
- If you are older than 55 years, you will probably live another 22 years.

The mathematics of chance or prediction is called **probability theory**.
Probability is that branch of mathematics that predicts the outcome of events.
The example of rolling a die will illustrate various terms associated with probability.

When you roll a single die there are 6 **equally likely** outcomes. Thus 1, 2, 3, 4, 5, or 6 has the same chance of being rolled on a fair die. The set of all possible outcomes 1, 2, 3, 4, 5, 6 is called the **sample space**. An outcome or set of outcomes is called an **event**. For example, when you roll a die, a roll of 3 is an example of an event.

The 2 is called the **outcome** of rolling the die.

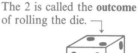

The notation used to indicate the probability of rolling a 3 is given by $P(3)$.

$$P(3) = \frac{1}{6}$$

$\leftarrow$ { The numerator shows the number of times the outcome can occur, (only 1 number on 1 roll).

$\leftarrow$ { The denominator shows the total number of possible outcomes—6 possible numbers might turn up.

The statement $P(3) = \frac{1}{6}$ is read as "The probability of rolling a 3 is $\frac{1}{6}$". The probability of the event $E$, of rolling a 5 or 6 on a die, is given by

$$P(E) = \frac{2}{6}$$

$\leftarrow$ { There are 2 possible, successful outcomes; namely you can obtain a 5 or a 6.

$\leftarrow$ { There are 6 possible numbers you can obtain on a roll of the die.

$$= \frac{1}{3}$$

Examples such as the above suggest the following definition for probability.

Probability of an event, $E = \dfrac{\text{number of favourable outcomes, } F}{\text{total number of possible outcomes, } T}$

You may write the above in a compact form.

$$P(E) = \frac{F}{T}$$

$\longleftarrow$ number of favourable outcomes

$\longleftarrow$ total number of possible equally likely outcomes.

**Example 1**    What is the probability of drawing a jack from a deck of 52 ordinary playing cards?

**Solution**    There are 4 jacks in a deck of cards. Thus, there are 4 favourable outcomes.

$$F = 4$$

There are 52 cards in a deck. Thus, there are 52 possible outcomes.

$$T = 52$$

$$P(E) = \frac{F}{T}$$

$$= \frac{4}{52} \text{ or } \frac{1}{13}$$

Thus, the probability of drawing a jack from a deck of cards is $\frac{1}{13}$.

**Impossible Event**
Rolling a 7 on a die is impossible.

$$P(7) = \frac{0}{6} \xleftarrow{\hspace{0.3cm}} \text{There are no faces with 7.}$$
$$\xleftarrow{\hspace{0.3cm}} \text{There are 6 possible}$$
$$= 0 \qquad \text{numbers to be rolled.}$$

Thus the probability of an **impossible event** or outcome is 0.

**Certain Event**
Rolling a number less than 7 on a die is a certainty.

$$P(E) = \frac{6}{6} \xleftarrow{\hspace{0.3cm}} \begin{array}{l}\text{Any number appearing on} \\ \text{the face of the die is} \\ \text{a favourable outcome.}\end{array}$$
$$= 1$$

The probability of a **certainty** is 1.

**Theoretical Probability**
When you roll a fair die you obtain one of 6 equally likely outcomes, namely, a 1, 2, 3, 4, 5, or 6. You can calculate the theoretical probability of rolling a 4 on a die.

$$P(4) = \frac{1}{6} \begin{array}{l} \xleftarrow{} \left\{\begin{array}{l}\text{There is one favourable outcome,} \\ \text{namely, rolling a 4 on a die.}\end{array}\right. \\ \xleftarrow{} \left\{\begin{array}{l}\text{There are 6 possible outcomes} \\ \text{when you roll a die.}\end{array}\right.\end{array}$$

Thus, the theoretical probability of rolling a 4 on a die is $\frac{1}{6}$.

**Experimental Probability**
Sometimes the theoretical probability of an event is not known. As a result, you need to rely on an experiment in order to obtain data on the favourable outcomes. For example, by rolling a die, you could obtain data experimentally to find the probability of rolling a 4 on a die.

Experiment A:

| Total number of rolls | 100 |
|---|---|
| Number of times a 4 is obtained | 13 |

$$P(4) = \frac{13}{100}$$
$$= 0.13$$

Based on the data of Experiment A, the probability (experimental) of rolling a 4 on a die is $\frac{13}{100}$ or 0.13.

Experiment B:

| Total number of rolls | 1000 |
|---|---|
| Number of times a 4 is obtained | 159 |

$$P(4) = \frac{159}{1000}$$
$$= 0.159$$

Based on the data of Experiment B, the probability (experimental) of rolling a 4 on a die is $\frac{159}{1000}$ or 0.159.

For some events, such as rolling a 4 on a die, you can obtain the experimental probability and then compare it with the theoretical probability, which is known. Thus, certain skills for probability can be obtained by comparing the results for experimental and theoretical probability. However, there are some situations, for which you can obtain only the experimental probability. This is shown in the experiment in Example 2.

**Example 2**   A thumbtack, when tossed, may land

up or down.

What is the probability of tossing a thumbtack so that it lands up?

**Solution**

| Number of thumbtacks tossed | 100 |
| Number of thumbtacks face up (U) | 61 |
| Number of thumbtacks face down (D) | 39 |

You need to perform an experiment to find an answer.

Based on the results of the data

$$P(U) = \frac{61}{100}$$
$$= 0.61$$

Thus, the probability of tossing a thumbtack face up is 0.61.   (Remember that the result is obtained by *experimental* probability.)

## 11.10   Exercise

**A** In the context of a question, you often need to decide whether *theoretical* or *experimental* probability is dealt with.

1   1000 tickets are sold to win a camper.
   (a) You buy one ticket. What is the probability that you will win the camper?
   (b) You buy 20 tickets. What is the probability that you will win the camper?

2  An envelope contains identical cards with one of each of the digits 0, 1, 2, . . . , 8, 9 written on them.

   (a) What is the probability of drawing an even digit?

   (b) What is the probability of drawing a number greater than, or equal to, 7?

3  A single die is rolled. What is the probability of rolling

   (a) a 3?          (b) an even number?          (c) a number greater than 1?

   (d) a number less than 4?          (e) a number greater than 6?

4  The 26 letters of the alphabet are placed in a box and all have an equal chance of being drawn. What is the probability of drawing

   (a) t?          (b) a, b, or c?          (c) the vowels?
   (d) letters that sound like "b" (bee)?

5  In a parking lot there are 42 compact cars and 36 full size cars. All the keys are placed in a box. What is the probability of taking a key for a compact car from the box?

6  On a popular game show one of each of the numbers 1, 2, 3, 4, 5, and 6 is written on a disc, and the discs placed in a box. The word "strike" is written on 3 similar discs and these discs are placed in the same box. What is the probability that you will draw

   (a) a number?          (b) a strike?

B  Express probability as required to 2 decimal places.

7  From experimental results, the probability that an electronic calculator has a defect is 0.04.

   (a) If 1246 calculators were manufactured, how many would you expect to be defective?

   (b) What is the probability that you will choose a calculator that will work?

8  In a class experiment, the data for tossing coins, 100 times by each of 36 students are recorded.

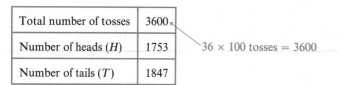

| Total number of tosses | 3600 |
| Number of heads ($H$) | 1753 |
| Number of tails ($T$) | 1847 |

36 × 100 tosses = 3600

   Based on the above data, what is the probability of tossing

   (a) a head, $P(H)$?          (b) a tail, $P(T)$?

9   Another class conducted the same experiment described in the previous question and obtained the following results. Based on the data at the right, what is the probability of tossing
(a) a head, $P(H)$?    (b) a tail, $P(T)$?

| Total number of tosses | 3200 |
|---|---|
| Number of heads ($H$) | 1523 |
| Number of tails ($T$) | 1677 |

10  (a) What is the theoretical probability of tossing a head, $P(H)$? a tail, $P(T)$?

   (b) How do your answers in Questions 8 and 9 compare to the theoretical probability of tossing a head and of tossing a tail?

   (c) Which of your answers in Questions 8 or 9 would you estimate to be more reliable? Give reasons for your choice.

11  A poll was conducted for a week to determine the probability of a certain law being passed by Parliament.

| Number of persons who said | Day of the week | | | | | | |
|---|---|---|---|---|---|---|---|
| | M | T | W | T | F | S | S |
| *yes* | 23 | 320 | 393 | 360 | 396 | 612 | 576 |
| *no* | 85 | 103 | 130 | 123 | 128 | 203 | 182 |
| *no comment* | 53 | 91 | 85 | 103 | 92 | 103 | 98 |

   (a) Based on the data, what percentage of the people said *yes* on Monday? on Tuesday?

   (b) Use the data in (a) to *predict* the approximate percentage of people who will say *yes* on Wednesday.

   (c) Use the data in the chart to *calculate* the percentage of people who said *yes* on Wednesday. How does your answer compare with (b)?

12  (a) To calculate the probability of persons saying *yes*, which data in the chart would you use?

   (b) Use the data in the chart to predict how many people out of 1000 will say *no comment* on weekends.

   (c) Use the data to predict how many out of 1000 will say *no* during the week.

## Computer Tip

A computer program can be used to do tedious calculations in statistics, such as finding the mean. What do the instructions mean in the program shown? Try the program. (Do you need to make any changes in the program?)

```
10  INPUT N
15  DIM X(100)
20  LET S = 0
30  FOR I = 1 TO N
40  INPUT X(I)
50  LET S = S + X(I)
60  NEXT I
70  LET M = S/N
80  PRINT "THE MEAN IS", M
90  END
```

## Complementary Probability

- The probability of rolling a 4 on a die is $\frac{1}{6}$.

$$P(\text{the event occurs}) = \frac{1}{6}$$

- The probability of rolling the numbers 1, 2, 3, 5, or 6 is $\frac{5}{6}$. You could interpret this result by saying the probability of not rolling a 4 is $\frac{5}{6}$.

$$P(\text{the event does not occur}) = \frac{5}{6}$$

From the above

$$P(\text{event occurs}) + P(\text{event does not occur}) = 1$$

You can use this result to calculate the probability of an event by using

$$P(\text{event occurs}) = 1 - P(\text{event does not occur})$$

or $\quad P(\text{event does not occur}) = 1 - P(\text{event occurs})$

13  (a) What is the probability of rolling a number greater than 2 on a die?

(b) Use your answer in (a) to calculate the probability of rolling a number not greater than 2.

14  On rolling a die, what is the probability that you will not

(a) roll a 6?                    (b) roll a 1 or a 6?

15  A pair of football tickets was won by a class. There are 34 students and names are to be drawn to find the winner of the tickets.

(a) If there are 14 girls, what is the probability of drawing a girl's name?

(b) What is the probability of *not drawing* a girl's name?

16  A box contains 36 red chips, 24 blue chips and 40 green chips. If you take a chip from the box, what is the probability it will be

(a) a red chip?                  (b) not a red chip?

(c) not a green chip?            (d) a blue chip?

17  Based on the number of games yet to play, the probability of the Eskimos finishing in first place is 0.46. What is the probability that they will not finish in first place?

18  From experimental results, the probability that a battery taken from a production line is defective is 0.003.

(a) Interpret the meaning of the above statement.

(b) What is the probability that a battery taken from the same production line is not defective?

## 11.11 Sample Spaces: Charts and Tree Diagrams

To calculate the probability of an event, you need to know the sample space or population. That is, you need to know the total possible outcomes for that event. For example, if you toss 3 coins at the same time, what is the probability of tossing 3 heads? You could answer the question by doing an experiment to calculate the experimental probability or draw a diagram to show the different possibilities and determine the sample space.

**Chart**

A chart shows the different possibilities of tossing 3 coins.

| Penny | H | H | H | H | T | T | T | T |
|-------|---|---|---|---|---|---|---|---|
| Nickel | H | H | T | T | H | H | T | T |
| Dime | H | T | H | T | H | T | H | T |

One combination is ↑ⓉⒽⓉ.

**Tree Diagram**

A tree diagram also shows the possibilities of tossing 3 coins.

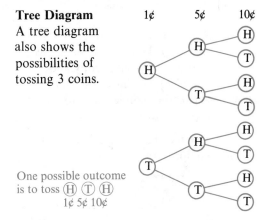

One possible outcome is to toss ⒽⓉⒽ
1¢ 5¢ 10¢

**Example**    What is the probability of tossing 3 coins and obtaining 3 heads?

**Solution**    Refer to the chart or tree diagram above.
The probability of tossing 3 heads is given by

$$P(3H) = \frac{\text{number of favourable outcomes}}{\text{number of total outcomes}} \longleftarrow \text{This is the sample space or population.}$$

$$= \frac{1}{8} \begin{array}{l} \longleftarrow \text{Only one combination in the diagram gives 3 heads.} \\ \longleftarrow \text{There are 8 possible outcomes when you toss 3 coins.} \end{array}$$

## 11.11 Exercise

**A** Use the chart or tree diagram to answer Questions 1 and 2.

1   Refer to the diagram. What is the probability of

**PSP**    Record this strategy in your PSP chart.

(a) tossing 3 tails?          (b) not tossing 3 tails?
(c) tossing a tail and 2 heads?     (d) not tossing a tail or 2 heads?

2   What is the probability of tossing
(a) 2 tails and a head?    (b) all the same?    (c) 2 coins the same?
(d) not tossing 2 heads?    (e) not tossing a head on any coin?

**B** To calculate the probability, you need to determine the sample space.

3   (a) Construct a tree diagram to show the sample space obtained when you toss 4 coins.

    (b) Use your chart. What is the probability of tossing all coins the same?

4   Refer to the previous question. What is the probability of tossing

    (a) 4 heads?  (b) 2 heads and 2 tails?

    (c) not tossing 2 heads?  (d) not tossing 3 tails?

5   (a) A pair of dice are rolled. To find out what the different sums are that may be rolled, copy and complete the chart. The chart shows the sample space for rolling a pair of dice.

    (b) Use the chart in (a). Copy and complete the following.

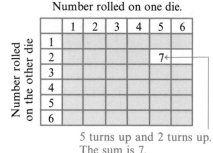
Number rolled on one die.

5 turns up and 2 turns up.
The sum is 7.

| Sum of | 2 | 3 | 4 | 5 | 6 | 7 | 8 | 9 | 10 | 11 | 12 |
|---|---|---|---|---|---|---|---|---|---|---|---|
| Frequency | | | | | | | | | | | |

---

Use your results in Question 5 to answer Questions 6 to 9.

6   What is the probability of rolling a sum of

    (a) 3?  (b) 6?  (c) 2?  (d) 11?

    (e) Which of the sums has an equal probability of being obtained?

7   Which sums are more likely to be rolled?

    (a) a 3 or a 7?  (b) a 5 or an 8?  (c) a 6 or a 9?  (d) a 2 or an 11?

8   What is the probability of not rolling

    (a) a sum of 2?  (b) a sum of 7?  (c) an even sum?  (d) an odd sum?

9   What is the probability of rolling a sum  (a) greater than 8?  (b) less than 4?

**C** 10   (a) Three dice are tossed. Design a diagram of your own to list the sample space for the sums of tossing 3 dice.

    (b) What is the probability of obtaining a sum of 12 on the toss of 3 dice?

    (c) Create a question based on your sample space in (a). Write a solution for your question.

# 11.12 Applications: Statistics and Probability

You may apply your skills in probability and statistics to solve problems. **PSP** In Example 1 statistical methods are used to collect the data, and then skills in probability are applied to answer the questions.

**Example**  A random sample was obtained from 1000 people for their responses to the question

"Are television series becoming too violent?"

The results were: 686 *agreed* (A), 235 disagreed (D) and the remainder had *no comment*, (NC). What is the probability that another person selected at random will

(a) *agree?*  (b) *disagree?*  (c) have *no comment?*

**Solution**  (a) Probability of *agree* (A)

**PSP**  Refer to your *Problem-Solving Plan.*

$$P(A) = \frac{686}{1000} \begin{array}{l} \longleftarrow \text{number that } agreed \\ \longleftarrow \text{total number} \end{array}$$

$$= 0.686$$

The probability of another person selected at random who will agree is 0.686.

(b) Probability of *disagree* (D)

$$P(D) = \frac{235}{1000} = 0.235$$

The probability of another person selected at random who will disagree is 0.235.

(c) Probability of *no comment* (NC)

$$P(NC) = \frac{79}{1000} \longleftarrow \begin{array}{l} \text{number of people} \\ \text{with } no \; comment \end{array}$$

$$= 0.079$$

The probability of another person selected at random who will have no comment is 0.079.

Based on the previous results, you could interpret them and say that the next person sampled randomly is *more likely to agree* than *to disagree*.

## 11.12  Exercise

**B**  Use your calculator efficiently to do each calculation.

1   To determine the popularity
of various cars these data
were randomly collected.

| Car | A | B | C | D | E | F | G | H | I | J |
|---|---|---|---|---|---|---|---|---|---|---|
| Frequency of responses | 21 | 4 | 11 | 11 | 9 | 1 | 25 | 3 | 6 | 26 |

(a) What is the probability
that a person chosen at random from the above students has selected Car C?

(b) What is the probability that a person will choose car D?

2   Refer to the chart in the previous question.

(a) What are the two most popular choices of cars?

(b) What is the probability that another person chosen randomly from the
same population will choose the two most popular cars?

(c) What is the probability that another person chosen randomly from the
same population will not choose car D?

3   On an experimental agriculture farm, 60 plants are selected at random.
Their heights in centimetres after 3 weeks of growth are recorded as follows.

```
 7   15   19   13   21   12   20   10   14   14   17   12   14   22   12
17   18   14   10   13   12   15   16   11   11    9   16   13   16   11
11   19   16   15   18   14   22   19   13   15   16   10   10   12   15
 9   20   17    8   23   12   10   11   13   14   18   15   20   12   14
```

(a) Construct a frequency distribution of the data.

(b) Construct a histogram of the data. Use class intervals $4 - 5$, $6 - 7$,
$8 - 9$, $10 - 11$, etc.

(c) For the data, calculate the mean.

(d) What percentage of the plants are within 2 cm of the mean?

4   Refer to the data in question 3. From the field you randomly select plants.
Calculate the probability that you will pick a plant which is

(a) $12 - 13$ cm high.          (b) between 10 cm and 15 cm inclusive.

(c) as long in length as the mode.     (d) less in length than the mean.

5   Refer to the data in Question 3.

(a) Calculate the median.

(b) What percentage of the plants are within 2 cm of the mode?

(c) What is the probability that another plant selected randomly will have
a height within 2 cm of the median?

6   Refer to the previous data for the agriculture farm.

   (a) What is the probability that another plant selected randomly from the same population will occur in the interval 8 cm to 9 cm?

   (b) What is the probability that another plant selected randomly from the same population will have a height less than the mean?

   (c) Create a question based on the data. Write a solution for the question you have created.

7   An optical illusion is shown.

   (a) Which of the following responses do you think most people would choose?

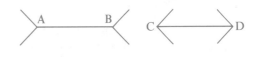

      1. AB is equal to CD.          2. AB is longer.          3. CD is longer.

   (b) Use a questionnaire based on the above information and have different persons complete it.

   (c) Use the data in (b) to make a prediction. Which statement is most likely to be chosen? Least likely to be chosen?

   (d) Use other samples to collect data for the questionnaire in (b).

   (e) In a group of 100 people, predict the percentage that will choose each statement.

   (f) What is the probability that another person selected randomly from the same population will choose AB is longer?

8   (a) Predict what you think is the average pulse rate for the members of your class.

   (b) Collect data to verify your prediction.

   (c) In a group of 100 people, what percentage will be within 3 or less beats of the average pulse rate? What assumption do you make in finding your answer?

   (d) Based on your results, what is the probability that another person selected randomly from the same population will have a pulse rate within the range
      A: 50 − 70 beats?          B: 65 − 85 beats?

## Math Tip

- It is important to clearly understand the vocabulary of mathematics to solve problems. Make a list of all the new words you have learned in this chapter. Provide a simple example of your own to remind you of the meaning of each word.

- Make a list of the strategies for problem solving  that you have learned in this chapter. Place them in your chart for the *Problem-Solving Plan.*

# 11.13 Independent Events

How many heads of a coin can you toss in a row? Suppose you toss a coin 5 times and obtain 5 heads, what is the probability that you will obtain another head on the next toss? Even though you have obtained 5 heads already, the probability of getting a head on the next toss is

$$P(H) = \frac{1}{2}.$$

Tossing a coin 5 times and getting 5 heads does not influence the outcome of the 6th toss. The 6th toss is *independent* of the previous results. Experiment A is said to be **independent** of experiment B if the results of one do not influence the results of the other.

**Example**    A coin is tossed and a die is rolled. What is the probability of tossing a head on the coin and rolling a six on the die?

To answer the question, you need to list the sample space.

**Solution**    For the coin, you can obtain a head (H) or tail (T).
For the die, you can obtain a 1, 2, 3, 4, 5, or 6.
Use a tree diagram to show the sample space.

There are 12 possible outcomes.
Thus, the probability of tossing

a head and rolling a 5 is    $P(H, 5) = \dfrac{1}{12}.$

Tossing a head on a coin and rolling a 5 on a die are **independent events**. The probability of each event can be calculated.

Tossing a head    $P(H) = \dfrac{1}{2}$          Rolling a 5    $P(5) = \dfrac{1}{6}$

Note that    $P(H) \times P(5) = \dfrac{1}{2} \times \dfrac{1}{6}$

$$= \frac{1}{12}$$

**PSP**    Remember: To solve a problem you must learn the precise meaning of each word or symbol.

Which is the same result as was obtained by listing the sample space. This observation is summarized in the general statement for independent events.

For the independent events, $E_1$, and $E_2$, you calculate the probability of both events occurring, $P(E_1, E_2)$, by calculating the individual probabilities.

$$P(E_1 \text{ and } E_2) = P(E_1) \times P(E_2)$$

probability of event $E_1$ and $E_2$ occurring

product of the probability of each event

## 11.13 Exercise

**A** You may express your answers in fractional form.

1 A coin is tossed and a die is rolled. Copy and complete the chart.

| | A | B | C |
|---|---|---|---|
| | Probability of tossing | Probability of rolling | Probability of tossing and rolling |
| (a) | a tail ? | a 5 ? | a tail and a 5 ? |
| (b) | a head ? | a 2 ? | a head and a 2 ? |
| (c) | a tail ? | an odd number ? | a tail and an odd number ? |

(d) How are the probabilities in Column A and Column B related to those in Column C?

2 (a) In an experiment, a nickel and a dime are tossed and a die is rolled. Construct the sample space for the experiment.

(b) What is the probability of tossing 2 heads and of rolling a 4?

3 Use the sample space in the previous question. What is the probability of tossing and rolling

(a) two heads and a 6?      (b) a tail, a head and a 4?

(c) two tails and an odd number?

4 (a) Construct a sample space for tossing 4 coins.

(b) What is the total number of possibilities of tossing 4 coins?

(c) What is the probability of tossing 3 tails and 1 head?

5 Refer to the previous question. What is the probability of tossing

(a) all heads?      (b) all tails?

(c) two heads, two tails?      (d) 3 heads, 1 tail?

6 A coin is tossed twice. You may draw a tree diagram to illustrate the sample space. Use a sample space to calculate the probability of tossing

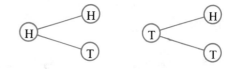

(a) 2 heads in a row      (b) 1 head and 1 tail

(c) Calculate the above probabilities using products.

**B** To answer the following questions, you need to determine the sample space.

7    Three coins are tossed in a row. What is the probability of tossing
     (a) three heads?    (b) 2 heads and a tail?    (c) 2 tails and a head?

8    In addition to 3 coins tossed in a row, a die is rolled. What is the
     probability of
     (a) tossing 3 heads in a row and rolling a 4?
     (b) tossing 2 heads and a tail and rolling an even number?

9    A deck of 52 cards is shuffled. After one card is drawn from the deck it is
     returned to the pack before the next draw. Calculate the probability of
     drawing
     (a) the ace of diamonds and then a 4 of clubs.
     (b) a 10 and then a 5.                    (c) a queen and then an ace.
     (d) a jack and not drawing another jack.
     (e) a black card followed by another black card.

10   A multiple choice test
     is constructed as shown.
     (a) What is the probability of getting
         a perfect score by guessing?
     (b) Express your answer in (a), as a
         per cent, to 2 decimal places.

| Question | Possible answers |
|----------|------------------|
| 1        | A  B  C          |
| 2        | A  B  C          |
| 3        | A  B  C          |
| 4        | A  B  C          |

11   Each question on a multiple choice test has 5 possible answers.
     (a) There are 4 questions. If you guess randomly at the answers, what is
         the probability of a perfect score, as a per cent, to 2 decimal places?
     (b) What is the probability of passing if you guess randomly at the
         answers?

**C** 12   To win a prize in the 5 – 9 lottery, you need to complete a card by
     writing a number between 1 and 9 inclusive in each space. Susan's choice of
     5 numbers was as follows.

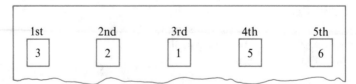

| 1st | 2nd | 3rd | 4th | 5th |
| 3 | 2 | 1 | 5 | 6 |

What is the probability of her choosing the prize-winning number?

# Problem Solving: Simulating Experiments

Often to solve a problem you need to do an experiment. For example, to answer the following question, you might do an experiment of tossing coins:

"What is the probability of obtaining a head in 1000 tosses of a coin?"

A more efficient method of simulating the toss of a coin is to use a calculator or computer that generates random numbers. Random numbers are numbers that have an equal chance of occurring, and are obtained on a calculator by using the key $\boxed{RAN\#}$.

output

$\boxed{C}$ $\boxed{RAN\#}$ 0.362    The output is a random number 0.000 to 0.999 inclusive.

To simulate the above experiment follow these steps.

*Step 1:* Assign heads (H) to even digits 0, 2, 4, 6, 8 of the random number and tails (T) to odd digits 1, 3, 5, 7, 9 of the random numbers.

*Step 2:* Use the calculator key $\boxed{RAN\#}$ to obtain random numbers.

| Random Numbers | 0.463 | 0.892 | 0.130 | 0.025 | and so on |
|---|---|---|---|---|---|
| Assign H or T | H H T | H T H | T T H | H H T | and so on |

From the data given by 1000 digits of random numbers you can answer the original question without actually flipping coins.

To simulate an experiment with 4 different outcomes, you again use the digits of the random numbers.

| Random Number | Multiply by 4 | Round up to the nearest whole number. |
|---|---|---|
| 0.736 | 2.944 | 3  These whole numbers |
| 0.515 | 2.060 | 2  simulate the outcome |
| 0.226 | 0.904 | 1  1, 2, 3, or 4 of the |
| 0.998 | 3.992 | 4  experiment. |

13  Use random numbers on a calculator to simulate each experiment.

(a) Rolling a fair die ten times. Based on the results, what is the probability of tossing 5 on the die?

(b) Tossing 2 coins. Based on the results, what is the probability of tossing 2 heads?

(c) Design an experiment of your own. Create a question based on the experiment involving probability. Answer the question.

14  On a computer, the command PRINT RND(1) provides an output of a random number in decimal form. If you want to obtain the random output of 1 to 4, then the computer program instruction is

PRINT INT (4 ∗ RND(1)) + 1

A bag contains 4 different coloured balls. Write a computer program to simulate the experiment of choosing a particular colour from the bag, 100 times.

# Practice and Problems: Review

1 Which of these estimates or predictions are based on the mean, the mode, or the median? Justify your answers.
(a) The average salary of students is $32.50 per week.
(b) The middle mass of the football players is 70 kg.
(c) Most snowmobile accidents occur in winter.   (d) The middle mark was 64.
(e) The average speed on our highways is 85 km/h.
(f) The average score at hockey games is 3.2 goals per team.
(g) More people golf than play billiards.   (h) The favorite song is Sunshine.

2 Illustrate the meaning of each word by an example of your own.
(a) range   (b) mean deviation   (c) box and whisker diagram   (d) scatter diagram
(e) line of best fit   (f) probability of an event   (g) complementary probability

3 The price of apples is seasonal. Helena purchased these amounts over 3 months.
3.2 kg @ $1.69/kg     4.6 kg @ $2.29/kg     1.9 kg @ $3.08/kg     2.8 kg @ $2.03/kg
What is (a) the average price?   (b) the weighted mean price per kilogram?

4 Based on collected data, the probability of the Canucks winning the game is 0.76 and of tying the game is 0.12. What is the probability that the Canucks will lose?

# Practice Test

1 Illustrate the meaning of each type of sample by an example of your own.

(a) random             (b) clustered           (c) stratified          (d) destructive

2 These data show the marks on an examination that is used each year.

61  66  71  42  69  86  98  52  68  64  92  59  81  74  61  96  76  56  67
72  82  91  51  64  83  61  91  73  84  73  62  87  48  55  77  88  56  58
86  77  57  77  73  76  65  85  66  73  61  77  69  92  68  58  67  63
(a) Calculate the mean, the median, and the mode.
(b) Use the data in (a). Predict what the histogram for these marks might look like.
(c) Construct a histogram. How does your histogram compare to the one in (b)?
(d) If the exam is used again next year, predict how many persons will obtain
    A: more than 60% on the exam.       B: over 80 marks on the exam.

3 A box has 10 foreign silver coins, 20 Canadian silver coins, and 10 pennies.
After a coin is taken from the box, it is returned to the box before another
coin is taken. Calculate the probability of taking
(a) a silver foreign coin   (b) a penny   (c) a silver foreign coin followed by a penny
(d) 2 pennies followed by a Canadian silver coin
(e) a penny and not followed by a Canadian silver coin

# 12

# *Process of Trigonometry: Applications*

Using similar triangles, developing mathematics, tangent of angle, concepts and skills of trigonometry, using calculators, trigonometric values, solving problems, angle of elevation and depression, applications, strategies and problem-solving

## Introduction

Often, the interaction between nations can act as a stimulant for new ideas in mathematics. For example, during the active trading between Egypt and Greece, the ideas of the Ancient Egyptians acted as a stimulant for the Greeks in their study of mathematics. Thus, Thales (640–546 B.C.) expanded his study of geometry as a result of a visit to Egypt. Although no records were kept, he has been credited with the introduction of the study of geometry to Greece.

The roots of trigonometry also occurred in Ancient Times and since then it has flourished as an important branch of mathematics. For example, the Ancient Greeks used the study of angles and sides to solve problems involving triangles. The word *trigonometry* is derived from their vocabulary.

| *tri* | *gono* | *metry* |
|:---:|:---:|:---:|
| tri-three | gonia-angle | metria-measurement |

*One of the earliest uses of trigonometry was in surveying. The concepts and skills of trigonometry have been applied to the construction of many of the structures you see about you: buildings, bridges, towers, etc.*

*Once co-ordinate geometry was introduced by Rene Descartes, the study of trigonometry was studied from a different point of view. The concepts and skills developed have now been applied to the study of electricity, economics, science, oil exploration, to name a few.*

# 12.1 Similar Triangles

While you learn mathematics, make comparisons to help you remember concepts and skills.

**Congruent triangles** have the same size and shape.

**Similar triangles** have the same shape but are different in size.

Similar triangles have the following properties.

Property I  Corresponding pairs of angles are equal.

$\triangle ABC \sim \triangle DEF$  $\angle A = \angle D$
$\angle B = \angle E$
$\angle C = \angle F$

↑
This symbol means "is similar to".

Property II  Corresponding pairs of sides are proportional.

$\triangle ABC \sim \triangle DEF$  $\dfrac{AB}{DE} = \dfrac{AC}{DF} = \dfrac{BC}{EF}$

You can use the following two postulates about similar triangles to solve problems.

- If the corresponding angles of two triangles are equal then the triangles are similar.

| If you know | then you know | This means |
|---|---|---|
| For $\triangle ABC$ and $\triangle DEF$ | | For $\triangle ABC$ and $\triangle DEF$, |
| $\angle A = \angle D$ <br> $\angle B = \angle E$ <br> $\angle C = \angle F$ | $\triangle ABC \sim \triangle DEF$ | $\dfrac{AB}{DE} = \dfrac{AC}{DF} = \dfrac{BC}{EF}$ |

- If the corresponding sides of two triangles are proportional, then the triangles are similar.

| If you know | then you know | This means |
|---|---|---|
| For $\triangle ABC$ and $\triangle DEF$ | | For $\triangle ABC$ and $\triangle DEF$ |
| $\dfrac{AB}{DE} = \dfrac{AC}{DF} = \dfrac{BC}{EF}$ | $\triangle ABC \sim \triangle DEF$ | $\angle A = \angle D$ <br> $\angle B = \angle E$ <br> $\angle C = \angle F$ |

**Example**  Find the missing measures.

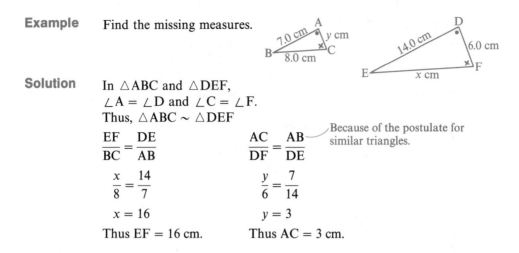

**Solution**  In △ABC and △DEF,
∠A = ∠D and ∠C = ∠F.
Thus, △ABC ~ △DEF

$$\frac{EF}{BC} = \frac{DE}{AB}$$   $$\frac{AC}{DF} = \frac{AB}{DE}$$

Because of the postulate for similar triangles.

$$\frac{x}{8} = \frac{14}{7}$$   $$\frac{y}{6} = \frac{7}{14}$$

$$x = 16$$   $$y = 3$$

Thus EF = 16 cm.   Thus AC = 3 cm.

You use your earlier skills in geometry to solve problems about similar triangles.
- Record the given information on a diagram.
- Plan your solution by recording other facts on the diagram.
- Write a concluding statement to answer the question.

**PSP**

## 12.1 Exercise

**A** Remember: Sketch a diagram and record the given information.

1  Which triangles are similar? Why?

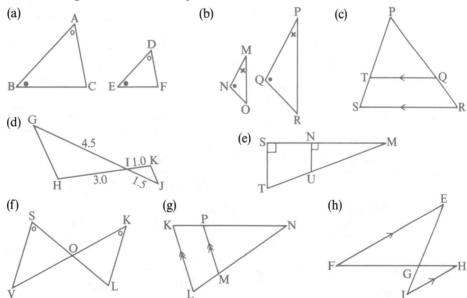

2   Complete the following.

(a) If △PQR ~ △ABC then (i) side PQ is proportional to ?.
(ii) side QR is proportional to ?.
(iii) side RP is proportional to ?.

(b) If △DEF ~ △STU then (i) ∠D = ?    (ii) ∠E = ?    (iii) ∠F = ?

3   Find the missing information.

| If you know | then you know |
|---|---|
| (a) △STU ~ △ABC | ? |
| (b) △PQR ~ △VXW | ? |

4   Find the missing measures in each triangle.

(a) △ABC ~ △DEF                    (b) △STV ~ △MNP

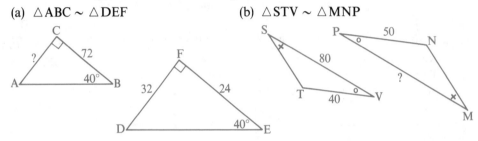

5   In △ADC and △BAC, AC = 10, DC = 8, and AD = 6.

(a) Why is △ADC ~ △BAC?

(b) Find AB.

(c) Find BC.

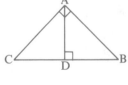

6   Refer to the diagram.
ST ∥ QR, PQ = 8, PS = 7, PT = 4.

(a) Which triangles are similar?
Give reasons for your answer.

(b) Find TR.

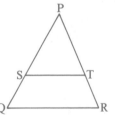

B   Remember: To find the missing measures,
you need to identify similar triangles.

7   Refer to the diagram.

(a) Which triangles are similar?
Give reasons for your answer.

(b) Why is $\frac{p}{90} = \frac{16}{24}$? Find the
value of p.

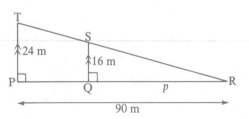

**8** Refer to the diagram.

(a) Which triangles are similar?
Give reasons for your answer.

(b) Find the value of *s*.

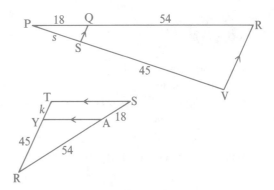

**9** Refer to the diagram.

(a) Which triangles are similar?

(b) Why is $\dfrac{k + 45}{45} = \dfrac{72}{54}$?

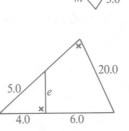

**10** Find the missing measures.

(a)

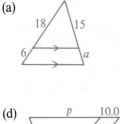

(b)

(c)

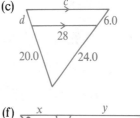

(d)

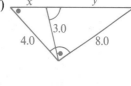

(e)

(f)

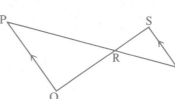

**11** For the diagram given
QR = 18.4, RS = 8.1, ST = 4.3.
Find the measure of PQ to
1 decimal place.

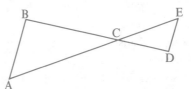

**C 12** For each diagram,
- record the given information on a sketch of your own.
- find the missing measures.

(a) PT = 13.6 cm,
TS = 18.6 cm,
QR = 10.8 cm,
PQ ‖ TR.
Find QS.

(b) AB ⊥ BD, DE ⊥ BD, DE = 18.6 cm,
CD = 28.8 cm, BC = 55.5 cm. Find AB.

The properties of similar triangles can be used to solve problems. Refer to the *Problem-Solving Plan* to organize your work.

You would not use a tape measure to measure directly the height of a tree or the height of a tower. Instead you would find each height by using indirect measures, as shown in the following example.

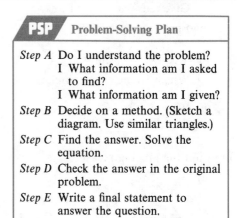

**PSP** | **Problem-Solving Plan**

*Step A* Do I understand the problem?
    I What information am I asked to find?
    I What information am I given?

*Step B* Decide on a method. (Sketch a diagram. Use similar triangles.)

*Step C* Find the answer. Solve the equation.

*Step D* Check the answer in the original problem.

*Step E* Write a final statement to answer the question.

**Example**    On a sunny day, a tree casts a shadow, 36.0 m long, while a person, 1.7 m in height, casts a shadow 4.0 m long. Calculate the height of the tree, to the nearest metre.

**Solution**    Let $h$, in metres, represent the height of the tree.

    Think: Draw a diagram to show the given information.

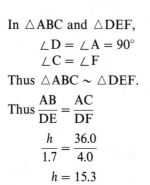

In $\triangle ABC$ and $\triangle DEF$,
$$\angle D = \angle A = 90°$$
$$\angle C = \angle F$$
Thus $\triangle ABC \sim \triangle DEF$.

Thus $\dfrac{AB}{DE} = \dfrac{AC}{DF}$

$$\frac{h}{1.7} = \frac{36.0}{4.0}$$

$$h = 15.3$$

The angles at which the sun's rays strike the ground are equal. $\angle C = \angle F$. (Property of similar triangles)

Thus, the height of the tree is 15 m to the nearest metre.

Be sure to make a final statement.

To solve problems involving indirect measurement, you will combine various skills.

- You will use your skills in solving equations
- You will use your skills in similar triangles.
- You will refer to the *Problem-Solving Plan* to plan your solution.

## 12.2 Exercise

**A** Express the answer to each problem to the accuracy given in the problem.

1 In order to find the height, DE, of a tower, the measurements shown at the right were made.

(a) Which triangles are similar?

(b) Write an equation to find $x$.

(c) How tall is the tower?

2 To calculate the length, WE, of a pond the measurements shown at the right were taken.

(a) Which triangles are similar?

(b) Write an equation to find $d$.

(c) How long is the pond?

3 To find the width, AB, of a river the following measurements were made.

(a) Which triangles are similar?

(b) Write an equation to find $w$.

(c) How wide is the river?

4 To calculate the height, AB, of the pole, a scale diagram was drawn.

(a) Why is $\triangle DEF \sim \triangle ABC$?

(b) If BC = 24.0 m, DE = 4.2 cm, EF = 2.4 cm, find the height, $h$.

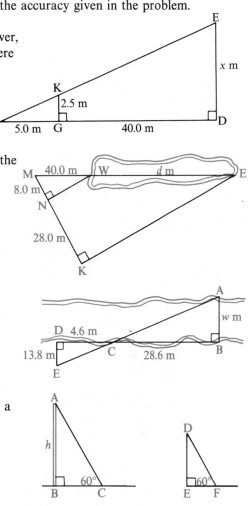

**B** Remember: Plan your solution. Refer to the *Problem-Solving Plan* to help you.    PSP

5 To find the length of a pond, the following measurements were made. How long is the pond?

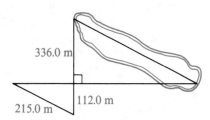

6   To find the length of a small lake the
    following measurements were made. How
    long is the lake?

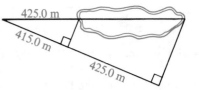

7   To find the width of a strait, the following
    measurements were made. Find the width of
    the strait.

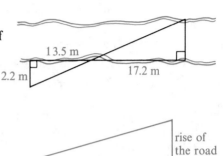

8   The following terms are used, not only in
    analytic geometry but also in road
    construction. A mountain road rises 4.3 m
    for every 18.2 m of run. Calculate the rise
    of the road for a run of 1.0 km.

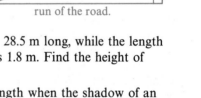

9   (a) On a sunny day, the shadow of a tower is 28.5 m long, while the length
        of the shadow of a pole, 2.3 m in height, is 1.8 m. Find the height of
        the tower.

    (b) The shadow of a metre stick is 1.8 m in length when the shadow of an
        apartment building is 106.0 m. Calculate the height of the apartment
        building.

    (c) A ski tow rises 36.0 m for a run of 100.0 m. How far would you have
        risen after 40.0 m of run?

10  The following procedure can be used to calculate the height of a building
    or a tree. A mirror is placed
    on the ground so that the reflection
    of the top of the building is seen.

    (a) Which triangles are similar?

    (b) Use the measures in the diagram.
        Calculate the height of the building.

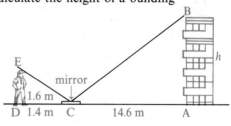

11  At eye level, 1.5 m above the ground, it is possible to see the top of a
    building just over the top of a tree when standing 20.0 m from the tree. If
    the tree is 11.5 m tall and the building is 66.5 m tall, how far is the
    building from the viewpoint?

C 12  (a) A plane climbs 30.0 m for every 100.0 m of run. If the speed of the
          plane is 225.0 km/h, find how high the plane will be in 6.0 s.

      (b) What assumption do you make in finding your answer in (a)?

## 12.3 **PSP** Problem-Solving: What If . . . ?

Many important developments in
mathematics are the result of a person
attempting to answer the question "What
if . . . ?" For example, to solve a problem
using similar triangles, you need to obtain
at least 3 measurements. What if you are
not able to obtain one of the measurements?
What if the diagram of the similar triangles
that you construct to determine a
measurement, places one of the vertices in
the middle of a swamp?

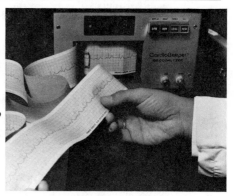

In the exercise, you will develop some important properties of special
similar triangles. Those special similar triangles are ones with right angles.
The useful mathematics that will result from your work will allow you to
calculate an indirect measurement without needing to work in a swamp.

These special words refer to the sides
of a right triangle. Side BC is said to
be adjacent to ∠B. Side AC is said to
be opposite to ∠B.

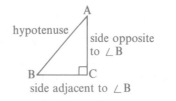

## 12.3 Exercise

**B** When you are exploring the properties of similar triangles,
construct accurate diagrams.

1 Refer to the diagram.

(a) Which triangles are similar?

(b) Measure the sides of △QRS
to 1 tenth of a centimetre.

(c) Measure the sides of △PRT
to 1 tenth of a centimetre.

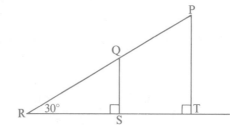

(d) Find the missing values in the
table. Round your answer to
2 decimal places.

What do you notice about the
values?

| | | | |
|---|---|---|---|
| △QRS | $\dfrac{QS}{RS} = ?$ | $\dfrac{QS}{QR} = ?$ | $\dfrac{RS}{QR} = ?$ |
| △PRT | $\dfrac{PT}{RT} = ?$ | $\dfrac{PT}{PR} = ?$ | $\dfrac{RT}{PR} = ?$ |

2   Calculate the following ratios for
    △ABC. Round your answers
    to 2 decimal places.

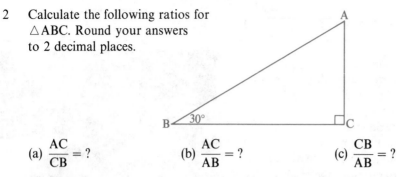

(a) $\dfrac{AC}{CB} = ?$     (b) $\dfrac{AC}{AB} = ?$     (c) $\dfrac{CB}{AB} = ?$

(d) How do your answers compare to those in Question 1?

3   In △DEF, ∠E = 30°. In △PQR, ∠Q = 30°.

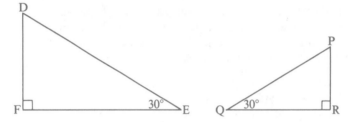

(a) Measure the sides to 1 tenth of a centimetre.

(b) Complete the table. Round your calculations to 2 decimal places.

|  | $\dfrac{\text{opposite side to } 30°}{\text{adjacent side to } 30°} = ?$ | $\dfrac{\text{opposite side to } 30°}{\text{hypotenuse}} = ?$ | $\dfrac{\text{adjacent side to } 30°}{\text{hypotenuse}} = ?$ |
|---|---|---|---|
| △DEF | | | |
| △PQR | $\dfrac{\text{opposite side to } 30°}{\text{adjacent side to } 30°} = ?$ | $\dfrac{\text{opposite side to } 30°}{\text{hypotenuse}} = ?$ | $\dfrac{\text{adjacent side to } 30°}{\text{hypotenuse}} = ?$ |

(c) How do your answers in (b) compare to those in Questions 1 and 2?

4   For △DEF, the values $t$, $s$, and $c$ are defined.

$$t = \frac{\text{measure of side opposite } \angle F}{\text{measure of side adjacent to } \angle F}$$

$$s = \frac{\text{measure of side opposite } \angle F}{\text{measure of hypotenuse}}$$

$$c = \frac{\text{measure of side adjacent to } \angle F}{\text{measure of hypotenuse}}$$

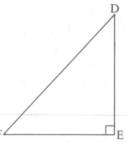

For ∠F = 30°, what are the following values
expressed to 2 decimal places?

(a) $t = ?$     (b) $s = ?$     (c) $c = ?$

5 **Step 1** Construct the triangle for each sketch. Measure each side to 1 tenth of a centimetre.

**Step 2** Calculate the values of $t$, $s$, and $c$ to 2 decimal places.

**Step 3** Record your answers in the chart.

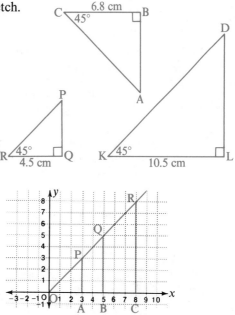

|  | value of $t$ | value of $s$ | value of $c$ |
|---|---|---|---|
| △PQR | ? | ? | ? |
| △ABC | ? | ? | ? |
| △DKL | ? | ? | ? |

6 Refer to the diagram.
Copy and complete the chart for ∠O.

|  | value of $t$ | value of $s$ | value of $c$ |
|---|---|---|---|
| △OPA | ? | ? | ? |
| △OQB | ? | ? | ? |
| △ORC | ? | ? | ? |

7 Use the steps in Question 5 to complete the following table. You need to construct at least 1 triangle containing the angle measure, for each angle.

Copy and complete the chart. Express your answers to 2 decimal places.

| angle measure | value of $t$ | value of $s$ | value of $c$ |
|---|---|---|---|
| 10° | ? | ? | ? |
| 15° | ? | ? | ? |
| 20° | ? | ? | ? |
| 25° | ? | ? | ? |
| 30° | ? | ? | ? |
| 35° | ? | ? | ? |
| 40° | ? | ? | ? |
| 45° | ? | ? | ? |

| angle measure | value of $t$ | value of $s$ | value of $c$ |
|---|---|---|---|
| 50° | ? | ? | ? |
| 55° | ? | ? | ? |
| 60° | ? | ? | ? |
| 65° | ? | ? | ? |
| 70° | ? | ? | ? |
| 75° | ? | ? | ? |
| 80° | ? | ? | ? |
| 85° | ? | ? | ? |

## Problem-Solving  `PSP`

To solve some problems, you often need to experiment to find a pattern. Try this problem.

Line segment AB is chosen as the hypotenuse of a right triangle. Two possible triangles are drawn with $P_1$ and $P_2$ at the right angle.

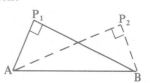

If other vertices $P_3$, $P_4$, etc are chosen, what pattern do you see? Can you describe the path of all vertices $P_1$, $P_2$, $P_3$, etc?

## 12.4 Process of Mathematics: Tangent of an Angle

In the previous section, you found the values for $t$ for different angles in a right triangle. Thus,

for $\angle B$, $t = \dfrac{\text{measure of opposite side}}{\text{measure of adjacent side}}$

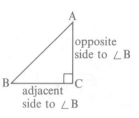

opposite side to $\angle B$

adjacent side to $\angle B$

Thus, for an angle of 30° of any right triangle, you found that the corresponding value of $t$ did not change. Thus, $t = 0.58$ to 2 decimal places.

The table you completed for values of $t$ provides an important strategy for calculating distances.

| measure of $\angle B$ | 10° | 15° | 20° | 25° | 30° | 35° | 40° | 45° | 50° | 55° | 60° | 65° | 70° | 75° | 80° |
|---|---|---|---|---|---|---|---|---|---|---|---|---|---|---|---|
| corresponding value of $t$ | 0.18 | 0.27 | 0.36 | 0.47 | 0.58 | 0.70 | 0.84 | 1.00 | 1.19 | 1.42 | 1.73 | 2.14 | 2.74 | 3.73 | 5.67 |

To calculate the height of a tree you need only make two measurements.

Measure one angle.          Measure one side.
$\angle PQR = 40°$          PQ, the distance to the tree

From the diagram, $h$ is the height of the tree in metres. Use the ratio for $t$.

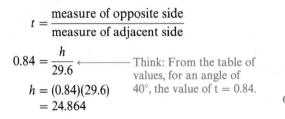

$t = \dfrac{\text{measure of opposite side}}{\text{measure of adjacent side}}$

$0.84 = \dfrac{h}{29.6}$ ⟵ Think: From the table of values, for an angle of 40°, the value of t = 0.84.

$h = (0.84)(29.6)$
$\quad = 24.864$

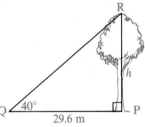

Thus, the height of the tree is 24.9 m to 1 decimal place.

While you are solving problems, you should always be asking yourself: "Is there a more efficient method of solving this problem?" In the past, the answer to this question has often resulted in the development of more useful mathematics. For example, the advantage of the method above for calculating a missing measurement is that you can base your calculation on a suitable choice of one triangle.

**PSP**

For *any* right triangle, the mathematical name given to the ratio, $t$, for an angle B, is the **tangent of angle B**. Thus,

$$\text{tangent of } \angle B = \frac{\text{measure of opposite side}}{\text{measure of adjacent side}} \qquad \tan B = \frac{\text{opposite side}}{\text{adjacent side}}$$

The definition of the tangent is always the same no matter the position of $\angle B$. You need only identify the adjacent and opposite sides with respect to $\angle B$.

## 12.4 Exercise

**A** Review the meaning of *opposite side*, *adjacent side*, and *hypotenuse*, for a right triangle.

1   To find $h$ in the diagram, 2 measures are given.

$$\tan S = \frac{\text{opposite side}}{\text{adjacent side}}$$

(a) Write an equation to find $h$.

(b) What is the value of $h$, to 1 decimal place?

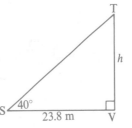

2   From the table of values, $\tan 25° = 0.47$. Calculate the height, $h$, of the balloon in the diagram.

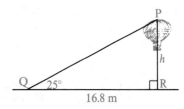

3   For each triangle, the tangent value is given for the measured angle. Calculate the value of $d$, to 1 decimal place.

(a) $\tan 35° = 0.70$      (b) $\tan 75° = 3.73$      (c) $\tan 60° = 1.73$

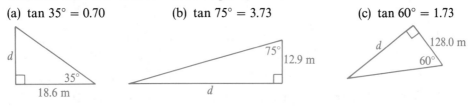

**B** For each of the following questions, the values of the tangent for each given angle occur in the table of values for $t$.

4   On a sunny day, the sun's rays meet the ground at an angle of 35°. A pole casts a shadow 21.3 m in length. Use the diagram to calculate the height of the pole.

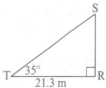

5   From a boat, 350.0 m from the base of an
    iceberg, measurements are taken of the tip
    of the iceberg. Use the diagram. Calculate
    the height of the iceberg.

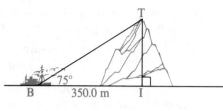

6   To measure the width of a gravel pit,
    measurements are made and recorded on a
    diagram. Calculate the width, AB, of the
    gravel pit.

7   A sighting is made of the top of a tree.
    The distance from the tree is 23.2 m.
    Find the height of the tree.

8   An airplane takes off at an angle of 15° with the ground. If the plane
    continues along its take-off path, how high will it be when the distance
    measured along the ground is 1.8 km?

9   A ladder is placed against a wall,
    making an angle of 20° with the wall. If
    TA = 8.5 m, how far is the base of the
    ladder from the wall?

PSP   10   (a) If EXERCISE has a value of 128, then what value would FITNESS have?
           (b) Goats and chickens are in a yard. If there are 60 eyes and 88 feet,
               then how many of each animal are there? List any assumptions you make
               in answering this question.
           (c) How would you measure exactly 5 L of water if the only containers you have
               are a 4-L and a 7-L container?

C  11   The length of a string for a kite is 320.0 m. The angle that the kite string
        makes with the ground is 60°. How high is the kite?

# 12.5 Concepts of Trigonometry

In your previous work with a right triangle, certain names were given to its sides. By using the measures of one side and one angle of a right triangle, and by using the meaning of the tangent of an angle, you used the values of the tangent to solve certain problems.

$$\text{tangent of } \angle A = \frac{\text{side opposite } \angle A}{\text{side adjacent to } \angle A}$$

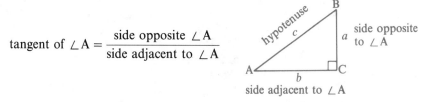

To obtain a method of solving any problem involving finding measures, other ratios for a right triangle are introduced. These ratios are the primary ratios of trigonometry.

| *Ratio* | *Abbreviation* |
|---|---|
| sine of $\angle A = \dfrac{\text{side opposite } \angle A}{\text{hypotenuse}}$ | sin A |
| cosine of $\angle A = \dfrac{\text{side adjacent to } \angle A}{\text{hypotenuse}}$ | cos A |
| tangent of $\angle A = \dfrac{\text{side opposite } \angle A}{\text{side adjacent to } \angle A}$ | tan A |

**Example 1**    Find the primary trigonometric ratios of $\angle A$ and $\angle B$ of $\triangle ABC$.

**Solution**    First find AB.   $AB^2 = 5^2 + 12^2$
$$= 25 + 144$$
$$= 169$$
Thus, $AB = 13$

Use the definitions.

$$\sin A = \frac{5}{13} \qquad \cos A = \frac{12}{13} \qquad \tan A = \frac{5}{12}$$

$$\sin B = \frac{12}{13} \qquad \cos B = \frac{5}{13} \qquad \tan B = \frac{12}{5}$$

The trigonometry that you will use is based on the measures of sides and angles of triangles. The word trigonometry is derived from the following words.

| tri | gono | metry |
|---|---|---|
| three | angle | measurement |

If you are given one of the trigonometric ratios, you can find the other ratios, as shown in Example 2.

**Example 2**    In $\triangle PQR$, $\angle R = 90°$ and $\cos Q = \frac{7}{25}$. Find sin Q and tan P.

**Solution**    Show the information in a diagram. **PSP**    Think: Since $\cos Q = \frac{7}{25}$ then QR = 7 and PQ = 25.

$$PR^2 + QR^2 = QP^2$$
$$x^2 + 7^2 = 25^2$$
$$x^2 = 625 - 49$$
$$= 576$$
$$x = 24 \text{ (Since RP is a measure, } x \text{ is positive.)}$$

$$\sin Q = \frac{PR}{QP} = \frac{24}{25} \qquad \tan P = \frac{QR}{PR} = \frac{7}{24}$$

## 12.5 Exercise

**A** Express trigonometric ratios in radical form except where otherwise indicated.

1   Calculate the tan of each angle.
    (a) $\angle POV$    (b) $\angle QOT$    (c) $\angle ROS$
    Why should your answers in (a) to (c) be equal?

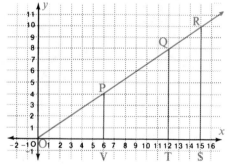

2   (a) Calculate the lengths of OP, OQ, OR.
    (b) Use the values in (a) to find the cosine of $\angle POV$, $\angle QOT$, $\angle ROS$.
    (c) Why should your answers in (b) be equal?

3   Find the primary trigonometric ratios of $\angle M$.
    (a)    (b)    (c)    (d)

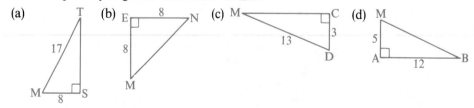

**4**  Find the value of tan A.

(a)

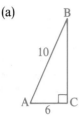

(b)

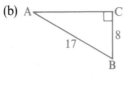

(c)

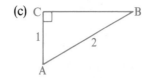

**5**  A triangle is given by the information:

$\angle P = 90°$      QP = 8      RP = 3

(a) Draw the triangle.      (b) Find cos Q and sin R.

**6**  For each of the following
- draw a triangle. Record the given information.
- then, answer the question.

(a) In $\triangle$PQR, $\angle Q = 90°$, PQ = 12, QR = 5. Find cos R.

(b) In $\triangle$STU, $\angle U = 90°$, TU = 2, ST = 4. Find sin T.

(c) In $\triangle$RAK, $\angle A = 90°$, RK = 10, AR = 6. Find tan R.

(d) In $\triangle$STU, $\angle U = 90°$, UT = 7, ST = 10. Find cos S.

**7**  Find each trigonometric ratio. Round off your answers to 2 significant digits.

(a) sin 40°      (b) cos 40°      (c) tan 50°

**8**  Find each trigonometric ratio. Round off your answers to 2 significant digits.

(a) cos 65°      (b) tan 65°      (c) tan 25°

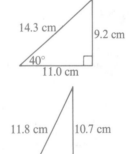

**B**  In your previous work, you have, by measurement, calculated the values of $s$, the sine of an angle, and $c$, the cosine of an angle. In the following questions, these values are used to solve problems.

**9**  A diagram is used to find the height, $h$, of a kite.

(a) When is $\dfrac{h}{128.0} = \sin 65°$?

(b) Use sin 65° = 0.91. Find the value of $h$.

(c) How high is the kite?

10    A guy-wire, AB, in the diagram, is 23.6 m
      in length.

      (a) When is $\dfrac{h}{\text{AB}} = \cos 60°$?

      (b) Use the equation in (a).
          Find the value of $h$.

      (c) How far from the base of the tower is the guy-wire attached?

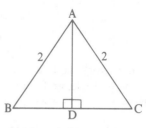

11    In each diagram, find the missing value, $d$. Use the given value of the
      trigonometric ratio.

      (a)  $\tan 70° = 2.7$          (b)  $\sin 25° = 0.42$          (c)  $\cos 65° = 0.42$

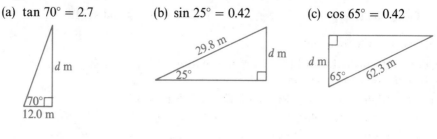

12    For $\triangle$DEF, DE $= 1$ unit.

      (a) Why is EF $= 1$ unit?

      (b) Why is DF $= \sqrt{2}$ units?

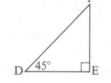

13    Use Question 12 to find each ratio.

      (a)  $\sin 45°$               (b)  $\cos 45°$                     (c)  $\tan 45°$

14    $\triangle$ABC is equilateral with sides 2 units in length and AD $\perp$ BC.

      (a) Show BD $=$ DC.

      (b) Find the length of AD as a radical.

      (c) Why is $\cos 60° = \frac{1}{2}$?

15    Use Question 14. Find each ratio.

      (a)  $\sin 60°$   (b)  $\cos 60°$   (c)  $\tan 60°$

      (d)  $\sin 30°$   (e)  $\cos 30°$   (f)  $\tan 30°$

C 16   Calculate each of the following.

      (a)  $\sin 45° + \cos 45°$                     (b)  $(\cos 60°)(\sin 30°)$

      (c)  $(\tan 30°)(\cos 45°)$                    (d)  $\sin^2 45°$   or $(\sin 45°)(\sin 45°)$

      (e)  $(\sin 45°)(\cos 45°) - \sin^2 60°$       (f)  $\sin^2 45° + \cos^2 45°$

# 12.6 Trigonometric Values

Earlier you used measured values to calculate values of the tangent, sine, and cosine of an angle. To obtain more accurate answers, the values shown in the chart are expressed correct to 4 decimal places. Computers have used advanced formulas to generate the values in the chart.

## Example 1

What are the value of each of the following?

(a) sin 67°    (b) cos 29°

(c) tan 78°    (d) sin 13°

(e) cos 63°    (f) tan 18°

## Solution

(a) sin 67° = 0.9205

(b) cos 29° = 0.8746

(c) tan 78° = 4.7046

(d) sin 13° = 0.2250

(e) cos 63° = 0.4540

(f) tan 18° = 0.3249

A calculator is a useful device. You can use it to obtain trigonometric values. For example, to find sin 69°, you follow the steps shown. Since calculators vary, refer to

**Table of Trigonometric Values**

| ∠A degrees | sin A | cos A | tan A | ∠A degrees | sin A | cos A | tan A |
|---|---|---|---|---|---|---|---|
| 1 | 0.0175 | 0.9998 | 0.0175 | 46 | 0.7193 | 0.6947 | 1.0355 |
| 2 | 0.0349 | 0.9994 | 0.0349 | 47 | 0.7314 | 0.6820 | 1.0724 |
| 3 | 0.0523 | 0.9986 | 0.0524 | 48 | 0.7431 | 0.6691 | 1.1106 |
| 4 | 0.0698 | 0.9976 | 0.0699 | 49 | 0.7547 | 0.6561 | 1.1504 |
| 5 | 0.0872 | 0.9962 | 0.0875 | 50 | 0.7660 | 0.6428 | 1.1918 |
| 6 | 0.1045 | 0.9945 | 0.1051 | 51 | 0.7771 | 0.6293 | 1.2349 |
| 7 | 0.1219 | 0.9925 | 0.1228 | 52 | 0.7880 | 0.6157 | 1.2799 |
| 8 | 0.1392 | 0.9903 | 0.1405 | 53 | 0.7986 | 0.6018 | 1.3270 |
| 9 | 0.1564 | 0.9877 | 0.1584 | 54 | 0.8090 | 0.5878 | 1.3764 |
| 10 | 0.1736 | 0.9848 | 0.1763 | 55 | 0.8192 | 0.5736 | 1.4281 |
| 11 | 0.1908 | 0.9816 | 0.1944 | 56 | 0.8290 | 0.5592 | 1.4826 |
| 12 | 0.2079 | 0.9781 | 0.2126 | 57 | 0.8387 | 0.5446 | 1.5399 |
| 13 | 0.2250 | 0.9744 | 0.2309 | 58 | 0.8480 | 0.5299 | 1,6003 |
| 14 | 0.2419 | 0.9703 | 0.2493 | 59 | 0.8572 | 0.5150 | 1.6643 |
| 15 | 0.2588 | 0.9659 | 0.2679 | 60 | 0.8660 | 0.5000 | 1.7321 |
| 16 | 0.2756 | 0.9613 | 0.2867 | 61 | 0.8746 | 0.4848 | 1.8040 |
| 17 | 0.2924 | 0.9563 | 0.3057 | 62 | 0.8829 | 0.4695 | 1.8807 |
| 18 | 0.3090 | 0.9511 | 0.3249 | 63 | 0.8910 | 0.4540 | 1.9626 |
| 19 | 0.3256 | 0.9455 | 0.3443 | 64 | 0.8988 | 0.4384 | 2.0503 |
| 20 | 0.3420 | 0.9397 | 0.3640 | 65 | 0.9063 | 0.4226 | 2.1445 |
| 21 | 0.3584 | 0.9336 | 0.3839 | 66 | 0.9135 | 0.4067 | 2.2460 |
| 22 | 0.3746 | 0.9272 | 0.4040 | 67 | 0.9205 | 0.3907 | 2.3559 |
| 23 | 0.3907 | 0.9205 | 0.4245 | 68 | 0.9272 | 0.3746 | 2.4751 |
| 24 | 0.4067 | 0.9135 | 0.4452 | 69 | 0.9336 | 0.3584 | 2.6051 |
| 25 | 0.4226 | 0.9063 | 0.4663 | 70 | 0.9397 | 0.3420 | 2.7475 |
| 26 | 0.4384 | 0.8988 | 0.4877 | 71 | 0.9455 | 0.3256 | 2.9042 |
| 27 | 0.4540 | 0.8910 | 0.5095 | 72 | 0.9511 | 0.3090 | 3.0777 |
| 28 | 0.4695 | 0.8829 | 0.5317 | 73 | 0.9563 | 0.2924 | 3.2709 |
| 29 | 0.4848 | 0.8746 | 0.5543 | 74 | 0.9613 | 0.2756 | 3.4874 |
| 30 | 0.5000 | 0.8660 | 0.5774 | 75 | 0.9659 | 0.2588 | 3.7321 |
| 31 | 0.5150 | 0.8572 | 0.6009 | 76 | 0.9703 | 0.2419 | 4.0108 |
| 32 | 0.5299 | 0.8480 | 0.6249 | 77 | 0.9744 | 0.2250 | 4.3315 |
| 33 | 0.5446 | 0.8387 | 0.6494 | 78 | 0.9781 | 0.2079 | 4.7046 |
| 34 | 0.5592 | 0.8290 | 0.6745 | 79 | 0.9816 | 0.1908 | 5.1446 |
| 35 | 0.5736 | 0.8192 | 0.7002 | 80 | 0.9848 | 0.1736 | 5.6713 |
| 36 | 0.5878 | 0.8090 | 0.7265 | 81 | 0.9877 | 0.1564 | 6.3138 |
| 37 | 0.6018 | 0.7986 | 0.7536 | 82 | 0.9903 | 0.1392 | 7.1154 |
| 38 | 0.6157 | 0.7880 | 0.7813 | 83 | 0.9925 | 0.1219 | 8.1443 |
| 39 | 0.6293 | 0.7771 | 0.8098 | 84 | 0.9945 | 0.1045 | 9.5144 |
| 40 | 0.6428 | 0.7660 | 0.8391 | 85 | 0.9962 | 0.0872 | 11.4301 |
| 41 | 0.6561 | 0.7547 | 0.8693 | 86 | 0.9976 | 0.0698 | 14.3007 |
| 42 | 0.6691 | 0.7431 | 0.9004 | 87 | 0.9986 | 0.0523 | 19.0811 |
| 43 | 0.6820 | 0.7314 | 0.9325 | 88 | 0.9994 | 0.0349 | 28.6363 |
| 44 | 0.6947 | 0.7193 | 0.9657 | 89 | 0.9998 | 0.0175 | 57.2900 |
| 45 | 0.7071 | 0.7071 | 1.0000 | 90 | 1.0000 | 0 | Not defined |

the manual provided with the calculator. Be sure that the calculator is in the degree mode.

output

| CE/C | 69 | SIN | 0.9335804

Thus, sin 69° = 0.9335804 (to the accuracy provided by the calculator).

Once you decide the trigonometric value from a calculator, you need to decide how many decimal places you need in a problem to do the calculation. You can also use the process above in reverse. If you are given a tangent, sine, or cosine value, you can determine the angle, as shown in the following

sin A = 0.5736        tan K = 2.4751        cos C = 0.6428        Think: Refer to the
                                                                 values in the table.
∠A = 35°              ∠K = 68°              ∠C = 50°

You can use a calculator to find the angle if you are given the values of any trigonometric ratio.

         Find the angle              Calculator procedure

                                                               Output

     Find ∠B if cos B = 0.7314      | CE/C | 0.7314 | INV | COS | 42.99611

                                     ∠B = 43°, rounded to the nearest degree.

To find the measures of the angle in a right triangle, all you need to know are the measures of two sides, as shown in the next example.

**Example 2**   Use the information on the diagram.
               Find the measure of ∠P and of ∠Q.

**Solution**    In △PQR, tan P = $\dfrac{23}{37}$

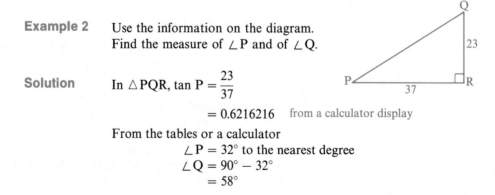

                          = 0.6216216    from a calculator display

               From the tables or a calculator
                          ∠P = 32° to the nearest degree
                          ∠Q = 90° − 32°
                             = 58°

To do the calculations in the previous solution on a calculator, try these steps.

                                            Output

| CE/C | 23 | ÷ | 37 | = | INV | TAN | 31.865978.    ∠P = 32° to the nearest degree.

## 12.6 Exercise

**A** Refer to the table of trigonometric values or use a calculator. Express angles to the nearest degree.

1 Find the value of each trigonometric ratio.
   (a) cos 42°    (b) sin 36°    (c) cos 24°    (d) tan 76°    (e) sin 58°
   (f) tan 36°    (g) sin 12°    (h) cos 48°    (i) tan 18°    (j) tan 58°

2 Which is greater in value?
   (a) sin 36° or cos 36°    (b) cos 72° or sin 72°    (c) sin 86° or tan 86°

3 (a) Use a calculator. Find the sine of 15°, 20°, 37°, 42°, 71° and 86°.
   (b) Round your answers in (a) to 4 decimal places. Compare your answers to those in the trigonometric tables.

4 (a) Use a calculator. Find the cosine of 9°, 12°, 27°, 39°, 45°, 63° and 72°.
   (b) Round your answers in (a) to 4 decimal places. Compare your answers to those in the trigonometric tables.

5 (a) Find sin A for these angles: ∠A = 17°, 27°, 36°, 45°, 53°, 69°.
   (b) How do the values of sin A change as ∠A increases?

6 (a) Find cos A for these angles: ∠A = 15°, 20°, 35°, 45°, 60°, 72°.
   (b) How do the values of cos A change as ∠A increases?

7 (a) Find tan A for these angles: ∠A = 8°, 23°, 35°, 49°, 61°, 76°.
   (b) How do the values of tan A change as ∠A increases?

8 Refer to the tables, or use a calculator. Find each angle.
   (a) sin A = 0.7193    (b) cos P = 0.5150    (c) tan Q = 0.7265
   (d) cos U = 0.8090    (e) sin B = 0.7986    (f) tan R = 2.9042

**B** When necessary, express angles to the nearest degree and lengths to 1 decimal place.

9 Find the measures of ∠P and ∠Q in each of the following.
   (a)
   (b)
   (c)

10 Find the missing length of each triangle. All measures are expressed in metres.

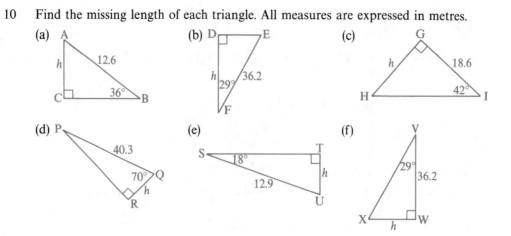

(a) A — 12.6, h, 36°, C, B

(b) D — E, h, 29°, 36.2, F

(c) G, h, 18.6, H, 42°, I

(d) P, 40.3, 70° Q, h, R

(e) S, 18°, T, h, 12.9, U

(f) V, 29°, 36.2, X, h, W

11 A sighting is made of the cloud shown in the diagram. Calculate the height of the cloud.

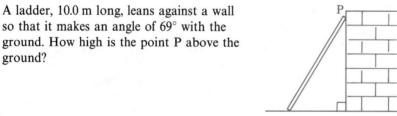

41°
1.6 km

12 Refer to the data given in the diagram. Find the height of the tree.

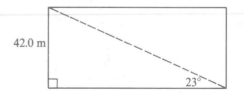

63°
21.6 m

13 A ladder, 10.0 m long, leans against a wall so that it makes an angle of 69° with the ground. How high is the point P above the ground?

C 14 Use the information in the diagram to calculate the area of the rectangle.

42.0 m

23°

# 12.7 Using Trigonometry: Problem-Solving

The process of solving problems in trigonometry involves principles similar to those needed to solve problems in any branch of mathematics. For example, you must know the answers to these two important questions, before you can solve any problem.

I What information am I asked to find?

II What information do I know?

You have already used the *Problem-Solving Plan*. To solve problems in trigonometry you also need to organize your solution. The missing parts of the chart are the skills you have learned about trigonometry.

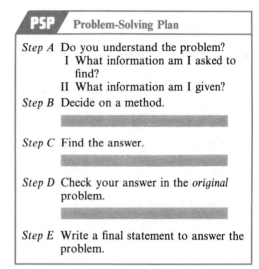

**PSP** / **Problem-Solving Plan**

*Step A* Do you understand the problem?
  I What information am I asked to find?
  II What information am I given?

*Step B* Decide on a method.

*Step C* Find the answer.

*Step D* Check your answer in the *original* problem.

*Step E* Write a final statement to answer the problem.

**Example**   A ladder, 9.2 m long, just reaches a second floor window. The base of the ladder is 2.3 m from the wall. Find the measure of the angle that the ladder makes with the ground, to the nearest degree.

**Solution**   From the diagram

$$\cos Q = \frac{2.3}{9.2}$$

$$= 0.25$$

Think: Sketch a diagram.
Record the given information.

From the tables or on a calculator

$$Q = 76° \text{ (to the nearest degree)}$$

Thus, the measure of the angle between the ladder and the ground is 76° (to the nearest degree).

---

# 12.7 Exercise

**A** The questions in Part A review essential skills.

1   Find the following trigonometric values.

(a) $\cos 15°$   (b) $\tan 46°$   (c) $\sin 28°$   (d) $\tan 36°$   (e) $\cos 78°$   (f) $\tan 82°$

2    Find the sine of each angle.
     (a) 15°       (b) 30°       (c) 45°       (d) 60°       (e) 75°       (f) 90°

3    Find the cosine of each angle.
     (a) 15°       (b) 30°       (c) 45°       (d) 65°       (e) 75°       (f) 90°

4    Find the measure of each angle.
     (a) sin A = 0.9135          (b) cos B = 0.8746          (c) tan D = 9.5144

5    Find each angle to the nearest degree.
     (a) cos A = 0.3842          (b) sin B = 0.2487          (c) tan P = 0.3920

6    Find the measure indicated.
     (a) a                       (b) d                       (c) ∠A

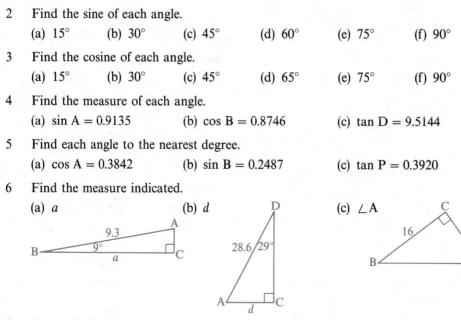

7    For each diagram,
     • decide on the trigonometric ratio you use to find h
     • find the value of h.
     (a)                         (b)                         (c)

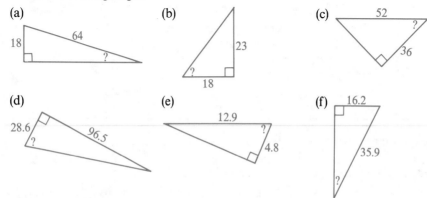

8    For each triangle,
     • decide on which trigonometric ratio you will use to find the missing
       angle
     • find the missing angle.
     (a)                         (b)                         (c)

     (d)                         (e)                         (f)

**B** Organize your solutions. Refer to the *Problem-Solving Plan.*

9  (a) Use the diagram. Find the height of the tower.

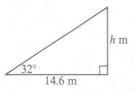

(b) Guy wires are attached to an antenna, 12.5 m high. Find the length of the guy wire, TB

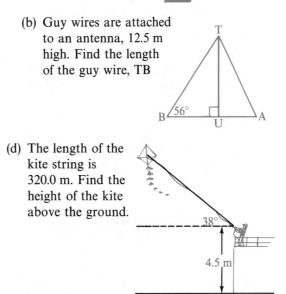

(c) Find the width in metres.

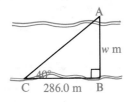

(d) The length of the kite string is 320.0 m. Find the height of the kite above the ground.

10  (a) A tree 18.0 m high casts a shadow 22.0 m long. Calculate the inclination of the sun to the horizontal at this time of day.

(b) A 10.5 m ladder is leaned against a wall, with the foot of the ladder 1.6 m from the wall. Find the angle between the ladder and the ground.

11  A monument casts a shadow that is 43.5 m. The rays of the sun strike the ground at an angle of 36°. Calculate the height of the monument.

12  A tower is supported by a guy wire 18.5 m in length and meets the ground at an angle of 59°. At what height on the tower is the guy wire attached?

13  At a construction site, the brace used to retain a wall is 9.6 m in length. The distance from the wall to the lower end of the brace (on the ground) is 5.3 m. Calculate the angle at which the brace meets the wall.

14  A mountain road drops 5.2 m for every 22.5 m of road. Calculate the angle at which the road is inclined to the horizontal.

15  These letters belong: B, C, D, E, H, ?, ?—but these do not: A, F, G, J, L, ... What are the next two letters? Give reasons for your answer.

**C** 16  A punch bowl is in the shape of a hemisphere with diameter 53.5 cm. How deep is the punch in the bowl if the punch begins to pour when the bowl is tilted 30° to the horizontal?

# 12.8 Nature of Solving Problems: Trigonometry

Sometimes you are not able to solve a problem because the words used in the problem are unfamiliar. Often, there are certain words particular to a branch of mathematics. It is essential that their meanings be understood clearly. In solving some problems in trigonometry special sightings are made. After the sighting is made, the recorded angle is used to do calculations.

The names of these sightings are often used in the instructions of a problem.

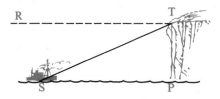

∠PST is called the **angle of elevation**.

∠RTS is called the **angle of depression**.

The angle of elevation is measured upwards from the horizontal.

The angle of depression is measured downwards from the horizontal.

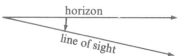

**Example**   From the top of a building, the angle of depression of a band shell is 56°. If the band shell is 86.5 m from the base of the building, what is the height of the building to the nearest metre?

**Solution**   Let $h$ represent the height of the building.
In $\triangle$PSR, ∠PRS = 56°

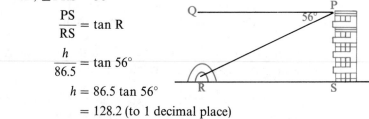

$$\frac{PS}{RS} = \tan R$$

$$\frac{h}{86.5} = \tan 56°$$

$$h = 86.5 \tan 56°$$

$$= 128.2 \text{ (to 1 decimal place)}$$

The height of the building is 128 m (to the nearest metre).

## 12.8 Exercise

**A** Review the meaning of *angle of elevation* and *angle of depression*.

1 For each diagram, find the distance *d*.

(a) Angle of elevation is 46°.

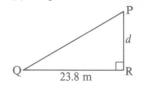

(b) Angle of depression is 53°.

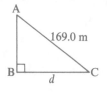

2 How high above the ground is the kite? The angle of elevation is 76°.

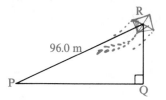

3 The angle of elevation of a glider is 28°. Use the data in the diagram to calculate the height.

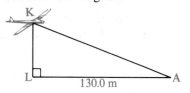

4 A sighting is made of a sailboat from a lighthouse. If the lighthouse is 123.5 m above the level of the water, how far is the sailboat from shore?

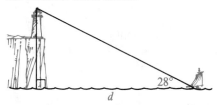

5 Use the data in the diagram. How high is the weather balloon? The angle of elevation is 59°.

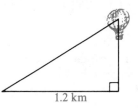

6 To calculate height, a transit is often used, as shown in the diagram. Calculate the height of the tree using the measurements on the diagram.

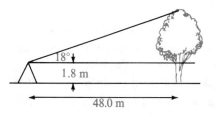

7  From the top of a building, these measurements are made of a building on the other side. Use the diagram to calculate the height of the building to the nearest metre.

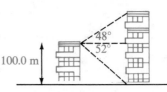

100.0 m

**B** To solve the following problems, you need to sketch a diagram. Be sure to make a final statement.   **PSP**

8  (a) The angle of elevation of the top of a tower is 27° from a point 19.0 m from its base. Calculate the height of the tower.

(b) The angle of elevation of the top of a cliff, taken from a point 126.0 m from the base of the cliff, is 36°. How high is the cliff?

9  (a) From the top of the cliff, the angle of depression of a sailboat is 32°. If the cliff is 62.0 m high, how far away is the sailboat from the base of the cliff?

(b) From a balloon, 600.0 m high, the angle of depression of a car is 52°. Calculate how far the balloon is from the car.

10  From a point 60.5 m above the ground in an airport control tower, the angle of depression to a Cessna airplane from the observer is 51°.

(a) How far is the plane from the observer in the control tower?

(b) What assumptions did you make in solving the problem?

11  An observer 185 cm tall finds the angle of elevation of the top of a cliff is 59°. If the observer is 40.8 m from the base of the cliff, find the height of the cliff.

12  By using sonar, a captain detects a school of fish at a depth of 56.6 m. If the angle of depression of the sounding is 15°, how far is the trawler from the school of fish?

13  A diagonal of a rectangle meets the longer side at an angle of 18°. If the width is 3.8 cm, find the measure of the longer side.

**C** 14  A business jet travels at a speed of 350.0 km/h, heading due South. However, the speed of the wind causes the jet's actual path to be 8° off course, towards the West.

(a) Find the actual distance travelled South after 1 h.

(b) Find the amount of the jet's drift towards the West after the hour.

# Practice and Problems: Review

1  (a) The shadow of an apartment is 32.8 m long, while the length of the shadow of a fence, 2.1 m high, is 2.9 m. Find the building's height.

   (b) By how much will the building's shadow decrease if its height decreases by 10 m?

2  A wire supports an FM antenna, and makes an angle of 35° with the flat roof. A guy-wire, GU, is attached, 10.8 m from the base, B, of the antenna. Find the height of the antenna.

3  (a) The altitude of an equilateral triangle is 27.0 cm. Calculate the lengths of the sides.

   (b) Calculate the area of each triangle.

4  (a) Calculate the length of the diagonals of a 6.5 cm by 8.6 cm rectangle.

   (b) Find the measure of the acute angle formed at the intersection of the diagonals.

# Practice Test

1  Refer to the diagram.

   (a) Which triangles are similar?

   (b) Find the length of DC.

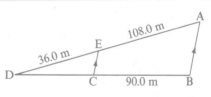

2  In △STU, ∠U = 90°, TU = 2.3, ST = 4.1. Find sin T, cos S and tan T.

3  Find each angle. (a) cos P = 0.8090   (b) tan S = 1.4826   (c) sin R = 0.3256

4  • Decide on the trigonometric ratio to find *h*.   • Find h.

   (a)   (b)   (c)

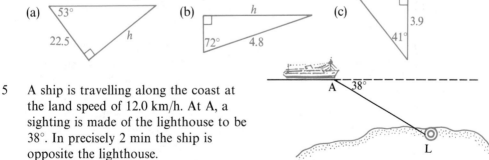

5  A ship is travelling along the coast at the land speed of 12.0 km/h. At A, a sighting is made of the lighthouse to be 38°. In precisely 2 min the ship is opposite the lighthouse.

   (a) Calculate how close the ship comes to the lighthouse.

   (b) What assumption do you make in finding your answer in (a)?

# Cumulative Review (9 to 11)

1  Prove each of the following properties.

(a) If the diagonals of a quadrilateral bisect each other, then the quadrilateral is a parallelogram.

(b) If the diagonals of a quadrilateral are right bisectors of each other then the quadrilateral is a rhombus.

(c) If the diagonals of a parallelogram bisect the angles, then it is a rhombus.

2  Use the diagram.  
Prove that BC = DC.

3  Use the diagram to prove that RT bisects the exterior ∠ QRS.

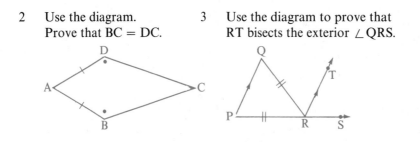

4  A commercial jet carries 221 passengers. The airline obtained a sample from the records of 75 flights of a particular jet. The data in the chart represent the number of passengers of each of those flights

| 132 | 142 | 161 | 123 | 184 | 129 | 157 | 118 | 140 | 178 | 159 | 149 | 138 | 119 | 186 |
| 175 | 183 | 173 | 197 | 169 | 191 | 174 | 165 | 198 | 180 | 182 | 159 | 191 | 154 | 221 |
| 115 | 143 | 156 | 207 | 95 | 172 | 155 | 182 | 161 | 203 | 189 | 192 | 142 | 195 | 146 |
| 185 | 167 | 104 | 184 | 176 | 160 | 164 | 170 | 206 | 173 | 124 | 214 | 137 | 200 | 175 |
| 173 | 167 | 198 | 147 | 156 | 192 | 116 | 151 | 138 | 199 | 104 | 138 | 183 | 219 | 181 |

(a) Construct a diagram to display the data. Analyze the data. What observations can you make?

(b) Create a problem based on the data. Write a solution to answer your problem.

5  When the Canada Winter Games were held in Saskatoon, a mountain had to be created. Approximately 750 000 m³ of material was used to create a conical hill for which the height was approximately equal in length to the diameter of the base.

(a) Write a formula for the volume of a cone for which the diameter of the base has the same measure as the height. Express the formula in terms of the radius of the cone.

(b) Calculate the height of the mountain in Saskatoon to the nearest ten metres.

# 13 Inventing Mathematics: Vectors and Matrices

Concept of vectors, vectors as line segments, operations with vectors, scalar products, vectors and polygons, co-ordinates and vectors, proving deductions, applications with vectors, concept of matrices, operations with matrices, inverse of a matrix, matrices and codes, strategy for solving linear systems, solving problems

## Introduction

The invention of the language of algebra had a great impact on the study of mathematics. It opened up many applications in astronomy, engineering, economics, and in many other fields such as those depicted on the stamps.

In this chapter, you will explore two other inventions in mathematics, namely, *vectors* and *matrices*. The concepts and properties of vectors and matrices you will examine have undergone an evolution since they were first introduced. The mathematician explores the properties of vectors and develops a consistent system. The scientist then uses the various properties of vectors and applies them in various fields of study, such as electricity, magnetism, and sound engineering. Today, with the flow of so much data, a study of matrices is important in the harnessing of the computer for the purposes of analyzing and interpreting the volumes of data.

> How can it be
> that mathematics being after all
> a product
> of human thought independent of experience
> is
> so admirably adapted
> to the objects of reality?

Albert Einstein

# 13.1  Vectors as Directed Line Segments

The English Channel lies between the shores of England and France, and has presented a challenge to swimmers for some time. The first person to swim the English Channel was Matthew Webb. Although the English Channel is about 34 km wide, he had to swim about 61 km. Why was this so?

An important factor that affected Matthew Webb's swim was the current in the English Channel. He had to know the *direction* of the current, as well as the speed of the current, namely, its *magnitude*.

When you swim across a body of water, the current in the water will cause you to land at D instead of A.

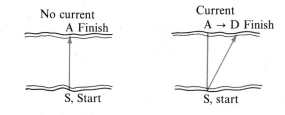

The current in the English Channel is an example of a **vector quantity**. A vector quantity has both a direction and a magnitude. Vector quantities can be represented by arrows, called **directed line segments**.

The arrow indicates the direction.
vector
A
B
The length of the line segment represents the magnitude.

The symbol $\overrightarrow{AB}$ is invented to represent the vector.

The following are other examples of vector quantities or vectors
- A wind velocity has direction and magnitude.
- Kicking a football requires a force that has direction and magnitude.
- Pushing a toboggan involves direction and magnitude.

A quantity that is indicated by magnitude only is called a **scalar quantity**. Each of the following are specified by a real number. (A magnitude only is represented.)
- the number of cars in a parking lot
- the number of persons on a basketball team
- your age
- your height

## Equal Vectors

Two scalar quantities are equal if they have the same magnitude. Two vector quantities are equal if they have the same magnitude *and* direction.

$\overrightarrow{AB}$ and $\overrightarrow{CD}$ show equal vectors.

$\vec{a}$ and $\vec{b}$ show equal vectors.

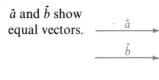

$$\overrightarrow{AB} = \overrightarrow{CD}$$

$$\vec{a} = \vec{b}$$

Vector $\overrightarrow{AB}$ is drawn on a grid.

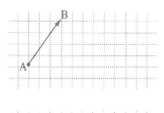

|  PSP | To solve the problem you must know the meaning of words. |

It has a *horizontal component*, 3 units, and a *vertical component*, 4 units.

The following symbol is used to represent the vector $\overrightarrow{AB}$ in component form.

$$\overrightarrow{AB} = [3, 4]$$

horizontal ⎣— vertical
component    component

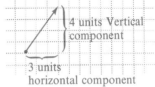

When expressed in component form, two vectors $[a, b]$ and $[c, d]$ are equal if and only if, $a = c$ and $b = d$.

If you are given the component pair that names a vector, you can calculate its magnitude by using your earlier skills with the Pythagorean Theorem.

**Example**     Find the magnitude of the vector $[12, 5]$.

**Solution**     In $\triangle ABC$, $AB^2 = AC^2 + CB^2$
$$= 12^2 + 5^2$$
$$= 169$$
$$|\overrightarrow{AB}| = 13$$

The vector may be shown on the grid as a directed line segment.

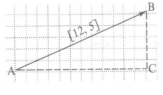

The magnitude of a vector is always positive. The form $|\overrightarrow{AB}|$ is used to represent the magnitude of a vector

The magnitude of $\overrightarrow{AB}$, with components $[12, 5]$, is 13 units.

If an object is moved from one position to another it is said to be displaced. A vector may be used to show a **displacement** on a grid

A displacement of 10 units to the right and 4 units up.

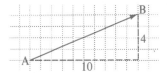

A displacement of 8 units to the left and 3 units down.

The vector $[10, 4]$ shows the displacement $\overrightarrow{AB}$.

The vector $[-8, -3]$ shows the displacement $\overrightarrow{CD}$.

You can use a **scale diagram** to show a displacement.    *PSP*

A displacement of 17.5 m Northwest

A displacement of 6.25 km Southeast

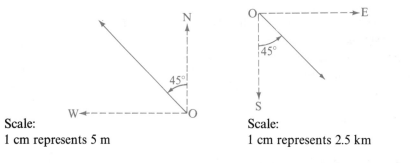

Scale:
1 cm represents 5 m

Scale:
1 cm represents 2.5 km

## 13.1  Exercise

**A** Review the meaning of *scalar quantity, vector quantity, component form.*

1  Use S for scalar and V for vector to classify each of the following.
   (a) the wind on the island
   (b) the number of broken windows
   (c) the current in the lake
   (d) the amount of money in a lottery
   (e) the volume of a cylinder
   (f) the life of a tow truck

2  List three other quantities that are
   (a) scalar                     (b) vector

3  A vector $\overrightarrow{AB}$ is shown on the grid.
   (a) Write $\overrightarrow{AB}$ using components of the form $[a, b]$.
   (b) Calculate the magnitude of $\overrightarrow{AB}$.
   (c) Write the components of $\overrightarrow{BA}$.
   (d) How are $\overrightarrow{AB}$ and $\overrightarrow{BA}$ the same? How are they different?

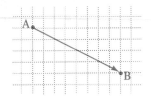

4   For each vector,

  • write its components in the form $[a, b]$.

  • calculate its magnitude. You may express your answer in radical form.

(a)   (b)   (c)   (d)

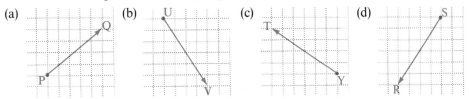

5   Draw each of the following vectors on a grid. Calculate the magnitude of each vector.

(a) $[3, 6]$    (b) $[-2, 5]$    (c) $[3, -5]$    (d) $[-2, 6]$    (e) $[-8, 5]$

B   Remember: If $[a, b] = [c, d]$ then $a = c$ and $b = d$.

6   Find pairs of vectors from the grid that are equal. Give reasons for your answers.

7   Find the value of $m$ and $n$ if the vectors are equal.

(a) $[2m, 16] = [m + 8, 4n]$

(b) $\left[\dfrac{m}{2}, n + 6\right] = [8, 2]$

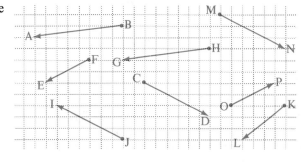

8   (a) Use a grid to draw the vectors $\overrightarrow{AB} = [6, 8]$ and $\overrightarrow{CD} = [-6, -8]$.

(b) What is the magnitude of each vector in (a)?

(c) Find the slope of the segments $\overrightarrow{AB}$ and $\overrightarrow{CD}$. Why is $\overrightarrow{AB} \parallel \overrightarrow{CD}$?

(d) Use your answer in (c) to explain why the vectors $\overrightarrow{AB}$ and $\overrightarrow{CD}$ are not necessarily equal, even if the line segments $\overrightarrow{AB} \parallel \overrightarrow{CD}$ and $|\overrightarrow{AB}| = |\overrightarrow{CD}|$.

(e) Explain why $\overrightarrow{AB}$ and $\overrightarrow{CD}$ are parallel but not equal.

9   Write each displacement in the form $[a, b]$.

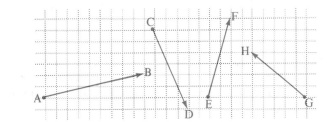

10    Use a scale diagram to draw each displacement.

| Magnitude of Displacement | Direction of Displacement |
|---|---|
| (a)   12 km | S30°W |
| (b)   20 km | N45°E |
| (c)   125 km | N60°W |
| (d)   250 km | S30°E |

11    Use a scale diagram to draw each force.

| Magnitude of Force | Direction of Force | |
|---|---|---|
| (a)   20 N (Newtons) | Northeast | means N45°W |
| (b)   65 N | Southeast | |
| (c)   120 N | Northwest | |

12    A path is shown on the grid. What is the magnitude and the direction of
the vector to show the displacement $\overrightarrow{SF}$?

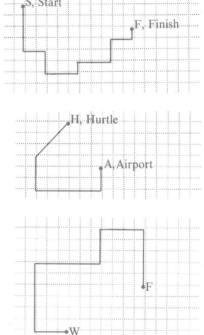

(a)                F, Finsh          (b)        S, Start

                                              F, Finish

S, Start

13    A jet begins at an airport, A, and flies to a
city, Hurtle, after a number of stops. Use a
vector in the form [a, b] to show the jet's
displacement $\overrightarrow{AH}$.

H, Hurtle

A, Airport

14    A truck makes deliveries from the
warehouse, W, to a final destination, F. The
scale of the diagram is 1 unit presents 1.5 km.

(a) What is the magnitude of the
displacement?

(b) What is the direction of the
displacement?

F

W

c  15    A cruiser begins at Port A and travels to the islands E, G, D, and K.
Express the displacement of the cruiser as a vector if its final destination
is at H. The co-ordinates of the ports are given by A(10, 2), E(3, 10),
G(0, 7), D(−10, 7), K(−10, −3), and H(4, 0).

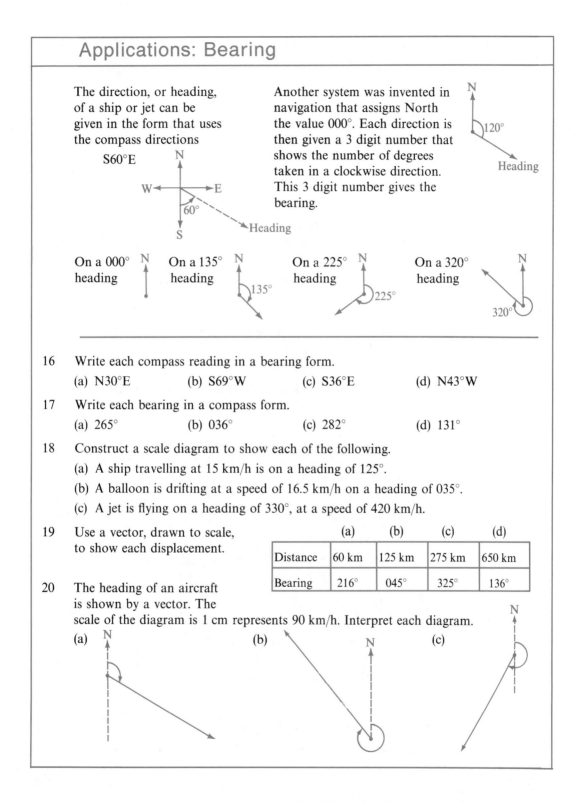

## Applications: Bearing

The direction, or heading, of a ship or jet can be given in the form that uses the compass directions

S60°E

Another system was invented in navigation that assigns North the value 000°. Each direction is then given a 3 digit number that shows the number of degrees taken in a clockwise direction. This 3 digit number gives the bearing.

120°

Heading

On a 000° heading

On a 135° heading

135°

On a 225° heading

225°

On a 320° heading

320°

16 Write each compass reading in a bearing form.
(a) N30°E        (b) S69°W        (c) S36°E        (d) N43°W

17 Write each bearing in a compass form.
(a) 265°        (b) 036°        (c) 282°        (d) 131°

18 Construct a scale diagram to show each of the following.
(a) A ship travelling at 15 km/h is on a heading of 125°.
(b) A balloon is drifting at a speed of 16.5 km/h on a heading of 035°.
(c) A jet is flying on a heading of 330°, at a speed of 420 km/h.

19 Use a vector, drawn to scale, to show each displacement.

|          | (a) | (b) | (c) | (d) |
|----------|-----|-----|-----|-----|
| Distance | 60 km | 125 km | 275 km | 650 km |
| Bearing  | 216° | 045° | 325° | 136° |

20 The heading of an aircraft is shown by a vector. The scale of the diagram is 1 cm represents 90 km/h. Interpret each diagram.
(a)        (b)        (c)

## 13.2 Vectors and Co-ordinates

Co-ordinates can be used to name a vector. For example, you can use a directed line segment on the co-ordinate plane to show a displacement. A ship has travelled from

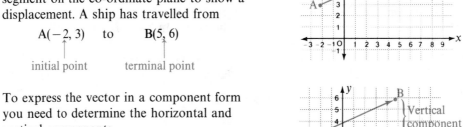

$$A(-2, 3) \quad \text{to} \quad B(5, 6)$$

initial point      terminal point

To express the vector in a component form you need to determine the horizontal and vertical components

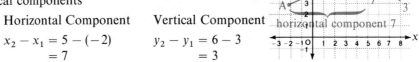

| Horizontal Component | Vertical Component |
|---|---|
| $x_2 - x_1 = 5 - (-2)$ | $y_2 - y_1 = 6 - 3$ |
| $= 7$ | $= 3$ |

In general, the components of a vector AB with co-ordinates $A(x_1, y_1)$, and $B(x_2, y_2)$ are given by $[x_2 - x_1, y_2 - y_1]$.

You can use your earlier skills to find the components of vectors given on the co-ordinate plane.

**Example**    Find the components of $\overrightarrow{AB}$ if the co-ordinates of A and B are $(-3, -5)$ and $(6, 1)$ respectively. What is the magnitude of $\overrightarrow{AB}$?

**Solution**    From the diagram, horizontal component

Sketch a diagram to help you interpret the problem    **PSP**

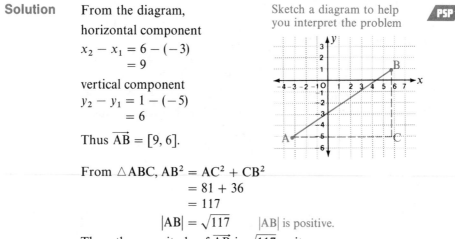

$$x_2 - x_1 = 6 - (-3)$$
$$= 9$$

vertical component
$$y_2 - y_1 = 1 - (-5)$$
$$= 6$$

Thus $\overrightarrow{AB} = [9, 6]$.

From $\triangle ABC$, $AB^2 = AC^2 + CB^2$
$$= 81 + 36$$
$$= 117$$
$$|AB| = \sqrt{117} \qquad |AB| \text{ is positive.}$$
Thus, the magnitude of $\overrightarrow{AB}$ is $\sqrt{117}$ units.

## 13.2 Exercise

**A** You may express magnitudes in radical form.

1. A vector $\overrightarrow{CD}$ is shown on the co-ordinate plane.
   (a) Write $\overrightarrow{CD}$ using the component form $[a, b]$.
   (b) Calculate the magnitude of $\overrightarrow{CD}$.
   (c) Write the vector components of $\overrightarrow{DC}$.
   (d) How are the vectors $\overrightarrow{CD}$ and $\overrightarrow{DC}$ alike? How are they different?

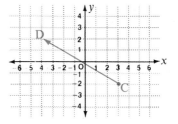

2. For each vector on the co-ordinate plane,
   - write its components in form $[a, b]$.
   - calculate each magnitude. You may express your answer in radical form.

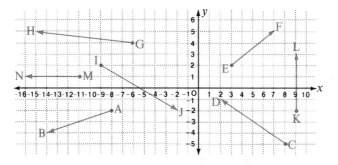

3. Points on the plane have co-ordinates $P(-4, -2)$, $Q(2, 2)$, $R(3, -2)$, and $S(-5, 3)$. Express each vector in the form $[m, n]$ and calculate each magnitude.
   (a) $\overrightarrow{PQ}$      (b) $\overrightarrow{QP}$      (c) $\overrightarrow{RS}$      (d) $\overrightarrow{QS}$

4. The vector $\overrightarrow{AB} = [4, -3]$. Find the co-ordinates of point B if point A has co-ordinates.
   (a) $(7, 2)$      (b) $(0, 6)$      (c) $(-5, 2)$      (d) $(-6, -5)$

5. The initial point, P, of a vector $\overrightarrow{PQ}$ has co-ordinates $P(-3, 2)$. Find the co-ordinates of the terminal point Q, if $\overrightarrow{PQ}$ is given by
   (a) $[3, -2]$      (b) $[3, 6]$      (c) $[-3, -4]$      (d) $[-5, -3]$

6. The terminal point S of a vector $\overrightarrow{RS}$ has co-ordinates $S(-3, 2)$. Find the co-ordinates of R if $\overrightarrow{RS}$ is equal to
   (a) $[0, 3]$      (b) $[-3, 0]$      (c) $[6, -2]$      (d) $[-6, 2]$

**B** Your skills in co-ordinate geometry can be used to solve problems about vectors.

7   A displacement $\vec{d} = [-6, 3]$ is shown.

(a) Find the co-ordinates of the terminal point if the initial point is C(4, 3).

(b) Find the co-ordinates of initial point if for $\vec{d}$ the terminal point is F(−6, −4).

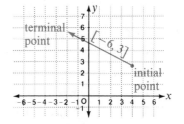

8   A ship has position A(3, 6). A wind, given by the vector [8, 3], pushes the ship to a new position B. Find the co-ordinates of B.

9   A rock is placed at (−3, 6). A force, shown by the vector [4, −8] moves the rock. Find the co-ordinates of the final position of the rock.

10   A ship is stationed at P(2, 0) and leaves for Sable Island at S(7, 3). It sails from Sable Island to Kingswood Port at K(−2, 6). From there it sails to a final destination at the Cameries at F(−4, −3).

(a) Draw a scale diagram to show the path of the ship.

(b) Write a vector in the form [a, b] to show its displacement $\overrightarrow{PF}$.

(c) What is the bearing of F from P?

11   ABCD is a square.

(a) Express the vectors in the component form [a, b].

(b) Calculate the magnitude of $\overrightarrow{AC}$ and $\overrightarrow{DB}$. What do you notice?

12   △PQR is drawn on the co-ordinate plane. S and T are the midpoints of PQ and PR respectively.

(a) Express $\overrightarrow{ST}$ and $\overrightarrow{QR}$ in component form.

(b) Calculate the magnitude of $\overrightarrow{ST}$ and $\overrightarrow{QR}$. What do you notice?

(c) Find the slope of $\overrightarrow{ST}$ and $\overrightarrow{QR}$. What do you notice?

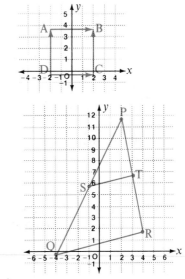

**C** 13   Refer to the previous question.

(a) Repeat the steps for a △PQR of your own choice.

(b) Interpret your results geometrically. What conclusion can you make based on the results of your calculations?

# 13.3 Combining Vectors

John pushes a desk from A to B. The vector, $\overrightarrow{AB}$, is used to show the result of this move.

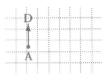

Jenny pushes the same desk from A to D. The vector, $\overrightarrow{AD}$, is used to show the result of this move.

If John and Jenny were to push the desk at the same time, the desk would follow a path, $\overrightarrow{AC}$, as shown in the diagram. In order to find the exact path, you need to find the single vector that gives the same result as $\overrightarrow{AB}$ and $\overrightarrow{AD}$.

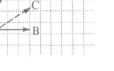

**Adding parallel vectors**
A vector, $\mathring{a}$, shows the displacement $\overrightarrow{AB}$, and $\mathring{b}$ shows the displacement $\overrightarrow{BC}$. $\overrightarrow{AC}$ shows the displacement obtained when $\overrightarrow{AB}$ is followed by $\overrightarrow{BC}$. $\overrightarrow{AC}$ is called the sum of the vectors $\mathring{a}$ and $\mathring{b}$.

$$\overrightarrow{AC} = \mathring{a} + \mathring{b} \quad \text{or} \quad \overrightarrow{AC} = \overrightarrow{AB} + \overrightarrow{BC}$$

$\overrightarrow{AC}$ is called the **resultant vector** of $\overrightarrow{AB}$ and $\overrightarrow{BC}$.

Thus, you can add vectors that are parallel.

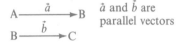

$\mathring{a}$ and $\mathring{b}$ are parallel vectors

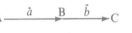

**Adding Non Parallel Vectors**
You can also add vectors such as $\mathring{a}$ and $\mathring{b}$, that are not parallel.
The effect of *vector $\mathring{a}$ followed by vector $\mathring{b}$* is given by the vector $\overrightarrow{AC}$. By representing the vectors as the sides of $\triangle ABC$, you have constructed the sum of the vectors $\mathring{a}$ and $\mathring{b}$.

$$\overrightarrow{AC} = \overrightarrow{AB} + \overrightarrow{BC}$$
$$= \mathring{a} + \mathring{b}$$

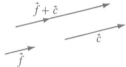

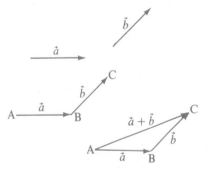

This method of adding vectors is called the **triangle method**. The vector $\overrightarrow{AC}$ is called the **resultant vector** of $\overrightarrow{AB}$ and $\overrightarrow{BC}$. Thus, you can combine vectors by adding them using the **triangle law of vectors**.

**Triangle Law of Vectors**
For any two vectors $\overrightarrow{AB}$ and $\overrightarrow{BC}$,
$$\overrightarrow{AC} = \overrightarrow{AB} + \overrightarrow{BC}$$

Vectors $\dot{a}$ and $\dot{b}$ are drawn from the same initial point. A parallelogram can be drawn with two sides as vectors.

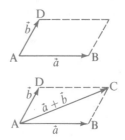

The resultant vector of vectors $\dot{a}$ and $\dot{b}$ is represented by the diagonal of the parallelogram. This method of combining vectors, is called the **parallelogram method**.

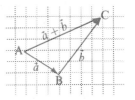

**Parallelogram Law of Vectors**
For any two vectors, $\dot{a}$ and $\dot{b}$,
$$\overrightarrow{AC} = \dot{a} + \dot{b}$$

If vectors are shown in the component form $[m, n]$ and if you know the components of each vector, you can add the vectors algebraically.

Vectors are shown on the grid.                    Use a vector diagram to show the sum.
$$\dot{a} = [3, -2] \qquad \dot{b} = [4, 5]$$

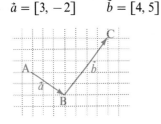

For the above vectors, you note that

$$\dot{a} + \dot{b} = [3, -2] + [4, 5]$$
$$= [3 + 4, -2 + 5]$$
$$= [7, 3]$$

From the diagram, the effect of $\dot{a}$ followed by $\dot{b}$ is shown by $\overline{AC}$. The components of $\overline{AC}$ are given by $[7, 3]$.

Based on examples such as those above, you can combine vectors by adding the corresponding components.

If $\dot{a} = [a_1, a_2]$ and $\dot{b} = [b_1, b_2]$ then $\dot{a} + \dot{b} = [a_1 + b_1, a_2 + b_2]$
$$\dot{a} + \dot{b} = [a_1 + b_1, a_2 + b_2]$$

## 13.3  Exercise

**A** What is meant by the *triangle method* and the *parallelogram method* of adding vectors?

1  Refer to the diagram.
   (a) What are the components of $\dot{a}$? of $\dot{b}$?
   (b) What are the components of $\dot{a} + \dot{b}$?
   (c) Which vector is called the resultant vector?

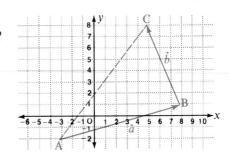

2   Refer to the diagram.

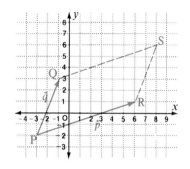

(a) What are the components of $\vec{p}$? of $\vec{q}$?

(b) What are the components of $\vec{p} + \vec{q}$?

(c) Which vector is called the resultant vector?

3   (a) Find $\vec{a} + \vec{b}$ if $\vec{a} = [6, 2]$ and $\vec{b} = [-3, 5]$.

(b) Draw a vector diagram to show the resultant.

(c) Calculate the magnitude of $\vec{a} + \vec{b}$.

4   (a) If $a = [-1, 5]$, $b = [4, 5]$, use the parallelogram method to find $\vec{a} + \vec{b}$.

(b) Write $\vec{a} + \vec{b}$ in the form $[m, n]$ and calculate its magnitude.

5   Express each of the following as a single vector.

(a) $[6, 3] + [4, 5]$          (b) $[8, 2] + [-3, 1]$          (c) $[0, 8] + [6, -4]$

(d) $[3, 0] + [-5, 2]$          (e) $[-6, -3] + [2, 6]$          (f) $[-6, 5] + [6, -5]$

6   Two vectors are added as shown.

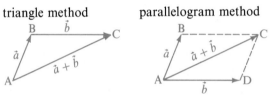

triangle method          parallelogram method

(a) What is the resultant vector for each method?

(b) How are the methods alike? How do they differ?

7   For each pair of vectors,

• draw an accurate diagram to find the sum.

• measure the magnitude of the resultant vector.

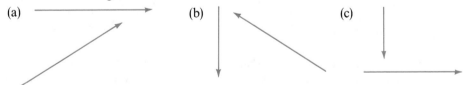

(a)          (b)          (c)

**B** Remember: To find combined vectors you express them in component form.

8   Vectors are given by $\vec{a} = [3, 5]$ and $\vec{b} = [4, 2]$. Construct a diagram to show

(a) $\vec{a} + \vec{b}$          (b) $\vec{b} + \vec{a}$

(c) What do you notice about your results for $\vec{a} + \vec{b}$ and $\vec{b} + \vec{a}$?

9 (a) Sketch each pair of vectors on the co-ordinate plane.
A: $[4, 3], [-4, -3]$      B: $[0, 3], [0, -3]$
C: $[4, 0], [-4, 0]$      D: $[-6, 3], [6, -3]$

(b) Find the resultant of each pair of vectors. What do you notice about your answers?

10 For each sum, find the missing components.
(a) $[3, 2] + [a, b] = [0, 0]$      (b) $[a, b] + [-3, 6] = [0, 0]$
(c) $[0, b] + [a, -3] = [0, 0]$      (d) $[a, 5] + [4, b] = [0, 0]$

11 A grid is used to find the sum of three vectors.
(a) Explain why $\overrightarrow{AC}$ is the resultant vector of $\overrightarrow{AB}$ and $\overrightarrow{BC}$.

(b) Explain why $\overrightarrow{AD}$ is the resultant vector of $\overrightarrow{AC}$ and $\overrightarrow{CD}$.

(c) What is the resultant vector of $\overrightarrow{AB}$, $\overrightarrow{BC}$, $\overrightarrow{CD}$?

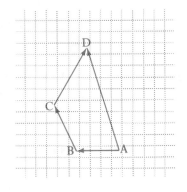

12 Find the sum of each of the following.
(a) $[2, -1], [3, 6], [4, 2]$
(b) $[4, -6], [-2, 3], [-2, 5]$

13 A box is placed at $(0, -3)$. A displacement, $\vec{p}$, given in component form, $[2, 3]$, is applied, followed by another displacement $\vec{q} = [3, 2]$.
(a) What is the resultant force shown in component form?
(b) After both forces are applied, what is the final position of the box?

14 A ship is on a course N45°E at a speed of 12 km/h. After 2.5 h, the ship changes its heading to S30°E at a speed of 20 km/h. After 1.5 h it arrives at its destination.
(a) Draw a vector diagram to show the ship's course.
(b) Find the resultant vector. What is the magnitude and direction?
(c) Interpret your answer in (b).

15 A light aircraft is on a heading of N60°W at an air speed of 120 km/h. A 25 km/h wind in a N30°E direction acts on the plane during the 2.5 h trip.
(a) Draw a vector diagram to show the aircraft's course.
(b) Find the resultant vector. What is its magnitude and direction?
(c) Interpret your answer in (b).

C 16 If $\vec{a} = [a_1, a_2]$, $\vec{b} = [b_1, b_2]$ and $\vec{c} = [c_1, c_2]$ prove that
(a) $\vec{a} + \vec{b} = \vec{b} + \vec{a}$      (b) $\vec{a} + (\vec{b} + \vec{c}) = (\vec{a} + \vec{b}) + \vec{c}$

# Subtracting Vectors

The **opposite**, or **additive inverse**, of vector $\vec{b}$ is $-\vec{b}$. Opposite vectors have the same magnitude but opposite directions. The subtraction of vectors is defined in terms of the addition of opposite vectors. Thus, to find $\vec{a} - \vec{b}$ you add $\vec{a}$ and $-\vec{b}$.

$\vec{a} - \vec{b} = \vec{a} + (-\vec{b})$ —— To subtract $\vec{b}$, add its opposite.

The **inverse of** $[a, b]$ is $[-a, -b]$.

$[a, b] + [-a, -b] = [0, 0]$ —— $[0, 0]$ represents the **identity vector**.

You can use the triangle or parallelogram methods to subtract vectors. To find $\vec{a} - \vec{b}$ follow these steps.

Draw $\vec{a}$ and $\vec{b}$.　　　　Draw $-\vec{b}$.　　　　Draw $\vec{a} + (-\vec{b}) = \vec{a} - \vec{b}$.

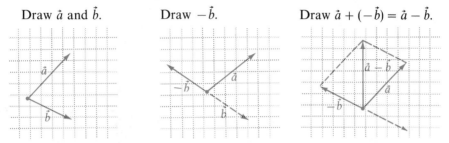

When vectors are expressed in component form, you can subtract the components to subtract the vectors.

If $\vec{a} = [a_1, a_2]$ and $\vec{b} = [b_1, b_2]$ then $\vec{a} - \vec{b} = [a_1 - b_1, a_2 - b_2]$.

---

17 (a) Draw a vector diagram for $[8, 6]$ and its opposite vector.

(b) How is a vector and its opposite alike? How are they different?

18 Write the opposite vector of each of these vectors.

(a) $[3, 2]$ (b) $[4, -3]$ (c) $[-5, 2]$ (d) $[-6, -8]$ (e) $[-2, 0]$ (f) $[0, 5]$

19 Use $\vec{p} = [3, 5]$ and $\vec{q} = [2, -3]$.

(a) Use the triangle method to find the vector represented by $\vec{p} - \vec{q}$.

(b) What is the magnitude of $\vec{p} - \vec{q}$?

20 Use $\vec{a} = [3, 2]$ and $\vec{b} = [-4, 3]$.

(a) Draw a diagram to find the vector $\vec{a} - \vec{b}$.

(b) What are the components of $\vec{a} - \vec{b}$?

21 Use $\vec{a} = [3, 4]$ and $\vec{b} = [-2, 6]$. Draw a vector diagram for

(a) $\vec{a}$ (b) $\vec{b}$ (c) $-\vec{a}$ (d) $-\vec{b}$ (e) $\vec{a} - \vec{b}$ (f) $\vec{b} - \vec{a}$

# 13.4   Vector and Scalar Products

You have seen that a vector quantity has magnitude and direction. A scalar quantity has only magnitude and may be represented by a real number.

The diagram shows the vector $\overrightarrow{AB}$.

$$\overrightarrow{AB} = \vec{v}$$

In component form, $\overrightarrow{AB} = [3, 2]$

or $\qquad\qquad \vec{v} = [3, 2] \qquad$ ①

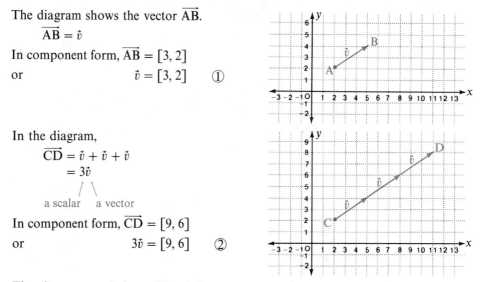

In the diagram,

$$\overrightarrow{CD} = \vec{v} + \vec{v} + \vec{v}$$
$$= 3\vec{v}$$

a scalar    a vector

In component form, $\overrightarrow{CD} = [9, 6]$

or $\qquad\qquad 3\vec{v} = [9, 6] \qquad$ ②

The above example from ① and ② suggests a method for multiplying a vector by a real number.

If $m$ is a real number and $\vec{v} = [v_1, v_2]$ then $m\vec{v}$ is given by

$$m\vec{v} = [mv_1, mv_2]$$

The **scalar product**, $m\vec{v}$, has been invented to give a meaning to the multiplication of a vector *by a scalar*. Scalar products can be interpreted on a grid.

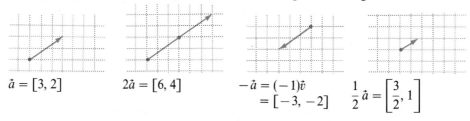

$\vec{a} = [3, 2]$ $\qquad$ $2\vec{a} = [6, 4]$ $\qquad$ $\begin{aligned} -\vec{a} &= (-1)\vec{v} \\ &= [-3, -2] \end{aligned}$ $\qquad$ $\dfrac{1}{2}\vec{a} = \left[\dfrac{3}{2}, 1\right]$

The diagrams above illustrate the following properties of the scalar product. The vectors $2\vec{a}$, $-\vec{a}$, $\frac{1}{2}\vec{a}$ are said to be **scalar multiples** of the vector $\vec{a}$.

- If $s$ is a scalar and $\vec{a}$ is a vector, then $s\vec{a}$ is a vector with the same direction as $\vec{a}$ and magnitude $s|\vec{a}|$.
- If $s = 1$, then $s\vec{a} = \vec{a}$.
- If $s > 0$, then $s\vec{a}$ has the same direction as $\vec{a}$.
- If $s < 0$, then $s\vec{a}$ has the opposite direction to $\vec{a}$.
- If, for two vectors $\vec{a}$ and $\vec{b}$, there is a real number $k$ such that $\vec{a} = k\vec{b}$ then $\vec{a}$ and $\vec{b}$ are said to be **parallel vectors**. $\vec{b}$ is said to be a scalar multiple of $\vec{a}$.

# 13.4 Exercise

**A** Review the meaning of *scalar multiple of a vector.*

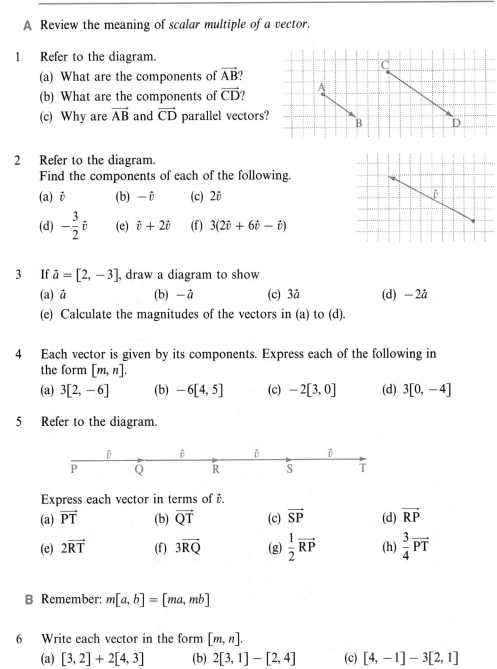

1 Refer to the diagram.
  (a) What are the components of $\overrightarrow{AB}$?
  (b) What are the components of $\overrightarrow{CD}$?
  (c) Why are $\overrightarrow{AB}$ and $\overrightarrow{CD}$ parallel vectors?

2 Refer to the diagram.
  Find the components of each of the following.
  (a) $\vec{v}$          (b) $-\vec{v}$          (c) $2\vec{v}$

  (d) $-\dfrac{3}{2}\vec{v}$      (e) $\vec{v} + 2\vec{v}$      (f) $3(2\vec{v} + 6\vec{v} - \vec{v})$

3 If $\vec{a} = [2, -3]$, draw a diagram to show
  (a) $\vec{a}$                (b) $-\vec{a}$                (c) $3\vec{a}$                (d) $-2\vec{a}$
  (e) Calculate the magnitudes of the vectors in (a) to (d).

4 Each vector is given by its components. Express each of the following in the form $[m, n]$.
  (a) $3[2, -6]$          (b) $-6[4, 5]$          (c) $-2[3, 0]$          (d) $3[0, -4]$

5 Refer to the diagram.

  Express each vector in terms of $\vec{v}$.
  (a) $\overrightarrow{PT}$          (b) $\overrightarrow{QT}$          (c) $\overrightarrow{SP}$          (d) $\overrightarrow{RP}$

  (e) $2\overrightarrow{RT}$          (f) $3\overrightarrow{RQ}$          (g) $\dfrac{1}{2}\overrightarrow{RP}$          (h) $\dfrac{3}{4}\overrightarrow{PT}$

**B** Remember: $m[a, b] = [ma, mb]$

6 Write each vector in the form $[m, n]$.
  (a) $[3, 2] + 2[4, 3]$          (b) $2[3, 1] - [2, 4]$          (c) $[4, -1] - 3[2, 1]$
  (d) $3[2, -1] - 2[4, 5]$          (e) $3[2, -1] + 5[3, -1]$
  (f) $-2[3, -1] - 3[5, -2]$          (g) $-4[5, 1] + 2[3, 1] - 5[2, 1]$

**7** Two vectors are given by $\vec{a} = [6, 3]$ and $\vec{b} = [-2, 8]$.

(a) Illustrate the vectors $2\vec{a} + \vec{b}$, $\vec{a} + 2\vec{b}$ on a grid.

(b) Express each vector in (a) in component form.

(c) Find the magnitudes of the vectors in (b).

**8** If $\vec{a} = [3, -8]$ and $\vec{b} = [-2, 4]$, express each of the following in the form $[a, b]$.

(a) $2\vec{a}$      (b) $3\vec{a}$      (c) $-2\vec{a}$      (d) $-2\vec{b}$      (e) $2\vec{b}$

(f) $\frac{1}{2}\vec{b}$      (g) $\vec{a} - \vec{b}$      (h) $2\vec{a} + \frac{1}{2}\vec{b}$      (i) $3\vec{a} - 2\vec{b}$

**9** Find $m, n$ for each of the following.

(a) $[-2, 3] + [3, 5] = [m, n]$         (b) $2[4, 5] - [m, 4] = [6, n]$

**10** Solve for $x$ and $y$.

(a) $x[3, 5] = [15, 25]$         (b) $x[3, -1] + y[4, -3] = [1, 3]$

**11** Quadrilateral PQRS has co-ordinates $P(-7, -5)$, $Q(-3, 5)$, $R(7, 5)$, $S(5, -7)$.

(a) A, B, C, and D are the midpoints of each side of the quadrilateral. Find the co-ordinates of the midpoints.

(b) Express the vectors $\overrightarrow{AB}$, $\overrightarrow{BC}$, $\overrightarrow{DC}$, $\overrightarrow{AD}$ in component form.

(c) Use your results in (b). Which sides are parallel?

**C 12** Show that the result in the previous question is true for any quadrilateral.

---

## Problem-Solving   **PSP**

Much mathematics has been developed as a result of asking the question, "*What if . . . ?*" For example, *What if* the concept of vectors is extended to 3 dimensions? The skills you learn in two dimensions can be extended to skills in 3 dimensions. Use your knowledge of vectors in 2 dimensions to interpret each of the following terms about vectors in 3 dimensions.

- vector $[2, 3, 5]$       • magnitude of $[2, -3, 1]$
- components of a vector       • equality of vectors
- using arrows to represent a vector in 3 dimensions
- parallel vectors       • scalar multiple of vectors
- triangle law of vectors       • parallelogram law of vectors

Are there any concepts about vectors in 2 dimensions that do not extend to vectors in 3 dimensions?

# 13.5  Applications with Vectors

When flying a jet, pilots need to make allowances for the direction of the wind, in order to reach the correct destination. For example, the speed and direction of a plane in still air is shown by $\vec{p}$. The speed and direction of the wind is given by $\vec{w}$. If the pilot heads the plane towards destination, S, the plane in fact will arrive at P, because the wind $\vec{w}$ has blown the plane off course.

*In a modern jet, information is fed into an onboard computer which is connected to the plane's navigational system. The computer compensates for any wind factor and computes a course so that the plane will arrive at the correct destination.*

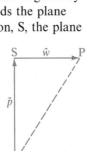

For the plane, A, to arrive at S, the pilot needs to compensate for the wind. In effect, a course is taken as shown by the diagram. The pilot actually flies in the direction of the vector $\overrightarrow{AT}$ shown by the vector $\vec{d}$.

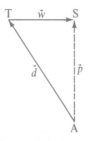

**Example** The direction and speed of the wind is 75 km/h due East. A plane flies due North at a speed of 150 km/h. Draw a scale diagram to find

(a) the distance flown after an hour.

(b) the direction of the plane after an hour.

**PSP** Use a scale diagram as a strategy.

**Solution** Use the scale 1 cm represents 25 km. The vector $\overrightarrow{AB}$ shows the path of the plane in still air, $\overrightarrow{BC}$ shows the wind current. By measurement, $\overrightarrow{AC}$ = 6.8 cm and $\angle BAC$ = 26°. 6.8 cm represents 6.8 × 25 km = 170 km. Thus, the plane travelled 170 km in a direction N26°E.

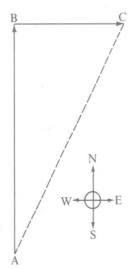

## 13.5 Exercise

**B** You may use scale diagrams to solve these problems. **PSP**

1   In still water, Les rows at a speed of 10 km/h. A river flows east to west at a speed of 4 km/h. If Les rows his boat in a northerly direction across the river, find
    (a) his actual direction.         (b) his actual speed.

2   An airplane travels 220 km/h when there is no wind. If the wind blows 80 km/h towards the west, then find the distance travelled by the airplane if it travels
    (a) due north for 2 h.           (b) N30°E for 4 h.

3   (a) Show the flight path of each aircraft during 2 h of flying. Use a suitable scale.
    (b) How far apart are the planes after 1 h?
    (c) What assumption do you make in (b)?

| Plane     | Direction | Speed     |
|-----------|-----------|-----------|
| piper cub | N40°W     | 250 km/h  |
| jet       | S60°W     | 550 km/h  |

4   (a) A plane flies due north at 200 km/h. Another plane flies N45°E at 250 km/h. How far apart are the planes after 3 h?
    (b) If there is an easterly wind of 50 km/h, what effect will this wind have on your answer in (a)?

5   (a) The direction of the ocean current is S40°W, and is moving at a speed of 10 km/h. A ship travels at a speed of 25 km/h in the direction W40°N. By how many kilometres will the ship be off course after 10 h?
    (b) What course should the captain take so that the ship will not be off course?

6   Two forces, at P, pull an object as shown.
    (a) Explain why the path of the object is shown by the vector $\overrightarrow{PQ}$.
    (b) Explain why $\overrightarrow{PQ}$ is the resultant force of $\vec{f_1}$ and $\vec{f_2}$.

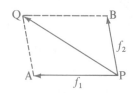

7   Two forces pull on an object at A. Draw a scale diagram to calculate the path of the object when pulled by the two forces.

8   Two forces of 100 N and 150 N are pulling on an object. The two forces are at an angle of 60° to each other.
    (a) Find the resultant force acting on the body.
    (b) What is the angle between the resultant force and the 100-N force?

# 13.6 Vectors and Polygons

Earlier, you used the triangle law of vectors to add vectors.

$$\overrightarrow{AB} + \overrightarrow{BC} = \overrightarrow{AC}$$

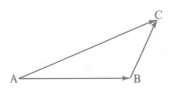

You can use vectors to represent the sides of any polygon. For rectangle ABCD, you can write various vector relations.

$$\overrightarrow{AB} + \overrightarrow{BC} = \overrightarrow{AC}$$
$$\overrightarrow{AD} + \overrightarrow{DC} = \overrightarrow{AC}$$
$$\overrightarrow{AD} = -\overrightarrow{DA}$$
$$\overrightarrow{CA} = -\overrightarrow{AC}$$

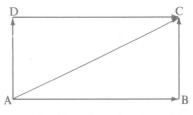

The properties of a rectangle can be used to write additional vector relations,

$$\overrightarrow{DC} = \overrightarrow{AB} \qquad \overrightarrow{AD} = \overrightarrow{BC}$$

The opposite sides of a rectangle have the same measure.

**Example**  Quadrilateral PQRS is a parallelogram. Express each of the following as one vector.

(a) $\overrightarrow{SR} + \overrightarrow{RQ}$  (b) $\overrightarrow{SP} + \overrightarrow{SR}$

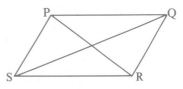

**Solution**  (a) Refer to the diagram.
$$\overrightarrow{SR} + \overrightarrow{RQ} = \overrightarrow{SQ}$$

(b) In parallelogram PQRS, $\overrightarrow{SR} = \overrightarrow{PQ}$.
Thus, $\overrightarrow{SP} + \overrightarrow{SR} = \overrightarrow{SP} + \overrightarrow{PQ} = \overrightarrow{SQ}$.

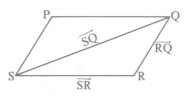

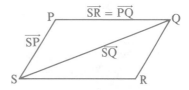

# 13.6 Exercise

**A** Remember to use the properties of the polygon to express vectors as sides of a polygon.

1  Refer to the diagram. Express each sum of vectors as one vector.

(a) $\overrightarrow{DA} + \overrightarrow{AB}$  (b) $\overrightarrow{DC} + \overrightarrow{CB}$

2 Quadrilateral PQRS is a square. Express each sum of vectors as one vector.

(a) $\overrightarrow{PQ} + \overrightarrow{PS}$
(b) $\overrightarrow{RS} + \overrightarrow{RQ}$

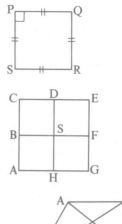

3 Refer to the diagram. The figures shown are congruent squares. Express each of the following as one vector.

(a) $\overrightarrow{AB} + \overrightarrow{BC}$
(b) $\overrightarrow{AB} + \overrightarrow{SD}$
(c) $\overrightarrow{AH} + \overrightarrow{HS}$
(d) $\overrightarrow{AH} + \overrightarrow{AB}$
(e) $\overrightarrow{AG} + \overrightarrow{GF}$
(f) $\overrightarrow{AG} + \overrightarrow{CE}$

4 For the diagram, write a single vector to show each of the following.

(a) $\overrightarrow{AB} + \overrightarrow{BC}$
(b) $\overrightarrow{DB} + \overrightarrow{BC}$
(c) $\overrightarrow{DB} + \overrightarrow{BA}$
(d) $\overrightarrow{DC} + \overrightarrow{CB} + \overrightarrow{BA}$

5 $\vec{a}$ and $\vec{b}$ are vectors shown by the diagram. Express each of the following in terms of $\vec{a}$ and $\vec{b}$.

(a) $\overrightarrow{DC}$
(b) $-\overrightarrow{CD}$
(c) $\overrightarrow{AD}$
(d) $\overrightarrow{AC}$
(e) $\overrightarrow{DB}$
(f) $-\overrightarrow{BD}$

6 Refer to the diagram. Express each vector as the sum of two or more vectors.

(a) $\overrightarrow{UT}$
(b) $\overrightarrow{RQ}$
(c) $\overrightarrow{RP}$
(d) $\overrightarrow{TS}$

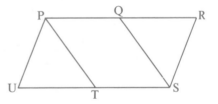

B In the next section, the skills you learned with polygons and vectors are used to prove properties.

**PSP** Place this information in your *Problem-Solving Plan.*

7 PQRS is a parallelogram. The midpoints of the sides are shown by A, B, C, and D. Express each of the following by one vector.

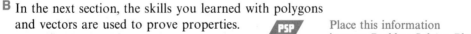

(a) $\overrightarrow{SD} + \overrightarrow{PB}$
(b) $\overrightarrow{QC} + \overrightarrow{PA}$
(c) $\overrightarrow{DS} + \overrightarrow{AP}$
(d) $\overrightarrow{BQ} + \overrightarrow{CR}$
(e) $\overrightarrow{DR} + \overrightarrow{RC} + \overrightarrow{BQ} + \overrightarrow{CQ}$

8 Refer to the diagram in the previous question.

(a) Write two relations about vectors that involve $\overrightarrow{SP}$.

(b) Write two relations about vectors that involve $\overrightarrow{DC}$.

9  For the rectangle, which of the following are true (T)? false (F)?
   (a) $\overrightarrow{DB} + \overrightarrow{BC} = \overrightarrow{DC}$     (b) $\overrightarrow{CB} + \overrightarrow{DB} = \overrightarrow{BC}$
   (c) $\overrightarrow{AB} = -\overrightarrow{BA}$     (d) $\overrightarrow{AB} - \overrightarrow{AC} = -\overrightarrow{BC}$
   (e) $\overrightarrow{BC} - \overrightarrow{DB} = \overrightarrow{CD}$     (f) $\overrightarrow{DB} - \overrightarrow{DB} = \overrightarrow{AD} - \overrightarrow{AD}$
   (g) $\overrightarrow{CB} + \overrightarrow{BA} = -\overrightarrow{AC}$     (h) $\overrightarrow{DB} = \overrightarrow{AD} + \overrightarrow{DB}$

10 For the parallelogram, give reasons why
   (a) $\overrightarrow{AD} = \overrightarrow{BC}$     (b) $\overrightarrow{AB} = \overrightarrow{DC}$     (c) $\overrightarrow{AC} \neq \overrightarrow{DB}$
   (d) $\overrightarrow{DE} = \overrightarrow{EB}$     (e) $\overrightarrow{AE} = \overrightarrow{EC}$     (f) $\overrightarrow{AD} + \overrightarrow{DE} = \overrightarrow{AE}$
   (g) $\overrightarrow{AB} + \overrightarrow{BC} = \overrightarrow{AC}$     (h) $\overrightarrow{AD} + \overrightarrow{AB} = \overrightarrow{AC}$

11 For the parallelogram ABCD, $\overrightarrow{AB} = \vec{a}$ and $\overrightarrow{AD} = \vec{b}$
   Express each of the following in terms of the vectors $\vec{a}$ and $\vec{b}$.
   (a) $\overrightarrow{DA}$     (b) $\overrightarrow{BA}$     (c) $\overrightarrow{DB}$     (d) $\overrightarrow{BD}$
   (e) $\overrightarrow{AD} + \overrightarrow{DC}$     (f) $\overrightarrow{AB} + \overrightarrow{BC}$     (g) $\overrightarrow{AD} + \overrightarrow{BC}$

12 The diagram consists of 6 congruent squares. Express the following in terms of the vectors $\overrightarrow{AB}$ and $\overrightarrow{AJ}$.
   (a) $\overrightarrow{KG} + \overrightarrow{DK}$     (b) $\overrightarrow{DF} + \overrightarrow{JD}$
   (c) $\overrightarrow{AC} + \overrightarrow{CF}$     (d) $\overrightarrow{BL} + \overrightarrow{CA}$
   (e) $\overrightarrow{FH} + \overrightarrow{GK}$     (f) $\overrightarrow{DJ} + \overrightarrow{JH}$

13 PQRS is a parallelogram. Show why, $\overrightarrow{SP} + \overrightarrow{PQ} = \overrightarrow{SR} + \overrightarrow{RQ}$.

14 ABCD is a square. Show why, $\overrightarrow{AB} + \overrightarrow{BC} = \overrightarrow{DC} + \overrightarrow{CB}$.

15 (a) In how many different orders can 5 people stand in a single line to buy tickets for a movie?
   (b) In how many different ways can 5 people sit around a round table? Justify your answer.

C 16 Refer to the diagram.
   Show why
   $\overrightarrow{HD} + \overrightarrow{DG} = \overrightarrow{GD} + \overrightarrow{DE} + \overrightarrow{EF}$.

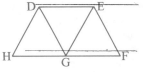

Vector notation was invented to represent a quantity that has direction and magnitude. You then developed various skills with vectors in the previous sections. By using vectors, you can now prove geometric deductions from another point of view.

To prove deductions using vectors, you need to interpret your results and express them in terms of geometry, as shown in the following example.

**Example**  In △PQR, S and T are the midpoints of PQ and PR respectively. Prove that QR = 2ST and ST∥QR.

 Think: Analyze the diagram. In terms of vectors, the result can be obtained if I can prove $\overrightarrow{QR} = 2\overrightarrow{ST}$. $\overrightarrow{QR}$ occurs in the large triangle PQR, and $\overrightarrow{ST}$ occurs in the small triangle PST. The large and small triangles are related by $\overrightarrow{QP} = 2\overrightarrow{SP}$, since S is the midpoint of $\overrightarrow{QP}$.

**Solution**  Given: △PQR with PS = SQ, PT = TR.
Required to prove: QR = 2ST, ST∥QR.

Proof:  Join ST.

| Statements | Reasons |
|---|---|
| In △PST, $\overrightarrow{ST} = \overrightarrow{SP} + \overrightarrow{PT}$ ① | triangle law of vectors |
| In △PQR, $\overrightarrow{QR} = \overrightarrow{QP} + \overrightarrow{PR}$ | triangle law of vectors |
| $= 2\overrightarrow{SP} + 2\overrightarrow{PT}$ | S midpoint $\overrightarrow{QP}$, T midpoint $\overrightarrow{PR}$ |
| $= 2(\overrightarrow{SP} + \overrightarrow{PT})$ | scalar product |
| $= 2\overrightarrow{ST}$ | from ①, $\overrightarrow{SP} + \overrightarrow{PT} = \overrightarrow{ST}$ |

Since $\overrightarrow{QR} = 2\overrightarrow{ST}$, then QR∥ST and QR = 2ST.

When proving deductions, you can apply the following skills with vectors.

- If $\overrightarrow{AB} = \overrightarrow{CD}$ then $\overrightarrow{AB} = -\overrightarrow{DC}$.
- In △ABC, $\overrightarrow{BC} = \overrightarrow{BA} + \overrightarrow{AC}$
  If $\overrightarrow{AB} = \overrightarrow{CD}$ then AB = CD and AB∥CD.
- You may replace a vector by an equal vector.
  For example, in square ABCD, AB = DC,
  AB∥DC. Then, $\overrightarrow{AB} = \overrightarrow{DC}$.
  Thus, $\overrightarrow{AB} + \overrightarrow{BC} = \overrightarrow{AC}$ or $\overrightarrow{DC} + \overrightarrow{BC} = \overrightarrow{AC}$.

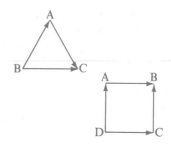

## 13.7 Exercise

**B** In your earlier work with deductions, you proved each of the following. Now use a vector method to prove each of the following deductions.

1   In quadrilateral ABCD, AB $\parallel$ DC and AB = DC. Show why
   (a) $\overrightarrow{BA} = \overrightarrow{CD}$   (b) $\overrightarrow{BC} = \overrightarrow{BA} + \overrightarrow{AC}$   (c) $\overrightarrow{AD} = \overrightarrow{AC} + \overrightarrow{CD}$
   (d) Use the above facts to prove that $\overrightarrow{AD} = \overrightarrow{BC}$ and thus AD = BC and AD $\parallel$ BC.

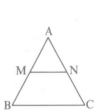

2   Use the diagram. AM = MB and MN $\parallel$ BC. Show why
   (a) $\overrightarrow{BA} = 2\overrightarrow{MA}$          (b) $\overrightarrow{MA} + \overrightarrow{AN} = \overrightarrow{MN}$
   (c) $\overrightarrow{BA} + \overrightarrow{AC} = \overrightarrow{BC}$       (d) Prove that AN = NC.

For Questions 3 to 8, you need to translate the given information and construct a diagram. Record the given information accurately.

3   In a quadrilateral PQRS, PS = QR and PS $\parallel$ QR. Prove PQ = SR and PQ $\parallel$ SR.

4   (a) PQRS is a parallelogram with A and B midpoints of PS and QR. Prove that AQ = SB.
   (b) In quadrilateral ABCD, E is the midpoint of AC. If AB = DC, prove that D, E, and B are collinear.
   (c) Two line segments AB and CD bisect each other at E. Prove that ACBD is a parallelogram.

5   In $\triangle$ PQR, the median PS is drawn to QR. Prove that PS = $\frac{1}{2}$(PQ + PR).

6   In trapezoid PQRS, A and B are the midpoints of PQ and RS respectively, and QR $\parallel$ PS. Prove that AB $\parallel$ QR.

7   (a) Prove that if a pair of opposite sides in a quadrilateral are equal and parallel then the quadrilateral is a parallelogram.
   (b) In a quadrilateral PQRS, the diagonals bisect each other. Prove that PQRS is a parallelogram.

**C** 8   Use a vector method to prove the following deduction: The quadrilateral formed by joining the midpoints of the sides of a quadrilateral, in succession, is a parallelogram.

## 13.8 Using a Matrix

In the study of mathematics, notation is often invented to represent much information in a compact way. For example, tables and charts are used to store information obtained in sports. The points scored by 3 teams in the month of January are shown in the chart.

| | Canucks | Jets | Saints |
|---|---|---|---|
| Home | 12 | 8 | 11 |
| Away | 16 | 13 | 9 |

Team

A more concise form, called a **matrix**, was invented to store this information. The plural of matrix is matrices. A **matrix** is an ordered array of numbers. These numbers occur in rows and columns placed within large parentheses as shown. In a matrix, the descriptive headings are omitted, but each number in the array is placed in the same position. The numbers displayed in the matrix are called **entries** or **components**. The **dimensions** or the **order** of a matrix is given by the number of rows and columns. Matrix A has order 2 by 3 (written as 2 × 3).

$$A = \begin{pmatrix} 12 & 8 & 11 \\ 16 & 13 & 9 \end{pmatrix}$$

This entry represents the points scored by the Jets in Away games.

### Row Matrix
For the previous data, the information for the home games is shown by a **row matrix**. The order of this row matrix is

$$1 \times 3 \text{ (one by three)}.$$

one row    3 columns

$$(12 \quad 8 \quad 11)$$

Remember: The numbers are placed in a specific order. The meaning of each entry is understood by its position in the array.

### Column Matrix
The information shown for the Canucks is shown by the **column matrix**. The order of the column matrix is

$$2 \times 1 \text{ (two by one)}$$

2 rows    1 column

$$\begin{pmatrix} 12 \\ 16 \end{pmatrix}$$

This entry means that the number of points scored by the Canucks on away games is 16.

A matrix with equal dimensions such as 2 × 2, or 3 × 3 is called a **square matrix**.

You will learn to perform operations on matrices in later sections.

## 13.8 Exercise

**A** Review the meaning of *matrix, column matrix, row matrix, order, dimensions.*

1 What is the order of each matrix?

(a) $\begin{pmatrix} 2 & 3 & 4 \\ 5 & 6 & 1 \end{pmatrix}$ (b) $\begin{pmatrix} 3 & 6 \\ 2 & 5 \end{pmatrix}$ (c) $\begin{pmatrix} 4 & 9 & 6 & 4 \\ 3 & 2 & 1 & 3 \\ 2 & 1 & 0 & 4 \end{pmatrix}$ (d) $\begin{pmatrix} 3 & 6 & 9 \\ 2 & 0 & 1 \\ 3 & 2 & 1 \end{pmatrix}$ (e) $\begin{pmatrix} 4 & 6 & 3 & 2 \\ 5 & 1 & 0 & 6 \end{pmatrix}$

(f) Which of the matrices above are square matrices?

2 How many rows and columns, does each matrix have?
(a) order $3 \times 1$  (b) order $2 \times 3$  (c) order $1 \times 2$
(d) order $2 \times 2$  (e) order $5 \times 2$  (f) order $2 \times 4$

3 Refer to matrix E.
(a) What are the dimensions of matrix E?
(b) What are the components of the third row?
(c) What are the entries of the fourth column?
(d) What is the component in the first row, third column?
(e) What is the entry in the second row, fifth column?

$$E = \begin{pmatrix} 1 & 15 & 8 & 3 & 13 \\ 11 & 7 & 17 & 12 & 5 \\ 16 & 19 & 2 & 20 & 18 \\ 4 & 10 & 6 & 14 & 7 \end{pmatrix}$$

4 Refer to the matrix for the Canucks, Jets, and Saints on the previous page. What do each of the following entries in the matrix represent?
(a) 8  (b) 13  (c) 9  (d) 16

5 In February, the following points were scored by the teams.

| Canucks | Jets | Saints |
|---|---|---|
| Home 16, Away 13 | Home 14, Away 15 | Home 13, Away 16 |

Record these points in a suitable matrix form.

6 Refer to the previous question.
(a) A row matrix records the home game points.

$(16 \quad 14 \quad 13)$

What does each entry represent in this row matrix?

(b) Record a row matrix for the away game points. What does each entry represent in game matrix?

(c) A column matrix is recorded for the Saints. $\begin{pmatrix} 13 \\ 16 \end{pmatrix}$
What do the entries mean?

(d) Construct a similar column matrix for the Canucks and the Jets.

**B** Remember: Each entry in a matrix has a special meaning.

7   The number of pizzas sold at
    Pizza Place *last week* are shown
    in the table.

    (a) Construct a matrix for the
        data given in the table. What
        is the order of the matrix?

Number of Pizzas sold (last week)

|         | Small | Medium | Large |
|---------|-------|--------|-------|
| Regular | 42    | 108    | 92    |
| Deluxe  | 28    | 76     | 83    |

    (b) The number of pizzas sold *this week* are given below. Record the
        information in matrix form.

        regular small 38,   deluxe small 36,    regular medium 92,
        deluxe medium 72,   regular large 82,   deluxe large 79

    (c) Use a matrix to show the combined sales of pizzas for this week
        and last week.

8   The soft drink sales during the day shift are given by the following data.
    Small (S), Regular (R), Large (L).

        Cola 36 S, 42 R, 18 L;       Orange 31 S, 36 R, 12 L;
        Ginger Ale 18 S, 24 R, 6 L;  Root Beer 12 S, 30 R, 25 L.

    (a) Construct a matrix to show the cola sales. What is the order of the
        matrix?

    (b) Construct a matrix to show the cola and orange sales. What is the
        order of the matrix?

    (c) Construct a matrix to represent all the data. What is the order of the
        matrix?

9   The games played part way into the season by each team in the Canadian
    Football League (CFL) are shown as follows: Win (W), Tie (T), Loss (L).

        Vancouver 6W, 2L, 4T; Edmonton 7W, 3L, 3T; Calgary 5W, 1L, 5T;
        Regina 8W, 2L, 2T; Winnipeg 6W, 3L, 2T; Toronto 7W, 2L, 4T;
        Hamilton 8W, 1L, 3T; Ottawa 9W, 2L, 1T; Montreal 7W, 3L, 2T.

    (a) Construct a matrix to show the wins and losses of the Western
        teams. What is the order of the matrix?

    (b) Construct a matrix to show all the results for the Western teams.
        What is the order of the matrix?

    (c) Construct a matrix to show the wins and losses of the Eastern teams.
        What is the order of the matrix?

    (d) Construct a matrix to show all the results for the Eastern teams.
        What is the order of the matrix?

    (e) Construct a matrix to show all the results. What is the order of
        the matrix?

# Applications: Communication Networks

A matrix can be used to show a communications network.

*The telephones that link you up with your friends is an example of a complex communications network.*

For example, the diagram shows how three people, ①, ② and ③, are linked by a communication network. The arrows show the direction in which communications are sent.

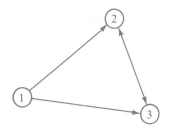

Sending Messages
① can send message to ② and ③.
② can send to ③.
③ can send to ②.

Receiving Messages
① does not receive messages.
② receives messages from ① and ③.
③ receives messages from ① and ②.

The above information can be represented by a communications network matrix as shown below. The rows of the matrix show the relation *sends*. The columns of the matrix show the relation *receives*.

The components of the communications matrix shown below are the numbers 0 or 1. They are interpreted as follows:

1 shows that there is a relation, namely receives or sends messages.
0 shows that there is no relation. It is used to show the relation of a sender
  with himself/herself, namely, you don't send or receive messages to yourself.

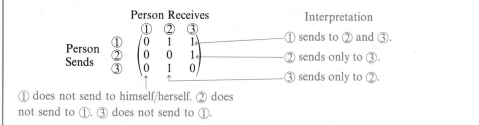

① does not send to himself/herself. ② does not send to ①. ③ does not send to ①.

*Continued*

10 Each matrix represents a communications network. Interpret the components of each matrix.

(a) $\begin{pmatrix} 0 & 1 & 0 \\ 1 & 0 & 0 \\ 1 & 1 & 0 \end{pmatrix}$ (b) $\begin{pmatrix} 0 & 1 & 1 \\ 0 & 0 & 0 \\ 1 & 1 & 0 \end{pmatrix}$ (c) $\begin{pmatrix} 0 & 1 & 1 \\ 0 & 0 & 1 \\ 1 & 1 & 0 \end{pmatrix}$

(d) How many stations are involved in each of the above matrices? Draw a diagram to show how the network is set up in each of (a), (b), (c).

11 A communications network in the form of a matrix A is shown for 4 people. Interpret the components of the

(a) first row. (b) second column.

(c) third row. (d) fourth column.

$\begin{pmatrix} 0 & 1 & 0 & 1 \\ 0 & 0 & 1 & 1 \\ 1 & 0 & 0 & 1 \\ 0 & 1 & 0 & 0 \end{pmatrix}$

12 Refer to the previous question. The 4 stations linked by the communications network are represented by the diagram.

(a) Make a copy of the diagram. Two arrowheads have been drawn. Draw the remaining arrowheads.

(b) Changes are made in the communication matrix as shown. Draw an appropriate diagram to represent the matrix.

$\begin{pmatrix} 0 & 1 & 0 & 1 \\ 0 & 0 & 1 & 1 \\ 1 & 1 & 0 & 1 \\ 1 & 1 & 0 & 0 \\ 1 & 1 & 0 & 0 \end{pmatrix}$

13 The matrix represents a communications network.

(a) How many stations are involved in the network?

(b) Interpret each row of the matrix.

(c) Use your answer in (b). Construct a diagram to show the communications network.

$\begin{pmatrix} 0 & 1 & 0 & 1 \\ 1 & 0 & 0 & 0 \\ 1 & 1 & 0 & 1 \\ 1 & 0 & 1 & 0 \end{pmatrix}$

14 Use a matrix to represent each communications network.

(a) (b) (c)

15 Ships, A, B, and C, are linked by communications devices. A sends messages to B and C, B sends messages to A and C, but C does not send messages.

(a) Draw a diagram to show the communications network.

(b) Use a matrix to show the network in (a).

(c) A fourth ship D is added to the network, but only A and D communicate with each other. Construct a diagram to show the network. Use a matrix to show this network.

# 13.9 Operations with Matrices

The matrix is useful in today's world of data because now data can be recorded in the form of a matrix, and the matrix can be readily stored in a computer. The components of matrices can be added or subtracted. For example, the sales of video cassette recorders (VCR) and compact disc players (CDP) at three branches for August and September are shown.

August Sales

| Store | VCR | CDP |
|---|---|---|
| Woodglen | 52 | 28 |
| Radford | 69 | 31 |
| Harwood | 45 | 19 |

September Sales

| Store | VCR | CDP |
|---|---|---|
| Woodglen | 35 | 17 |
| Radford | 41 | 19 |
| Harwood | 30 | 13 |

Total Sales
August-September

| Store | VCR | CDP |
|---|---|---|
| Woodglen | 87 | 45 |
| Radford | 110 | 50 |
| Harwood | 75 | 32 |

The data above can also be recorded in a matrix. To find the total sales, the matrices are added.

August sales    September sales     Total sales

$$\begin{pmatrix} 52 & 28 \\ 69 & 31 \\ 45 & 19 \end{pmatrix} + \begin{pmatrix} 35 & 17 \\ 41 & 19 \\ 30 & 13 \end{pmatrix} = \begin{pmatrix} 52+35 & 28+17 \\ 69+41 & 31+19 \\ 45+30 & 19+13 \end{pmatrix} = \begin{pmatrix} 87 & 45 \\ 110 & 50 \\ 75 & 32 \end{pmatrix}$$

Matrices can be added only if they have the same dimensions. Two matrices with the same dimensions can also be subtracted. To find how many more sales occurred in August, than in September, you subtract the corresponding entries.

$$\begin{pmatrix} 52 & 28 \\ 69 & 31 \\ 45 & 19 \end{pmatrix} - \begin{pmatrix} 35 & 17 \\ 41 & 19 \\ 30 & 13 \end{pmatrix} = \begin{pmatrix} 52-35 & 28-17 \\ 69-41 & 31-19 \\ 45-30 & 19-13 \end{pmatrix} = \begin{pmatrix} 17 & 11 \\ 28 & 12 \\ 15 & 6 \end{pmatrix}$$

**Scalar Multiplication**

In your previous work in algebra, you learned that $3k$ means $k + k + k$. In a similar way for matrices, you invent the multiplication of a matrix by a real number.

$$3\begin{pmatrix} 2 & -2 \\ 1 & 0 \end{pmatrix} \text{ means } \begin{pmatrix} 2 & -2 \\ 1 & 0 \end{pmatrix} + \begin{pmatrix} 2 & -2 \\ 1 & 0 \end{pmatrix} + \begin{pmatrix} 2 & -2 \\ 1 & 0 \end{pmatrix} = \begin{pmatrix} 2+2+2 & -2-2-2 \\ 1+1+1 & 0+0+0 \end{pmatrix}$$

$$= \begin{pmatrix} 6 & -6 \\ 3 & 0 \end{pmatrix}$$

The number 3 is called a **scalar**. To find the product, each entry of the matrix is multiplied by the scalar.

$$3\begin{pmatrix} 2 & -2 \\ 1 & 0 \end{pmatrix} = \begin{pmatrix} 3 \times 2 & 3 \times (-2) \\ 3 \times 1 & 3 \times 0 \end{pmatrix} = \begin{pmatrix} 6 & -6 \\ 3 & 0 \end{pmatrix}$$

## 13.9 Exercise

**A** Remember: Matrices with the same dimensions can be added or subtracted.

1 Simplify.

(a) $\begin{pmatrix} 3 & -6 & 0 \\ 2 & 1 & 2 \end{pmatrix} + \begin{pmatrix} 4 & 6 & 3 \\ 1 & -3 & -1 \end{pmatrix}$

(b) $\begin{pmatrix} 9 & 12 & 0 \\ -1 & 0 & 3 \\ -2 & 1 & 5 \end{pmatrix} - \begin{pmatrix} 6 & 8 & 3 \\ -2 & 6 & -3 \\ 2 & 1 & 7 \end{pmatrix}$

2 Write each of the following as one matrix.

(a) $2\begin{pmatrix} 3 & -6 \\ 3 & 1 \end{pmatrix} + \begin{pmatrix} 2 & -3 \\ 4 & 2 \end{pmatrix}$

(b) $\begin{pmatrix} 8 & 6 & 2 \\ 1 & -3 & 2 \end{pmatrix} - 3\begin{pmatrix} 6 & 9 & 2 \\ 3 & 0 & 1 \end{pmatrix}$

(c) $3\begin{pmatrix} 3 & 6 & 1 \\ 9 & 2 & 1 \\ 4 & 3 & 0 \end{pmatrix} - 2\begin{pmatrix} 6 & 9 & -1 \\ 0 & 3 & -1 \\ 2 & 1 & 6 \end{pmatrix}$

3 Matrices are given as follows.

$A = \begin{pmatrix} 6 & 9 & 3 \\ 2 & 1 & 8 \end{pmatrix}$

$B = \begin{pmatrix} 3 & -2 & 6 \\ -1 & -8 & 4 \end{pmatrix}$

$C = \begin{pmatrix} 1 & 9 & 3 \\ -1 & 4 & -6 \\ 3 & 7 & 7 \end{pmatrix}$

$D = \begin{pmatrix} 2 & 0 & 9 \\ 7 & 11 & 4 \end{pmatrix}$

$E = \begin{pmatrix} 9 & 4 & 5 \\ -6 & 1 & 11 \\ 2 & 8 & -7 \end{pmatrix}$

Write each of the following as a single matrix.

(a) A + B
(b) B − D
(c) C + E
(d) D − A
(e) A + B + D
(f) E − C
(g) 4B
(h) 2C
(i) 2A − B
(j) C − 3E
(k) 3B − D
(l) 3C − 2E

**B** Throughout the following questions, use a matrix form to express your answers.

4 Data for the sales of pizza are shown in the tables.

**Number Sold Saturday**

|  | Regular | Deluxe |
|---|---|---|
| Small | 12 | 19 |
| Medium | 16 | 17 |
| Large | 18 | 21 |

**Number Sold Sunday**

|  | Regular | Deluxe |
|---|---|---|
| Small | 9 | 17 |
| Medium | 12 | 14 |
| Large | 21 | 16 |

(a) Write the total data for Saturday and Sunday in a matrix form.
(b) Find the total sales.

5   The charts show the number of hobby kits produced at three plants.

October Production

| Plant \ Hobby kits | 1 | 2 | 3 |
|---|---|---|---|
| A | 42 | 46 | 36 |
| B | 36 | 50 | 32 |
| C | 40 | 48 | 34 |

November Production

| Plant \ Hobby kits | 1 | 2 | 3 |
|---|---|---|---|
| A | 60 | 69 | 50 |
| B | 50 | 75 | 45 |
| C | 56 | 72 | 46 |

(a) Represent the information for each month as a matrix.

(b) How much did the production in November increase from October?

(c) Production in November was to be increased by 1.5 times over October. Show this information in matrix form.

(d) Compare the actual production in November with the expected production in (c). Use a matrix form to show your answer.

6   The inventory of batteries at 3 stores is given.

Store A has 12 AA, 90 C, 100 D, 8 9-V batteries.
Store B has 96 AA, 24 C, 38 D, 12 9-V batteries.
Store C has 46 AA, 36 D, 48 C, 16 9-V batteries.

(a) Represent the inventory at each store as a matrix.

(b) Write the total inventory as a matrix. Did you add to find the total inventory?

(c) Create a problem based on the matrices. Solve your problem.

7   Find the components for the missing matrices.

(a) $\begin{pmatrix} 3 & 6 \\ 2 & 1 \end{pmatrix} + X = \begin{pmatrix} 2 & 1 \\ 6 & 3 \end{pmatrix}$

(b) $2Y + \begin{pmatrix} 4 & -3 \\ 2 & 1 \end{pmatrix} = \begin{pmatrix} 6 & 3 \\ -1 & 0 \end{pmatrix}$

(c) $\begin{pmatrix} 4 & -3 \\ 1 & 2 \end{pmatrix} - Z = \begin{pmatrix} 3 & 0 \\ 1 & -5 \end{pmatrix}$

8   (a) Three matrices are given by $A = \begin{pmatrix} 6 & 1 & 3 \\ 2 & 1 & 0 \end{pmatrix}$   $B = \begin{pmatrix} 9 & 6 & -1 \\ 3 & 2 & 1 \end{pmatrix}$   $C = \begin{pmatrix} 8 & 9 & -3 \\ 0 & 1 & 2 \end{pmatrix}$

Complete each step.

*Step 1:* Show whether $A + B \overset{?}{=} B + A$

*Step 2:* Show whether $A + (B + C) \overset{?}{=} (A + B) + C$

*Step 3:* Show whether $3(A + B) \overset{?}{=} 3A + 3B$

(b) Repeat *Steps* 1, 2, and 3 for matrices of your own choice. What do you notice?

(c) Based on your results in (a) and (b), what generalizations can you make?

## 13.10 Multiplying Matrices

Many businesses use computers to store data. These data are often in a matrix form. The owner can obtain information about the sales at each outlet. This notation was invented to accommodate any situation that might arise.

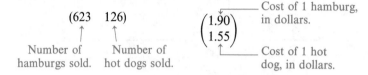

The following expression is used to calculate the total sales for one outlet.

$$623(\$1.90) + 126(\$1.55)$$

number of   cost of 1   number of   cost of 1
hamburgs   hamburg   hot dogs   hot dog

If more than one outlet is involved, the data can be recorded in a matrix form.

$$\begin{array}{cc} & \text{number of} \quad \text{number of} \\ & \text{hamburgs} \quad \text{hot dogs} \\ \text{Store A} \longrightarrow & \begin{pmatrix} 623 & 126 \\ 496 & 186 \\ 782 & 212 \end{pmatrix} \\ \text{Store B} \longrightarrow & \\ \text{Store C} \longrightarrow & \end{array}$$

To calculate the sales of each outlet, multiply the matrices,

$$\begin{pmatrix} 623 & 126 \\ 496 & 186 \\ 782 & 212 \end{pmatrix} \begin{pmatrix} 1.90 \\ 1.55 \end{pmatrix} = \begin{pmatrix} 623 \times 1.90 + 126 \times 1.55 \\ 496 \times 1.90 + 186 \times 1.55 \\ 782 \times 1.90 + 212 \times 1.55 \end{pmatrix}$$

$$= \begin{pmatrix} 1379.00 \\ 1230.70 \\ 1814.40 \end{pmatrix} \leftarrow \text{This component means the total sales at outlet B.}$$

Examples, such as those above, suggest a method for multiplying matrices.

$$(a \quad b \quad c)\begin{pmatrix} e \\ f \\ g \end{pmatrix} = (ae + bf + cg) \qquad \begin{pmatrix} a & b \\ c & d \end{pmatrix}\begin{pmatrix} e \\ f \end{pmatrix} = \begin{pmatrix} ae + bf \\ ce + df \end{pmatrix}$$

The diagram shows the entries used to find the product of matrices.

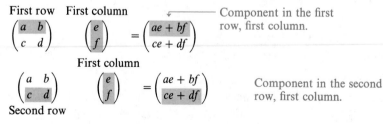

First row   First column

$$\begin{pmatrix} a & b \\ c & d \end{pmatrix} \qquad \begin{pmatrix} e \\ f \end{pmatrix} = \begin{pmatrix} ae + bf \\ ce + df \end{pmatrix}$$

Component in the first row, first column.

First column

$$\begin{pmatrix} a & b \\ c & d \end{pmatrix} \qquad \begin{pmatrix} e \\ f \end{pmatrix} = \begin{pmatrix} ae + bf \\ ce + df \end{pmatrix}$$

Second row

Component in the second row, first column.

A similar procedure is followed to find the product of matrices of other orders.

$$\begin{pmatrix} a & b \\ c & d \end{pmatrix}\begin{pmatrix} e & g \\ f & h \end{pmatrix} = \begin{pmatrix} ae + bf & ag + bh \\ ce + df & cg + dh \end{pmatrix}$$

1st row   1st column         Component in

$$\begin{pmatrix} a & b \\ c & d \end{pmatrix} \quad \begin{pmatrix} e & g \\ f & h \end{pmatrix} = \begin{pmatrix} \square & \\ & \end{pmatrix}$$
1st row, 1st column.

2nd row   1st column

$$\begin{pmatrix} a & b \\ c & d \end{pmatrix} \quad \begin{pmatrix} e & g \\ f & h \end{pmatrix} = \begin{pmatrix} & \\ \square & \end{pmatrix}$$
Component in
2nd row, 1st column.

Two matrices can be multiplied if the number of columns in the first matrix is the same as the number of rows in the second matrix.

Matrix A                Matrix B
2 × 3                   3 × 1

The number     equals     The number
of columns                of rows

## 13.10 Exercise

**A 1** (a) Find the product of the matrices $\begin{pmatrix} 3 & 6 \\ 2 & 1 \end{pmatrix}\begin{pmatrix} -3 \\ 2 \end{pmatrix}$.

(b) How are the orders of the matrices in (a) related to the order of the product?

2 Calculate each of the following.

(a) $(4 \ \ 6 \ \ 3)\begin{pmatrix} 0 \\ -1 \\ 2 \end{pmatrix}$   
(b) $\begin{pmatrix} 6 & 9 \\ -3 & 2 \end{pmatrix}\begin{pmatrix} 4 \\ 5 \end{pmatrix}$   
(c) $\begin{pmatrix} 8 & 9 \\ -3 & 0 \end{pmatrix}\begin{pmatrix} 6 & 0 \\ -3 & 2 \end{pmatrix}$   
(d) $\begin{pmatrix} 6 & 8 \\ 3 & -2 \end{pmatrix}\begin{pmatrix} 5 & 0 \\ 0 & 4 \end{pmatrix}$

3 For each of the following products,
- decide how to obtain each component of the answer matrix.
- then find the product.

(a) $\begin{pmatrix} 3 & 6 & 9 \\ 4 & 8 & 2 \end{pmatrix}\begin{pmatrix} 4 & 2 \\ 6 & 3 \\ 1 & 9 \end{pmatrix}$      
(b) $\begin{pmatrix} -3 & 9 & 2 \\ 0 & 4 & -3 \\ 0 & 0 & 6 \end{pmatrix}\begin{pmatrix} 3 & -9 & 0 \\ -2 & 6 & -3 \\ 4 & -2 & 1 \end{pmatrix}$

4 Remember: $M^2$ means $M \times M$. Find each product.

(a) $\begin{pmatrix} 3 & 6 \\ 1 & -2 \end{pmatrix}^2$     
(b) $\begin{pmatrix} 2 & 0 \\ 0 & 3 \end{pmatrix}^2$     
(c) $\begin{pmatrix} 3 & 6 & 0 \\ -3 & 2 & 0 \\ 1 & -4 & 6 \end{pmatrix}^2$

5  (a) Find each product. What do you notice about your answers?

$$\begin{pmatrix} 3 & -6 \\ -2 & 1 \end{pmatrix}\begin{pmatrix} 1 & 0 \\ 0 & 1 \end{pmatrix} \qquad \begin{pmatrix} -2 & 3 \\ -4 & 5 \end{pmatrix}\begin{pmatrix} 1 & 0 \\ 0 & 1 \end{pmatrix}$$

   (b) Why would the name **identity matrix** be a suitable description of the matrix $\begin{pmatrix} 1 & 0 \\ 0 & 1 \end{pmatrix}$?

**B** Products of matrices are used to solve problems. **PSP**

Questions 6 to 11 are based on the given information. The current standings of three soccer teams are shown in the chart. The points awarded for a win, a loss, and a tie are shown by the $3 \times 1$ matrix.

|  | Wins | Losses | Ties |
|---|---|---|---|
| Riders | 21 | 1 | 4 |
| Bears | 6 | 12 | 8 |
| Tigers | 10 | 10 | 4 |

Points
$$\begin{pmatrix} 2 \\ 0 \\ 1 \end{pmatrix} \begin{array}{l} \longleftarrow \text{win} \\ \longleftarrow \text{loss} \\ \longleftarrow \text{tie} \end{array}$$

6  (a) Interpret the meaning of this product of matrices.

$$(21 \quad 1 \quad 4)\begin{pmatrix} 2 \\ 0 \\ 1 \end{pmatrix}$$

   (b) Find the product in (a).

7  (a) Why can you not give a meaning to this product of the matrices?

$$(6 \quad 12)\begin{pmatrix} 2 \\ 0 \\ 1 \end{pmatrix}$$

   (b) Change the product in (a) so that you can obtain an answer.

8  (a) What is the interpretation of this product?

$$\begin{pmatrix} 21 & 1 & 4 \\ 6 & 12 & 8 \end{pmatrix}\begin{pmatrix} 2 \\ 0 \\ 1 \end{pmatrix}$$

   (b) Write the answer in (a) as a matrix. Interpret each component of this matrix.

9  (a) What matrices would you multiply to find the standings of all the teams?
   (b) Write a matrix to show the points standings of the teams.

10  During the next two weeks, the teams had the record shown at right. Represent in a matrix the up-to-date information on wins, losses, and ties for the three teams. What operation did you use?

Week 1
$$\begin{pmatrix} 2 & 2 & 1 \\ 3 & 1 & 1 \\ 4 & 1 & 0 \end{pmatrix}$$

Week 2
$$\begin{pmatrix} 3 & 1 & 1 \\ 0 & 1 & 4 \\ 2 & 1 & 1 \end{pmatrix}$$

11  Find the total number of points scored by each team. What operation did you use?

Questions 12 to 16 are based on the following information. At the Photo Shop's two outlets, the inventory of camera models A, B and C is to be sold in two ways:

(i) at the regular price, camera and case

(ii) at a promotion price, to include 3 films and processing

The data are recorded in these charts.

Number of Cameras

| Store \ Camera model | A | B | C |
|---|---|---|---|
| Ryder Rd. | 40 | 30 | 25 |
| Beck St. | 35 | 20 | 15 |

Selling Price ($)

| Camera Model \ Selling Method | Regular | Promotion |
|---|---|---|
| A | $90.35 | $102.80 |
| B | $193.25 | $201.90 |
| C | $292.60 | $302.65 |

12 Represent the information using matrices.

13 Based on the data, how would you interpret each product of matrices?

(a) $(40 \quad 30 \quad 25)\begin{pmatrix} 90.35 \\ 193.25 \\ 292.60 \end{pmatrix}$

(b) $(35 \quad 20 \quad 15)\begin{pmatrix} 102.80 \\ 201.90 \\ 302.65 \end{pmatrix}$

14 (a) Write a product of matrices to show the total value of the cameras at the Beck Street outlet selling at regular price.

(b) Find the total value in (a).

15 (a) Write a product of matrices to show the total value of cameras at both outlets selling at the regular price.

(b) Find the total value in (a).

16 (a) Write a product of matrices to show the total value of all cameras at both outlets.

(b) Find the value in (a).

17 (a) Matrices M and N are given as $M = \begin{pmatrix} -6 & 3 \\ 2 & 1 \end{pmatrix}$ $N = \begin{pmatrix} 3 & -9 \\ 2 & 5 \end{pmatrix}$
Show that $M \times N \neq N \times M$.

(b) Choose 2 matrices of your own, with order $2 \times 2$. Show that $M \times N \neq N \times M$.

C 18 (a) Matrix $K = \begin{pmatrix} 0 & -1 \\ 1 & 0 \end{pmatrix}$. Find the matrix represented by $K^2$, $K^3$, $K^4$.

(b) Based on your results, predict the matrix represented by $K^5$. Check your prediction by finding $K^5$.

(c) Write a formula to show the components of the matrix $K^n$.

# 13.11 Inverse of a Matrix

Questions asked in previous branches of mathematics, are often asked again in later branches.

*Real Numbers:* Does the real number $\frac{1}{2}$ have an inverse with respect to the operation of multiplication?

$$\left(\frac{1}{2}\right)(2) = 1$$

The product of $\frac{1}{2}$ and its inverse is the identity with respect to multiplication.

The identity with respect to the operation of multiplication is 1.

*Matrices:* Does a matrix have an inverse with respect to the operation of multiplication?

To find the inverse of a matrix, you need to know the identity matrix. In an earlier exercise you found that an identity matrix occurs with respect to multiplication for a $2 \times 2$ matrix.

$$I = \begin{pmatrix} 1 & 0 \\ 0 & 1 \end{pmatrix}$$

$$\begin{pmatrix} 3 & -2 \\ -1 & 6 \end{pmatrix}\begin{pmatrix} 1 & 0 \\ 0 & 1 \end{pmatrix} = \begin{pmatrix} 3 & -2 \\ -1 & 6 \end{pmatrix} \qquad \begin{pmatrix} 1 & 0 \\ 0 & 1 \end{pmatrix}\begin{pmatrix} 3 & -2 \\ -1 & 6 \end{pmatrix} = \begin{pmatrix} 3 & -2 \\ -1 & 6 \end{pmatrix}$$

Matrices A and B are inverses if their product equals the identity matrix. Namely, $AB \times BA = I$.

To find the inverse of a matrix, a real number called the **determinant** of a matrix is defined. For a $2 \times 2$ matrix $A = \begin{pmatrix} a & b \\ c & d \end{pmatrix}$. The determinant of A is given by

$$\det A = ad - bc.$$

For example, if $A = \begin{pmatrix} 7 & -3 \\ 1 & -2 \end{pmatrix}$ then

$$\begin{aligned}
\det A &= ad - bc \\
&= (7)(-2) - (-3)(1) \\
&= -14 + 3 \\
&= -11
\end{aligned}$$

For any matrix A where $\det A \neq 0$, then you can find the inverse matrix for A. The inverse matrix, given by $A^{-1}$, is obtained as shown.

$$A = \begin{pmatrix} a & b \\ c & d \end{pmatrix} \qquad A^{-1} = \frac{1}{\det A}\begin{pmatrix} d & -b \\ -c & a \end{pmatrix}$$

This is a real number, or scalar.

**Example**   Find the inverse matrix, $B^{-1}$, where $B = \begin{pmatrix} -2 & 1 \\ 5 & 0 \end{pmatrix}$.

**Solution**   Use $a = -2$, $b = 1$, $c = 5$, $d = 0$.

$$\det B = ad - bc$$
$$= (-2)(0) - (1)(5)$$
$$= -5$$

$$B^{-1} = \frac{1}{\det B} \begin{pmatrix} d & -b \\ -c & a \end{pmatrix}$$

$$= \frac{1}{-5} \begin{pmatrix} 0 & -1 \\ -5 & -2 \end{pmatrix}$$

$$= \begin{pmatrix} 0 & \dfrac{1}{5} \\ 1 & \dfrac{2}{5} \end{pmatrix}$$

**PSP**

You can check your work by showing $B \times B^{-1} = I$.

## 13.11   Exercise

**A** Remember: Review the meaning of the symbols det A, $A^{-1}$.

1   Find the determinant of each matrix.

(a) $\begin{pmatrix} 6 & -1 \\ -2 & 3 \end{pmatrix}$    (b) $\begin{pmatrix} 4 & -1 \\ 5 & -9 \end{pmatrix}$    (c) $\begin{pmatrix} 6 & -3 \\ 1 & 2 \end{pmatrix}$    (d) $\begin{pmatrix} 2 & 1 \\ 5 & -4 \end{pmatrix}$

(e) $\begin{pmatrix} 1 & 5 \\ 0 & -2 \end{pmatrix}$    (f) $\begin{pmatrix} 3 & 1 \\ 6 & 2 \end{pmatrix}$    (g) $\begin{pmatrix} 4 & 0 \\ 4 & -4 \end{pmatrix}$    (h) $\begin{pmatrix} -1 & 4 \\ 2 & -1 \end{pmatrix}$

Based on your results in (a) to (h), which matrix does not have an inverse?

2   A matrix is given by $Y = \begin{pmatrix} 1 & 1 \\ 2 & 1 \end{pmatrix}$.

Which of the following is the inverse matrix for Y?

(a) $\begin{pmatrix} -1 & -1 \\ 2 & 1 \end{pmatrix}$    (b) $\begin{pmatrix} -1 & 1 \\ -2 & -1 \end{pmatrix}$    (c) $\begin{pmatrix} -1 & 1 \\ 2 & -1 \end{pmatrix}$    (d) $\begin{pmatrix} 1 & -1 \\ 2 & -1 \end{pmatrix}$

3   Find the inverse for each matrix.

(a) $\begin{pmatrix} 1 & 1 \\ 2 & 1 \end{pmatrix}$    (b) $\begin{pmatrix} 2 & 1 \\ 1 & 1 \end{pmatrix}$    (c) $\begin{pmatrix} 1 & 2 \\ 1 & 1 \end{pmatrix}$    (d) $\begin{pmatrix} 1 & 1 \\ 1 & 2 \end{pmatrix}$

4   A matrix is given by $M = \begin{pmatrix} 6 & 0 \\ 0 & 3 \end{pmatrix}$.

(a) Find the components of the inverse matrix, $M^{-1}$.

(b) Find the product $M \times M^{-1}$ and the product $M^{-1} \times M$. What do you notice?

5   If $K = \begin{pmatrix} 3 & 0 \\ -2 & 4 \end{pmatrix}$, find    (a) $K^{-1}$    (b) $K \times K^{-1}$    (c) $K^{-1} \times K$

**B** Remember: For a matrix A to have an inverse, det A $\neq$ 0.

6  Show that $E = \begin{pmatrix} 4 & -2 \\ -3 & -1 \end{pmatrix}$ and $F = \begin{pmatrix} \dfrac{1}{10} & -\dfrac{1}{5} \\ -\dfrac{3}{10} & -\dfrac{2}{5} \end{pmatrix}$ are inverses of each other.

7  A matrix is given by $A = \begin{pmatrix} 8 & -3 \\ 5 & -6 \end{pmatrix}$.

   (a) Find the components of the inverse matrix $A^{-1}$.

   (b) Find the products $A \times A^{-1}$ and $A^{-1} \times A$.

   (c) What do you notice about your answers?

8  Find the inverse of each matrix, where possible.

   (a) $\begin{pmatrix} 4 & -2 \\ 1 & 1 \end{pmatrix}$
   (b) $\begin{pmatrix} 2 & 1 \\ 1 & -2 \end{pmatrix}$
   (c) $\begin{pmatrix} 3 & -4 \\ 2 & 1 \end{pmatrix}$
   (d) $\begin{pmatrix} 4 & 6 \\ 1 & -3 \end{pmatrix}$

   (e) $\begin{pmatrix} 4 & 5 \\ 6 & -1 \end{pmatrix}$
   (f) $\begin{pmatrix} 6 & -8 \\ 2 & 0 \end{pmatrix}$
   (g) $\begin{pmatrix} 3 & 4 \\ 9 & 12 \end{pmatrix}$
   (h) $\begin{pmatrix} -7 & 1 \\ 8 & -2 \end{pmatrix}$

**C** 9  A product of matrices is equal to the identity matrix. $\begin{pmatrix} a & b \\ c & d \end{pmatrix}\begin{pmatrix} x_1 & x_2 \\ x_3 & x_4 \end{pmatrix} = \begin{pmatrix} 1 & 0 \\ 0 & 1 \end{pmatrix}$

   (a) Why is $ax_1 + bx_3 = 1$?    (b) Why is $ax_2 + bx_4 = 0$?

   (c) By equating components in the above product of matrices, write the remaining equations.

   (d) Solve the equations in (a) to (c) for the variables $x_1$, $x_2$, $x_3$, and $x_4$.

   (e) Based on your results in (a) to (d), what are the components of the inverse matrix for $\begin{pmatrix} a & b \\ c & d \end{pmatrix}$?

---

## Math Tip

- The following list are key words that you have learned. Do you have a clear understanding of each of the following? If not, use the *Index* to locate the word and refresh your memory.

  *system of linear equations, rational expression, function, vector, vertical line test, inequation, relation, linear function, intercept, radical, tangent, parallel postulate, parallel lines, congruence, similar figures, matrix, sine, congruence postulates, mean, histogram, slope, perpendicular lines, cosine*

- Use the *Index* of this book on pages 559 and 560. List the words you do not fully understand and then refer to its meaning on the referenced page.

# Applications: Matrices and Codes

Inverse matrices can be used to send secret messages. Each letter of the alphabet is assigned a number. Both the sender (encoder) and receiver (decoder) of the message must know how the letters and numbers correspond. For example, one letter-number correspondence is shown.

A B C D E F G H I J K L M N O P Q R S T U V W X Y Z
↕ ↕ ↕ ↕ ↕ ↕ ↕ ↕ ↕ ↕ ↕ ↕ ↕ ↕ ↕ ↕ ↕ ↕ ↕ ↕ ↕ ↕ ↕ ↕ ↕ ↕
26 25 24 23 22 21 20 19 18 17 16 15 14 13 12 11 10 9 8 7 6 5 4 3 2 1

A 2 × 2 matrix and its inverse are used to encode and decode messages.

$$\text{Encoder Matrix, } M = \begin{pmatrix} 2 & 3 \\ 1 & 2 \end{pmatrix} \qquad \text{Decoder Matrix, } M^{-1}\begin{pmatrix} 2 & -3 \\ -1 & 2 \end{pmatrix}$$

**Encoding**  To encode a message, such as HELP ME, you follow these steps.

*Step 1:* Record the number—letter correspondence.

| H | E | L | P | M | E |
|---|---|---|---|---|---|
| 19 | 22 | 15 | 11 | 14 | 22 |

*Step 2:* Pair the numbers to form 1 × 2 row matrices.

$$\begin{matrix} A & B & C \\ (19 \quad 22) & (15 \quad 11) & (14 \quad 22) \end{matrix}$$

*Step 3:* Multiply each matrix by the encoder matrix.

$$\begin{matrix} A \\ (19 \quad 22)\begin{pmatrix} 2 & 3 \\ 1 & 2 \end{pmatrix} \\ = (38 + 22 \quad 57 + 44) \\ = (60 \quad 101) \end{matrix} \qquad \begin{matrix} B \\ (15 \quad 11)\begin{pmatrix} 2 & 3 \\ 1 & 2 \end{pmatrix} \\ = (30 + 11 \quad 45 + 22) \\ = (41 \quad 67) \end{matrix} \qquad \begin{matrix} C \\ (14 \quad 22)\begin{pmatrix} 2 & 3 \\ 1 & 2 \end{pmatrix} \\ = (28 + 22 \quad 42 + 44) \\ = (50 \quad 86) \end{matrix}$$

*Step 4:* The message you send is written as   60   101   41   67   50   86

---

10   Use the decoder matrix $M^{-1} = \begin{pmatrix} 2 & -3 \\ -1 & 2 \end{pmatrix}$. Find each product.

(a) $(60 \quad 101)\begin{pmatrix} 2 & -3 \\ -1 & 2 \end{pmatrix}$   (b) $(41 \quad 67)\begin{pmatrix} 2 & -3 \\ -1 & 2 \end{pmatrix}$   (c) $(50 \quad 86)\begin{pmatrix} 2 & -3 \\ -1 & 2 \end{pmatrix}$

What results did you expect to obtain in (a) to (c)?

11   Use the letter-number correspondence above and encoder matrix $M = \begin{pmatrix} 2 & 3 \\ 1 & 2 \end{pmatrix}$.

Write each of the following messages in code.

(a) I GOT IT     (b) EUREKA     (c) TRAVEL CANADA     (d) MATH IS IT

12   Use the letter-number correspondence above and decoder matrix $M^{-1} = \begin{pmatrix} 2 & -3 \\ -1 & 2 \end{pmatrix}$.

Decode the following message.

49   80   49   76   53   84   45   74   48   74   33   59   59   92   54
94   33   59   34   64   24   40   38   64   36   66   59   99   25   44

# 13.12 Matrices for Solving Linear Systems

You have already developed methods for solving a linear system of equations. When a linear system of equations occurs in matrix form, you invent matrix methods to solve the system.

Linear System

$$5x + 2y = 14$$
$$3x - 7y = 33$$

Linear System in Matrix Form

$$\begin{pmatrix} 5 & 2 \\ 3 & -7 \end{pmatrix}\begin{pmatrix} x \\ y \end{pmatrix} = \begin{pmatrix} 14 \\ 33 \end{pmatrix}$$

This matrix is called the coefficient matrix, C.

This matrix is called the variable matrix, V.

As in your earlier work in solving equations, the principle is to isolate the variables. Similarly to solve a system of linear equations written in matrix form, you wish to isolate the variables. In matrix form, the linear system becomes

$$C \times V = \begin{pmatrix} 14 \\ 33 \end{pmatrix}$$

To solve the system, you can multiply the matrix equation by the inverse of C. The following steps illustrate this principle.

$$C \times V = \begin{pmatrix} 14 \\ 33 \end{pmatrix}$$

$$C^{-1}(C \times V) = C^{-1}\begin{pmatrix} 14 \\ 33 \end{pmatrix}$$

$$V = C^{-1}\begin{pmatrix} 14 \\ 33 \end{pmatrix} \quad \text{since } C \times C^{-1} = I$$

Thus, to solve the system, you need to find the inverse of the coefficient matrix, as shown in the following example.

**Example**   Solve $5x + 2y = 14$, using a matrix method.
$$3x - 7y = 33$$

**Solution**   Write the system in the form of a matrix equation.

$$\begin{pmatrix} 5 & 2 \\ 3 & -7 \end{pmatrix}\begin{pmatrix} x \\ y \end{pmatrix} = \begin{pmatrix} 14 \\ 33 \end{pmatrix}$$

$$\underset{C}{\uparrow} \quad \underset{V}{\uparrow}$$

Find the inverse matrix, $C^{-1}$.

$$\det C = ad - bc$$
$$= (5)(-7) - (2)(3)$$
$$= -41$$

$$C^{-1} = \frac{1}{\det C}\begin{pmatrix} d & -b \\ -c & a \end{pmatrix}$$

$$= \frac{1}{-41}\begin{pmatrix} -7 & -2 \\ -3 & 5 \end{pmatrix}$$

$$= \begin{pmatrix} \dfrac{7}{41} & \dfrac{2}{41} \\ \dfrac{3}{41} & \dfrac{-5}{41} \end{pmatrix}$$

Solve the matrix equation. Multiply both sides of the matrix equation by $C^{-1}$.

$$\begin{pmatrix} \dfrac{7}{41} & \dfrac{2}{41} \\ \dfrac{3}{41} & -\dfrac{5}{41} \end{pmatrix} \begin{pmatrix} 5 & 2 \\ 3 & -7 \end{pmatrix} \begin{pmatrix} x \\ y \end{pmatrix} = \begin{pmatrix} \dfrac{7}{41} & \dfrac{2}{41} \\ \dfrac{3}{41} & -\dfrac{5}{41} \end{pmatrix} \begin{pmatrix} 14 \\ 33 \end{pmatrix}$$

$$\begin{pmatrix} 1 & 0 \\ 0 & 1 \end{pmatrix} \begin{pmatrix} x \\ y \end{pmatrix} = \begin{pmatrix} \dfrac{98 + 66}{41} \\ \dfrac{42 - 165}{41} \end{pmatrix}$$

$$\begin{pmatrix} x \\ y \end{pmatrix} = \begin{pmatrix} \dfrac{164}{41} \\ -\dfrac{123}{41} \end{pmatrix}$$

$$\begin{pmatrix} x \\ y \end{pmatrix} = \begin{pmatrix} 4 \\ -3 \end{pmatrix} \qquad \text{The check is left for you to verify.}$$

Thus, from the matrix form $x = 4$, $y = -3$.

The significance of solving a linear system by using a matrix form is that the method can be applied to any number of variables. For such systems, the method of using matrices can be computer programmed.

## 13.12 Exercise

B Review the method of finding the inverse of a matrix.

1 Write each linear system of equations as a matrix equation.

(a) $x - y = 6$
$3x + 4y = 7$

(b) $2x + y = -1$
$-3x - y = 6$

(c) $7x - 4y = -1$
$2x + y = 5$

(d) $x = 4y - 3$
$2x + y = 7$

2 Find the inverse matrix, you would need to solve each system of linear equation. Then solve each system.

(a) $\begin{pmatrix} 7 & 1 \\ 2 & -3 \end{pmatrix} \begin{pmatrix} x \\ y \end{pmatrix} = \begin{pmatrix} 13 \\ 12 \end{pmatrix}$

(b) $\begin{pmatrix} 4 & 5 \\ 4 & -5 \end{pmatrix} \begin{pmatrix} x \\ y \end{pmatrix} = \begin{pmatrix} 8 \\ 6 \end{pmatrix}$

(c) $\begin{pmatrix} 6 & 2 \\ 3 & 5 \end{pmatrix} \begin{pmatrix} x \\ y \end{pmatrix} = \begin{pmatrix} 9 \\ -3 \end{pmatrix}$

3 Solve each linear system. Use a matrix method.

(a) $x + 3y = 1$
$3x - y = 3$

(b) $2x - 3y = 7$
$3x + 2y = 4$

(c) $3x - y = -9$
$x - 2y = -3$

(d) $2x + y = 6$
$3x - 2y = 9$

(e) $2x + y = 6$
$x - y = -3$

(f) $3x - 4y = -2$
$2x + y = 5$

(g) $3x - 2y = 10$
$x + 5y = -3$

(h) $4x = 11 + 3y$
$2x = 9 + 5y$

# Practice and Problems: Review

1   A coast guard patrol leaves home base and travels North at 18.0 km/h. After 2 h, it changes course and travels on a heading of 110°. After a half hour it changes its course to 215°. After 2.5 h it arrives at Bell Island.

   (a) Construct a scale diagram for the coast guard patrol.
   (b) How far is the coast guard from home base?
   (c) What is the bearing of its final destination from home base?
   (d) Use a vector in the form $[a, b]$ to show its displacement.

2   In △ABC, M is the midpoint of AB. If MN is parallel to BC, prove that AN = NC.

3   On Monday, 28 adult and 23 children tickets were sold. On Tuesday, 12 adults and 16 children tickets were sold. On Wednesday 15 adult and 18 children tickets were sold. The cost of tickets was $6 for adults and $3 for children.

   (a) Represent the total ticket sales as a 3 × 2 matrix.
   (b) Represent the cost of tickets in a column matrix.
   (c) Use matrix multiplication to find the value of tickets sold each day.

# Practice Test

1   Use a scale diagram to draw the velocity of each current in a river.

   | Magnitude of Current | Direction of Current |
   |---|---|
   | (a) 5.0 km/h | S40°W |
   | (b) 5 km/h | N60°E |

2   An object undergoes a displacement. Find the missing values in each case.

   | | Displacement | Co-ordinates of original position | Co-ordinates of final position |
   |---|---|---|---|
   | (a) | $[-3, 4]$ | $(-3, 5)$ | $(?, ?)$ |
   | (b) | $[8, -2]$ | $(?, ?)$ | $(6, 2)$ |
   | (c) | $[-6, -9]$ | $(-3, ?)$ | $(?, 8)$ |

3   Write each as one matrix. (a) $2\begin{pmatrix} 2 & -3 \\ 4 & 1 \end{pmatrix} + 3\begin{pmatrix} -3 & 6 \\ 2 & 0 \end{pmatrix}$   (b) $6\begin{pmatrix} -3 & 1 \\ 2 & 1 \end{pmatrix}\begin{pmatrix} 2 & 6 \\ -3 & 1 \end{pmatrix}$

4   (a) Illustrate what is meant by adding vectors using the parallelogram law.
   (b) Find the resultant of the vectors represented by $[4, 2]$ and $[6, -3]$.

5   Two vectors are given by $\vec{a} = [3, 6]$, $\vec{b}\,[-1, 3]$.
   (a) Illustrate vector $\vec{a} + 2\vec{b}$ on a grid.   (b) Find the magnitude of vector $2\vec{a} - \vec{b}$.

6   M and N are the midpoints of AD and BC respectively in rectangle ABCD. Use vectors to prove MN = AB and MN ‖ AB.

# 14

# *Transformations: Concepts and Co-ordinates*

language of transformations, translations and mappings, properties of reflections, rotations, and dilatations, invariant properties, proving deductions, transformations and equations, matrices and transformations, skills, strategies, problem solving

## Introduction

As you study mathematics, you are developing for yourself a framework for a *Problem-Solving Plan*. A plan is to help you to develop your ability to solve problems in any problem-solving situation, whether in mathematics, or in another discipline. Throughout your study, you have continued to build your plan by placing skills and strategies into the appropriate shaded part of the *Problem-Solving Plan* **PSP**.

In this chapter, you will explore skills and strategies of another geometry.

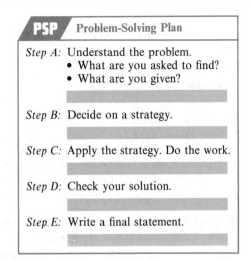

**PSP** Problem-Solving Plan

*Step A:* Understand the problem.
- What are you asked to find?
- What are you given?

*Step B:* Decide on a strategy.

*Step C:* Apply the strategy. Do the work.

*Step D:* Check your solution.

*Step E:* Write a final statement.

- In plane geometry you studied relations and properties among geometric shapes. You also learned to prove deductions.

- In co-ordinate geometry you used co-ordinates to locate points and figures on the plane. You also learned important strategies and skills for solving problems.

- In this chapter on transformational geometry, you will study the properties and applications of translations, reflections, rotations, and dilatations, which are collectively called **transformations**. If the shape, size, or position of a figure changes, then the figure is said to have undergone a transformation. You will use the skills and strategies in this chapter to prove properties about figures. As this chapter unfolds, place the skills and strategies into the appropriate place in your *Problem-Solving Plan* **PSP**.

## 14.1 Translations and Mappings

A translation is a transformation that relates points on a plane in a particular way.

**Translation Postulate**
The correspondence
$A \longrightarrow A', B \longrightarrow B', C \longrightarrow C'$
is a translation, if and only if
- $AA' = BB' = CC'$ and
- $AA' \parallel BB' \parallel CC'$

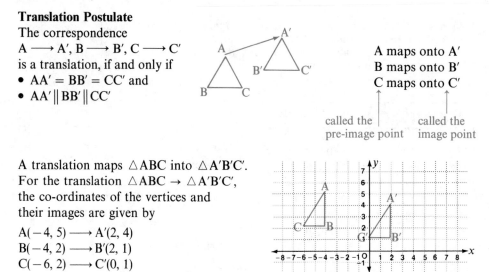

A maps onto A'
B maps onto B'
C maps onto C'

called the pre-image point        called the image point

A translation maps $\triangle ABC$ into $\triangle A'B'C'$.
For the translation $\triangle ABC \rightarrow \triangle A'B'C'$,
the co-ordinates of the vertices and
their images are given by

$A(-4, 5) \longrightarrow A'(2, 4)$
$B(-4, 2) \longrightarrow B'(2, 1)$
$C(-6, 2) \longrightarrow C'(0, 1)$

A transformation can be shown as a mapping of ordered pairs. The previous translation can be represented by the following mapping rule:

$(x, y) \qquad (x + 6, y - 1)$

**Example**  The co-ordinates of the vertices of $\triangle PQR$ are $P(-1, 3)$, $Q(2, 6)$ and $R(6, -2)$. A translation, given by the mapping rule $(x, y) \longrightarrow (x - 2, y - 5)$, is applied to $\triangle PQR$.

(a)  Find the co-ordinates of the vertices of the translation image of $\triangle PQR$.

(b)  Use a Cartesian grid to show $\triangle PQR$ and its translation image.

**Solution**  (a) $(x, y) \longrightarrow (x - 2, y - 5)$
$P(-1, 3) \longrightarrow P'(-3, -2)$
$Q(2, 6) \longrightarrow Q'(0, 1)$
$R(6, -2) \longrightarrow R'(4, -7)$

(b)

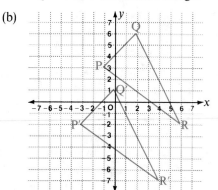

When a transformation is applied to a figure, the figure may undergo a change in position, size, or shape. Some properties or characteristics may change, but others may not. Those properties or characteristics that do not change are said to be **invariant**. For the translation of △PQR in the example,

- which properties change?
- which properties are invariant?

 Remember: To solve problems, you need to know the vocabulary.

## 14.1 Exercise

**A** Review the meaning of *pre-image point*, *image point*, *mapping rule*, and *translation*.

1   Find the co-ordinates of the image point of each of the following, for the translation given by $(x, y) \longrightarrow (x + 4, y - 1)$.

   (a) $(2, 5)$         (b) $(-3, 0)$        (c) $(-2, 3)$       (d) $(1, -4)$

2   Find the co-ordinates of the pre-image points, if each of the following are the image points for the translation given by $(x, y) \longrightarrow (x - 3, y - 6)$.

   (a) $(-2, 3)$       (b) $(8, 2)$          (c) $(4, -5)$       (d) $(-2, -3)$

3   Write the mapping rule to describe each of the following translations.

   (a) $△PQR \longrightarrow △P'Q'R'$

   (b) Square ABCD $\longrightarrow$ Square A'B'C'D'

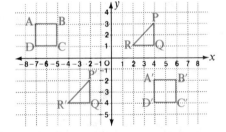

**B** You need to use your skills with co-ordinate geometry in the following questions.

 Refer to your *Problem-Solving Plan*. Is your list of skills and strategies up to date?

4   △ABC has vertices given by A(3, 2), B(3, −1), and C(6, −1). Use the mapping rule $(x, y) \longrightarrow (x - 2, y + 3)$.

   (a) Find the co-ordinates of the image points A', B', and C'.

   (b) Calculate the slopes of AB and A'B'. What do you notice?

   (c) Calculate the slopes of AC and A'C'. What do you notice?

   (d) Calculate the slopes of BC and B'C'. What do you notice?

   (e) What conclusion can you come to about the slope of a line and the slope of its translation image?

5   The vertices of $\triangle$LMN are L($-3$, $-2$), M(1, 0), and N($-5$, 2). Use the translation given by $(x, y) \longrightarrow (x + 5, y - 4)$.

(a) Find the translation image of $\triangle$LMN. Show $\triangle$LMN and $\triangle$L'M'N' on a Cartesian grid.

(b) Find the lengths LM and L'M'. What do you notice?

(c) Compare the lengths MN and M'N'. What do you notice?

(d) Calculate the lengths LN and L'N'. What do you notice?

(e) What probable conclusion can you arrive at about the length of a line segment and the length of its translation image?

6   Refer to the triangles in Questions 4 and 5.

(a) Which triangles are congruent? Justify your answer.

(b) Calculate the area of each triangle. Which triangles have equal areas?

(c) Describe the orientation of the pre-image and image triangles. What do you notice?

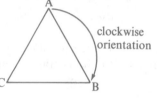

clockwise orientation

7   Based on your results in the previous questions, which of the following are invariant for a translation?

(a) lengths of line segments     (b) slopes of line segments

(c) measures of angles           (d) the orientation of the vertices

(e) areas of the figures

8   (a) Use an illustration of your own to show each property of translations.

(b) Which properties in (a) are invariant?

9   A translation, in general, is given by the mapping rule
$$(x, y) \longrightarrow (x + a, y + b), \quad a, b \in R.$$
Two points, A($x_1$, $y_1$) and B($x_2$, $y_2$) are mapped onto A' and B' by the above translation.

(a) Prove that AB and A'B' have the same slope, and therefore, are parallel.

(b) Prove that AB and A'B' are equal in length.

(c) Justify each of the following statements:
   • For a translation, slopes of line segments are invariant.
   • For a translation, lengths of line segments are invariant.

## 14.2 Reflections and Properties

A reflection is a transformation that relates
points on a plane in a particular way.

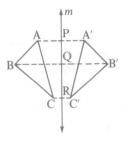

**Reflection Postulate**

The correspondence

$$A \longrightarrow A', \; B \longrightarrow B', \; C \longrightarrow C'$$

is a reflection, if, and only if,

- $AP = A'P$, $BQ = B'Q$, $CR = C'R$
- $AA' \perp$ mirror line m, $BB' \perp$ mirror line m,
  $CC' \perp$ mirror line m

A reflection in the $y$-axis is used to
relate $\triangle ABC$ to $\triangle A'B'C'$. For the
reflection $\triangle ABC \longrightarrow \triangle A'B'C'$, the
co-ordinates of the vertices, and their
images are

$$A(6, 7) \longrightarrow A'(-6, 7)$$
$$B(3, 3) \longrightarrow B'(-3, 3)$$
$$C(7, 1) \longrightarrow C'(-7, 1)$$

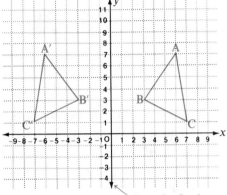

The reflection in the $y$-axis can be
described by the mapping rule

$$(x, y) \longrightarrow (-x, y)$$

line of reflection

The form of the mapping rule depends on the line
of reflection, as shown in the following example.

**Example**   $\triangle XYZ$ is reflected in the $x$-axis.

(a) List the co-ordinates of the
vertices of $\triangle XYZ$ and the
corresponding co-ordinates
of their reflection images.

(b) Express the reflection in the
$x$-axis as a mapping rule
$(x, y) \longrightarrow (?, ?)$

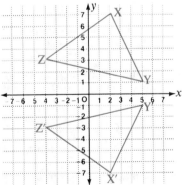

**Solution**   (a) $X(2, 7) \longrightarrow X'(2, -7)$,
$Y(5, 1) \longrightarrow Y'(5, -1)$,
$Z(-4, 3) \longrightarrow Z'(-4, -3)$

(b) The mapping rule for the reflection in the $x$-axis is given by

$$(x, y) \longrightarrow (x, -y).$$

Compare this mapping rule to the
one given for a reflection in the $y$-axis.

**PSP**

To learn mathematics, ask yourself: How are the properties of reflections
and translations   • alike?     • different?     **PSP**

## 14.2 Exercise

**A** 1   A mapping rule is given by $(x, y) \longrightarrow (x, -y)$. Find the co-ordinates of the
image of each of the following.
   (a) A(3, −6)                (b) B(2, −2)                (c) C(4, 5)
   (d) △DEF where, D(5, 3), E(6, −2), F(2, −2).
   (e) Why does the mapping rule describe a reflection in the $x$-axis?

2   A mapping rule is given by $(x, y) \longrightarrow (-x, y)$. Find the co-ordinates of the
image of each of the following.
   (a) A(3, −2)                (b) B(−6, 4)                (c) C(−7, −6)
   (d) △DEF where D(1, 3), E(4, −3), F(3, −5).
   (e) Why does the mapping rule describe a reflection in the $y$-axis?

3   Find the co-ordinates of the image point if each of the following points
are reflected in the $x$-axis.
   (a) (2, 3)                (b) (−2, 3)                (c) (−2, −4)
   (d) Use your results in (a) to (c) to describe the reflection in the $x$-axis as a
       mapping rule $(x, y) \longrightarrow (?, ?)$.

4   Find the co-ordinates of the image point if each of the following points
are reflected in the $y$-axis.
   (a) (3, 4)                (b) (−3, 4)                (c) (−5, −2)
   (d) Use your results in (a) to (c) to describe the reflection in the $y$-axis as a
       mapping rule $(x, y) \longrightarrow (?, ?)$.

5   A mapping rule is given by $(x, y) \longrightarrow (y, x)$. Find the co-ordinates of the
image of each of the following.
   (a) P(4, −3)                (b) Q(5, 2)                (c) R(−1, 0)
   (d) △GHI where G(3, 4), H(−1, 5), and I(−4, −2)
   (e) Why does the mapping describe a reflection in the line $y = x$?

6   A mapping is given by $(x, y) \longrightarrow (-y, -x)$. Find the co-ordinates of the
image of each of the following.
   (a) X(5, 3)                (b) Y(−2, 7)                (c) Z(6, −4)
   (d) △RST where R(0, 5), S(−3, −5) and T(−2, 4)
   (e) Why does the mapping describe a reflection in the line $y = -x$?

7   Find the image of each point for the reflection line given.

(a) $(2, -3)$, $x$-axis

(b) $(-4, -6)$, $y$-axis

(c) $(3, -8)$, $y = x$.

(d) $(-2, 6)$, $y = -x$.

**B** 8   $\triangle ABC$, given by $A(-3, 5)$, $B(-2, 1)$ and $C(-6, 2)$ is reflected in the $x$-axis.

(a) Plot $\triangle ABC$ and its reflection image $\triangle A'B'C'$.

(b) Find the slopes of AB, A'B'; BC, B'C'; and AC, A'C'.

(c) What do you notice about the pairs of slopes in (b)?

(d) What probable conclusion can you come to about the slope of a line segment and the slope of its reflection image?

9   $\triangle NPQ$, given by $N(3, -2)$, $P(3, 6)$ and $Q(7, -2)$, is reflected in the $y$-axis.

(a) Plot $\triangle NPQ$ and its reflection image $\triangle N'P'Q'$.

(b) Find the lengths of NP, N'P'; PQ, P'Q'; and NQ, N'Q'.

(c) What do you notice about the pairs of lengths in (b)?

(d) What probable conclusion can you come to about the length of a line segment and the length of its reflection image?

10   Refer to the triangles in Questions 8 and 9.

(a) Which triangles are congruent? Justify your answers.

(b) Calculate the areas of the triangles. Which triangles have equal areas?

(c) Describe the orientation of the pre-image and the image triangles. What do you notice?

11   Refer to your results in the previous questions.

(a) If a figure is reflected in a line, which properties are invariant? Which are not?

(b) List the properties of a reflection. Use an illustration of your own to show each property of a reflection.     **PSP**

**C** 12   A reflection in the $x$-axis maps points $A(x_1, y_1)$ and $B(x_2, y_2)$ onto A' and B'. Prove AB and A'B' are equal in length.

---

Math Tip     **PSP**

You do not need to memorize the mapping rules for reflections with different lines of reflections. When you are working with a particular reflection, make up a simple triangle, and test the effect of the reflection in the given line of reflection.

# 14.3  Describing Rotations

A rotation is a transformation that relates points on a plane in a
particular way. For a rotation, you must specify
- the rotation centre
- the rotation angle
- the direction of rotation

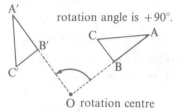

shows a positive
rotation

shows a negative
rotation

rotation angle is +90°.

O rotation centre

**Rotation Postulate**

The correspondence

$$A \longrightarrow A', B \longrightarrow B', C \longrightarrow C'$$

is a rotation, if, and only if,
- $OB = OB'$, $OA = OA'$, $OC = OC'$
- $\angle BOB' = \angle AOA' = \angle COC'$

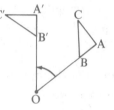

In the figure, a rotation of +180°
about the origin is used to relate
△ABC to △A'B'C'. For the rotation
△ABC $\longrightarrow$ △A'B'C' the co-ordinates
of the vertices and their images are

$$A(3, 8) \longrightarrow A'(-3, -8)$$
$$B(8, 2) \longrightarrow B'(-8, -2)$$
$$C(3, 2) \longrightarrow C'(-3, -2)$$

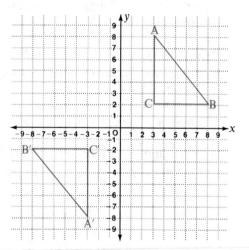

The rotation of +180° about the origin
can be described by the mapping rule

$$(x, y) \longrightarrow (-x, -y)$$

The mapping rule for a rotation
depends on the rotation angle, as
shown in the following example.

  Record any additional
skills or strategies in
your *Problem-Solving Plan.*

**Example** $\triangle$LMN is rotated $+90°$ about the origin.

(a) List the co-ordinates of the vertices of $\triangle$LMN and the corresponding co-ordinates of the rotation image.

(b) Express the rotation of $+90°$ about the origin as a mapping rule $(x, y) \longrightarrow (?, ?)$.

**Solution** (a) $L(-3, 8) \longrightarrow L'(-8, -3)$
$M(6, 4) \longrightarrow M'(-4, 6)$
$N(-3, 4) \longrightarrow N'(-4, -3)$

(b) The mapping rule for a rotation of $+90°$ about the origin is given by $(x, y) \longrightarrow (-y, x)$.

Remember: To learn mathematics, make comparisons.
How are the properties of translations, reflections, and rotations
• the same?  • different?

## 14.3 Exercise

**A** Review the rotation postulate and the meaning of *rotation image, rotation angle*, and *rotation centre*.

1  $\triangle$FGH is rotated $-90°$ about the origin.

(a) What are the co-ordinates of the image of each vertex?

(b) Express the rotation of $-90°$ about the origin as a mapping rule

$(x, y) \longrightarrow (?, ?)$.

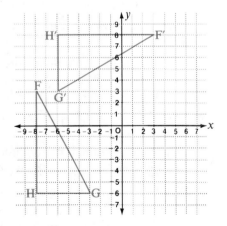

2  $\triangle$UVW is given by U(3, 0), V(7 $-4$), and W(0, $-6$), and is rotated $+270°$ about the origin.

(a) Write the co-ordinates of the image of each vertex.

(b) Express the rotation of $+270°$ about the origin as a mapping rule.

(c) What negative rotation angle gives the same image as $+270°$ about the origin?

3    $\triangle$RST is given by R(6, 7), S(2, 3) and T($-2$, 7). $\triangle$RST is rotated $+180°$ about the origin.

(a) Write the co-ordinates of the image of each vertex.

(b) Express the rotation of $+180°$ about the origin as a mapping rule.

4    A mapping rule is given by $(x, y) \longrightarrow (-y, x)$. Find the co-ordinates of the image of each of the following.

(a) A(2, 5)                    (b) B(4, $-3$)                    (c) C($-1$, $-4$)

(d) $\triangle$DEF where D($-2$, 5), E($-6$, 0), and F($-3$, $-5$)

(e) Describe the rotation obtained by the mapping rule.

5    A mapping rule is given by $(x, y) \longrightarrow (-x, -y)$. Find the co-ordinates of the image of each of the following.

(a) G(5, 0)                    (b) H($-3$, 7)                    (c) I($-5$, $-3$)

(d) $\triangle$JKL where J(3, 3), K(3, 8), and L($-2$, 3)

(e) Describe the rotation obtained by the mapping rule.

6    A mapping rule is given by $(x, y) \longrightarrow (y, -x)$. Find the co-ordinates of the image of each of the following.

(a) M(4, 7)                    (b) N($-6$, $-3$)                    (c) P(2, $-7$)

(d) $\triangle$QRS where Q($-2$, 3), R($-8$, 3), and S($-2$, $-5$)

(e) Describe the rotation obtained by the mapping rule.

7    Find the image of each point for the rotation angle given. The rotation centre is the origin.

(a) (4, 7), $+180°$     (b) ($-5$, 3), $+90°$     (c) (6, $-3$), $+270°$   (d) ($-4$, $-5$), $-90°$

**B**  The following questions explore the properties of a rotation. Which properties are invariant?

8    $\triangle$PQR, given by P(4, 2), Q(4, 7), and R($-3$, 7), is rotated $+180°$ about the origin.

(a) Plot $\triangle$PQR and its rotation image $\triangle$P'Q'R'.

(b) Find the lengths of PQ, P'Q'; QR, Q'R'; and PR, P'R'.

(c) What do you notice about the pairs of lengths in (b)?

(d) What probable conclusion can you come to about the length of a line segment and the length of its rotation image?

9    $\triangle$XYZ, given by X(2, 3), Y(2, 8), and Z(6, 5), is rotated $+90°$ about the origin.

(a) Find the image of each vertex.

(b) Plot △XYZ and its rotation image △X'Y'Z'.

(c) Find the slopes of XY, X'Y'; of YZ, Y'Z'; and of XZ, X'Z'.

(d) What do you notice about the pairs of slopes in (c)?

(e) What probable conclusion can you come to about the slope of a line segment and the slope of its image rotated $+90°$ about the origin?

10 Repeat the steps in the previous question for each of the following rotation angles.

(a) $-90°$    (b) $+180°$    (c) $-180°$    (d) $+270°$

11 Refer to the triangles in Questions 8 to 10.

(a) Which triangles are congruent? Justify your answers.

(b) Calculate the areas of the triangles. Which triangles have equal areas?

(c) Describe the orientation of the pre-image and image triangles. What do you notice?

12 Based on your results in the previous questions, which of the following are invariant for a rotation?

(a) lengths of line segments    (b) slopes of line segments

(c) measures of angles    (d) orientation    (e) area of figures

13 Refer to your results in the previous questions.

(a) List all the properties of a rotation.

(b) Use an illustration of your own to show each property in (a).  Which properties are invariant?

---

## Computer Tip

To write a program for a computer, you must first learn and understand the mathematics. Then you apply the programming skills you have learned to write the appropriate computer program.

- A formula can be used to find the roots of any quadratic equation given in the form $ax^2 + bx + c = 0$. Do research to find how the formula is developed.

Roots are given by

$$x = \frac{-b \pm \sqrt{b^2 - 4ac}}{2a}$$

- The computer program shown in BASIC calculates the roots of a quadratic equation $ax^2 + bx + c = 0$. Refer to the quadratic equations given in Chapter 2, Section 2.11. Run the program for these quadratic equations, as well as equations of your own choice.

```
10 INPUT A, B, C
20 LET D = B↑2 − 4 ∗ A ∗ C
30 IF D < 0 THEN 80
40 LET X1 = (−B + SQR(D))/(2 ∗ A)
50 LET X2 = (−B − SQR(D))/(2 ∗ A)
60 PRINT "THE ROOTS ARE"; X1, X2
70 GO TO 90
80 PRINT "THE ROOTS ARE UNREAL"
90 END
```

## 14.4 Dilatations and Properties

A dilatation is a transformation that relates points on a plane in a particular way. It is a transformation that enlarges or reduces the dimensions of a figure by a **scale factor**, $k$.

**Dilatation Postulate**
The correspondence

$A \longrightarrow A'$, $B \longrightarrow B'$, $C \longrightarrow C'$

is a dilatation, if, and only if
- O, A, and, A′ are collinear
  O, B, and B′ are collinear
  O, C, and C′ are collinear
- $OA' = k(OA)$, $OB' = k(OB)$, $OC' = k(OC)$

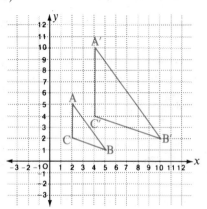

For example, in the figure on the right, a dilatation with centre the origin and dilatation factor 2, is used to transform △ABC. For the dilatation $\triangle ABC \longrightarrow \triangle A'B'C'$, the co-ordinates of the vertices and the images are

$A(2, 5) \longrightarrow A'(4, 10)$,
$B(5, 1) \longrightarrow B'(10, 2)$,
$C(2, 2) \longrightarrow C'(4, 4)$

The dilatation with dilatation centre the origin and dilatation factor 2 can be described by the mapping rule

$(x, y) \longrightarrow (2x, 2y)$.

## 14.4 Exercise

**A** The dilatations that you will work with in this section all have the origin as their dilatation centre.

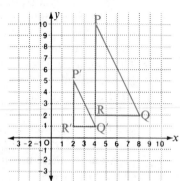

1  A dilatation with factor $\frac{1}{2}$ is applied to △PQR.

   (a) What are the co-ordinates of the image of each vertex?

   (b) Express the dilatation as a mapping rule.

2  △XYZ has vertices X(3, 3), Y(6, 2), and Z(4, −4). A dilatation with scale factor −2 is applied to △XYZ.

   (a) Write the co-ordinates of the image vertices.

(b) Plot $\triangle XYZ$ and $\triangle X'Y'Z'$ on the co-ordinate plane. What do you notice?

(c) Express the dilatation as a mapping rule.

3   A mapping is given by $(x, y) \longrightarrow (4x, 4y)$. Find the co-ordinates of the image of each of the following.

(a) P(1, 1)                (b) Q(−2, 2)                (c) R(3, −1)

(d) $\triangle STU$ where S(−2, 3), T(2, 4), and U(1, 5)

(e) Describe the dilatation given by the mapping rule.

4   A mapping rule is given by $(x, y) \longrightarrow (−3x, −3y)$. Find the co-ordinates of the image of each of the following.

(a) A(2, 1)                (b) B(−3, 1)                (c) C(−1, −3)

(d) $\triangle DEF$ where D(0, 2), E(3, 2), and F(1, −2)

(e) Describe the dilatation given by the mapping rule.

**B** 5   $\triangle FGH$ is given by F(1, 1), G(5, 0), and H(2, 3). A dilatation, with scale factor 2, is applied to $\triangle FGH$.

(a) Plot $\triangle FGH$ and its dilatation image $\triangle F'G'H'$.

(b) Find the slopes of FG, F'G'; of GH, G'H'; and of FH, F'H'.

(c) What do you notice about the pairs of slopes in (b)?

(d) What probable conclusion can you come to about the slope of a line segment and the slope of its dilatation image?

6   Repeat the steps in the previous question for each of the following scale factors.

(a) −3                (b) $-\dfrac{1}{2}$                (c) $\dfrac{3}{2}$

7   Refer to the triangles in Questions 5 and 6.

(a) Which triangles are similar? Justify your answers.

(b) Calculate the areas of corresponding triangles. What probable conclusion can you come to about the relationship between the area of a triangle and the area of its dilatation image?

(c) Describe the orientation of the pre-image and the image triangles. What do you notice?

8   Based on your results in the previous questions, which of the following are invariant for a dilatation?

(a) slopes of line segments            (b) lengths of line segments

(c) measures of angles      (d) orientation of figures      (e) areas of figures

## 14.5 Working With Isometries

There are some special words that are used in the study of transformations which refer to important concepts.

An **isometry** is a transformation that preserves length. (It is derived from the Greek *isos* meaning *same* and *metria* meaning *measure*.) Since an isometry preserves length, if two figures are related by an isometry, then the figures are congruent. An isometry is often referred to as a **congruence transformation**.

- An isometry that preserves the orientation of the vertices is a **direct congruence**. In the diagram, the translation that relates △ABC to △A′B′C′ is an isometry for these reasons:
  (i) Since a translation is applied, then △ABC ≅ △A′B′C′.
  (ii) The orientation of the triangles is the same.

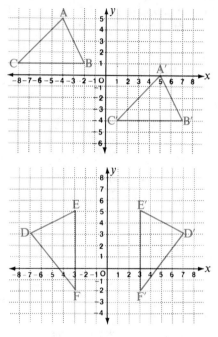

- An isometry that does not preserve the orientation of the vertices is called an **opposite congruence**. In the diagram, the reflection that relates △DEF to △D′E′F′ is an isometry for these reasons:
  (i) Since a reflection is applied, then △DEF ≅ △D′E′F′.
  (ii) The orientation of △DEF is clockwise, whereas, the orientation of △D′E′F′ is counter-clockwise.

## 14.5 Exercise

**A 1** A translation relates △GHJ to △G′H′J′.

(a) Is the translation an isometry? Justify your answer.

(b) Is the translation a direct congruence or an opposite congruence? Justify your answer.

(c) Express the translation as a mapping rule.

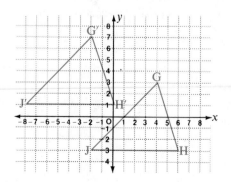

2   A reflection relates △KLM to
    △K′L′M′.

    (a) Is the reflection an isometry?
        Justify your answer.

    (b) Is the reflection a direct congruence
        or an opposite congruence? Justify
        your answer.

    (c) Express the reflection as a
        mapping rule.

3   A rotation relates △PQR to △P′Q′R′.

    (a) Is the rotation an isometry? Justify
        your answer.

    (b) Is the rotation a direct congruence
        or an opposite congruence? Justify
        your answer.

    (c) Express the rotation as a mapping
        rule.

4   A dilatation relates △STU to
    △S′T′U′.

    (a) Is the dilatation an isometry?
        Justify your answer.

    (b) Is the dilatation a direct
        congruence or an opposite
        congruence? Justify your answer.

    (c) Express the dilatation as a
        mapping rule.

 Record any new words,
skills, or strategies in
your *Problem-Solving Plan*.

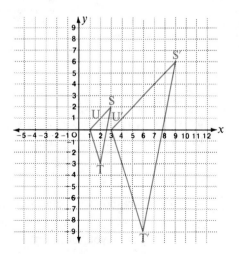

**B** Review the properties of the various transformations you have learned so far.

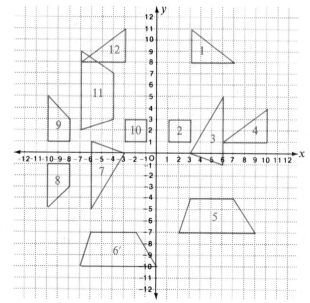

5   A number of figures are shown.
   • Decide which figures are congruent. Describe the isometry that relates the figures.
   • Decide whether the congruence is direct or opposite.
   • Write the isometry by naming the correspondence between the numbered shapes, e.g. 2 ⟶ 14.

6   Use the chart to summarize the properties of transformations. Copy and complete the chart. Use T for true and F for false. Be sure that you can provide an illustration to justify your answers.

| Transformation / Property | Opposite congruence | Direct congruence | Isometry | Areas invariant | Orientation invariant | Angles invariant | Slopes invariant | Lengths invariant |
|---|---|---|---|---|---|---|---|---|
| Translation | ? | ? | ? | ? | ? | ? | ? | ? |
| Reflection | ? | ? | ? | ? | ? | ? | ? | ? |
| Rotation | ? | ? | ? | ? | ? | ? | ? | ? |
| Dilatation | ? | ? | ? | ? | ? | ? | ? | ? |

7   Identify the following transformations.
   (a) An isometry has opposite congruence.
   (b) An isometry has direct congruence and the slopes are invariant.
   (c) An isometry has direct congruence and the slopes are not invariant.

8   (a) Create two additional questions based on the chart in Question 6.
   (b) Write an answer to your questions in (a). Use an example of your own to justify your answers.

# 14.6 **PSP** Problem-Solving: What If . . . ?

When you are studying mathematics, the answer to an important question often leads to the development of additional mathematics, or to the invention of useful vocabulary. For example, what if two or more transformations are applied, in succession, to a figure? Can the resulting image be described by a single transformation? The process of applying one transformation followed by another transformation is called the **composition of transformations**. For example, two transformations applied in succession can be described by one translation.

$$\triangle ABC \longrightarrow \triangle A'B'C' \qquad \triangle A'B'C' \longrightarrow \triangle A''B''C'' \qquad \triangle ABC \longrightarrow \triangle A''B''C''$$
$$(x, y) \longrightarrow (x + 2, y - 3) \qquad (x, y) \longrightarrow (x - 1, y + 2) \qquad (x, y) \longrightarrow (x + 1, y - 1)$$

However, not all composition of transformations can be described by a single transformation, as shown in the following example.

**Example**  $\triangle ABC$ is given by A(11, −5), B(11, −2), and C(4, −2). $\triangle ABC$ is reflected in the x-axis. The reflection image, $\triangle A'B'C'$, is then translated using the mapping rule $(x, y) \longrightarrow (x - 9, y)$.

(a) Use a Cartesian grid to show $\triangle ABC$, its reflection image, $\triangle A'B'C'$, and then the final translation image, $\triangle A''B''C''$.

(b) Compare $\triangle ABC$ and the final image $\triangle A''B''C''$. Can $\triangle ABC$ be related to $\triangle A''B''C''$ by an isometry?

(c) Is there a single transformation that transforms $\triangle ABC$ to $\triangle A''B''C''$?

**Solution**  (a) Plot the various triangles

(b) $\triangle ABC \longrightarrow \triangle A'B'C'$ is a reflection. Thus,
$\triangle ABC \cong \triangle A'B'C'$  ①
$\triangle A'B'C' \longrightarrow \triangle A''B''C''$
is a translation. Thus,
$\triangle A'B'C' \cong \triangle A''B''C''$  ②
From ① and ②.
$\triangle ABC \cong \triangle A''B''C''$.
The combination of transformations results in an isometry.

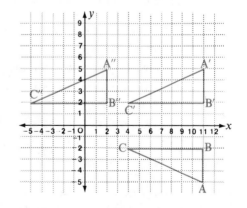

(c) The mapping $\triangle ABC \longrightarrow \triangle A''B''C''$ does not satisfy the postulates for any of the transformations studied. Thus, there is no single transformation that relates $\triangle ABC$ to $\triangle A''B''C''$.

The composition of transformations used in the previous example, is given the special name **glide-reflection**. A glide-reflection consists of a reflection followed by a translation parallel to the line of reflection.

You will investigate the effect of other compositions of transformations in the following exercise. You will identify whether they are isometries, with direct or opposite congruence, and whether they are equivalent to a single transformation.

## 14.6  Exercise

**B 1**  Refer to the glide-reflection in the previous example.

(a) Compare the orientation of $\triangle ABC$ with that of $\triangle A''B''C''$. What do you notice?

(b) Compare the slopes of corresponding line segments. Is slope preserved?

(c) List other properties of glide-reflections.

2  $\triangle PQR$ is given by $P(2, -2)$, $Q(4, -3)$ and $R(3, -5)$.

(a) Translate $\triangle PQR$ by using the mapping rule $(x, y) \longrightarrow (x + 1, y - 2)$ to obtain $\triangle P'Q'R'$. Then translate $\triangle P'Q'R'$ by using the mapping rule $(x, y) \longrightarrow (x + 2, y - 3)$.

(b) What single transformation has the same effect on $\triangle PQR$ as the combination of the translations in (a)? Express this transformation as a mapping rule.

(c) Is the transformation in (b) an isometry? Is it a direct congruence or an opposite congruence?

3  Square ABCD is given by $A(-7, 3)$, $B(-5, 3)$, $C(-5, 1)$, and $D(-7, 1)$.

(a) Reflect square ABCD in the $y$-axis to obtain $A'B'C'D'$.

(b) Translate the image $A'B'C'D'$, using the mapping rule $(x, y) \longrightarrow (x - 4, y)$, to obtain $A''B''C''D''$.

(c) What type of transformation relates ABCD to its final image $A''B''C''D''$?

(d) Is the transformation in (c) an isometry? Is it a direct congruence or an opposite congruence?

4  $\triangle KLM$ is given by $K(5, 4)$, $L(5, 1)$ and $M(1, 1)$.

(a) Rotate $\triangle KLM + 180°$ about the origin to obtain $\triangle K'L'M'$.

(b) Reflect $\triangle K'L'M'$ in the $y$-axis to obtain $\triangle K''L''M''$.

(c) What single transformation relates $\triangle KLM$ to $\triangle K''L''M''$? Justify your answer.

**Exploration I:** Questions 5 to 8 explore the composition of two reflections, when the lines of reflection are parallel.

5   $\triangle ABC$ is given by A(6, 5), B(8, 2), C(6, 2).

(a) Reflect $\triangle ABC$ in the $y$-axis to obtain $\triangle A'B'C'$.

(b) Reflect $\triangle A'B'C'$ in the line $x = -3$ to obtain $\triangle A''B''C''$.

(c) Is there a single transformation that relates $\triangle ABC$ to $\triangle A''B''C''$? Justify your answer.

6   Parallelogram DEFG is given by D(8, 0), E(4, 0), F(2, $-3$), and G(6, $-3$).

(a) Reflect DEFG in the line $y = 1$ to obtain D'E'F'G'.

(b) Reflect D'E'F'G' in the $x$-axis to obtain D''E''F''G''.

(c) What single transformation relates DEFG to D''E''F''G''? Express the transformation as a mapping rule.

7   (a) $\triangle ABC$ is given by A(4, 3), B(7, 1), and C(7, 4). Choose any two parallel lines, $m_1$ and $m_2$. Reflect $\triangle ABC$ in the line $m_1$ to obtain $\triangle A'B'C'$. Then reflect $\triangle A'B'C'$ in the line $m_2$ to obtain $\triangle A''B''C''$.

(b) What single transformation gives the same result as that obtained in (a)?

(c) Repeat (a) and (b) for other figures of your own choice.

8   Based on your results in the previous question,

(a) why can you say that two successive reflections in parallel lines may be given by a translation? Give examples to illustrate your answer.

(b) what are the properties of a transformation consisting of two successive reflections in two parallel mirror lines?

**Exploration II:** Questions 9 to 12 explore the composition of two reflections when the lines of reflection intersect.

9   Two mirror lines are perpendicular as shown.

(a) Reflect the figure in the line $m_1$ followed by a reflection in $m_2$.

(b) What one transformation may be used to obtain the same result in (a)?

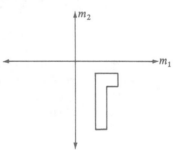

10  ST is given by S(1, 2), T(4, 3).

(a) Reflect ST with respect to the $y$-axis. Then reflect the image S'T' with respect to the $x$-axis.

(b) Name another single transformation that would obtain the same result as in (a).

11    $\triangle$KLM is given by K($-2$, $-2$), L(3, $-5$), and M($-2$, $-5$).

(a) Reflect $\triangle$KLM in the *x*-axis to obtain $\triangle$K'L'M'.

(b) Reflect $\triangle$K'L'M' in the line $y = x$ to obtain $\triangle$K"L"M".

(c) What single transformation relates $\triangle$KLM to $\triangle$K"L"M"? Give reasons for your answer.

12    Refer to your results in the previous questions.

(a) Why can you say that two successive reflections in intersecting lines can be shown by a rotation? Give examples to illustrate your answer.

(b) How is the angle of rotation related to the angle between the two mirror lines?

(c) What are the properties of a transformation consisting of two successive reflections in two intersecting lines?

**PSP**   **Exploration III:** Questions 13 and 14 explore the composition of three reflections in any three lines of reflection.

13    (a) Make a copy of the diagram. Reflect figure F with respect to the line $m_1$. Then reflect this image with respect to the line $m_2$. Finally, reflect this image with respect to the line $m_3$.

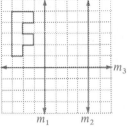

(b) What single transformation relates the original pre-image with its final image? Justify your answer.

14    (a) Draw a figure on the plane. Draw three parallel lines. Reflect the figure successively in the three mirror lines.

(b) What single transformation relates the pre-image with its final image?

(c) Repeat (a) and (b) except use three intersecting (concurrent) lines, as mirror lines, as shown at the right. What conclusion can you come to?

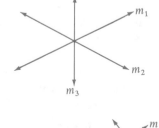

(d) Repeat (a) and (b) for the reflection lines shown at the right. What conclusion can you come to, based on your results?

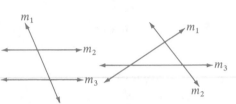

C 15    List the transformations that are the only isometries. Which properties are invariant? Which transformations are direct congruences, and which are opposite congruences?

# 14.7 PSP Transformations: Proving Properties

In your study of mathematics, there is often a parallel study.

| Plane geometry | You are given postulates. SSS SAS ASA | You develop proofs for deductions. |
|---|---|---|
| Transformation geometry | You are given postulates. translations, reflections rotations, dilatations | You develop proofs for deductions. |

To prove deductions involving transformations, you will use many of the geometric results you learned in your earlier work, as shown in the following example.

**Example**   A'B' is the image of AB for a rotation of $+180°$ about O. Prove that A'B' = AB.

**Solution**   Given: A'B' is the rotation image of AB.
Required to prove: A'B' = AB
Proof: *Statements*

| Statements | Reasons |
|---|---|
| In $\triangle OA'B'$ and $\triangle OAB$, | |
| AO = A'O | Rotation postulate |
| BO = B'O | Rotation postulate |
| $\angle AOA' = \angle BOB'$ | Rotation postulate |
| But   $\angle AOA' = \angle AOB + \angle BOA'$ | Rotation is $+180°$ |
| and   $\angle BOB' = \angle A'OB' + \angle BOA'$ | |
| Thus, $\angle AOB = \angle A'OB'$ | SAT |
| Thus, $\triangle AOB \cong \triangle A'OB'$ | SAS postulate |
| Thus,      AB = A'B' | |

# 14.7 Exercise

A In this exercise, you will use the Translation, Reflection and Rotation Postulates to prove certain properties.

1   P'Q' is the translation image of PQ.
Use the following steps to prove PQ $\parallel$ P'Q'.

(a) Why is PP' = QQ'?

(b) Why is PP' $\parallel$ QQ'?

(c) Why is PP'Q'Q a parallelogram?

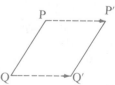

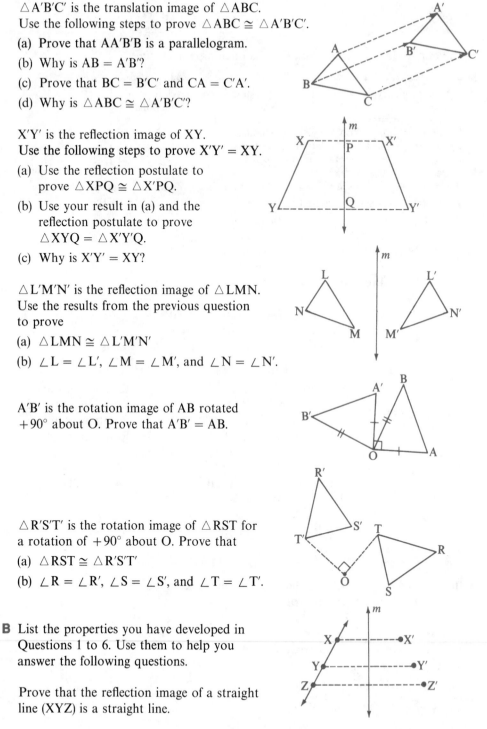

2 &triangle;A′B′C′ is the translation image of &triangle;ABC.
Use the following steps to prove &triangle;ABC ≅ &triangle;A′B′C′.

(a) Prove that AA′B′B is a parallelogram.

(b) Why is AB = A′B′?

(c) Prove that BC = B′C′ and CA = C′A′.

(d) Why is &triangle;ABC ≅ &triangle;A′B′C′?

3 X′Y′ is the reflection image of XY.
Use the following steps to prove X′Y′ = XY.

(a) Use the reflection postulate to
prove &triangle;XPQ ≅ &triangle;X′PQ.

(b) Use your result in (a) and the
reflection postulate to prove
&triangle;XYQ = &triangle;X′Y′Q.

(c) Why is X′Y′ = XY?

4 &triangle;L′M′N′ is the reflection image of &triangle;LMN.
Use the results from the previous question
to prove

(a) &triangle;LMN ≅ &triangle;L′M′N′

(b) ∠L = ∠L′, ∠M = ∠M′, and ∠N = ∠N′.

5 A′B′ is the rotation image of AB rotated
+90° about O. Prove that A′B′ = AB.

6 &triangle;R′S′T′ is the rotation image of &triangle;RST for
a rotation of +90° about O. Prove that

(a) &triangle;RST ≅ &triangle;R′S′T′

(b) ∠R = ∠R′, ∠S = ∠S′, and ∠T = ∠T′.

**B** List the properties you have developed in
Questions 1 to 6. Use them to help you
answer the following questions.

7 Prove that the reflection image of a straight
line (XYZ) is a straight line.

8    Prove that the translation image of a straight line (PQR) is a straight line.

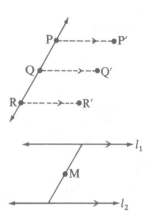

9    A′ is the translation image of A. Prove that the translation image of any line through A is the parallel line through A′.

10   Prove that for a rotation of $+180°$, the image of a line is a parallel line such that the centre of the rotation is the midpoint of any transversal between the parallel lines.

11   Prove that, if two lines intersect, then they are the reflection images of each other in a line of reflection that is the bisector of the angle between the two intersecting lines.

12   Two circles are congruent (have the same radius), and the image of the centre, C, of the first circle is the centre, C′, of the image circle. Prove that the image circle is a translation image of the original circle.

13   Prove that if two circles are congruent, then their centres are reflection images in the line that is the perpendicular bisector of the line joining their centres.

14   Prove that two intersecting congruent circles are reflection images in the line passing through their points of intersection.

15   Prove that if two circles are congruent, then they are related by a rotation of $+180°$ about the midpoint of the line joining their centres.

16   Refer to the results of the questions in this exercise.
     (a) Make a list of the various properties. Organize them under the headings: translations, reflections, rotations.
     (b) Illustrate each property in (a) with a diagram.

## Problem-Solving

If you use pipe A, a reservoir can be emptied in 40 min. If you use pipe B it takes only 30 min. How long would it take to empty the reservoir if both pipes were used?

Often in mathematics, there is more than one way of proving a result. You can use your skills with plane geometry, co-ordinate geometry, or even vector geometry. In this section, you will see how some earlier results can be proved using the properties of transformations, as shown in the following example.

**Example**   In $\triangle ABC$, $AB = AC$. The bisector of $\angle A$ meets BC at D. Prove
(a) $\angle B = \angle C$     (b) $AD \perp BC$

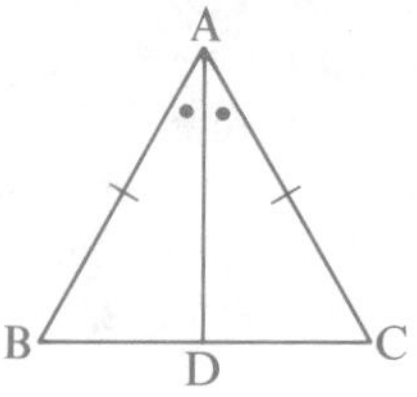

Record the given information on a diagram.

**Solution**   Given: $\triangle ABC$, $AB = AC$,
$\angle BAD = \angle CAD$

Required to prove:
(a) $\angle B = \angle C$
(b) $AD \perp BC$

Proof:

| Statements | Reasons |
|---|---|
| Think of AD as a line of reflection. (a) In $\triangle ABD$ and $\triangle ACD$, | |
| $\quad\quad A \longrightarrow A$ $\quad\quad D \longrightarrow D$ $\quad\quad AB \longrightarrow AC$ | on the line of reflection $\angle BAD = \angle CAD$ and $AB = AC$ |
| Thus, $B \longrightarrow C$ Thus, $\angle ACD$ is the reflection image of $\angle ABD$. Thus, $\angle B = \angle C$. (b) Since $B \longrightarrow C$, and since AD is the line of reflection, then $BC \perp AD$ | Reflection postulate: BC $\perp$ line of reflection |

## 14.8 Exercise

**B** Review the properties of transformations. You will need them in the following exercise.

1   In the diagram, MJ bisects $\angle LMN$ and $\angle LKN$. Consider MJ as a line of reflection. Prove that MJ is the perpendicular bisector of LN.

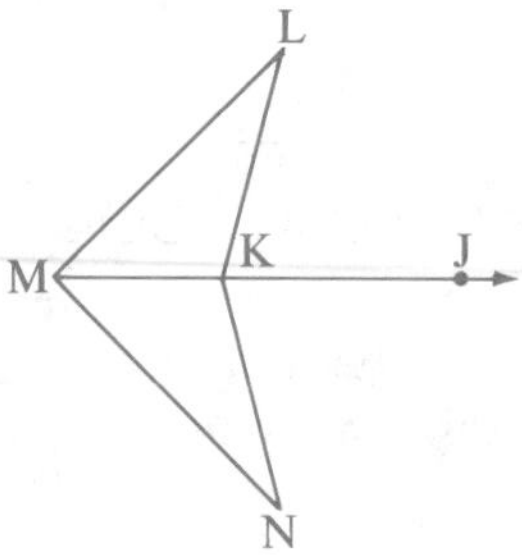

2 P and Q are the centres of two congruent circles. RST is parallel to PQ. Use the translation P ⟶ Q to prove that △PRS is equilateral.

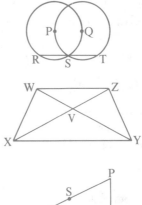

3 In quadrilateral WXYZ, the diagonals intersect so that WV = VZ and VX = VY. Prove that △WXY ≅ △ZYX.

4 △PQR is rotated through a half-turn about the midpoint S of PQ so that R ⟶ R'. Prove that

(a) R, S, R' are collinear.     (b) RS = R'S.

(c) Use the above results to show that the diagonals of a parallelogram bisect each other.

5 Use the diagram. If CP = PH, use your work with reflections to prove that OP ⊥ CH.

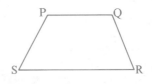

6 Use the diagram. PQ ∥ SR and ∠S = ∠R. Prove that ∠P = ∠Q.

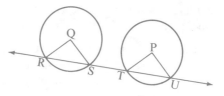

7 In the diagram, P and Q are the centres of congruent circles. If QR ∥ PT prove that SQ ∥ UP.

8 In a circle with centre O, two chords PQ and RS are drawn so that QOR is a diameter and RP ∥ SQ. Prove that P, O, S, are collinear.

9 Two congruent rectangles PQRS and PQVT have a common base PQ, but are on opposite sides of PQ. The midpoints of SV, PV and SP are A, B, and C respectively. The midpoints of RT, TQ and QR are D, E, and F respectively. Prove that △ABC ≅ △DEF.

# 14.9 Equations of Lines: Transformations

By applying a transformation, you can transform a figure on the co-ordinate plane. If the figure has an equation, you can use the mapping rule that describes the transformation to find the equation of the image.

For example, the diagram at the right shows a reflection in the $x$-axis, given by the mapping rule $(x, y) \longrightarrow (x, -y)$. The line $x + 2y = 6$, and its reflection image are shown.

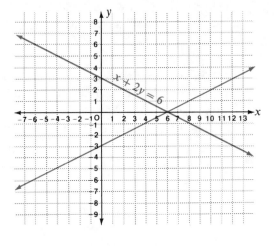

One method of finding the equation of the imagine line is to use your skill with co-ordinate geometry. Choose two points, A(0, $-3$) and B(6, 0), on the image line to find the slope of the image line.

$$\text{slope AB} = \frac{-3 - 0}{0 - 6}$$

$$= \frac{-3}{-6} \text{ or } \frac{1}{2}$$

From the graph, the $y$-intercept of the image line is $-3$. Thus, the equation of the image line is given by

$$y = mx + b$$

$$y = \frac{1}{2}x - 3 \text{ or } x - 2y = 6$$

Another approach you can take to find the equation of the image line is to use the mapping rule that describes the transformation. For example, the line of reflection is the $x$-axis. You can use the following steps whenever you know the mapping rule.

*Step 1:* Let $(X, Y)$ be the co-ordinates of any point on the image line. Let $(x, y)$ be the corresponding point on the original line.

*Step 2:* But the mapping rule for the reflection gives the image point

$$(x, y) \longrightarrow (x, -y)$$

Thus, $(x, -y) = (X, Y)$     ①

since both are the image points of $(x, y)$.

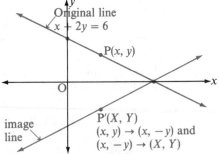

*Step 3:* From the ordered pairs ① $x = X$ and $-y = Y$ or $y = -Y$.
Thus, any point $(x, y)$ on the original line is also given by the form $(X, -Y)$.

*Step 4:* $(x, y)$ or $(X, -Y)$ satisfies the equation $x + 2y = 6$. Use $x = X$, $y = -Y$.

$$x + 2y = 6$$
$$X + 2(-Y) = 6$$
$$X - 2Y = 6$$

But $(X, Y)$ is any point on the image line. Thus, $X - 2Y = 6$ is the equation of the image line. Since the axes are labelled $x$ and $y$, the equation is given by $x - 2y = 6$.

Note, that the equation of the image line, obtained by either method, is the same. However, the method of using the mapping rule to find the equation of the image figure extends to the finding of the equations of the images of advanced figures when the mapping rule is given.

## 14.9 Exercise

**B** Remember: To find the equation of the image line, use the mapping rule of the transformation.

1 A reflection in the $y$-axis is shown by the mapping rule $(x, y) \longrightarrow (-x, y)$. Find the equation of each image line for a reflection in the $y$-axis.
   (a) $2x - y = 3$ 　　　　　　　　　　　(b) $-x + 3y = -2$

2 Each line is reflected in the $x$-axis. Find the equation of each image line.
   (a) $x - 3y = 8$ 　　　　　　　　　　　(b) $2x + 3y = 5$

3 The line $x + y = 2$ is translated using the mapping rule $(x, y) \longrightarrow (x + 1, y - 2)$. Find the equation of the image line.

4 The line $3x - 2y = 6$ is rotated $+90°$ about the origin. The rotation is given by the mapping rule $(x, y) \longrightarrow (-y, x)$. Find the equation of the image line.

5 A rotation of $-90°$ about the origin is shown by the mapping rule $(x, y) \longrightarrow (y, -x)$. Find the equation of each image line for the above rotation.
   (a) $2x + 3y = 6$ 　　　　　　　　　　　(b) $2x - 4y = 8$

6 The line $-5x + 3y = 10$ is reflected in the line $y = -x$. The reflection is given by the mapping rule $(x, y) \longrightarrow (-y, -x)$. Find the equation of the image line.

7 In general, a translation is given by the mapping rule $(x, y) \longrightarrow (x + a, y + b)$. Find the equation of the translation image of the line $Ax + By = C$.

## 14.10　Nature of Mathematics: Applying Matrices to Transformations

In the development of mathematics, newly invented skills are often applied to situations that had not been previously imagined. For example, the language and symbols of matrices can be applied to transformations. Matrices provided a convenient and compact way of representing reflections, rotations, and dilatations. The co-ordinates of a point, $(x, y)$, are represented by a column matrix $\begin{pmatrix} x \\ y \end{pmatrix}$.

An earlier observation about the product of matrices, leads to an important result: The product of a $2 \times 2$ matrix and a $2 \times 1$ column matrix results in a $2 \times 1$ column matrix.

$$\begin{pmatrix} a & b \\ c & d \end{pmatrix} \begin{pmatrix} x \\ y \end{pmatrix} = \begin{pmatrix} ax + by \\ cx + dy \end{pmatrix}$$

If transformations can be represented by a $2 \times 2$ matrix, then the results of transformation can be related to the product of matrices.

For example, a reflection in the $y$-axis is given by the mapping rule

$$(x, y) \longrightarrow (-x, y).$$

This transformation can be described by the $2 \times 2$ matrix $\begin{pmatrix} -1 & 0 \\ 0 & 1 \end{pmatrix}$.

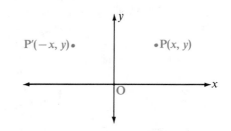

The product of matrices can be used to find the co-ordinates of image points.

$$\begin{pmatrix} -1 & 0 \\ 0 & 1 \end{pmatrix} \begin{pmatrix} x \\ y \end{pmatrix} = \begin{pmatrix} (-1)x + (0)y \\ (0)x + (1)y \end{pmatrix} \quad \text{or} \quad \begin{pmatrix} -x \\ y \end{pmatrix}$$

The significance of this result is that work with transformations can be programmed on a computer. Many complex figures required in designs and in engineering can be handled in this way.

 Remember: Continue to build your vocabulary list.
Provide your own example to illustrate each meaning.
You can't solve a problem if you don't know the key words.

**Example**  The vertices of $\triangle ABC$ are recorded in matrix form as

$$\begin{pmatrix} -3 & -6 & -6 \\ 2 & 2 & 7 \end{pmatrix}$$ ← This row shows the $x$ co-ordinates.
← This row shows the $y$ co-ordinates.

This column is interpreted to mean the co-ordinates of vertex $C(-6, 7)$.

A transformation, given by the matrix $\begin{pmatrix} -1 & 0 \\ 0 & -1 \end{pmatrix}$ is applied to $\triangle ABC$.

(a) Find the product $\begin{pmatrix} -1 & 0 \\ 0 & -1 \end{pmatrix}\begin{pmatrix} -3 & -6 & -6 \\ 2 & 2 & 7 \end{pmatrix}$.

(b) Find the co-ordinates of the image of $\triangle ABC$.

(c) Plot $\triangle ABC$ and its image, $\triangle A'B'C'$.

(d) What transformation is represented by the matrix $\begin{pmatrix} -1 & 0 \\ 0 & -1 \end{pmatrix}$?

**Solution**  (a) 
$$-1(-3) + 0(2)$$
$$\begin{pmatrix} -1 & 0 \\ 0 & -1 \end{pmatrix}\begin{pmatrix} -3 & -6 & -6 \\ 2 & 2 & 7 \end{pmatrix} = \begin{pmatrix} 3 & 6 & 6 \\ -2 & -2 & -7 \end{pmatrix}$$
$$0(-3) + (-1)2$$

(b) From the results in (a), the co-ordinates of the vertices of the image triangle are: A'(3, −2), B'(6, −2), C'(6, −7).

(c)

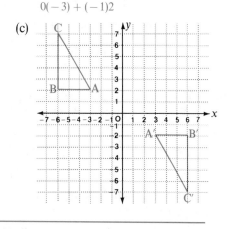

(d) The matrix $\begin{pmatrix} -1 & 0 \\ 0 & -1 \end{pmatrix}$ represents a rotation of $+180°$ about the origin.

## 14.10 Exercise

**B** Review your skills for multiplying matrices.

1  A matrix is given by $\begin{pmatrix} 1 & 0 \\ 0 & -1 \end{pmatrix}$ and operates on the point A with co-ordinates shown by $A\begin{pmatrix} 4 \\ 5 \end{pmatrix}$.

(a) Find the product $\begin{pmatrix} 1 & 0 \\ 0 & -1 \end{pmatrix}\begin{pmatrix} 4 \\ 5 \end{pmatrix}$.

(b) Find the co-ordinates of the image of A $\begin{pmatrix} 4 \\ 5 \end{pmatrix}$ if A is reflected in the $x$-axis.

(c) What do you notice about your answers in (a) and (b)?

(d) What transformation is represented by the matrix $\begin{pmatrix} 1 & 0 \\ 0 & -1 \end{pmatrix}$?

2   A matrix is given by $\begin{pmatrix} 0 & -1 \\ 1 & 0 \end{pmatrix}$ and operates on the point M with

co-ordinates shown by M $\begin{pmatrix} 0 \\ 4 \end{pmatrix}$.

(a) Find the product $\begin{pmatrix} 0 & -1 \\ 1 & 0 \end{pmatrix}\begin{pmatrix} 0 \\ 4 \end{pmatrix}$.

(b) M is rotated $+90°$ about the origin. Find the co-ordinates of M′ in
the form M′$\begin{pmatrix} ? \\ ? \end{pmatrix}$.

(c) M is rotated $-270°$ about the origin. Find the co-ordinates of M′ in
the form M′$\begin{pmatrix} ? \\ ? \end{pmatrix}$.

(d) What do you notice about your answers in (a), (b) and (c)?

(e) What transformation is represented by the matrix given by $\begin{pmatrix} 0 & -1 \\ 1 & 0 \end{pmatrix}$?

3   A matrix is given by $\begin{pmatrix} 0 & 1 \\ -1 & 0 \end{pmatrix}$. This matrix is an operator on the figure
whose co-ordinates are written in the form $\begin{pmatrix} 8 & 10 & 12 & 10 \\ 0 & -2 & 0 & 2 \end{pmatrix}$.

(a) Find the co-ordinates of the resulting figure.

(b) What transformation is equivalent to the result obtained in (a)? (Draw
the original figure and the resulting figure in (a) to help you.)

(c) What other transformation is equivalent to the result obtained in (a)?

4   A matrix is given by $\begin{pmatrix} -1 & 0 \\ 0 & -1 \end{pmatrix}$. This matrix is an operator on the
figure whose co-ordinates are written in the form $\begin{pmatrix} -7 & -9 & -6 \\ 0 & 4 & 4 \end{pmatrix}$.

(a) Find the co-ordinates of the resulting figure.

(b) What transformation is equivalent to the result obtained in (a)?

(c) What other transformation is equivalent to the result obtained in (a)?

5  A matrix is given by $\begin{pmatrix} 2 & 0 \\ 0 & 2 \end{pmatrix}$. This matrix is an operator on the square

ABCD whose co-ordinates are written in the form $\begin{pmatrix} 0 & 3 & 3 & 0 \\ 0 & 0 & 3 & 3 \end{pmatrix}$.

(a) Find the co-ordinates of the resulting image.

(b) What transformation is equivalent to the result obtained in (a)?

6  A matrix is given by $\begin{pmatrix} 0 & 1 \\ 1 & 0 \end{pmatrix}$. This matrix is an operator on the figure

whose co-ordinates are written in the form $\begin{pmatrix} 3 & 3 & 5 \\ 2 & 1 & 2 \end{pmatrix}$.

(a) Find the co-ordinates of the resulting figure.

(b) What transformation is equivalent to the result obtained in (a)?

7  Eight matrices are given.

$$A = \begin{pmatrix} 0 & 1 \\ -1 & 0 \end{pmatrix} \qquad B = \begin{pmatrix} 1 & 0 \\ 0 & -1 \end{pmatrix} \qquad C = \begin{pmatrix} 0 & -1 \\ 1 & 0 \end{pmatrix} \qquad D = \begin{pmatrix} -1 & 0 \\ 0 & 1 \end{pmatrix}$$

$$E = \begin{pmatrix} -1 & 0 \\ 0 & -1 \end{pmatrix} \qquad F = \begin{pmatrix} 4 & 0 \\ 0 & 4 \end{pmatrix} \qquad G = \begin{pmatrix} 0 & -1 \\ -1 & 0 \end{pmatrix} \qquad H = \begin{pmatrix} 0 & 1 \\ 1 & 0 \end{pmatrix}$$

Which of the following transformations gives the same result as when one of the above matrices operates on the co-ordinates of a figure?

(a) a reflection in the $x$-axis

(b) a rotation of $+180°$ about the origin

(c) a reflection in the line $y = x$

(d) a dilatation with scale factor 4

(e) a rotation of $+90°$ 　　　　(f) a reflection in the $y$-axis

(g) a reflection in the line $y = -x$

(h) a rotation of $+270°$ 　　　　(i) a rotation of $-90°$

8  Use the matrices in the previous question to find the co-ordinates of the image for each of the following.

(a) ABCD, given by A(3, 1), B(5, 3), C(7, $-2$), D(3, $-5$), is reflected in the $x$-axis.

(b) PQRS, given by P($-7$, 3), Q($-4$, 2), R($-5$, $-1$), S($-8$, 0), is rotated $+180°$.

(c) $\triangle$MNQ, given by M(5, 8), N(11, 8), Q(9, 4), is reflected in the $y$-axis.

(d) EFGH, given by E($-5$, $-4$), F(0, $-3$), G(0, $-8$), H($-5$, $-9$), is rotated $+90°$.

(e) WXYZ, given by W(3, 6), X(9, 9), Y(12, 3), Z(6, $-3$), is transformed by a dilatation with scale factor $\frac{1}{3}$.

(f) $\triangle$JKL, given by J($-7$, 2), K(3, $-5$), L(5, 6), is reflected in the line $y = x$.

# Answers

Answers to Chapter Reviews, Chapter Tests, and Cumulative Reviews will be included in the Teacher's Resource Masters.

## CHAPTER 1

### 1.1 Exercise, page 11

1.a)−4 b)−1 c)2 d)−9 e)0 f)11 2.a)12 b)24 c)120 d)9 e)−9 f)−8 g)0 h)8 i)−18 j)−112 k)1 l)18 3.a)−9 b)2 c)45 d)−25 e)−9 f)9 g)−5 h)−5 4.a)−16 b)−6 c)−7 d)3 e)−11 f)−3 5.a)> b)< c)> d)> e)< f)> 6.a)51 b)−3 c)−1003 d)297 e)−7 f)−2 7.a)−6 b)−2 c)1 8.a)−4 b)9 c)11 d)−12 e)−3 f)3 g)−5 h)1 9.a)−18 b)59 c)−23 d)24 10.a){3, 5, 7, 9} b){−5, −1, 3} c){−1, 2, 3, 2, −1} d){11, 4, 1, 2, 7} 11. 2, 3; 1, 2, 3

### 1.2 Exercise, page 15

1.a)$\frac{1}{2}$ b)$-\frac{2}{3}$ c)$\frac{1}{5}$ d)$-\frac{1}{5}$ e)$\frac{7}{5}$ f)$-\frac{1}{2}$ 2.a)$-1$ b)$-5$ c)$-\frac{8}{3}$

d)$\frac{9}{13}$ e)1 3.a)$-\frac{1}{2}$ b)$\frac{7}{6}$ c)$-\frac{1}{2}$ d)$-\frac{27}{20}$ e)$-\frac{19}{12}$ f)$-\frac{95}{12}$ g)$-\frac{5}{2}$

h)$-\frac{19}{6}$ i)$-\frac{41}{20}$ j)$-\frac{3}{8}$ k)$\frac{4}{3}$ 4.a)$-\frac{16}{25}$ b)$\frac{9}{5}$ c)$\frac{2}{15}$ d)$\frac{3}{2}$ e)$\frac{1}{5}$ f)2

g)10 h)$\frac{3}{10}$ i)$\frac{1}{2}$ j)$-\frac{17}{5}$ k)$-\frac{96}{5}$ l)$\frac{775}{24}$ 5.a)2 b)$-\frac{19}{4}$ c)$\frac{16}{9}$

d)$-\frac{9}{2}$ e)$\frac{15}{2}$ f)$\frac{2}{3}$ 6.a)$\frac{1}{5}$ b)$-\frac{9}{5}$ c)$\frac{3}{10}$ d)$\frac{43}{40}$ e)$\frac{4}{3}$ f)$-\frac{2}{3}$ 7.a)<

b)> c)> d)< 8.a)$\frac{1}{4}$ b)$\frac{1}{36}$ c)$\frac{289}{144}$ d)$\frac{1}{36}$ 9.a)$\left\{\frac{7}{4}, -\frac{3}{2}, -\frac{5}{8}\right\}$

b)$\left\{-1, -\frac{1}{4}, -\frac{1}{2}, -\frac{3}{8}\right\}$ 10.a)$\frac{1}{6}$ b)$-\frac{7}{6}$ c)$\frac{5}{6}$ d)$-\frac{17}{6}$ e)$-\frac{7}{12}$

11.a)52 b)$\frac{1}{12}$ c)$\frac{1}{12}$ 12.a)$\frac{1}{2}, \frac{2}{3}, \frac{3}{5}, \ldots$ b)$\frac{89}{144}$ 13.a)0.75,

none b)−0.5625, none c)$1.\overline{2}$: 2, 1 d)2.25, none e)$0.\overline{35}$: 35, 2 f)$-1.1\overline{36}$: 36, 2 g)$-0.90\overline{74}$: 074, 3 h)0.53, none

i)$3.0\overline{6}$: 6, 1 j)$-0.4\overline{6}$: 6, 1 14.a)$\frac{6}{25}$ b)$-\frac{9}{26}$ c)$\frac{6}{29}$ d)$-\frac{1}{14}$

15.a)$\frac{2}{5}$ b)$\frac{4}{9}$ c)$\frac{4}{45}$ d)$\frac{11}{30}$ e)$\frac{4}{11}$ f)$\frac{1}{11}$ g)$\frac{82}{25}$ h)$-\frac{35}{111}$ i)$-\frac{79}{33}$

j)$-\frac{518}{495}$ 16.a)$\frac{1}{3}$ b)$\frac{2}{45}$ c)$\frac{67}{99}$ d)$\frac{11}{90}$

### 1.3 Exercise, page 19

1.a)$2\sqrt{7}$ b)$2\sqrt{2}$ c)$\sqrt{163}$ d)$2\sqrt{19}$ e)$\sqrt{183}$ f)$\sqrt{205}$ g)$4\sqrt{6}$ h)$\sqrt{69}$ i)$\sqrt{133}$ j)$\sqrt{271}$ 2.a)5.66 b)5.66 c)same 3.a)17.32 b)17.32 c)same 4.a)11.1 b)13.0 c)37.1 d)14.4 e)18.2 f)23.3 g)18.9 h)24.6 i)20.6 j)12.7 5.a)6.93 b)31.30 c)61.64 d)4.84 e)6.97 f)11.50 g)3.86 h)6.24 i)17.72 j)16.90 6.b)$\sqrt{18}$ c)$\sqrt{72}$ d)$\sqrt{192}$ e)$\sqrt{80}$ f)$\sqrt{567}$ g)$\sqrt{160}$ h)$\sqrt{800}$ i)$\sqrt{200}$ j)$\sqrt{126}$ k)$\sqrt{180}$ l)$\sqrt{54}$ m)$\sqrt{324}$ 7.b)$5\sqrt{2}$ c)$2\sqrt{5}$ d)$2\sqrt{7}$ e)$4\sqrt{2}$ f)$2\sqrt{3}$ g)$5\sqrt{5}$ h)$10\sqrt{2}$ i)$3\sqrt{3}$ j)$2\sqrt{6}$ k)$7\sqrt{2}$ l)$6\sqrt{2}$ m)$10\sqrt{3}$ n)$4\sqrt{13}$ o)$5\sqrt{7}$ p)$4\sqrt{15}$ 8.a)2.45 b)4.90 c)3.16 d)4.24 e)6.32 f)5.92 g)6.93 h)8.37 i)5.48 9.a)9.9 r/min b)7.4 r/min c)8.5 r/min 10. 8.4 r/min 11. 7.1 r/min 12.a)6.6 r/min b)5.7 r/min 13.a)6.3 r/min b)16.8 m c)31.8 m 14.a)yes b)decrease $N$ to 6.8 r/min

### 1.4 Exercise, page 23

1.a)natural b)rational c)irrational d)real e)whole f)integers 3.b)(i)yes (ii)yes (iii)no 5.a)$-\frac{5}{24}$ b)$\frac{7}{24}$ c)$-\frac{5}{24}$ d)$-\frac{13}{48}$ e)$\frac{3}{64}$ 7.a)yes 9. $\bar{Q}$ 10. $Q$: (a), (d), (f); $\bar{Q}$: (b), (c), (e)

### 1.5 Exercise, page 27

2.a)$10^{11}$ b)$10^{12}$ c)$10^6$ d)$10^3$ e)$10^4$ f)$-10^2$ g)$-10^4$ h)$-10^{12}$ 3.a)$x^3$ b)$k^9$ c)$a^5b^5$ d)$\frac{k^3}{m^3}$ e)$m^{10}$ f)$a^6$ g)$m^{11}$ h)$\frac{125}{x^3}$ i)$81a^4$ j)$x^{12}$ k)$8x^3y^3$ l)$y^{10}$ m)$x^{12}$ n)$\frac{27}{8}$ o)128 p)$m^9$ q)$x^4y^4$ r)0 s)$x^3y^3$ 4.a)$x^2y^2$ b)$2ab^5$ c)$a^8b$ d)$-x^2y^4$ e)$-x^5y^4$ f)$a^{12}b^2$ g)$x^7y^2$ h)$\frac{x^8}{y^2}$ 5.a)(i)32 (ii)32 6.a)(i)64 (ii)−64 7.a)−1 b)−2 c)−1 d)1 e)$\frac{1}{4}$ f)1 8.a)$2^7$ b)$3^7$ c)$3^4$ d)$10^4$ 9.a)$2^7$ b)$2^{n+3}$ c)$2^{3x}$ d)$2^{4x}$ e)$2^4$ f)$2^{2x}$ g)$2^{3x+3}$ h)$2^{4x+2}$ i)$2^{8x-4}$ 10.b)$a^{2m}$ c)$a^{4n}$ d)$a^{3n+4}$ e)$a^{4m}$ f)$a^5$ g)$a^{n+2}$ 11.a)1 b)−1 12.a)1 b)−1 c)−1 d)−1 e)1 f)−1 g)−1 13.a)7 b)7 c)6 d)1

### 1.6 Exercise, page 32

1.a)27 b)$\frac{1}{3}$ c)1 d)16 e)$\frac{1}{4}$ f)5 g)$\frac{1}{4}$ h)$\frac{1}{9}$ i)$\frac{1}{9}$ j)$-\frac{1}{16}$ k)16 l)$\frac{1}{16}$ 2.a)3 b)3 c)4 d)4 e)−4 f)2 g)−2 h)−9 i)−10 j)8 k)−5 l)10 3.a)16 b)−16 c)$\frac{1}{16}$ d)$-\frac{1}{16}$ 4.a)9, 9, 9 b)same 5.a)1 b)−9 c)1 d)$\frac{1}{2}$ e)$-\frac{1}{9}$ f)$-\frac{1}{25}$ g)$-\frac{1}{5}$ h)$\frac{1}{25}$ i)−1 j)−9 k)81 l)16 6.a)9 b)2 c)128 d)6 e)$\frac{1}{81}$ f)256 g)1 h)4 i)16 j)1 k)81 l)$\frac{4}{9}$ m)$\frac{1}{8}$ n)$\frac{7}{3}$ o)3 7.a)$-\frac{5}{3}$ b)$-\frac{4}{3}$ c)$-\frac{7}{4}$ d)8 e)$\frac{1}{3}$ f)$-\frac{5}{2}$ g)$-\frac{1}{3}$ h)14 i)$\frac{5}{3}$ 8.a)$10^2$ b)$10^7$ c)$10^4$ d)$10^{-3}$ e)$10^{-10}$ f)$10^{12}$ g)$10^6$ h)$10^0$ i)$10^{-2}$ 9.a)all $a^{-6}$ b)same 10.a)$a^6$ b)$a^6b^2$ c)$a^3b^3$ d)$x^{-9}$ e)$b^{-4}$ f)$a^2$ g)$m^{-2}n^{-4}$ h)$a^{-4}b^2$ i)$a^{-2}b^{-4}$ j)$x^{-6}y^{-4}$ k)$a^{-6}b^{-4}$ l)$m^3n^3$ 11.a)$x^4$ b)$\frac{x}{y^2}$ c)$-\frac{m}{n}$ d)$\frac{a^5}{b^7}$ e)$-\frac{t^4}{s}$ f)$\frac{x^9}{y^3}$ g)$s^7$ h)$-\frac{1}{m}$ 12.a)$a^2b^{-2}$ b)$-x^{-2}$ c)$-m^9n$ d)$x^{-4}y^5$ e)$-a^5b^{-6}$ f)$-n^{-1}$ g)$-a^5b$ h)$-s^9t^4$ 13.a)(i)2 (ii)$\frac{1}{18}$ (iii)$-\frac{1}{18}$ 14.a)−1 b)−2 c)$-\frac{3}{2}$ d)1 e)$-\frac{3}{4}$ f)4 g)6 h)$-\frac{5}{4}$ 15. true: C, D; false: A, B 16.a)3 b)$2\sqrt{2}$ c)4 d)2 e)5 f)4 17.a)2 b)2 c)3 d)5 e)4 18.a)$\frac{1}{2}$ b)$\frac{1}{3}$ c)2 d)2 e)4

### 1.7 Exercise, page 36

1.a)$4\sqrt{2}$ b)$4\sqrt{2}$ 2.a)$10\sqrt{8}$, $20\sqrt{2}$ b)$20\sqrt{2}$ 3.a)$3\sqrt{2}$ b)$2\sqrt{3}$ c)$5\sqrt{2}$ d)$3\sqrt{3}$ e)$4\sqrt{2}$ f)$2\sqrt{2}$ g)$2\sqrt{6}$ h)$10\sqrt{10}$ i)$5\sqrt{5}$ j)$2\sqrt{7}$ k)$3\sqrt{7}$ l)$2\sqrt{5}$ 4.a)$-10\sqrt{2}$ b)$9\sqrt{2}$ c)$\sqrt{6}$ d)$6\sqrt{3}$ e)$-2\sqrt{2}$ f)$\sqrt{5}$ g)$-10\sqrt{3}$ h)$-12\sqrt{5}$ i)$12\sqrt{3}$

**j)**$4\sqrt{10}$ **5.a)**$8\sqrt{2}$ **b)**$3\sqrt{2}$ **c)**$6\sqrt{3}$ **d)**$-3\sqrt{3}$ **e)**$-\sqrt{5}$ **f)**$10\sqrt{5}$
**6.a)**$6\sqrt{2}$ **b)**$0$ **c)**$-5\sqrt{5}$ **d)**$-27\sqrt{7}$ **e)**$\frac{11}{12}\sqrt{5}$ **f)**$-\sqrt{2}$

**7.a)**$7\sqrt{2}-2\sqrt{3}$ **b)**$3\sqrt{3}-2\sqrt{2}$ **c)**$7\sqrt{5}-3\sqrt{2}$
**d)**$2\sqrt{7}-2\sqrt{3}$ **e)**$7\sqrt{2}+3\sqrt{3}$ **f)**$4\sqrt{3}$ **8.a)**$-10\sqrt{2}$ **b)**$4\sqrt{3}$ **c)**$13\sqrt{2}$
**d)**$7\sqrt{5}-30\sqrt{3}$ **e)**$\sqrt{3}$ **f)**$-6\sqrt{6}$ **9.a)**$-\sqrt{2}$ **b)**$-22\sqrt{3}$
**c)**$16\sqrt{5}$ **d)**$-21\sqrt{3}$ **e)**$48\sqrt{2}$ **f)**$-71\sqrt{3}$ **10.a)**$-2\sqrt{2}$
**b)**$-6\sqrt{3}$ **c)**$5\sqrt{2}-5\sqrt{3}$ **d)**$\sqrt{2}+\sqrt{3}$ **e)**$-4\sqrt{3}$ **f)**$-\sqrt{5}$
**g)**$\sqrt{3}-\sqrt{2}$ **h)**$8\sqrt{5}-13\sqrt{3}$ **12.a)**$21\sqrt{2}-\sqrt{3}$ **b)**$4\sqrt{2}-4\sqrt{3}$
**c)**$2\sqrt{2}+10\sqrt{3}$ **d)**$24\sqrt{3}-30$ **13.a)**$10\sqrt{2}+10\sqrt{3}$ units
**b)**$4\sqrt{2}+9\sqrt{3}$ units **14.a)**ABCD; $2\sqrt{3}+4\sqrt{2}-4$ units
**15.** true: (b); false: (a), (c), (d)

**1.8 Exercise, page 38**
**1.a)**$\sqrt{6}$ **b)**$6\sqrt{6}$ **c)**$6\sqrt{35}$ **d)**$\sqrt{15}$ **e)**$6\sqrt{15}$ **f)**$15\sqrt{30}$
**2.a)**$3\sqrt{5}$ **b)**$30\sqrt{3}$ **c)**$2\sqrt{5}$ **d)**$16\sqrt{5}$ **e)**$72$ **f)**$-54\sqrt{2}$
**3.b)**(i)$4\sqrt{30}$ (ii)$24\sqrt{2}$ (iii)$200$ **4.a)**$4\sqrt{15}$ **b)**$90\sqrt{6}$
**c)**$480$ **d)**$108\sqrt{6}$ **e)**$144\sqrt{6}$ **f)**$60\sqrt{10}$ **5.a)**$8$ **b)**$27$ **c)**$18$
**d)**$320$ **e)**$288$ **f)**$200$ **g)**$648$ **h)**$7938$ **6.a)**$6\sqrt{2}-3\sqrt{6}$
**b)**$6\sqrt{10}-2\sqrt{15}$ **c)**$4\sqrt{10}-12$ **7.a)**$24$ **b)**$8$ **c)**$-24$
**8.a)**$22-8\sqrt{3}$ **b)**$-16\sqrt{3}$ **9.a)**$36.74$ **b)**$7.07$ **c)**$7.76$ **d)**$1.10$
**e)**$-10.05$ **f)**$-19.10$ **10.a)**$8\sqrt{3}-11\sqrt{2}$ **b)**$14\sqrt{3}-19\sqrt{2}$
**c)**$3\sqrt{6}+12\sqrt{3}-16\sqrt{2}-6$ **d)**$38-15\sqrt{6}$ **12. B**

**1.9 Exercise, page 41**
**1.a)**$\frac{5\sqrt{3}}{3}$ **b)**$-3\sqrt{2}$ **c)**$5\sqrt{5}$ **d)**$2\sqrt{3}$ **e)**$\frac{4\sqrt{6}}{3}$ **f)**$-3\sqrt{2}$
**g)**$\frac{-2\sqrt{15}}{5}$ **h)**$\sqrt{10}$ **i)**$-\frac{\sqrt{5}}{10}$ **j)**$-\frac{\sqrt{2}}{2}$ **2.a)**$\frac{\sqrt{2}}{4}$ **b)**$3\sqrt{2}$ **c)**$\frac{\sqrt{6}}{12}$
**d)**$\frac{\sqrt{3}}{2}$ **e)**$2\sqrt{5}$ **f)**$-2\sqrt{7}$ **g)**$-\frac{\sqrt{6}}{2}$ **h)**$\frac{3}{2}\sqrt{5}$ **i)**$\frac{9\sqrt{2}}{4}$ **j)**$\frac{10\sqrt{3}}{3}$
**k)**$\frac{-3\sqrt{15}}{5}$ **l)**$\frac{-5\sqrt{30}}{48}$ **3.a)**$\frac{\sqrt{6}-2}{2}$ **b)**$\frac{6+\sqrt{6}}{3}$ **c)**$\frac{\sqrt{10}+2}{4}$
**d)**$\frac{-3\sqrt{10}+4}{6}$ **4.a)**$1.73$ **b)**$-0.20$ **c)**$0.87$ **d)**$1.22$ **e)**$-2.04$
**f)**$-1.73$ **5.a)**$\frac{8\sqrt{3}-3}{3}$ **b)**$2\sqrt{2}+3\sqrt{6}$ **c)**$\frac{\sqrt{10}-3}{3}$
**d)**$\frac{4-3\sqrt{2}}{2}$ **6.a)**$-1.326$ **b)**$17.487$ **c)**$-3.674$ **7.a)**$\frac{24-4\sqrt{6}}{3}$
**b)**$4.734$ **8.a)**$1.95$ **b)**$3.24$ **9.a)**$\frac{3\sqrt{6}-4}{4}$ **b)**$\frac{3\sqrt{6}}{8}$ **c)**$\frac{4\sqrt{6}-9}{9}$
**d)**$\frac{3\sqrt{3}-2\sqrt{2}}{4}$ **e)**$\frac{3\sqrt{6}+8\sqrt{2}-4}{4}$ **f)**$\frac{9-4\sqrt{6}}{9}$
**10.a)**$3\sqrt{2}-2\sqrt{3}$ units **b)**$0.779$ units, $4.899$ units
**11.a)**$6\sqrt{6}-18$ **b)**$4\sqrt{3}-2\sqrt{5}$ **c)**$3\sqrt{2}+\sqrt{3}$
**12.a)**$\frac{5\sqrt{3}+3\sqrt{5}}{15}$ **b)**$\frac{4\sqrt{3}-9\sqrt{2}}{6}$ **c)**$\frac{4\sqrt{5}-15\sqrt{2}}{10}$ **d)**$\frac{29\sqrt{2}}{70}$
**e)**$\frac{7\sqrt{3}}{36}$ **f)**$\frac{45\sqrt{2}+8\sqrt{3}}{180}$ **13.a)**$2.09$ **b)**$-0.32$ **c)**$1.59$ **d)**$-0.01$

**1.10 Exercise, page 44**
**1.a)**$10.0$ **b)**$6.9$ **c)**$10.0$ **d)**$11.4$ **e)**$20.8$ **f)**$81.4$ **2.a)**$20.00$
**b)**$32.00$ **c)**$48.00$ **d)**$21.17$ **e)**$81.58$ **f)**$59.71$ **3.a)**$25$ **b)**$10$
**c)**$19.1$ **4.a)**$\sqrt{5}$ **b)**$2\sqrt{14}$ **c)**$\frac{\sqrt{803}}{2}$ **5.a)**$8.6$ cm

**b)**$10.8$ cm **6.a)**$31.2$ cm **b)**$10.6$ cm **c)**$6.9$ cm **d)**$18.8$ cm
**7.a)**$30.6$ cm **b)**$28$ cm **8.a)**$8.9$ cm **b)**$33.9$ cm **9.a)**$\sqrt{2}, \sqrt{5}$

**1.12 Exercise, page 49**
**1.a)**$3.8$ m **b)**$100.0$ m **c)**$5.69$ m **2.a)**$9.4$ km **b)**$7.6$ km
**c)**$8.9$ km **3.** $9.7$ m **4.** $12.5$ m **5.** $144.4$ m **6.a)**$96.7$ m
**b)**$67.9$ km **7.** $2.8$ m **8.** $5.8$ m **9.** $179$ km
**10.a)**$25.5$ km **b)**$2.2$ km **11.a)**$86.5$ km **b)**$103.8$ km
**c)**$164.0$ km **12.a)**$96.7$ km **b)**$2.8$ km **13.** $34.3$ m

**1.13 Exercise, page 53**
**1.a)**$6$ **b)**$8$ **c)**$6$ **2.a)**$1$ **b)**$3$ **c)**$1$ **d)**$1$ **3.a)**$1$ **b)**$5$
**4.a)**$14; 1, 5, 14$ **b)**$14$ **c)**$55$ **5.** Morris and Sonja;
Kevin and Terry; Jacques and Melanie **6.** $45$ **7.** $99$

**CHAPTER 2**

**2.1 Exercise, page 59**
**1.a)**$4, y$ **b)**$-6, x^2$ **c)**$\frac{2}{3}, x$ **d)**$-12, ab$ **e)**$36, x^2y$ **f)**$\frac{2}{3}, kp$

**g)**$-16, p^2$ **h)**$-\frac{3}{5}, xy$ **2.a)**trinomial **b)**binomial

**c)**monomial **d)**binomial **e)**trinomial **f)**binomial
**g)**monomial **h)**trinomial **3.a)**$6a^3b^3$ **b)**$6a^3b^3$ **c)**$6a^3b^3$
**4.a)**$-8x^4y^3$ **b)**$-8$ **5.a)**$4a^2b^4$ **b)**$576$ **6.a)**$6x^2y+9xy^2-6x^2y^2$
**b)**$-432$ **7.a)**$-6y^2$ **b)**$12x^4$ **c)**$18a^2$ **d)**$-24m^4$ **e)**$-28a^2$
**f)**$-18y^3$ **g)**$-6a^3$ **h)**$12x^3$ **8.a)**$-6xy$ **b)**$9x^2$ **c)**$8x^2y^2$ **d)**$-6a^2b^2$
**e)**$-12x^4$ **f)**$6y^3$ **g)**$6x^3y^3$ **h)**$-9a^3b^2$ **i)**$-12a^4b^2$ **j)**$-6m^3n^2$
**k)**$-6p^4q^3$ **l)**$-8a^4b^3$ **9.a)**$9x^2$ **b)**$4a^4$ **c)**$16x^2y^2$ **d)**$4m^2n^2$
**e)**$9m^2n^4$ **f)**$4x^4y^2$ **10.a)**$-24m^2n^3$ **b)**$-12x^6$ **c)**$2x^2y^5$ **d)**$-6x^5y^4$
**e)**$-12a^3b^3$ **f)**$-6m^3n^3$ **11.a)**$36$ **b)**$4320$ **c)**$864$ **d)**$432$ **e)**$27\,216$
**f)**$144$ **g)**$120$ **h)**$-504$ **12.a)**$28.8$ **b)**$-86.4$ **c)**$207.36$
**d)**$-29.4912$ **e)**$-20.736$ **f)**$-29.4912$ **13.a)**$3x+6$ **b)**$-4k+8$
**c)**$-6x^2+18x$ **d)**$-2y^2+10y$ **e)**$2x^2+2xy$ **f)**$-6x^2+3xy$
**g)**$-3x^2+6x+15$ **h)**$-12x-6x^2+18x^3$ **i)**$12-8y-4y^2$
**j)**$-12y+18y^2+24y^3$ **k)**$-3a^3b^2+6ab^3$
**l)**$2p^4q-2p^2q^3+2p^2q$ **14.a)**$-18$ **b)**$-504$ **c)**$12$
**15.a)**$-151.2$ **b)**$0.549$ **c)**$-2.49$ **16.a)**$300$ **b)**$300$ **c)**$648$
**d)**$3.468$ **e)**$78$ **17.a)**$9a^2b^4$ **b)**$4x^3y+6x^2y^2-2xy^3$
**18.** $80$ square units when $x=5, y=1$

**2.2 Exercise, page 63**
**1.a)**$x^4$ **b)**$2a$ **c)**$3x^2$ **d)**$-4y$ **e)**$-2p^2$ **f)**$4q^2$ **g)**$3m$ **h)**$-3$ **2.a)**$3a^2b$
**b)**$6$ **3.a)**$-2$ **b)**$-8$ **c)**$8$ **d)**$2$ **4.a)**$-2p^2$ **b)**$-18$ **5.b)**$2p-3$ **6.a)**$3$
**b)**$y$ **c)**$-3y$ **d)**$-4x^2$ **e)**$-3c$ **f)**$5n$ **g)**$6b$ **h)**$-2a$ **i)**$2x$ **j)**$-3a$
**k)**$4m^2$ **l)**$-4m$ **m)**$-6x^2y^2$ **n)**$6a^2$ **o)**$7m$ **7.a)**$-4a$ **b)**$3b$ **c)**$5a^2$
**d)**$-3ab^2$ **e)**$-7mt^2$ **f)**$7x^2y$ **g)**$-2mn$ **h)**$-8m$ **8.a)**$6$ **b)**$-4$ **c)**$-9$
**d)**$24$ **e)**$-12$ **f)**$-72$ **g)**$15$ **h)**$-54$ **i)**$4$ **9.a)**$-4y$ **b)**$x^2$ **c)**$2ab$ **d)**$3b$
**e)**$-4m$ **f)**$4x$ **g)**$-2$ **h)**$x$ **i)**$m$ **10.a)**$1-2y$ **b)**$4-2m$ **c)**$5m-y$
**d)**$-2x-4x^2$ **e)**$-3y+4$ **f)**$-3x+2a$ **g)**$-10n+5m$
**h)**$y-1+x$ **i)**$-a+a^2+3b$ **j)**$-3x+2y-5xy$
**k)**$-3am+2m+6a$ **l)**$-5p^2+q^3-4p$ **11.a)**$-8$
**b)**$-8$ **c)**same **12.a)**$5$ **b)**$-7$ **c)**$-6$ **d)**$-9$ **13.a)**$6$ **b)**$-2m^4$ **c)**$-3x$
**d)**$-9x^3y^2$ **e)**$b^2$ **f)**$2b^3$ **g)**$-3ab^2$ **h)**$-3ab$ **14.** T, V **15.** A

**2.3 Exercise, page 67**
**1.a)**$6p$ **b)**$2y$ **c)**$2y$ **d)**$-10x$ **e)**$11p$ **f)**$11s$ **2.a)**$5a-2b$
**b)**$8x-3y$ **c)**$m-2n$ **d)**$5x-y$ **e)**$5p+q$ **f)**$m$ **3.a)**$7x-3y$
**b)**$2a-8b$ **c)**$3m$ **d)**$5x^2-5x+3$ **e)**$-6y-9$ **4.a)**$8a-6b$
**b)**$8a-6b$ **5.a)**$x^2-5xy-y^2$ **b)**$25$ **6.a)**$2x^2+2x-8$
**b)**$2x^2+2x-8$ **7.a)**$3y^2-5y-4$ **b)**$-4-5y+3y^2$
**8.a)**$3x+2y$ **b)**$8p-6q$ **c)**$0$ **d)**$10x-10y$ **e)**$-8a+6b$
**f)**$6m-3n$ **g)**$2x^2+x+10$ **h)**$4y^2-10y-8$

**9.a)**$x - 5y$ **b)**$5a - 12b$ **c)**$-13m + 3n$ **d)**$7x - 12y + 5z$
**e)**$-a - 10b + 5c$ **10.a)**$-4x^2 + 6x - 5$ **b)**$-48$ **c)**$2x^2 + 5x$
**d)**$-5y^2 + 9y$ **11.a)**$72$ **b)**$99$ **c)**$-33.22$ **d)**$4.96$ **e)**$8.25$
**f)**$98.01$ **12.a)**$2x - 3y$ **b)**$2x - 3y$ **c)**$2x - 3y$ **d)**$2x - 3y$
**14.a)**$10$ **b)**$18$ **c)**$-81$ **d)** $-51$ **15.** B **16.** A **17.a)**$14$ units
**b)**$12$ units **c)**$10$ units **d)**$7$ **18.a)**$6$ square units **b)**$8$ square
units **c)**$6$ square units **d)**$2$ **19.a)**$2x + 12$ **b)**$12x - 2x^2$
**c)**$10$ square units, $14$ units; $16$ square units,
$16$ units **20.a)**$4$ **b)**$32$ **c)**$24$ units **21.a)**$18$ **b)**$144$

## 2.4 Exercise, page 70
**1.a)**$3$ **b)**$2$ **2.a)**$6$ **b)** $-11$ **c)**$6$ **d)**$4$ **e)**$3$ **f)**$2$ **g)**$3$ **h)** $-1$ **i)**$41$

**3.a)**$24$ **b)**$2$ **c)**$10$ **d)**$17$ **e)**$17$ **4.a)**$m = \dfrac{F}{a}$ **b)**$M = DV$

**c)**$r = \dfrac{C}{2\pi}$ **d)**$R = \dfrac{E}{I}$ **e)**$t = \dfrac{v^2 - u^2}{30}$ **f)**$n = \dfrac{S}{180} + 2$

**g)**$p = \dfrac{t}{3} - s$ **h)**$l = \dfrac{P}{2} - w$ **i)**$m = \dfrac{y - b}{x}$ **j)**$a = x - \dfrac{y}{m}$

**k)**$u = \dfrac{2S}{t} - v$ **l)**$P = 2l + 2w$ **m)**$\dfrac{v - u}{t}$ **5.a)**$17$ **b)**$9.1$

**c)**$487.3$ **6.** 62 adults, 147 students **7.** 20 cm by 14 cm
**8.** \$18 000, \$9000, \$6000 **9.** 25, 75 **10.** \$4.50 **11.** \$2400

## 2.5 Exercise, page 73
**1.a)**$y^2 + 5y + 6$ **b)**$k^2 + 7k + 6$ **c)**$y^2 - y - 42$
**d)**$y^2 - 5y + 6$ **e)**$x^2 - x - 6$ **f)**$a^2 - 2a - 15$ **g)**$y^2 + y - 42$
**h)**$y^2 - 49$ **i)**$x^2 - y^2$ **3.a)**$2x^2 - 4x + 2$ **b)**$4x^2 - 4x + 1$
**4.a)**$3y^2 + 4y - 15$ **b)**$6a^2 - 2a - 28$ **c)**$3t^2 - 6t - 9$
**d)**$y^2 - 16$ **e)**$x^2 - 4x - 12$ **f)**$m^2 + 9m + 14$
**g)**$4x^2 + 26x - 14$ **h)**$2x^2 - 17xy - 9y^2$ **i)**$x^2 + 9x + 8$
**j)**$24 + 10k + k^2$ **k)**$9k^2 - 4$ **l)**$9x^2 - 1$ **5.a)**$3x^2 - 15x + 12$
**b)**$-8x^2 + 44x - 60$ **c)**$27k^2 + 18k + 3$
**d)**$48y^2 - 128y - 48$ **e)** $-2x^2 + 4xy - 2y^2$ **f)** $-12x^2 + 3y^2$
**g)** $-2k^2 - 4k + 96$ **h)** $-2m^2 + 9m - 9$ **i)**$3x^2 - 30x + 75$
**j)**$12p^2 - 10pq + 2q^2$ **k)**$8x^2 - 8xy + 2y^2$ **l)** $-2a^2 - 2a + 60$
**6.a)**$x^4 - 11x^2 + 24$ **b)**$8 + 10a + 2a^2$ **c)**$12y^4 + 8y^2 - 7$

**d)**$x^2 - \dfrac{1}{16}$ **e)**$4x^2 - 4x + 1$ **f)**$9y^2 - 30y + 25$

**g)**$a^2b^2 - 36$ **h)**$4x^2 - 2x + \dfrac{1}{4}$ **i)**$16x^2 - 20x + \dfrac{25}{4}$

**7.a)**$4x^2 - 6x - 10$ **b)** $-2x + 14$ **8.a)** $-x^2 - 9x + 52$
**b)** $-7y^2 + y + 138$ **c)**$10a^2$ **d)**$9m^2 - 56m + 12$
**e)**$7x^2 - 30x + 75$ **f)**$a^2 - 6a + 1$ **g)**$9y^2 - 3xy$
**h)** $-10a^2 + 4ab + 5b^2$ **i)**$x^2 - 10x + 1$ **j)**$5x^2 - 10x$
**k)** $-16x^2 + 3x - 16xy + 48y^2$ **l)** $-y^2 + 10y - 23$
**9.a)**$2x^3 + 3x^2y - y^3$ **b)**$6a^3 - 7a^2b + b^3$
**c)**$6x^3 - 10x^2 + 7x - 2$ **d)**$3a^3 - 8a^2b + 5ab^2 - 2b^3$
**e)**$x^3 - 3x^2y + 3xy^2 - y^3$ **f)**$8m^3 + 12m^2 + 6m + 1$
**g)**$27a^3 - 54a^2b + 36ab^2 - 8b^3$ **10.a)**$107$ **b)** $-18$
**c)**$14$ **d)** $-3$ **e)** $-54$ **11.a)**$29$ square units **b)** $86$ square units
**c)**$173$ square units **12.a)**$21.2$ square units **b)**$62.64$ square
units **c)**$8087.13$ square units **14.a)**$3x^2 - 10x + 8$
**b)**$16$ square units **15.a)**$6x^2 + 5x + 1, 6x^2 - 5x + 1$ **b)**$10x$

## 2.6 Exercise, page 77
**1.a)**$3x$ **b)**$2a$ **c)** $-3x$ **d)**$3y$ **e)**$5xy$ **f)** $-2x$ **g)** $-3x^2y$ **h)**$2a^2b$
**i)**$3x$ **j)** $-3a$ **k)** $-3x$ **l)** $-2m$ **m)** $-a^2$ **n)** $-2x$ **o)** $-p$ **2.a)**$4xy$
**b)**$4xy$ **c)**$8ab$ **d)**$3x^2$ **e)**$y^2$ **f)**$5m$ **g)**$a$ **h)**$6a$ **i)**$25ax$ **3.a)** $-4y$
**b)** $-3xy$ **c)** $-3x^2$ **d)** $-3ab$ **e)**$2ab$ **f)** $-4x^3y^2$ **g)**$2y^2$ **h)** $-3x^2y$
**4.a)** $-2x(x - y)$ **5.a)**$3$ **b)**$x - y$ **c)**$2x$ **d)**$2a - 3$ **e)**$x^3$ **f)**$2xy$
**g)**$x^2 - 2x + 3$ **h)**$2c^3 - 3bc^2 - 4a$ **6.a)** $-4(3x - y)$

**b)**$4x(a - 2b)$ **c)**$2a(a - 3)$ **d)** $-13a(b + 3c)$ **e)**$9a^3(2a - 3)$
**f)**$2x(3x - 2)$ **g)**$5xy(3 - 2y)$ **h)**$6a(1 - 2a^4)$ **i)**$4a(7a - b)$
**j)**$7mn(7 - 2mn)$ **k)**$32x^4y^2(2x^2 - y^2)$ **7.a)**$x^2(x^2 - 5x + 3)$
**b)**$x(x + 4y - 1)$ **c)**$6(2x^2 - 4x + 5)$ **d)**$ab(x^2 + 6y - 8y^2)$
**e)**$ax(x^2 - 5x + 3)$ **f)**$10x(x^2 - 5x + 3)$ **g)**$2m(2m^2 - 4m + 3)$
**h)**$3(x^2 - 4xy + 3y^2)$ **i)**$15ab(3a - b - 4)$ **j)**$10ab(a^2b^2 -$
$2ab - 1)$ **k)**$3p^2q^2(2 + p - 3q)$ **l)**$3a(3x^2 - 6xy + 2y^2)$
**8.a)**$(a + b)(x + y)$ **b)**$(a - b)(2x - y)$ **c)**$(x + 1)(3x - 2)$
**d)**$(2a - 3b)(a - b)$ **e)**$(2x - 5y)(2x - 3y)$ **f)**$(a - 3b)(a + 2b)$
**9.** $(a + b)(2x - 3y)$ **10.a)**$(x - y)(2a - 3b)$ **b)**$(a - b)(a + c)$
**c)**$(m + n)(a + b)$ **d)**$(2m - 3n)(3a - b)$ **e)**$(b + c)(b - a)$
**f)**$(x - 1)(x - y)$ **g)**$2(m + 2)(x + y)$ **h)**$3x(m - n)(y - 2)$
**11.a)** $-84$ **b)** $-84$ **d)**(b) **12.a)** $-60$ **b)**$32$ **c)** $-36$ **d)**$432$
**e)**$48$ **f)**$912$ **13.a)**$1268.3$ m² **b)**$2\pi r(r + h)$, $1268.3$ m²
**14.a)**$878.3$ m² **b)**$207.3$ m² **15.a)**$232.4$ m² **16.a)**$31.4$m, 5
**b)**$31.4$ m, 3 **c)**$2\pi(R - r)$ **17.** $107.14$ m **18.** $113.54$ m

## 2.7 Exercise, page 82
**1.a)**$2, 3$ **b)**$(a + 2)(a + 3)$ **2.a)** $-6, -6$ **b)**$4, 4$ **c)** $-6, 8$
**d)** $-12, 6$ **e)**$(m - 6)(m - 6), (k + 4)(k + 4), (p - 6x)(p + 8x),$
$(x - 12y)(x + 6y)$ **3.a)**$m + 3$ **b)**$x - 6$ **c)**$y + 3$ **d)**$m - 4$
**e)**$x + 5y$ **f)**$a + 3b$ **4.a)**$7, 8$ **b)** $-8, 2$ **c)** $-4, 3$ **d)** $-5, 7$
**5.a)**$2, 8$ **b)** $-9, -1$ **c)** $-5, 4$ **d)** $-5, 3$ **e)** $-3, 6$ **f)** $-2, 5$
**g)**$1, 14$ **h)** $-2, 13$ **i)** $-8, -6$ **6.a)**$a^2$ **b)**$4m$ **c)**$9x^2$ **d)**$1$ **e)**$4$ **f)**$24a$
**7.a)**$(y + 4)^2$ **b)**$(m - 3)^2$ **c)**$(x - y)^2$ **d)**$(a + 1)^2$ **e)**$(2x + 9)^2$
**f)**$(5y - 2)^2$ **g)**$(2a + 1)^2$ **h)**$(5a - 4b)^2$ **8.a)**$(x + 3)(x + 5)$
**b)**$(y - 6)(y + 5)$ **c)**$3(a + 2)(a + 1)$ **d)**$(x - y)^2$
**e)**$(x + 2y)(x + y)$ **f)**$2(a + 2)^2$ **g)**$2(x - 1)(x + 2)$ **h)**$(x - 1)(x + 5)$
**9.a)**$(x - 5)(x - 4)$ **b)**$(m - 7)(m - 6)$ **c)**$(a + 3)^2$
**d)**$(5 - x)^2$ **e)**$(a - 5b)(a + 2b)$ **f)**$3(x - 1)(x + 2)$ **g)**$(x - 3)(x + 7)$
**h)**$(3x - 2)^2$ **i)**$(3 - x)(6 - x)$ **j)**$(m + 3n)(m + 5n)$
**k)**$2(5a + b)^2$ **l)**$3(y - 1)(y + 5)$ **10.a)**$y + 7$ **b)**$x - 2$ **c)**$y + 1$
**11.a)**$4$ **b)**$8$ **c)**$8$ **13.** $(3y + 1)(y + 3), (3x + 2)(x - 7)$

## 2.8 Exercise, page 85
**1.a)**$2, 3$ **b)**$(3x + 2)(x + 1)$ **2.a)** $-9, 2$ **b)**$3, 4$ **c)** $-15, -2$
**d)** $-10, 12$ **e)**$(3y + 1)(2y - 3), (2y + 1)(3y + 2),$
$(5y - 1)(2y - 3), (4y - 5)(2y + 3)$ **3.a)**$3, 9$ **b)** $-16, 4$
**c)** $-6, 8$ **d)** $-5, 2$ **4.a)** $-5, -3$ **b)** $-9, 3$ **c)** $-8, 1$ **d)** $-5, 8$
**e)** $-3, 5$ **f)** $-9, 6$ **g)** $-9, 3$ **h)** $-8, -7$ **i)** $-16, 3$ **j)** $-8, -2$
**5.b)**$(3x + 5)(2x + 1)$ **6.a)**$(x - 2)(3x + 2)$ **b)**$(a - 3)(2a - 3)$
**c)**$(x - y)(2x - y)$ **d)**$(2n - 1)(m - 3)$ **e)**$(x - 5y)(x - 5y)$
**f)**$(p + 3q)(p + 2q)$ **7.a)**$(2x + 1)(2x + 3)$ **b)**$(2x - 1)(2x - 3)$
**c)**$(2x - 1)(2x + 3)$ **d)**$(2x + 1)(2x - 3)$ **8.a)**$(3x + 1)(3x + 4)$
**b)**$(3x - 4)(3x - 1)$ **c)**$(3x + 1)(3x - 4)$ **d)**$(3x - 1)(3x + 4)$
**9.a)**$(2y + 1)(y + 1)$ **b)**$(3x + 1)(x - 2)$ **c)**$(2y - 3)(y + 4)$
**d)**$(2x + 1)(3x + 1)$ **e)**$(5x - 1)(x - 2)$ **f)**$(2m - 5)(3m + 2)$
**g)**$(y + 2)(2y + 1)$ **h)**$(3y - 2)(2y - 3)$ **i)**$(5m + 3)(2m - 1)$
**10.a)**$(x - 7y)(3x + 2y)$ **b)**$(3m + 1)(m + 4)$
**c)**$2(5x - 4)(x - 2)$ **d)**$(y - 3)(3y + 10)$ **e)**$(2y + 5)(4y - 3)$
**f)**$(4x + 3y)(x - 5y)$ **11.** (b), (d); (c), (l); (d), (f); (h), (k); (g), (h);
(c), (j) **12.a)**$(1 - x)(1 + x + x^2 + x^3 + x^4), (1 - x)(1 +$
$x + x^2 + x^3 + x^4 + x^5)$ **b)**$(1 - x)(1 + x + x^2 + \cdots +$
$x^8 + x^9), (1 - x)(1 + x + x^2 + \cdots + x^{99})$ **c)**$65\ 535$

## 2.9 Exercise, page 88
**1.a)**$x^2 - 25$ **b)**$9 - y^2$ **c)**$4x^2 - 9y^2$ **d)**$9m^2 - 1$ **e)**$k^2 - 16m^2$
**f)**$25y^2 - 4x^2$ **2.a)**$(2x - y)(2x + y)$ **b)**$(m - 3)(m + 3)$
**c)**$(x - 7y)(x + 7y)$ **d)**$(6 - 7x)(6 + 7x)$ **e)**$(4a - 5b)(4a + 5b)$
**3.a)**$(x - 5)(x + 5)$ **b)**$(n - 4)(n + 4)$ **c)** $(k - 7)(k + 7)$
**d)**$(a - 8)(a + 8)$ **e)**$(c - 10)(c + 10)$ **f)**$(m - 9)(m + 9)$
**4.a)**$(3x - 2)(3x + 2)$ **b)**$(8y - 1)(8y + 1)$ **c)**$(5p - 7)(5p + 7)$

d)$(2m - 3)(2m + 3)$ e)$(5s - 6)(5s + 6)$ f)$(20r - 7)(20r + 7)$
**5.a)**$(x - 2y)(x + 2y)$ **b)**$(5k - p)(5k + p)$ **c)**$(m - 10n)(m + 10n)$
**d)**$(10a - 7b)(10a + 7b)$ **e)**$(6y - 5x)(6y + 5x)$
**f)**$(4p - 5q)(4p + 5q)$ **6.b)**$2(3a - 2)(3a + 2)$ **7.a)**$(x^2 + 1)$
$(x - 1)(x + 1)$ **8.a)**$(y - 2)(y + 2)$ **b)**$(1 - 2m)(1 + 2m)$
**c)**$(4x - 3)(4x + 3)$ **d)**$(a - 6)(a + 6)$ **e)**$(3x - 1)(3x + 1)$
**f)**$(4x - 5y)(4x + 5y)$ **g)**$(7y - 1)(7y + 1)$ **h)**$(3 - 5x)(3 + 5x)$
**i)**$(2m - 5t)(2m + 5t)$ **j)**$(xy - 2)(xy + 2)$ **9.a)**$(a - b)(a + b)$
**b)**$2(x - y)(x + y)$ **c)**$3(a - 2b)(a + 2b)$ **d)**$(4p - 1)(4p + 1)$
**e)**$(1 - 6ab)(1 + 6ab)$ **f)**$2(x - 1)(x + 1)$
**g)**$10(x - 8)(x + 8)$ **h)**$(9m - 2n)(9m + 2n)$ **i)**$3(1 - 5y)(1 + 5y)$
**j)**$(4a - 3b)(4a + 3b)$ **k)**$(1 - 2a)(1 + 2a)$ **l)**$(7 - y)(7 + y)$
**m)**$(8 - xy)(8 + xy)$ **n)**$(4 - 3y)(4 + 3y)$ **o)**$2(xy - 2)(xy + 2)$
**10.b)**$(x - s)(x + s)$
**11.b)**$(m - 2n)(m + 2n), (m - 2n - 2t)(m + 2n + 2t)$
**12.b)**$(x - y)(x + y), (x + a - y - b)(x + a + y + b)$
**13.a)**$(a + b + c)(a + b - c)$ **b)**$(a - b + c)(a - b - c)$
**c)**$(x + y + k)(x - y - k)$ **d)**$(x + y - h)(x - y + h)$
**e)**$(c + 2a - b)(c - 2a + b)$ **f)**$(c + 4a - 2b)(c - 4a + 2b)$
**g)**$(a + b + y)(a + b - x - y)$ **h)**$(a - b + x - y)(a - b - x + y)$ **14.a)**$(m - s)(m + s)$ **b)**$(a - 2b)(a + 2b)$
**c)**$(2s - 3t)(2s + 3t)$ **d)**$(2a - b)(2a + b)$ **e)**$(y - x)(y + x)$

**f)**cannot be factored **g)**$\left(x - \dfrac{1}{2}\right)\left(x + \dfrac{1}{2}\right)$

**h)**$2(3k + 4m)(3k - 4m)$ **i)**$(2t - 5s)(2t + 5s)$ **j)**$\left(\dfrac{x}{5} - 1\right)\left(\dfrac{x}{5} + 1\right)$

**k)**$(x^2 + 1)(x - 1)(x + 1)$ **l)**$(4y - 5x)(4y + 5x)$
**m)**$(7 - 3m)(7 + 3m)$ **n)**$(3 - a + b)(3 + a - b)$ **o)**cannot
be factored **p)**$2(mn - 5)(mn + 5)$ **q)**$(1 - 8y^2)(1 + 8y^2)$
**r)**$(5xy - 1)(5xy + 1)$ **s)**$(3a - 3b - 1)(3a - 3b + 1)$
**t)**$b(2a - b)$ **u)**$(x - y - 2)(x - y + 2)$ **v)**$4(2x^2 - b^2)(2x^2 + b^2)$ **w)**$(3a + b)(-a - 3b)$ **x)**$(9 + 4x^2)(3 - 2x)(3 + 2x)$
**15.a)**399 **b)**899 **c)**3599 **d)**9996 **16.a)**280 **b)**480 **c)**660
**d)**1980 **e)**600 **f)**1800 **g)**5000 **h)**9200 **17.a)**$a^2 - b^2$
**18.a)**$(3a)^2 - (2b)^2$ **b)**$(3a - 2b)(3a + 2b)$
**19.a)**$(a^2 + 1)(a + 1)(a - 1)$ **b)**$(a^4 + 1)(a^2 + 1)(a + 1)(a - 1)$
**c)**$(a^8 + 1)(a^4 + 1)(a^2 + 1)(a + 1)(a - 1)$
**d)**$(a^{16} + 1)(a^8 + 1)(a^4 + 1)(a^2 + 1)(a + 1)(a - 1)$
**20.a)**183 376 cm³ **b)**183 376 cm³ **21.** 268 470 cm³
**22.** 41 910 cm³ **23.a)**0.67 m³ **b)**(i)578 (ii)1452 m³

## 2.10 Exercise, page 92
**1.** $3a(a + 2)$ **2.** $2x(1 - 4y)$ **3.** $(2a)(2a)(9a - 1)$
**4.** $(5a^2 - 3y^2)(5a^2 + 3y^2)$ **5.** $(x + 3)(x + 4)$
**6.** $3(a - b)(a + b)$ **7.** $(y - 7)(y - 4)$ **8.** $(4x - 1)^2$
**9.** $(a - 8b)(a + 7b)$ **10.** $(4x - 3)(x - 2)$ **11.** $(3k - 1)(3k + 1)$
**12.** $(1 + 2y)(1 + 16y)$ **13.** $2y^2(1 - 4y)$ **14.** $(x + 2)(x + 4)$
**15.** $(8x - 1)(7x + 2)$ **16.** cannot be factored
**17.** $2(4 - 5x)(2 - x)$ **18.** $(m^2 + 4)(m + 2)(m - 2)$
**19.** $(4 - 5y)(2 - y)$ **20.** $(a^2 + 1)(a + 1)(a - 1)$
**21.** $(m^2 + 4)(m + 3)(m - 3)$ **22.** $(3a + 1)(2a + 1)$
**23.** $(x^2 + y^2)(x + y)(x - y)$ **24.** $(p - 9q)(p + 7q)$
**25.** $(m^2 + 4)(m + 1)(m - 1)$ **26.** $x(x - y)$ **27.** $x(x + 3y - 1)$
**28.** $(a + 12)(a - 12)$ **29.** $3(a^2 - 12a + 12)$
**30.** $(a + b + c)(a + b - c)$ **31.** $-(a + b)^2$ **32.** cannot be
factored **33.** $(x^2 + 2)(x^2 + 16)$ **34.** $(m^2 + 7)(m + 4)(m - 4)$
**35.** $(x^4 + 1)(x^2 + 1)(x + 1)(x - 1)$ **36.** $2(y - 4)(y + 3)$
**37.** $2(x + 2)(x - 2)$ **38.** $4(y + 5)(y - 3)$ **39.** $(m^2 + 4)(m + 2)(m - 2)$ **40.** $2(x - 4)^2$ **41.** $x(x + y)(x - y)$
**42.** $(x + 2)(x + 1)(x - 2)(x - 1)$ **43.** $-3(16 + y^2)$
**44.** $xy^2(xyz - 2)$ **45.** $-4xy$ **46.** $4(2a + b)(a + 2b)$

**47.** $-3(5a + 7b)(a + 3b)$ **48.** $(19x + 4)(x + 6)$
**49.** $-4(3x + y)(x + 3y)$ **50.** $8(2x + y)(x + 8y)$

## 2.11 Exercise, page 94

**1.a)** $3, -4$ **b)**$6, -2$ **c)**$3, -\dfrac{1}{2}$ **d)** $-5$ **e)**$\dfrac{1}{3}, -2$ **f)**$0, 3$ **2.a)**$-1, 3$

**b)**$-\dfrac{1}{2}, 3$ **c)**$-\dfrac{2}{3}, \dfrac{1}{2}$ **d)** $-6, \dfrac{5}{3}$ **e)**$\dfrac{1}{3}, 3$ **f)** $0, 6$ **3.a)**$-2, 4$

**b)**$-6, -5$ **c)**$-2, 8$ **d)**$-4, 9$ **e)**$-4, 5$ **f)**$-7, 7$ **4.a)**$5, 10$

**b)**$-3, 8$ **c)**$-6, -3$ **d)**$5, 6$ **e)**$-9, 2$ **f)**$-\dfrac{3}{2}, \dfrac{3}{2}$ **5.a)**$\{4, 5\}$

**b)**$\{-8, 12\}$ **c)**$\{-25, 4\}$ **d)**$\{-6, -5\}$ **e)**$\{-2, 6\}$

**f)**$\left\{-\dfrac{4}{5}, \dfrac{4}{5}\right\}$ **6.a)**$x^2 + 5x - 24 = 0$ **b)**$x^2 - 4x - 12 = 0$

**7.a)**$x^2 - 9x + 20 = 0$ **b)**$x^2 - 5x - 24 = 0$
**c)**$x^2 + 8x + 16 = 0$ **d)**$x^2 - 6x - 27 = 0$ **e)**$3x^2 - 5x + 2 = 0$
**f)**$2x^2 - x - 6 = 0$ **g)**$x^2 - 1.5x + 0.54 = 0$
**h)**$6x^2 - x - 1 = 0$ **8.b)**$-4, 18$ **9.b)**$-4, 6$ **10.a)**$-8, 6$ **b)**$-3, 7$

**c)**$-2, 6$ **d)**$-\dfrac{10}{3}, 3$ **e)**$\dfrac{1}{6}, 1$ **f)**$-\dfrac{5}{3}, \dfrac{3}{4}$ **11.a)**$-3, 2$ **b)**$-6, 7$

**c)**$-9, 2$ **d)**$-\dfrac{5}{2}, \dfrac{3}{4}$ **e)**$-5, \dfrac{2}{3}$ **f)**$\dfrac{2}{3}, 2$ **12.a)**$\{-5, -3\}$ **b)**$\{4, 5\}$

**c)** $\{-5, 6\}$ **d)**$\left\{-\dfrac{1}{6}, 1\right\}$ **e)**$\left\{-\dfrac{3}{4}, 5\right\}$ **f)**$\left\{\dfrac{2}{5}, \dfrac{5}{2}\right\}$ **13.a)**$-3, \dfrac{5}{3}$ **b)**$\dfrac{6}{5},$

$4$ **c)**$-3, \dfrac{10}{3}$ **d)**$-\dfrac{5}{3}, \dfrac{3}{4}$ **e)**$-5$ **f)**$-2, 3$ **14.a)**$n = 2, x = \dfrac{1}{2}$

**b)**$n = 5, p = \dfrac{1}{3}$ **c)**$n = -1, y = -\dfrac{1}{2}$ **d)**$n = -1, m = \dfrac{3}{2}$

**15.** 15, 7 and $-15, -7$ **16.** 8 m × 12 m **17.** 12, 13 or $-13, -12$ **18.** 3 m × 9 m **19.** 30 cm, 40 cm

## 2.12 Exercise, page 97
**1.a)**6 **b)**15 **2.** 120 **3.** 1296 **4.** no **5.** 84
**6.** 7, 16, 6 **7.** 40 320

## CHAPTER 3

## 3.1 Exercise, page 100
**1.** $(y - 6)(y + 4)$ **2.** $2(m - 1)(m + 1)$ **3.** $(m - 7)(m - 4)$
**4.** $a(1 - 4a)$ **5.** $pq(r + s)$ **6.** $(x - 12)(x + 12)$ **7.** $k(k + 4)$
**8.** $(x - 20)(x - 4)$ **9.** $(p + 4)(p + 3)$ **10.** $(2y + 3)(y + 4)$
**11.** $2(y^2 + 2)$ **12.** $m(m - 10)(m + 1)$ **13.** $3(a - b)(a + b)$
**14.** $(3y)(3y)(4y - 1)$ **15.** $(5m^2 + 4y^2)(5m^2 - 4y^2)$
**16.** $(y + 3)(y - 3)(y + 2)(y - 2)$ **17.** $(2m - 3)(m - 4)$
**18.** $(x + 4)(x - 2)$ **19.** $(4y - 1)^2$ **20.** $2x^2(1 - 4x)$
**21.** $(2x - 5)(5x - 2)$ **22.** $-(x + y)^2$ **23.** $(2m + 1)(m + 1)$
**24.** $10(3x + 10)(3x - 10)$ **25.** $3(y^2 - 12y + 12)$
**26.** $(12 + y)(12 - y)$ **27.** $(5m + 4n)(5m - 4n)$ **28.** $(3x + 2)(4x - 5)$
**29.** $(m^2 + 4)(m + 3)(m - 3)$ **30.** $2a(a^2 - 2)$
**31.** $(5x^2 - y^2)(5x^2 + y^2)$ **32.** $2y(8y - 3)(3y + 5)$ **33.** $8(x^2 - 3y^2)$
**34.** $(m^2 + 1)(m + 2)(m - 2)$ **35.** $2y^2(y + 4)$ **36.** $(5x + 3)(2x - 5)$
**37.** $\left(\dfrac{1}{2}x - 1\right)^2$ **38.** $(x - 12)(x - 9)$ **39.** $(x^2 + y^2)(x + y)(x - y)$
**40.** $(8y + 1)(3y - 2)$ **41.** $(b - 8)(b - 7)$ **42.** cannot factor
**43.** $x(x + y)(x - y)$ **44.** $(y + 1)(y - 1)(y + 4)(y - 4)$
**45.** $(3n + 1)(3n - 1)$ **46.** $(x + 6)(x - 3)$ **47.** $9(4y + 1)$
**48.** $xy(4x - 3y)(x + 6y)$ **49.** $2(x - 4)^2$ **50.** $x^2(x + y)(x - y)$
**51.** $(2x - 5)(x + 7)$ **52.** $(y^2 + 1)(y + 1)(y - 1)$
**53.** cannot factor **54.** $(1 + 2x)(1 + 36x)$

$(y^2 - 4y + 12)(y - 6)(y + 2)$ **56.** $(3x + y)(x + 3y)$

**57.** $\left(x - \dfrac{5}{2}\right)\left(5x - \dfrac{1}{2}\right)$ **58.** $(m - 3)(m - 2)(m - 6)(m + 1)$

### 3.2 Exercise, page 101
**1.a)** $z \neq 0$ **b)** $a \neq 0$ **c)** $y \neq 1$ **d)** $m \neq -2$ **e)** $a \neq 0, b \neq 0$

**f)** $m \neq 0, n \neq 0$ **g)** $w \neq 0, -3$ **h)** $a \neq \dfrac{1}{2}$ **2.a)** $b \neq -1, 1$

**b)** $m \neq -n, n$ **c)** $x \neq 2, y \neq 3$ **d)** $c \neq 0, \dfrac{1}{2}$ **e)** $p \neq 0, q \neq 0,$

$r \neq 1$ **f)** $k \neq -2, 2$ **g)** $w \neq -\dfrac{3}{2}, 1$ **h)** $m \neq -\dfrac{1}{2}, 2$ **i)** $a \neq -3, 2$

**3.a)** $\dfrac{y + 4}{y + 8}, y \neq -8, 4$ **b)** $\dfrac{y + 3}{y - 3}, y \neq 3$ **c)** $\dfrac{y - 3}{y + 2}, y \neq -2, 2$

**d)** $-\dfrac{5}{4}b, a \neq 0, \dfrac{2}{3}$ **4.a)** 13 **b)** 13 **5.a)** $x - 8$ **b)** $-12$

**6.a)** $x \neq 5; \dfrac{x + 3}{4}$ **b)** $y \neq 1, 2; \dfrac{2}{y - 2}$ **c)** $y \neq -3, \dfrac{7}{2}; \dfrac{1}{y + 3}$

**d)** $x \neq -\dfrac{1}{2}, \dfrac{1}{2}; \dfrac{3x + 1}{2x + 1}$ **e)** $x \neq -5y, y \neq -\dfrac{x}{5}; x + 5y$

**f)** $x \neq -\dfrac{y}{3}, \dfrac{y}{2}, y \neq -3x, 2x; \dfrac{3x - y}{3x + y}$ **g)** $x \neq -1, 3; \dfrac{x + 3}{x - 3}$

**h)** $p \neq -q, \dfrac{q}{3}, q \neq 3p, -p; \dfrac{2p + q}{3p - q}$ **i)** $x \neq -\dfrac{3}{5}y, -y,$

$y \neq -\dfrac{5}{3}x, -x; \dfrac{5x - 3y}{x + y}$ **7.a)** $-3$ **b)** 2 **c)** $-5$

**d)** 8 **e)** $\dfrac{2}{3}$ **f)** 2 **8.a)** $3(3x - y)$ **b)** $\dfrac{x}{2x + y}$ **c)** $2(4x + y)$ **9.** C

### 3.3 Exercise, page 103
**2.a)** $12m$ **b)** $6x$ **c)** $xy$ **d)** $x^2y^2$ **e)** $6x$ **f)** $2ab$ **g)** $2x^2$ **h)** $x^2y$

**3.a)** $\dfrac{11}{4}x$ **b)** $\dfrac{11}{4a}$ **c)** $\dfrac{11x}{4a}$ **d)** $\dfrac{26}{15}x$ **e)** $\dfrac{26}{15a}$ **f)** $\dfrac{26x}{15a}$ **4.a)** $\dfrac{-5}{12m}$ **b)** $\dfrac{-17y}{6x}$

**c)** $\dfrac{x(2n - 3m)}{mn}$ **d)** $\dfrac{2(3y - 1)}{xy}$ **e)** $\dfrac{-2(4y + 3x)}{x^2y^2}$ **f)** $\dfrac{x(8a - 3)}{2a^2}$

**5.a)** $\dfrac{7}{4}x$ **b)** $\dfrac{7}{2}x$ **c)** $\dfrac{13}{20}x$ **6.a)** $\dfrac{7}{2a}$ **b)** $\dfrac{7x}{2a}$ **c)** $\dfrac{2y^2 - 5y - 6x}{xy^2}$

**d)** $\dfrac{a(2xy - 5x - 6y)}{x^2y}$ **7.a)** $\dfrac{2}{15}x$ **b)** $-\dfrac{a}{18}$ **c)** $\dfrac{17}{10}m$ **d)** $\dfrac{7x + 20}{12}$

**e)** $\dfrac{2y - 7}{12}$ **f)** $\dfrac{2x - 11}{6}$ **8.a)** $\dfrac{27x - 2}{12}$ **b)** $\dfrac{4m - 5}{18}$ **c)** $\dfrac{9y + 14}{6}$

**d)** $\dfrac{2x - 17}{6}$ **e)** $\dfrac{13x + 5}{18}$ **f)** $\dfrac{13t + 1}{12}$ **g)** $\dfrac{4x - 5}{6}$ **h)** $\dfrac{x + 31}{12}$

**9.a)** $\dfrac{4ay - 3bx}{2xy}$ **b)** $\dfrac{6y - 2}{xy}$ **c)** $\dfrac{8(y - x)}{x^2y^2}$ **d)** $\dfrac{2(2a - 3)}{a^2}$

**e)** $\dfrac{9x + 4y}{12x^2y^2}$ **f)** $\dfrac{2ax - 3by}{x^2y^2}$ **g)** $\dfrac{9}{2a}$ **h)** $\dfrac{m(3y^2 + 4x^2 - 1)}{6xy}$

**i)** $\dfrac{5 - 7x}{x^2}$ **10.a)** $-\dfrac{15}{6x}$ **b)** $\dfrac{x(2b - 4a + 3)}{2ab}$ **c)** $\dfrac{2an + 3bn - 2cm}{6mn}$

**d)** $\dfrac{8 - 13x}{2x^2}$ **e)** $\dfrac{2a(3x - 2xy - 4)}{x^2y}$ **f)** $\dfrac{m(q - 2q^2 - 3p)}{pq^2}$

**11.a)** $\dfrac{8m + 7}{4m}$ **b)** $\dfrac{9 - 14x}{10x}$ **c)** $\dfrac{3a^2 + 7ab - 2b^2}{6ab}$

**d)** $\dfrac{2x(3 - x) + y(2 + x)}{4x^2y}$ **e)** $\dfrac{x^2 - 6x + 1}{4x^2}$ **f)** $\dfrac{4y + 3}{6y^2}$ **12.a)** $\dfrac{x}{y}$

**b)** $-\dfrac{13a}{30b}$ **c)** $-\dfrac{4}{5}x$ **d)** $\dfrac{18x}{49}$ **13** **b)** F, S

**14.a)** 4 **b)** 64

### 3.4 Exercise, page 107
**1.a)** $x \neq 0, 4$ **b)** $a \neq -1, 0$ **c)** $x \neq -4, 2$ **d)** $x \neq -1, 2$
**e)** $x \neq -y, y, y \neq -x, x$ **f)** $x \neq -5, 6$ **g)** $x \neq 0, 3$

**h)** $x \neq -2y, 2y, y \neq -\dfrac{1}{2}x, \dfrac{1}{2}x$ **2a)** $\dfrac{x + 3}{2x}$ **b)** $\dfrac{x + 3}{2(x - 1)}$

**3.a)** $\dfrac{2x^2 + x + 1}{x^2}$ **b)** $\dfrac{2x^2}{(x - 1)^2}$ **4.a)** $\dfrac{a^2 + b^2}{ab}$ **b)** $\dfrac{2(a^2 + b^2)}{(a - b)(a + b)}$

**5.a)** $\dfrac{7a + 6}{a(a + 2)}$ **b)** $\dfrac{3a + 10}{a(a + 2)}$ **6.a)** $\dfrac{4(y + 6)}{(y - 2)(y + 2)}$ **b)** $\dfrac{4(2y + 3)}{(y - 2)(y + 2)}$

**7.a)** $\dfrac{x^2 + x - 3}{(x - 2)(x - 1)}$ **b)** $\dfrac{3y^2 + 13y + 6}{(y - 3)(y + 5)}$

**c)** $\dfrac{7b - a}{(a - b)(a + b)}$ **d)** $\dfrac{10x - 33}{(x - 6)(2x - 3)}$

**e)** $\dfrac{10 + 17y - 3y^2}{(y - 5)(y + 5)}$ **f)** $\dfrac{2x^2 - 9x - 15}{(x - 3)(x + 5)}$ **8.a)** $\dfrac{2(a - 5)}{a(a - 2)}$

**b)** $\dfrac{5a - 13}{a(a - 2)}$ **c)** $\dfrac{2(y - 3)}{y(y + 1)}$ **d)** $\dfrac{2(1 - 3y)}{y(y + 1)}$ **e)** $\dfrac{11x - 15}{(x - 3)(x + 3)}$

**f)** $\dfrac{2(5x - 2)}{(x - 2)(x + 2)}$ **g)** $\dfrac{9 - 2x}{(x - 3)(x + 3)}$ **h)** $\dfrac{7 - x}{(x - 2)(x + 2)}$

**9.a)** $\dfrac{3 - x}{x - 1}$ **b)** $\dfrac{3x - 2}{(x - 1)(x + 1)}$ **c)** $\dfrac{4a + 15}{(5 - a)(5 + a)}$

**d)** $\dfrac{-3a + 8}{(a - 2)(a + 2)}$ **e)** $\dfrac{3x - 2y}{(x - y)(x + y)}$ **f)** $\dfrac{7 + 4a}{(3 - a)(3 + a)}$

**g)** $\dfrac{x^2 + 2x + 2xy - y^2}{(x - y)(x + y)}$ **h)** $\dfrac{(3m + n)(m - 2n) - 6}{(m - n)(m + n)}$

**10.a)** $\dfrac{1}{8}$ **b)** $\dfrac{1}{8}$ **11.a)** $\dfrac{2}{5}$ **b)** $-\dfrac{13}{5}$ **c)** 1 **d)** $\dfrac{7}{3}$ **12.a)** $\dfrac{26}{45}$ **b)** $\dfrac{113}{168}$

### 3.5 Exercise, page 110
**1.a)** $\dfrac{mb}{na}$ **b)** $\dfrac{ma}{nb}$ **c)** $\dfrac{a}{b}$ **d)** $\dfrac{2x}{5}$ **e)** $-2x$ **f)** $-\dfrac{3x}{k}$ **g)** $\dfrac{5am}{4}$

**h)** $\dfrac{5m}{2}$ **i)** $-1$ **2.a)** $-\dfrac{y^4}{6}$ **b)** $-x^2$ **c)** $\dfrac{a^6}{18}$ **d)** $\dfrac{x}{y}$ **e)** $\dfrac{3a^2}{2b^4}$ **f)** $6y$

**3.a)** $-4$ **b)** $\dfrac{km}{2}$ **c)** $\dfrac{4x}{5}$ **d)** $\dfrac{3}{4y}$ **4.a)** $-\dfrac{4}{3x}$ **b)** $\dfrac{4x^4}{y}$ **c)** $4m$

**d)** $-4y$ **5.a)** $-\dfrac{x}{3y}$ **b)** $-\dfrac{y}{2x^2}$ **c)** $\dfrac{1}{2y}$ **d)** $-\dfrac{3}{2x}$ **e)** $\dfrac{4}{5y}$ **f)** $-\dfrac{5y}{3x}$

**6.a)** $\dfrac{xb}{ya}$ **b)** $\dfrac{xb}{ya}$ **c)** $-\dfrac{y}{b}$ **d)** $\dfrac{2}{21}x$ **e)** $-2y$ **f)** $-\dfrac{6k}{5y}$ **7.a)** $\dfrac{4xy}{5}$

**b)** $\dfrac{4}{5y^2}$ **c)** $\dfrac{4}{x}$ **d)** $-\dfrac{1}{5y}$ **e)** 1 **f)** $\dfrac{2ab}{5}$ **8.a)** $-b^2$ **b)** $-\dfrac{4a}{b}$

**c)** $-\dfrac{7a}{2b}$ **d)** $\dfrac{x^2}{y}$ **9.a)** $\dfrac{x^2}{y^2}$ **b)** $4a^2$ **c)** $\dfrac{b}{2a}$ **d)** $\dfrac{5}{x}$ **e)** $\dfrac{x^2}{y}$ **f)** $-\dfrac{16m^2}{n^2}$

**10.a)** $\dfrac{14}{5}x$ **b)** $\dfrac{2x(y + 6x)}{9y^2}$ **c)** $\dfrac{38}{51}$ **d)** $\dfrac{16a + 27b}{6ab}$ **11.a)** $\dfrac{6a^2}{5b^2}$ **b)** $\dfrac{16a^2}{25b^2}$

**c)** $\dfrac{9a^2}{4b^2}$ **d)** $-\dfrac{23a}{10b}$ **e)** $\dfrac{7a}{10b}$ **f)** $-\dfrac{7a}{10b}$ **g)** $-\dfrac{31a}{10b}$ **h)** $-\dfrac{37a}{10b}$ **i)** $\dfrac{23a}{10b}$

## 3.6 Exercise, page 113

1.b)$a \neq b$ c)$\frac{a+b}{a-b}$ 2.a)$x \neq 0, y, y \neq x; -2x$ b)$a \neq -b,$

$b \neq -a; -2$ c)$x \neq -y, y \neq -x; x^2$ d)$s \neq 5; \frac{s+3}{4}$

e)$m \neq \frac{1}{2}, 3; \frac{m+3}{m-3}$ f)$x \neq 4; \frac{x+4}{2}$ g)$a \neq -5b, 5b,$

$b \neq -\frac{a}{5}, \frac{a}{5}; \frac{a-5b}{a+5b}$ h)$m \neq -6, 6; \frac{4(m-3)}{m+6}$ 3.b)$\frac{1}{3y};$

$y \neq -1, 0, 1$ 4.a)$\frac{4}{y}; y \neq -2, 0$ b)$\frac{1}{3(x+1)}; x \neq -1, 0, 1$

c)$\frac{2}{y-3}; y \neq -2, 3$ d)$\frac{a+b}{a+4}; a \neq b, -4, 4, b \neq a$ e)$\frac{1}{x}; x \neq -1,$

$0, 1$ f)$\frac{3}{4}; x \neq -5, 0, 4$ 5.a)$-(x+3)$ b)$-(x+3)$

6.a)$-1$ b)$1$ c)$-1$ d)$1$ e)$1$ f)$-(m+n)$ g)$2a+b$

h)$\frac{-(x+2y)}{x+y}$ 7.a)$1$ b)$\frac{x}{y(x-1)}$ c)$-\frac{4}{3}$ d)$\frac{-1}{2(y+3)}$

e)$\frac{1}{2(x+y)}$ f)$\frac{1}{x}$ 8.a)$\frac{x+1}{x+3}$ b)$\frac{-(a+2)}{a(a+6)}$ c)$\frac{2(2a-3b)}{a}$

d)$\frac{2}{2a-1}$ 9.a)$\frac{1}{(x-1)(x+3)}$ b)$\frac{(x+y)^3}{x^2y}$ c)$\frac{a(a-1)}{3(a-3)}$

d)$\frac{-x(x-2)}{(x-4)(x+4)}$ e)$x$ 10. A 11. increases from $\frac{1}{2}$ to 1

## 3.7 Exercise, page 116

1.b)$-\frac{25}{36}$ 2.a)$4$ b)$-4, 3$ 3.a)$x \neq 0, 1$ b)$\left\{-\frac{3}{2}\right\}$ 4.b)$\{11\}$

5.a)$20$ 6.a)$\{2\}$ 7.a)$4$ b)$-\frac{1}{2}$ 8.a)$\{4\}$ b)$\{2\}$ 9.a)$-\frac{3}{2}; x \neq -\frac{4}{3},$

$-1$ b)$11; y \neq 3, 4$ 10.a)$-1$ b)$2$ c)$-9$ d)$12$ e)$3$ f)$\frac{1}{2}$

11.a)$1$ b)$-\frac{3}{2}$ c)$\frac{1}{3}$ d)$\frac{32}{9}$ e)$11$ f)$-\frac{21}{2}, 1$ 12.a)$-3, 2$ b)$-2$

## 3.8 Exercise, page 119

1. 18.0 km/h 2. 100.0 km/h 3. 0.5 m/s 4. 96.0 km/h
5. 18.0 km/h 6.a)80.0 km/h b)96.0 km/h
7. 18.0 km/h 8.a)12.0 km/h 9. bus: 14.0 h,
train: 11.2 h 10.a)6.0 km/h b)8.0 km/h 11. 5.0 h

## 3.9 Exercise, page 122

1.a)$y = -6$ b)$y \leq -6$ 2.a)$y > -16$ 3.b)$\{y | y \geq 2, y \in R\}$

4.b)$y \geq \frac{23}{11}$ 5.a)$p \geq -\frac{13}{2}$ b)$x < 3$ c)$y > \frac{9}{5}$ d)$y > 6$ 6.a)$y \geq 6$

b)$y < -2$ c)$m < 2$ d)$m \leq 1$ 7.a)$y \geq 4$ b)$k > -3$ c)$k \leq -2$

d)$y > 2$ e)$x < 6$ f)$y \leq 2$ 8.a)$x > -4$ b)$k > -2$

c)$m \leq 5$ d)$p \geq 40$ e)$y < 2$ 9.a)$y \leq 4$ b)C 10. (a), (d)

11. (a), (c)

## CHAPTER 4

## 4.1 Exercise, page 128

1.a)$(-4, 2)$ b)$(3, 3)$ c)$(2, -5)$ d)$(-4, -4)$ e)$(1, 5)$ f)$(6, -4)$
g)$(0, 0)$ 2.a)B b)R c)G d)U e)P f)L g)E h)T i)M j)J k)W l)S
3.a)$(0, 5)$ b)$(-6, 0)$ c)$(0, -4)$ 4.a)$(-4, -4)$ b)$(-7, -1)$

c)$(-4, -2)$ 5.a)$(-6, -6)$ b)$(-4, -4)$ c)$(3, 3)$ 6.a)I, D b)C,
Z c)G, P, M 7.a)A, J b)P, Z, L c)M, U, E 8.a)C, F, M, N,
P, Z b)3 9.a)B, G, S, N, C, P, M, F, Z, U, L, D or E b)12
c)2, 3, 4 10.a)B, D, E, G, L b)2, 4 11.a)H, I, K b)S, T, U, W
12.a)C, N b)F, M, Z 13.a)D(2, 3) b)H(3, -5) c)L(-6, -2)
14.b)parallelogram 16.b)C(-3, -4) 17. F(4, 6) 18. B, J, P,
M, O, D, F, G, L; E, A, N, I, K, C, H 20.b)straight line
graph 21.a)15 km b)30 km c)40 km d)7.5 km e)12.5 km
f)22.5 km 22.a)7 h b)2 h c)8 h d)3 h e)1.5 h f)4.5 h
23.a)60 km b)60 km c)20 km d)60 km e)55 km f)30 km
24.a)1.5 h b)3.25 h c)2.5 h d)2.0 h e)0.75 h f)4.0 h
25.a)12 km/h b)resting

## 4.2 Exercise, page 133

1.a)$D = \{-1, 2, 3, 4\}, R = \{-2, 1, 2, 3\}$ b)$D = \{-1, 0, 2, 3\},$
$R = \{-1, 2, 3\}$ c)$D = \{-2, 1, 3, 4\}, R = \{-2, 1, 3, 4\}$
2.a)$D = \{2, 3, 4, 5\}, R = \{1, 2, 3, 4\}$
3.a)$D = \{-7, -6, -5, -4, -3\}, R = \{-2, -1, 0, 1, 2\}$
4.a)$\{(0, 0), (1, 1), (2, 2), (3, 3)\}$ b)$D = \{0, 1, 2, 3\}$
c)$R = \{0, 1, 2, 3\}$ 5.b)$D = \{0, 1, 2, 3\}, R = \{0, 1, 4, 9\}$
8.a)$\{(-6, -2), (-3, 0), (0, 2), (3, 4), (6, 6), (9, 8)\}$
b)$D = \{-6, -3, 0, 3, 6, 9\}$ c)$R = \{-2, 0, 2, 4, 6, 8\}$
9.a)$\{(1, 1), (2, 2), (3, 3), (4, 4), (5, 5)\}; D = \{1, 2, 3, 4, 5\};$
$R = \{1, 2, 3, 4, 5\}$ b)$\{(-1, 4), (0, 3), (1, 2), (2, 1), (3, 0), (4, -1)\};$
$D = \{-1, 0, 1, 2, 3, 4\}; R = \{-1, 0, 1, 2, 3, 4\}$
c)$\{(1, 3), (1, 4), (1, 5), (1, 6), (2, 3), (2, 4), (2, 5), (3, 3), (3, 4), (4, 3)\};$
$D = \{1, 2, 3, 4\}; R = \{3, 4, 5, 6\}$ d)$\{(-1, -1), (-1, 0), (-1, 1),$
$(-1, 2), (-1, 3), (0, 0), (0, 1), (0, 2), (0, 3), (1, 1), (1, 2),$
$(1, 3), (2, 2), (2, 3), (3, 3)\}; D = \{-1, 0, 1, 2, 3\};$
$R = \{-1, 0, 1, 2, 3\}$ e)$\{(-1, -4), (-1, -3), (-1, -2),$
$(-1, -1), (0, -4), (0, -3), (0, -2), (1, -4), (1, -3), (2, -4)\};$
$D = \{-1, 0, 1, 2\}; R = \{-4, -3, -2, -1\}$ f)$\{(-3, 3),$
$(-2, 3), (-1, 3), (0, 3), (1, 3), (2, 3), (3, 3), (4, 3), (5, 3)\};$
$D = \{-3, -2, -1, 0, 1, 2, 3\}; R = \{3\}$
14.a)(team, number of losses) b)(Crescent, 4) c)(team, number
of points scored) d)(Oakdale, 222) 15.c)6, Oakdale
d)$D = \{Crescent, Meadowvale, Oakdale\}, R = \{5, 6, 7\}$

## 4.3 Exercise, page 138

1.a)$D = \{-5, -3, -1, 1, 3, 5\}, R = \{1, 2, 3, 4, 5, 6\}$
b)$D = \{-5, -3, -1, 1, 3\}, R = \{-1, 1, 3, 5, 7\}$
c)$D = \{-4, -3, -2, -1, 0, 1, 2\}, R = \{2, 3, 4, 5\}$
d)$D = \{-4, -3, -2, -1, 0, 1, 2, 3, 4\}, R = \{-3, -2, -1, 0, 1\}$
2.a)$D = \{x | -4 \leq x \leq 5, x \in R\}, R = \{y | -1 \leq y \leq 2, y \in R\}$
b)$D = \{x | -5 \leq x \leq 6, x \in R\}, R = \{y | 1 \leq y \leq 3, y \in R\}$
c)$D = \{x | -4 \leq x \leq 4, x \in R\}, R = \{y | 0 \leq y \leq 5, y \in R\}$
d)$D = \{x | -4 \leq x \leq 0, x \in R\}, R = \{y | 0 \leq y \leq 5, y \in R\}$
3.a)$x \in I$ b)$y \in I$ 4.a)$x \in R$ b)$y \in R$ 5.a)$\{(0, 0), (0, 1), (0, 2),$
$(0, 3), (0, 4), (0, 5), (0, 6), (1, 1), (1, 2), (1, 3), (1, 4), (1, 5), (1, 6),$
$(2, 2), (2, 3), (2, 4), (2, 5), (2, 6), (3, 3), (3, 4), (3, 5), (3, 6), (4, 4),$
$(4, 5), (4, 6), (5, 5), (5, 6), (6, 6)\}$ b)$D = \{0, 1, 2, 3, 4, 5, 6\}$
c)$R = \{0, 1, 2, 3, 4, 5, 6\}$ 7.b)A: $D = \{x \in I\},$
$R = \{y | y \geq 1, y \in I\}$; B: $D = \{x \in R\}, R = \{y | y \geq 1, y \in R\}$
8.a)$\{(-4, -4), (-4, -3), (-4, -2), (-4, -1), (-4, 0), (-4, 1),$
$(-4, 2), (-4, 3), (-4, 4), (-4, 5), (-3, -4), (-3, -3), (-3, -2),$
$(-3, -1), (-3, 0), (-3, 1), (-3, 2), (-3, 3), (-3, 4), (-3, 5),$
$(-2, -4), (-2, -3), (-2, -2), (-2, -1), (-2, 0), (-2, 1),$
$(-2, 2), (-2, 3), (-2, 4), (-2, 5), (-1, -4), (-1, -3), (-1, -2),$

$(-1, -1), (-1, 0), (-1, 1), (-1, 2), (-1, 3), (0, -4), (0, -3),$
$(0, -2), (0, -1), (0, 0), (0, 1), (1, -4), (1, -3), (1, -2), (1, -1),$
$(2, -4), (2, -3)\}$ **b)**$R = \{-4, -3, -2, -1, 0, 1, 2, 3, 4, 5\}$
**10.a)**$\{(-2, 0), (-2, 1), (-2, 2), (-1, 1), (-1, 2), (0, 2)\}$
**b)**$D = \{-2, -1, 0\}$ **c)**$R = \{0, 1, 2\}$ **12.a)**$\{3, 5, 7, 9, 11, 13, 15\}$
**b)**$\left\{1, \frac{2}{3}, \frac{1}{3}, 0, -\frac{1}{3}, -\frac{2}{3}, -1\right\}$ **c)**$\{-6, -5, -4, \ldots, 2, 3, 4\}$
**d)**$\left\{-\frac{5}{2}, -2, -\frac{3}{2}, -1, -\frac{1}{2}, 0, \frac{1}{2}, 1, \frac{3}{2}\right\}$ **e)**$\{1, 3, 5, \ldots, 17, 19, 21\}$
**13.** linear: (a), (c); non-linear: (b), (d)

### 4.4 Exercise, page 142
**1.** A, C, D, E **2.** P, R, S, U **3.** E, K **4.** M, P, S, T
**5.a)**$(3, 1)$ **b)**$(3, 4)$ **c)**$(2, 2)$ **d)**$(0, 5)$ **e)**$(3, 1)$ **f)**$(8, 3)$
**g)**$(-4, -2)$ **h)**$(3, 4)$ **i)**$(3, 10)$ **j)**$(1, 1)$ **6.** A, C **7.** D **8.a)**$(1, 3)$
**b)**$(1, 3)$ **c)**$(6, 4)$ **d)**$(1, 3)$ **e)**$(2, 6)$ **f)**$(2, 3)$ **g)**$(2, 3)$ **h)**$(-1, 2)$
**9.a)**$-1$ **10.a)**$1$ **11.a)**$2$ **b)**$-2$ **c)**$\frac{7}{2}$ **d)**$4$ **e)**$1$ **f)**$\frac{9}{4}$ **12.a)**$1$

### 4.5 Exercise, page 145
**1.a)**C **2.** (b), (c), (f) **4.a)**$x + 3y \geqq 3$ **b)**$3x + y < 3$
**c)**$3x - 3y \leqq -6$ **5.a)**A **b)**C **c)**F **d)**G **e)**J **f)**P **g)**Q
**9.a)**$y > -2x + 8$ **b)**$y > x - 6$ **c)**$y \geqq 2x - 4$
**d)**$y \leqq \frac{1}{2}x + 3$ **e)**$y \geqq 3x + 9$ **f)**$y > 3x - 6$

### 4.6 Exercise, page 148
**1.** $AB = \sqrt{74}$ units, $CD = \sqrt{137}$ units, $EF = 7$ units,
$GH = \sqrt{137}$ units, $IJ = 10$ units, $KL = 2\sqrt{29}$ units,
$MN = 9$ units, $PQ = 205$ units **2.** $MN = 19$ units,
$NL = 6$ units, $ML = \sqrt{397}$ units; $PQ = 7$ units,
$QR = 3\sqrt{5}$ units, $RS = 13$ units, $PS = 3\sqrt{5}$ units
**3.b)**$5\sqrt{2}$ units **4.b)**$36$ square units **5.b)**$\sqrt{3600}$ square
units **c)**$60.0$ square units **6.a)**$11$ units **b)**$11$ units
**c)**$6$ units **d)**$1$ unit **e)**$\sqrt{29}$ units **f)**$\sqrt{26}$ units **7.** CD
**8.a)**$PQ = RS = 4\sqrt{10}$ units, $QR = PS = 2\sqrt{10}$ units
**b)**$10\sqrt{2}$ units **9.b)**$40$ square units **10.a)**$6\sqrt{5}$ units
**b)**$4$ units **c)**$2\sqrt{37}$ units **d)**scalene **11.** $48$ square units
**12.b)**$AB = BD = 2\sqrt{10}$ units **c)**$AC = CE = 2\sqrt{10}$ units
**d)**$BC = 4$ units, $DE = 8$ units, $BC = \frac{1}{2}DE$
**13.a)**$4\sqrt{5}$ units **b)**$4\sqrt{5}$ units **c)**$8\sqrt{5}$ units

### 4.7 Exercise, page 151
**1.b)**$\sqrt{2}$ units **2.b)**$5\sqrt{2}$ units **3.a)**$\sqrt{26}$ units **b)**$5.1$ units
**4.** $AB = \sqrt{85}$ units, $CD = \sqrt{29}$ units, $EF = 2\sqrt{10}$ units,
$GH = 2\sqrt{5}$ units, $OP = \sqrt{65}$ units **5.a)**$\sqrt{13}$ units
**b)**$\sqrt{29}$ units **c)**$\sqrt{37}$ units **d)**$\sqrt{85}$ units **e)**$5\sqrt{5}$ units
**f)**$\frac{\sqrt{73}}{2}$ units **g)**$\frac{\sqrt{145}}{2}$ units **h)**$10$ units **6.a)**$\sqrt{29}$ units
**b)**$5$ units **c)**$2\sqrt{73}$ units **d)**$5\sqrt{2}$ units **e)**$\sqrt{146}$ units
**f)**$\sqrt{10}$ units **7.** $AB = GH = IJ, KL = EF = CD$
**8.** $AB = BC = 3\sqrt{10}$ units, $AC = 6\sqrt{2}$ units; isosceles
**9.** $(20 + 5\sqrt{10})$ units **10.a)**$V(-6, 1)$ **b)**$ST = UV = 3\sqrt{5}$ units,
$TU = SV = 4\sqrt{5}$ units **c)**$60$ square units **11.** F
**12.a)**$(\sqrt{61} + 14)$ units **b)**$(\sqrt{89} + 9)$ units **c)**$(\sqrt{122} +$
$\sqrt{117})$ units **d)**$(\sqrt{61} + \sqrt{89})$ units **13.a)**$R(7, 6)$ **b)**$160$ square
units **c)**$(9, 0)$ **d)**$(3, -2)$ **14.a)**$AB = BC = \sqrt{17}$ units,
$AC = 2\sqrt{17}$ units **b)**$2\sqrt{17}$ units **c)**B midpoint of AC

### 4.8 Exercise, page 154
**1.b)**$(5, 5)$ **2.a)**$(5, 6)$ **b)**$(-6, 3)$ **c)**$(6, -4)$ **d)**$(-7, 0)$ **e)**$(6, 4)$
**f)**$(3, 6)$ **3.a)**$(-4, 4)$ **b)**$(3, 2)$ **c)**$\left(\frac{3}{2}, 4\right)$ **d)**$(3, 2)$ **e)**$\left(\frac{13}{2}, -\frac{11}{2}\right)$
**f)**$(6, -2)$ **g)**$\left(\frac{1}{2}, 4\right)$ **h)**$\left(-\frac{3}{2}, -\frac{3}{2}\right)$ **i)**$\left(-6, -\frac{11}{2}\right)$ **4.a)**$(3, 4)$
**b)**$(-1, -1)$ **c)**$(0, -2)$ **5.a)**$(6, -3)$ **b)**$(5\sqrt{2}, -3\sqrt{3})$
**6.** AB: $(3, 3)$, AC: $(4, 1)$, BC: $(-5, 0)$ **7.** B$(0, 10)$ **8.** $(-9, -7)$
**9.a)**$(-5, 1)$ **b)**$(2, 8)$ **c)**$7\sqrt{2}$ units **d)**$14\sqrt{2}$ units **e)**$MN = \frac{1}{2}EF$
**12.** 1000

### 4.9 Exercise, page 157
**1.a)**$\frac{2}{3}$ **b)**$-\frac{1}{2}$ **c)**$0$ **2.** AB: $\frac{1}{3}$, CD: $-\frac{5}{4}$, EF: $-\frac{1}{2}$, GH: $-\frac{1}{2}$, IJ: $\frac{7}{4}$
KL: $-\frac{1}{2}$, MN: $2$, OP: $\frac{4}{9}$, QR: $2$ **3.b)**rise $= 4$, run $= 5$, slope $= \frac{4}{5}$
**4.a)**$-\frac{11}{8}$ **b)**$\frac{7}{3}$ **c)**$-\frac{2}{5}$ **d)**$\frac{11}{12}$ **e)**$-\frac{1}{4}$ **f)**$-\frac{13}{4}$ **5.** $\frac{4}{13}$ **6.a)**$\frac{1}{2}$ **b)**$\frac{1}{2}$
**7.a)**$\frac{3}{5}$ **b)**$-\frac{2}{5}$ **8.** $l_1: -\frac{3}{13}, l_2: -\frac{7}{2}, l_3: \frac{3}{4}$ **9.a)**$-\frac{3}{2}$
**10.a)**$0$ **11.a)**AB, CD: $\frac{2}{5}$, BC, AD: $2$, **12.a)**$l_1: \frac{7}{2}, l_2: \frac{3}{2}, l_3: \frac{2}{3}, l_4: \frac{1}{4}$
**b)**$l_1: -3, l_2: -\frac{7}{5}, l_3: -\frac{7}{9}, l_4: -\frac{1}{4}, l_5: -\frac{1}{10}$

### 4.10 Exercise, page 161
**1.a)**$-2$ **b)**$2$ **c)**$-2$ **d)**$-1$ **e)**$\frac{3}{2}$ **f)**$\frac{4}{5}$ **2.a)**$-\frac{4}{13}$ **b)**$\frac{5}{14}$
**3.b)**$3$ **4.a)**$2$ **b)**$3$ **c)**$\frac{3}{2}$ **d)**$2$ **e)**$\frac{2}{3}$ **f)**$-\frac{1}{2}$ **7.b)**$0$ **8.a)**$\frac{5}{2}$
**b)**$-\frac{5}{3}$ **9.a)**$-4$ **b)**$\frac{9}{2}$ **c)**$-15$ **d)**$6$ **10.a)**$\frac{2}{3}$ **b)**$\frac{2}{3}$ **12.** (c)
**13.a)**$m_{AB} = m_{CD} = 1, m_{BC} = m_{AD} = -1$ **15.** (b)

## CHAPTER 5

### 5.1 Exercise, page 168
**1.a)**$\{x \in R\}$ **b)**$\{y \mid y \geqq 0, y \in R\}$ **c)**function **2.a)**$\{x \mid x \geqq 0, x \in R\}$
**b)**$\{y \in R\}$ **c)**not a function **3.a)**Domain: $\{0, 1, 2, 3\}$;
Range: $\{0, 1, 2, 3\}$; function **b)**Domain: $\{1, 2, 3\}$;
Range: $\{1, 2, 3\}$; not a function **c)**Domain: $\{-3, -2, -1,$
$0, 1, 2, 3, 4\}$; Range: $\{2\}$; function **d)**Domain: $\{-3, -2, -1\}$;
Range: $\{-1, 0, 1, 2\}$; not a function **4.** functions: (a), (b), (e), (i)
**5.** functions: (a), (d), (e) **7.** not a function: (a), (b), (c);
Function: (d) **10.b)**function **11.b)**$|x| \leqq 5$ **12.** functions: (a), (d),
(e), (g) **13.a)**$-2$ **b)**$-5$ **c)**$1$ **d)**$7$ **e)**$-8$ **f)**$10$
**14.a)**$4$ **b)**$1$ **c)**$6$ **d)**$-2$ **e)**$8$ **f)**$-8$ **g)**$3$ **h)**$18$ **15.a)**$19$ **b)**$1$
**c)**$3$ **d)**$9$ **e)**$9$ **f)**$33$ **16.a)**(i)$0$ (ii)$1$ (iii)$-3$ (iv)$5$ (v)$-1$
**b)**(i)$0$ (ii)$1$ (iii)$-1$ (iv)$2$ (v)$-3$ **17.** Joe: dog; Jeff: mouse; Amy: cat
**18.a)**$0$ **b)**$-2, 1$

### 5.2 Exercise, page 172
**1.a)**$-4, 3, \frac{3}{4}$ **b)**$-2, -3, -\frac{3}{2}$ **c)**$6, -4, \frac{2}{3}$ **2.a)**$6$ **b)**$4$ **c)**$6$ **d)**$2$
**e)**$\frac{20}{3}$ **f)**$\frac{28}{5}$ **3.a)**$3$ **b)**$3$ **c)**$-2$ **d)**$2$ **e)**$10$ **f)**$-\frac{58}{25}$ **4.a)**$2, -6$

b)$4,\ -8$ c)$-2,\ 8$ d)$-3,\ 2$ e)$\dfrac{12}{5},\ \dfrac{12}{7}$ f)$\dfrac{45}{13},\ \dfrac{15}{2}$ **5.a)**$\dfrac{5}{2}$ b)$\left(\dfrac{5}{2},\ 0\right)$

**6.a)**$-6$ b)$(0,\ -6)$ **7.a)**$-\dfrac{2}{3}$ b)$x:\ 3,\ y:\ 2$ c)$(0,\ 2),\ (3,\ 0)$ **8.a)**$6,\ 2$

b)$2,\ 4$ c)$\dfrac{5}{2},\ -5$ d)$3,\ -\dfrac{3}{2}$ e)$-\dfrac{5}{2},\ 5$ f)$-2,\ \dfrac{2}{3}$ g)$-\dfrac{8}{3},\ 2$

h)$12,\ 18$ i)$36,\ -48$ **9.b)**$3$ c)$-\dfrac{9}{4}$ **10.b)**$2$ c)$-3$ **12.b)**$-\dfrac{9}{2}$ c)B

**13.b)**$-6$ c)yes, both **14.b)**$\dfrac{2}{3}$ c)$9$ **15.a)**$60$ km b)$1.5$ h

c)$40$ km/h d)$40$ **16.a)**$30$ km b)$2.25$ h c)$13.33$ km/h
d)$13.33$ **17.b)**$0$ c)$0$ km/h **18.a)**(i)OM: 30, MN: 0,
NP: 40 (ii)OM: 30 km/h, MN: 0 km/h, NP: 40 km/h

### 5.3 Exercise, page 176
**1.a)**$6,\ -3$ b)$3,\ 9$ c)$\dfrac{1}{2},\ -1$ d)$4,\ -6$ e)$4,\ 8$ f)$-10,\ 5$

g)$3,\ -9$ h)$6,\ -1$ i)$1,\ -\dfrac{4}{3}$ **2.a)**$x:\ 3,\ y:\ -9$ **3.a)**$x:\ 5,$

$y:\ -10$ **4.** $(8,\ 0),\ (0,\ -4)$; slope: $\dfrac{1}{2}$ **5.b)**$x:\ \dfrac{11}{2},\ y:\ \dfrac{11}{5}$

**6.b)**$1$ **7.b)**$(0,\ 0)$ **8.b)**$-\dfrac{7}{2}$ **9.b)**$6$ **11.** $(4,\ 2)$

### 5.4 Exercise, page 178
**1.a)**$\dfrac{1}{3}$ b)same **2.a)**$-\dfrac{3}{4}$ b)same **3.a)**$-\dfrac{1}{2}$ c)$-\dfrac{1}{2},\ -\dfrac{1}{2}$ **4.b)**$2$

**5.a)**$3$ b)$\dfrac{1}{2}$ c)$-2$ d)$-\dfrac{2}{3}$ **6.a)**$-\dfrac{1}{2}$ b)$-\dfrac{1}{2}$ **7.a)**$-3$ b)$-\dfrac{1}{2}$ c)$4$

d)$1$ **9.b)**$5$ **10.a)**$3$ b)$-1$ c)$4$ **11.b)**$-3$ **12.a)**$4$ b)$-4$ c)$\dfrac{2}{3}$

### 5.5 Exercise, page 183
**1.a)**$3,\ 6$ b)$-\dfrac{1}{2},\ 3$ c)$1,\ -3$ d)$-2,\ 3$ e)$-\dfrac{3}{2},\ 3$ f)$\dfrac{1}{2},\ \dfrac{3}{2}$

g)$-\dfrac{3}{2},\ 12$ h)$2,\ -\dfrac{3}{2}$ i)$\dfrac{1}{3},\ -2$ j)$2,\ -5$ k)$\dfrac{2}{3},\ -\dfrac{5}{3}$ l)$-1,\ 12$

**2.a)**$y = 2x + 3$ b)$y = 2x - 3$ c)$y = -2x + 3$
d)$y = \dfrac{1}{2}x - 4$ e)$y = -3x + \dfrac{1}{2}$ f)$y = -\dfrac{3}{4}x - \dfrac{1}{3}$ **3.a)**$8$

**4.a)**$(4,\ 0)$ b)$(0,\ 4)$ **5.a)**$(3,\ 0)$ b)$(0,\ 3)$ c)$(6,\ 0)$ d)$\left(0,\ -\dfrac{10}{3}\right)$

**6.** (a) and (d), (b) and (c) **7.** (b) and (g), (c) and (h),
(d) and (f), (e) and (i) **8.** 4 **9.a)**2 b)5 **10.a)**4 b)1 **11.** $-2$

**12.a)**$-1$ b)$1$ **13.a)**$-6$ b)$-\dfrac{3}{2}$ **14.** $(2,\ 0)$ **15.** $-\dfrac{4}{3}$ **16.** $\dfrac{1}{3}$

**17.a)**$y = \dfrac{3}{2}x + 3$ **18.a)**$-\dfrac{A}{B}$ b)$-\dfrac{C}{B}$ **19.a)**EF: 2, GH: $-\dfrac{1}{2}$;

AB: $-4$, CD: $\dfrac{1}{4}$; IJ: $-\dfrac{5}{3}$, KL: $\dfrac{3}{5}$ b)$-1,\ -1,\ -1$ **20.c)**$-1$

**21.a)**$1,\ -1$ b)$-1$ c)perpendicular **22.a)**perpendicular
b)$-1$ **23.b)**A and G, B and H, C and E, D and F

### 5.6 Exercise, page 187
**1.a)**$\dfrac{2}{3}$ b)$-\dfrac{4}{3}$ c)$-\dfrac{1}{3}$ d)$\dfrac{1}{2}$ **2.a)**$\dfrac{3}{4}$ b)$m = \dfrac{3}{4}$ **3.a)**$-\dfrac{1}{2}$ b)$-\dfrac{1}{m}$ **4.a)**$-\dfrac{1}{2}$

b)$-3$ c)$\dfrac{1}{4}$ d)$2$ e)$-\dfrac{2}{3}$ f)$-\dfrac{2}{7}$ g)$-\dfrac{1}{k}$ h)$m$ **5.** parallel: (b), (c), (h);

perpendicular: (d); neither: (a), (e), (f), (g) **6.a)**$\dfrac{7}{10},\ -\dfrac{10}{7}$

b)$-\dfrac{4}{9},\ \dfrac{9}{4}$ **7.a)**$2$ b)$-\dfrac{1}{2}$ **8.a)**$-\dfrac{1}{2}$ b)$-\dfrac{3}{2}$ c)$\dfrac{1}{2}$ d)$-\dfrac{1}{3}$ e)$-2$ f)$-\dfrac{1}{2}$

**9.** (a), (d), (e) **10.** parallel: A and E, H and I, C and G;
perpendicular: B and C, B and G, F and H, F and I

**11.b)**$k = -\dfrac{1}{12}$; $-\dfrac{1}{4}$ **12.b)**$16,\ 16$ **13.a)**$-2$ b)$-\dfrac{1}{3}$ c)$-\dfrac{4}{3}$ d)$\dfrac{14}{3}$

**14.a)**(i)$\dfrac{1}{10}$ (ii)$2$ (iii)$-2$ (iv)$-10$ b)none c)(i) and (iv)

**15.a)**(i)$4$ (ii)$-\dfrac{1}{2}$ (iii)$4$ (iv)$2$ b)(i) and (iii) c)(ii) and (iv)

**16.** perpendicular: (a), (d); parallel: (b), (e)
**17.a)**yes b)$\left(\dfrac{12}{7},\ \dfrac{15}{7}\right)$ or $\left(\dfrac{4}{9},\ -\dfrac{5}{3}\right)$ **19.** kictet **20.** $-\dfrac{4}{3}$ or $-\dfrac{3}{4}$

### 5.7 Exercise, page 191
**1.a)**$2$ b)$\dfrac{3}{2}$ c)$\dfrac{1}{4}$ d)$\dfrac{1}{2}$ e)$\dfrac{4}{3}$ f)$-\dfrac{2}{7}$ g)$\dfrac{3}{2}$ **2.b)**$2x - y + 7 = 0$

**3.a)**$1$ c)$x - y - 1 = 0,\ x - y - 1 = 0$ **4.a)**$(0,\ -1)$

c)$x - 2y - 2 = 0$ **5.a)**$(2,\ 0)$ c)$x + 2y - 2 = 0$ **6.a)**$\dfrac{2}{3}$

c)$2x - 3y + 6 = 0,\ 2x - 3y + 6 = 0$
**7.a)**$3x - 2y + 11 = 0$ b)$2x - y + 7 = 0$ c)$3x + y - 7 = 0$
d)$x - 2y - 9 = 0$ e)$x + 3y - 2 = 0$ f)$3x - 2y + 4 = 0$
g)$4x - y - 12 = 0$ h)$4x + 3y + 2 = 0$ **8.a)**$2x - y - 5 = 0$
b)$3x + y - 7 = 0$ c)$x - 2y + 5 = 0$ d)$2x + 3y + 12 = 0$
**9.a)**$x + 5y - 14 = 0$ b)$4x - 3y - 5 = 0$ c)$x + y - 7 = 0$
d)$4x - 3y - 1 = 0$ **10.a)**$2x - y - 3 = 0$ b)$3x + y - 2 = 0$
c)$x - 2y - 6 = 0$ d)$4x - 6y - 3 = 0$ **11.a)**$3x + y - 6 = 0$
b)$x - 2y + 3 = 0$ c)$6x - 3y - 4 = 0$ d)$3x + 6y + 4 = 0$
**12.a)**$2x + y - 4 = 0$ b)$2x - 3y + 6 = 0$ c)$x -$
d)$4x + y - 2 = 0$ e)$4x - 9y - 12 = 0$ f)$8x + 9y + 6 = 0$
**13.e)**all $3x + 5y - 15 = 0$ **14.a)**$4x - 3y + 12 = 0$
b)$2x + 3y + 6 = 0$ c)$x + 2y - 4 = 0$ **15.** $y = 0,\ x = 0$
**16.a)**$x - 2y - 5 = 0$ b)$x - 3y - 6 = 0$ c)$x + 4y + 1 = 0$
d)$2x - y - 7 = 0$ **17.a)**$5x + 3y - 4 = 0$ b)$2x - y + 6 = 0$
c)$x - 2y + 4 = 0$ d)$2x + 3y - 6 = 0$ e)$6x - 5y + 1 = 0$
f)$4x + 2y - 3 = 0$ g)$3x + 6y - 2 = 0$ h)$3x - y - 7 = 0$
i)$y + 3 = 0$ j)$x + 1 = 0$ **18.a)**AB: $3x - y - 5 = 0$,
BC: $x - 5y + 17 = 0$, AC: $5x + 3y + 1 = 0$ b)4
**19.a)**$11x - 3y + 59 = 0$ b)$3x + 11y - 43 = 0$
**20.** $m = -\dfrac{A}{B},\ b = -\dfrac{C}{B}$

### 5.8 Exercise, page 195
**1.a)**$x + 4 = 0$ b)$y + 3 = 0$ **2.a)**$x - 2y + 1 = 0$
b)$2x + y - 1 = 0$ **3.a)**$x + 2y + 4 = 0$ b)B
**4.a)**$x + 2y + 4 = 0$ b)$x + 4y - 4 = 0$
c)$5x + 4y + 12 = 0$ **5.a)**$x - y = 0,\ x - 5 = 0,$
$y + 4 = 0$ b)$9x - 4y + 36 = 0,\ 13x + 6y - 54 = 0,$
$2x + 5y + 8 = 0$ **6.a)**$3x - y + 9 = 0$
b)$x + 3y - 3 = 0$ c)$3x + 5y + 27 = 0$ **7.** 1 **8.** $\dfrac{14}{3}$

**9.** $\dfrac{3}{2}$ **10.** $4x - 3y - 12 = 0$ **11.** $x - 2y - 2 = 0$

### 5.9 Exercise, page 198
**1.a)**$y = 2x + 3$ b)$y = -3x + 3$ c)$y = x + 3$

d)$y = -x + 3$ e)$y = \dfrac{1}{2}x + 3$ f)$y = 0.5x + 3$

g) $y = -\dfrac{2}{3}x + 3$ h) $y = \dfrac{5}{2}x + 3$ **2.a)** $y = -3x + 3$

b) $y = -3x - 2$ c) $y = -3x + 5$ d) $y = -3x + \dfrac{1}{2}$

e) $y = -3x - 0.5$ f) $y = -3x + \dfrac{3}{2}$ g) $y = -3x - \dfrac{2}{3}$

h) $y = -3x + 1.6$ **3.a)** $y = 2x - 1$ **b)** $y = 2x + 5$

c) $y = 2x + 3$ d) $y = 2x + 6.5$ **4.a)** $y = -\dfrac{9}{4}x - 3$

b) $y = \dfrac{7}{6}x - 3$ c) $y = \dfrac{3}{4}x - 3$ d) $y = -\dfrac{5}{6}x - 3$

**5.a)** $y = 3x - 2$ **b)** $y = 3x - 5$ **c)** $y = 3x + 9$

**6.a)** $y = \dfrac{1}{2}x - 2$ **b)** $y = -\dfrac{5}{2}x - 2$ **c)** $y = -\dfrac{2}{3}x - 2$

**7.a)** $y = 3x + b$ **b)** $y = mx - 1$ **c)** $y = -\dfrac{2}{3}x + b$

d) $y = mx + 3$ e) $y = mx - 2$ f) $y = -3x + b$ **8.a)** slope: 3

b) $y$-intercept: $-2$ c) slope: $\dfrac{1}{2}$ d) $y$-intercept: $-\dfrac{2}{3}$

e) $y$-intercept: $-3$ f) $y$-intercept: $\dfrac{1}{3}$ g) $y$-intercept: $-m - 2$

h) $y$-intercept: 2 i) $y$-intercept: $-3m$ **9.a)** $y = mx - 3$

b) $y = -\dfrac{1}{3}x + b$ c) $y = mx + 3$ **10.a)** $y = -2x + b$

b) $y = \dfrac{1}{2}x + b$ c) $y = -\dfrac{1}{3}x + b$ d) $y = x + b$

e) $y = \dfrac{2}{3}x + b$ f) $y = -\dfrac{2}{3}x + b$ **11.a)** $y = -x + b$

b) $y = -x + 1$ **12.a)** $y = mx + 2$ **b)** $y = -\dfrac{5}{4}x + 2$

**13.a)** $y = -2x + b$ **b)** $y = -2x + 5$ **c)** $y = -2x - 6$

**14.a)** $y = -\dfrac{1}{2}x + b$ **b)** $y = -\dfrac{1}{2}x + 2$ **c)** $y = -\dfrac{1}{2}x - 8$

**15.a)** $y = 3x$ **b)** $y = \dfrac{1}{2}x + 4$ **c)** $y = \dfrac{2}{3}x - 2$ **d)** $y = 4x$

e) $y = \dfrac{5}{4}x + 8$ **16.a)** $y = \dfrac{1}{4}x + 3$ **b)** $y = 4x + 12$

c) $y = -\dfrac{1}{3}x + \dfrac{5}{3}$ d) $y = \dfrac{4}{3}x - 4$ e) $y = -\dfrac{3}{2}x + 5$

f) $y = -3$ **17.a)** $y = \dfrac{2}{3}x - 3$ **b)** $y = 3x + 5$

c) $y = -\dfrac{1}{2}x - \dfrac{3}{2}$ d) $y = 1$ e) $y = 3x - 2$ f) $y = -\dfrac{1}{2}x - \dfrac{1}{4}$

g) $y = -x - 1$ **18.a)** PQ: $y = -\dfrac{1}{6}x + 5$,

RS: $y = -\dfrac{1}{6}x - \dfrac{3}{2}$, QR: $y = 2x - 8$, PS: $y = 2x + 18$

**b)** PR: $y = -\dfrac{8}{9}x + \dfrac{2}{3}$, SQ: $y = \dfrac{4}{15}x + \dfrac{12}{5}$ **c)** not

perpendicular. **19.** $y = -3x - 2$ **20.** $y = 2x + 5$

**21.a)** $(-1, 3), 2$ **b)** $(3, -2), \dfrac{1}{2}$ **c)** $(1, -3), 3$ **d)** $(-1, 2), -2$

e) $(0, -5), 3$ f) $(-3, 0), \dfrac{2}{3}$ **22.a)** $(-2, -3)$ **b)** $x + 2 = 0$

**23.a)** $y + 1 = 3x$ **b)** $y = 3x - 1$ **24.a)** $y + 1 = m(x - 3)$

**b)(i)** $y + 1 = \dfrac{1}{2}(x - 3)$ **(ii)** $y + 1 = -\dfrac{5}{4}(x - 3)$

**(iii)** $y + 1 = -\dfrac{7}{3}(x - 3)$ **(iv)** $y + 1 = -\dfrac{1}{5}(x - 3)$

## CHAPTER 6

**6.1 Exercise, page 207**
**1.a)** $(3, 4)$ **b)** $(3, -2)$ **c)** $(-3, 2)$ **d)** $(-2, -1)$ **2.a)** yes
**b)** no **c)** no **d)** yes **e)** no **f)** no **3.a)** yes **b)** no **c)** yes **d)** yes
**e)** yes **f)** no **4.c)** $(2, 3)$ **5.a)** $(3, 6)$ **b)** $(-8, -11)$

**6.a)** $(-1, 1)$ **b)** $(1, -1)$ **c)** $(0, 3)$ **d)** $(-3, 0)$ **e)** $\left(\dfrac{11}{7}, \dfrac{6}{7}\right)$

**f)** $(-12, -8)$ **7.a)** $(3, 2)$ **b)** $(5, 1)$ **8.a)** $(-3, -2)$ **b)** $(-6, 4)$ **9.a)** $(3, 1)$
**b)** $(1, 4)$ **10.** $(1, 2)$ **11.** $(3, 2)$ **12.c)** $(4, -3)$ **13.** tug **14.** no

**6.2 Exercise, page 210**
**2.a)** $x = -3$, $x - 2y = 1$; $x = -3$, $y = -2$;
$x = -3$, $x + 3y = -9$; $x - 2y = 1$, $y = -2$;
$x - 2y = 1$, $x + 3y = -9$; $y = -2$, $x + 3y = -9$
**b)** $x = -3$, $y = -2$ **3.c)** same graph
**e)** $\{(x, y)\,|\,2x - y = 7\}$ **4.c)** parallel **e)** $\{\varnothing\}$ **5.c)** $(2, 1)$
**6.c)** $(2, 1)$ **7.a)** add: $8x - 7y = 15$, subtract:
$-4x + 13y = -17$ **b)** add: $13x - 9y = 22$,
subtract: $-5x + 21y = -26$ **c)** add: $12x - y = 13$,
subtract: $19y = -19$ **9.** consistent but independent
**10.** inconsistent **11.a)** consistent but independent **b)** inconsistent
**c)** consistent but dependent **d)** consistent but independent
**e)** inconsistent **f)** consistent but independent **g)** consistent
but dependent **h)** consistent but dependent

**6.3 Exercise, page 214**
**1.a)** $-3y + 4$ **b)** $2y + 8$ **c)** $3y - 5$ **d)** $-2y + 3$ **e)** $-2y + 8$
**f)** $\dfrac{y - 1}{2}$ **g)** $\dfrac{5y + 1}{2}$ **h)** $3y + 5$ **i)** $7y + 5$ **2.a)** $-3x + 2$

**b)** $4x + 5$ **c)** $2x - 3$ **d)** $3x - 6$ **e)** $x + 4$ **f)** $\dfrac{3x - 4}{2}$ **g)** $\dfrac{7x - 3}{2}$

**h)** $\dfrac{-3x + 1}{2}$ **i)** $\dfrac{3x + 1}{2}$ **3.a)** $3y + 5$ **b)** $2x - 6$ **c)** $-3a + 4$

**d)** $\dfrac{4m - 5}{2}$ **e)** $-3a + 5$ **f)** $\dfrac{5x + 4}{2}$ **4.a)** $-3$ **b)** $3$ **c)** $1$ **d)** $\dfrac{4}{3}$ **e)** $\dfrac{15}{2}$

**f)** $-\dfrac{13}{2}$ **g)** $3$ **h)** $7$ **5.** (a), (b), (d), (e) **6.b)** $\left(\dfrac{11}{5}, -\dfrac{2}{5}\right)$ **7.a)** $(-2, 0)$

**b)** $(3, 1)$ **c)** $(-2, 3)$ **8.a)** $(3, 1)$ **b)** $(3, 1)$ **9.a)** $(3, 1)$ **b)** $(2, 0)$
**c)** $(1, 0)$ **d)** $(-1, 1)$ **e)** $(0, -3)$ **f)** $(2, 1)$ **g)** $(3, 2)$ **h)** $(1, 4)$
**10.a)** $(1, 3)$ **b)** $(2, 1)$ **c)** $(3, -1)$ **d)** $(-2, 3)$ **e)** $(0, 3)$ **f)** $(-3, 0)$

**g)** $(1, 3)$ **h)** $\left(\dfrac{7}{2}, 2\right)$ **11.a)** $(2, 3)$ **b)** $(-1, 2)$ **c)** $(-3, -2)$

**12.a)** $(-3, -2)$ **13.a)** $\left(\dfrac{5}{3}, \dfrac{1}{3}\right)$ **b)** $(3, -1)$ **c)** $(2, 3)$ **d)** $(1, -1)$

**14.a)** $(2, 2)$ **b)** $(1, 3)$ **c)** $(-1, 1)$ **d)** $(1, -1)$ **15.a)** $(3, 2)$ **b)** $(3, 2)$
**c)** $(3, 2)$ **16.** $(-2, -5)$ **17.** economy: 330, first class: 60
**18.** $(40, 16)$ **19.a)** $(8, -3)$ **b)** $(4, 5)$ **c)** $(-2, 3)$ **d)** $(16, 4)$
**20.** $(-2, 3)$ **21.** Sheila: \$650, Brian: \$350

**6.4 Exercise, page 219**
**1.a)** $3x - y = 2$ **b)** $3y = -8$ **c)** $x - 3y = 3$ **d)** $x - 2y = 1$
**e)** $4y = 3$ **f)** $3x - 5y = -16$ **2.a)** $2x + y = 6$, $x = \dfrac{-y + 6}{2}$,

$y = -2x + 6$ **b)**$x + 2y = -12$, $x = -2y - 12$,

$y = \dfrac{-x - 12}{2}$ **c)**$x + 4y = 14$, $x = -4y + 14$,

$y = \dfrac{-x + 14}{4}$ **d)**$3x + y = 6$, $x = \dfrac{-y + 6}{3}$, $y = -3x + 6$

**e)**$x - 6y = -8$, $x = 6y - 8$, $y = \dfrac{x + 8}{6}$ **f)**$x + 2y = 22$,

$x = -2y + 22$, $y = \dfrac{-x + 22}{2}$ **3.b)**$(4, 2)$ **4.b)**$(2, 0)$ **5.a)**A

**b)**B **c)**A **d)**B **6.a)**$(3, 6)$ **7.a)**$(-1, 0)$ **8.a)**$(0, 3)$ **b)**$\left(\dfrac{13}{5}, \dfrac{11}{5}\right)$

**c)**$(1, 1)$ **d)**$(-1, 1)$ **9.a)**$(3, 3)$ **b)**$(0, 4)$ **c)**$(6, 1)$ **d)**$(3, 4)$ **e)**$(6, 6)$

**f)**$(6, 1)$ **10.a)**$(4, 3)$ **11.a)**$\left(\dfrac{9}{5}, \dfrac{14}{5}\right)$ **b)**$(3, -2)$ **c)**$(0, -2)$

**d)**$\left(\dfrac{16}{5}, \dfrac{39}{5}\right)$ **12.a)**$(0, -2)$ **b)**$(3, 0)$ **c)**$(2, 3)$ **13.a)**$(x, y) = \left(\dfrac{53}{20}, \dfrac{3}{20}\right)$

## 6.5 Exercise, page 222

**1.a)**$-2y + 8$ **b)**$3y + 4$ **c)**$2y - 3$ **d)**$-3y + 2$ **e)**$\dfrac{y + 6}{2}$

**f)**$\dfrac{6y + 2}{3}$ **2.a)**$-2x + 4$ **b)**$2x + 6$ **c)**$3x - 2$ **d)**$2x - 4$ **e)**$\dfrac{x + 8}{2}$

**f)**$-3x + 1$ **3.a)**$(2, 1)$ **b)**$(-1, 2)$ **c)**$(1, 0)$ **d)**$(1, 0)$ **e)**$(-1, -1)$

**f)**$(0, 1)$ **4.b)**$(2, 3)$ **5.a)**$(3, 2)$ **b)**$(3, 2)$ **6.a)**$(-2, 1)$ **b)**$(1, -1)$

**c)**$\left(-\dfrac{3}{5}, \dfrac{6}{5}\right)$ **d)**$(3, -2)$ **e)**$(-2, 3)$ **f)**$(5, 1)$ **7.a)**$(0, 2)$ **b)**$(-1, 1)$

**c)**$(1, 0)$ **d)**$(1, -1)$ **e)**$(2, 3)$ **f)**$(3, 2)$ **8.a)**$(4, 2)$ **b)**$(1, 0)$ **c)**$(0, -1)$

**d)**$(-1, -1)$ **e)**$\left(\dfrac{153}{35}, -\dfrac{2}{7}\right)$ **f)**$(-2, 3)$ **9.** $(1, 3)$ **10.a)**$(1, 2)$

**b)**$(3, 1)$ **c)**$(-1, 2)$ **11.a)**$(1, -1)$ **b)**$(2, 1)$ **c)**$(-1, -2)$

**12.b)**$(8, 4)$ **13.b)**$(-1, -1)$ **14.a)**$(3, 0)$ **b)**$(3, -2)$ **c)**$(1, 0)$

**d)**$(3, 0)$ **e)**$(-3, 2)$ **f)**$(0, 6)$ **g)**$(3, 2)$ **h)**$(0, 4)$ **15.** $p = \dfrac{3}{2}$, $q = 16$

## 6.6 Exercise, page 227

**1.a), b)**$(9, 3)$ **2.b)**$\{(2, 1)\}$ **3.a)**$(3, 1)$ **b)**$(2, -1)$ **c)**$(-1, 3)$

**d)**$(1, 0)$ **e)**$(0, -2)$ **f)**$(3, 1)$ **4.b)**$(-2, -2)$ **5.a)**$(0, 3)$ **b)**$(-1, 2)$

**c)**$(2, -3)$ **d)**$\left(\dfrac{40}{3}, 25\right)$ **e)**$(4, 0)$ **f)**$\left(\dfrac{19}{3}, 8\right)$ **g)**$(2, -3)$ **h)**$(4, 6)$

**i)**$(0, -2)$ **j)**$\left(\dfrac{7}{2}, -3\right)$ **k)**$(4, -6)$ **l)**$\left(\dfrac{16}{5}, \dfrac{39}{5}\right)$ **6.b)**$(4, -1)$

**7.** $(2, -1)$ **8.a)**$(-1, 0)$ **9.a)**$(-1, -1)$ **b)**$(0, -1)$

**10.a)**$(3, -2)$ **b)**$(1.2, 2.5)$ **c)**$(2, -1)$ **d)**$(1.2, 1.2)$ **11.a)**$(1, -1)$

**b)**$(-1, 4)$ **c)**$(0, -2)$ **d)**$(0, 3)$ **e)**$(-1, 4)$ **f)**$(3, 12)$ **12.** $(-1, 0)$

**13.** $(3, -2)$ **14.** $p = 45¢$, $t = 800¢ = \$8.00$ **15.a)**$(23, 750)$

**b)**$\$30.50$ **16.a)**$(62, 2300)$ **b)**$\$116.00$

## 6.7 Exercise, page 231

**1.b)**$(12, 24)$ **2.b)**$(4, 5)$ **3.b)**$\left(\dfrac{11}{40}, \dfrac{11}{21}\right)$ **4.a)**$\left(\dfrac{1}{3}, 1\right)$ **b)**$\left(2, \dfrac{2}{3}\right)$

**c)**$\left(-\dfrac{3}{4}, 3\right)$ **5.a)**$(5, -4)$ **b)**$(4, -8)$ **c)**$\left(\dfrac{34}{11}, \dfrac{37}{11}\right)$ **d)**$(1, 7)$

**6.** $(6, 4)$ **7.** $(7, 2)$ **8.** $(-3, 3)$ **9.** $m = 3$, $n = 2$

**11.b), c)**$y = \dfrac{af - cd}{ae - bd}$, $ae - bd \neq 0$ **12.a)**$(a, 2a)$

**b)**$(3m, -m)$ **c)**$(a, 2b)$ **d)**$(a + b, a - b)$

**e)**$\left(\dfrac{6 - 4b}{1 - ab}, \dfrac{4 - 6a}{1 - ab}\right)$, $ab \neq 1$ **f)**$\left(\dfrac{9}{b + 1}, \dfrac{6b - 3}{b + 1}\right)$, $b \neq -1$

## 6.8 Exercise, page 235

**1.a)**$(18, 1)$ **b)**$(2.50, -2.33)$ **c)**$(2, 3)$ **d)**$(2, -2)$

**e)**$(-1, 5)$ **f)**$(3, 3)$ **2.a)**$(0.6, 1.8)$ **b)**$(-0.6, 2.0)$

**c)**$(1.6, -0.1)$ **d)**$(2.1, 0.2)$ **3.a)**$(17.16, 25.57)$

**b)**$(-1.89, 2.38)$ **c)**$(1.00, 0.36)$ **d)**$(0.44, -0.98)$

## 6.9 Exercise, page 236

**1.a)**$\$20$ **b)**$\$0.08x$ **c)**$\$0.12(y + 2)$ **d)**$\$0.17x$ **2.a)**$\$(0.05x + 0.10y)$

**b)**$\$(0.06m + 0.08n)$ **c)**$\$(0.06x + 0.08y + 0.16)$

**d)**$\$(0.10x + 0.12y + 0.02)$ **3.a)**$50¢$ **b)**$10x¢$ **c)**$20x¢$ **d)**$(25y + 50)¢$

**e)**$5y¢$ **f)**$15x¢$ **g)**$(10m + 25n)¢$ **h)**$(25x + 10y + 40)¢$ **4.a)**$(10x + 25y)$

**b)**$(25m + 10n)¢$ **c)**$(5n + 25q)¢$ **d)**$(20x + 25y)¢$ **e)**$(15m + 20n)¢$

**f)**$(2x + 30y)¢$ **5.a)**$\$25.90$ **b)**$\$1.59x$ **c)**$\$(1.86x + 3.89y)$

**d)**$\$(3.09x + 1.19y + 2.38)$ **6.a)**$300$ km **b)**$50x$ km **c)**$12x$ km

**d)**$(60x + 100y)$ km **e)**$(5x + 10y)$ km **7.a)**$0.10x + 0.12y = 160$

**b)**$0.08x - 0.09y = 10$ **c)**$0.075x - 0.09y = -20$

**8.a)**$1.25x + 1.50y = 18.75$ **b)**$1.50x - 1.25y = 6.25$

**c)**$5.50x - 1.25y = 1.75$ **9.a)**$25x + 75y = 275$

**b)**$5x - 2y = -8$ **c)**$3x - 6y = 48$ **10.a)**$5n + 10d = 60$

**b)**$5n - 25q = 75$ **c)**$5n + 25q = 75$ **11.a)**$x + y = 48$

**b)**$x - y = 5$ **c)**$w + l = 96$ **d)**$2w + \dfrac{l}{2} = 86$ **12.a)**$384$, $896$ **b)**F, F

**13.a)**$h + j = 36$ **b)**$2w - d = 4$

## 6.10 Exercise, page 240

**1.a)**$x = y + 8$ **b)**$l + w = 48$ **c)**$2x - 3y = 83$ **d)**$x - \dfrac{y}{2} = 33$

**2.a)**$10x + y = 186$ **b)**$29x + 36y = 696$ **c)**$38x = 369 + 50y$

**3.a)**$d - 6 = z$ **b)**$5j + 3s = 103$ **c)**$j + 3m = 36$

**d)**$m + 4 = \dfrac{h + 4}{2}$ **e)**$5(h - 2) = (m - 2) + 3$ **4.a)**$12$, $60$

**b)**$4$, $146$ **c)**$36$, $48$ **5.a)**$40$ dimes, $36$ quarters **b)**$14$ nickels,

$36$ dimes **c)**$115$ adults, $76$ students **6.** $15$ \$2-bills,

$25$ \$5-bills **7.** $18$, $24$ **8.** \$500, \$700 **9.** $30$ **10.** $120$ wheat,

$75$ oats **11.** $50$ practice, $20$ game **12.** large: $300$ L,

small: $200$ L **13.** $65$

## 6.11 Exercise, page 242

**1.** Debbie: $18$, Klaas: $41$ **2.** $\$1100$ @ $10\%$, $\$900$ @ $9\%$

**3.** $10$ kg of $30\%$, $40$ kg of $40\%$ **4.** Janos: $16$, David: $18$

**5.** $\$400$ @ $6\%$, $\$600$ @ $8\%$ **6.** $\$300$ in savings, $\$450$ in

chequing **7.** $350$ **8.** city: $678$ km, highway: $522$ km

**9.a)**yes: $5 \times 1¢$, $2 \times 10¢$, $1 \times 5¢$, $1 \times 25¢$ **10.** $220$ g of A,

$180$ g of B **11.a)**$37.5$ kg **b)**$12.5$ kg **12.** $80$ kg of $\$2.30$/kg

$70$ kg of $\$3.20$/kg **13.** $115$ kg of red, $85$ kg of green

**14.** $20$ kg of $20\%$ mixture, $80\%$ of $40\%$ mixture

**15.** $240$ kg of Orange Pekoe, $160$ kg of Indian Tea

**16.** $60$ kg of $\$2.20$/kg, $40$ kg of $\$2.40$/kg

## 6.12 Exercise, page 246

**1.** J: $50$ km/h, P: $32$ km/h **2.** H: $37$ km/h, S: $40$ km/h

**3.** L: $68$ km/h, M: $50$ km/h **4.** M: $3$ km/h, Z: $6$ km/h

**5.** plane: $280$ km/h, wind: $40$ km/h **6.** $20$ km/h, $24$ km/h

**7.** $45$ km/h, $50$ km/h **8.** $1425$ km **9.a)**$170$ km **b)**$15$ km

**10.** $16$ km/h **11.** westbound: $42$ km/h, eastbound:

$50$ km/h **12.** $30$ km **13.a)**$500$ km/h **b)**$20$ km/h

# 6.13 Exercise, page 248
1. 26 h, 32 h 2. H: 82, M: 96 3. M: 16, L: 42
4. 3500 pike, 5500 perch 5. 236 chemists, 188 physicists
6. 38, 50 7. 400 in N.B., 800 out-of-province
8. L: $6300, D: $3700 9. 120 $2, 60 $5 10. 843 dimes,
6300 pennies 11. 45 km 12. 9 boys, 14 girls

# 6.14 Exercise, page 250
1. 483 chemists, 651 engineers 2. 180 3. 2000 bass,
8000 perch 4. 18, 30 5. 125 6. 35 dimes, 40 quarters
7. 20 kg of Red Barons, 80 kg of Bon Bons 8. 150 kg of
40% solution, 50 L of 60% solution 9. prop-jet: 280 km/h,
wind: 40 km/h 10. 153

# CHAPTER 7

## 7.1 Exercise, page 255
1. E 2. (a), (c) 3. A, C 4.a)$2x - 5y \leq 10$ b)$-2 \leq y < 3$
c)$2x + 5y > -10$ 5.a)$2x + y \geq 2$ and $x - 2y \leq -1$
b)$7x - 5y \geq 6$ and $7x + 3y < 30$ c)$x + y \leq 2$ and
$x - 2y < -1$ 6.a)$y = 0$ b)$x = 0$ c)1: $x > 0$ and $y > 0$,
2: $x < 0$ and $y > 0$, 3: $x < 0$ and $y < 0$, 4: $x > 0$ and
$y < 0$ 7.a)$-3 \leq y \leq 5$ b)$-4 \leq x < 3$ c)$0 \leq x \leq 5$
d)$2 \leq y \leq 6$ 9.a)$x + 3y \geq 3$ and $2x - y > -2$
b)$5x - 3y \leq -25$ and $2x + 3y < 6$ 11.a)$x + y < 6$,
$2x + 7y \geq 7$, $x \geq 0$ b)$x - y > -2$, $x + 2y < 4$ and $y \geq -3$

## 7.2 Exercise, page 259
1. 6 2. 24 3. 21 4. 600 5.a)220 b)17 6.a)min: 30,

max: 100 b)min: 80, max: 150 7.b)$\left(0, \dfrac{19}{3}\right)$, (0, 0),

$\left(\dfrac{31}{3}, 0\right)$, (5, 8) c)(i)42 (ii)29 8.b)(0, 8), (4, 3), (10, 0)

c)(i)16 (ii)17 9.a)13 b)22 10. 67 11. 320

## 7.3 Exercise, page 263
1.c)12 golf hats, 24 visors 2. 80 basketballs, 30 soccer
balls 3. 90 pillows, 40 cushions 4. 120 2-bulb lamps,
60 4-bulb lamps; $4500.00 5. $2800 6.a)Janet: 2 h,
Sam: 6 h b)Janet: 6 hockey sticks, 6 goalie sticks;
Sam: 6 hockey sticks, 24 goalie sticks
7.a)30 kg Husky, 20 kg Vibrant b)$1390
8.a)7.0 kg Erunam, 5.0 kg Goodwin b)$31.80

## 7.4 Exercise, page 268
1.a)$d = kt$ b)$g = km$ c)$A = kh$ d)$C = kl$ e)$A = kb$ 2.a)$5.00
b)$30.00 c)$42.50 3.a)4 h b)9 h c)7 h 4.a)$E = kt$ b)5
5.a)$C = 3.15\,m$ c)$14.18, interpolation d)9.5 kg,
extrapolation 6.c)1.50 7.c)(i)$4.50 (ii)$7.50 (iii)$0.75
8.a)$G = \dfrac{1}{5}N$ c)1060 t d)182 450 9.c)7.5 10.b)yes c)3.14

## 7.5 Exercise, page 272
1.a)2 b)12 c)4 d)$\dfrac{4}{9}$ e)2 2.a)$m = kn$ b)40 3.a)$x = ky$ b)64

4.a)$p = kq^2$ b)10.24 5.a)50 b)8 c)3 d)3.6 6.a)$\dfrac{8}{15}$ b)$\dfrac{8}{15}$

7.a)$m = kV$ b)480.0 g 8.a)98.0 cm b)12.0 g 9.a)480.0 L
10. 375.0 km 11. $45.33 12. $3.50 13. 5.08 cm³ 14. 12
15.a)2075.0 m b)10.4 s 16. 24.0 g

## 7.6 Exercise, page 275
1.a)$w = \dfrac{k}{f}$ b)$t = \dfrac{k}{s}$ c)$S = \dfrac{k}{A}$ 2.a)20 m b)9 m c)40 m

3.a)15 dB b)7 dB c)24 dB 4.a)$N = \dfrac{k}{d}$ b)600

5.a)80 units b)2.0 m c)80 6.a)inverse b)40.0 cm

c)100 7.a)$f = \dfrac{22\,380}{l}$ 8.a)$I = \dfrac{144}{R}$ 9.a)$V = \dfrac{6400}{A}$ 10.a)$t = \dfrac{24}{d^2}$

## 7.7 Exercise, page 278
1.a)$F = \dfrac{k}{s}$ b)$V = \dfrac{k}{A}$ 2.a)3072 b)128 c)192 3.a)$m = \dfrac{k}{n}$

b)54 4.a)32 b)4 5.a)$t = \dfrac{k}{s}$ b)2.0 h 6.a)$667

b)2.67 years 7. 2.5 h 8. 1.47 m 9.a)96.0 cm
b)30.0 cm 10. 6.4°C 11.a)A is halved b)D is halved

## 7.8 Exercise, page 281
1.a)$D = ks^2$ b)$I = \dfrac{k}{d^2}$ c)$d = kt^2$ d)$F = \dfrac{k}{r^2}$ e)$P = kI^2$

f)$C = kS^2$ 2.a)0.5 b)5400 3.a)60 b)48 4.a)$t = kq^2$

b)2025 5.a)$P = \dfrac{k}{V^2}$ b)100 6.a)$R = ks$ b)2 units

7.a)445.5 b)1.8 cm 8. 200.0 units 9. 2.0 units 10. 6.0 m/s
11. 5.0 cm 12. 27.4 min 13. 2.1 m 14. 1.7 s 15. 8.0 cm 16. 2.8 m

## 7.9 Exercise, page 283
1.a)$C = 6.00 + 0.75n$ 2.a)$C = 0.72 + 0.61n$
3.a)$C = 25.00 + 0.50n$ d)(i) 4.a)Ace: $C = 22.00 + 0.05n$,
Brights: $C = 35.00 + 0.02n$ d)433 km

## 7.10 Exercise, page 286
1.a)90 b)168 c)234 d)318 2.a)12 b)32 c)17 d)59 3. $L = 40$,
$s = 20$ 4.a)$1200.00 b)$1.20 5.b)$460.00 6.a)0.3 b)$265.00
7. $2096.00 8.a)$32.00 9. $8.38 10.a)$140 b)20 years

# CHAPTER 8

## 8.1 Exercise, page 292
1. Inductive 2. Deductive 3. Inductive
4. Deductive 5. Deductive 6. Inductive 7. Deductive
8. Deductive 9. Deductive 13. 15, 21 14.a)10 b)300

## 8.2 Exercise, page 296
12.a)1, 4; 1, 2; 2, 3; 3, 4; 9, 10; 9, 12; 10, 11; 11, 12; 5, 6;
6, 8; 7, 8; 5, 7 b)Same as (a) above 13.a)DK, HE b)A, H,
I; C, D, F; K, H, D, E; A, B, D; A, C, M c)$\angle 1, \angle 2, \angle 4$,
$\angle 5, \angle 7, \angle 8, \angle 9, \angle 10, \angle 13, \angle 14$ 14.a)$\overline{BC}$ b)$\overline{KE}$ c)$\overline{DG}$
15.a)$\overline{AB}, \overline{SQ}$ b)$\overline{RS}, \overline{QT}$ c)$\overline{WY}, \overline{XZ}, \overline{PK}, \overline{BT}$ d)$\overline{DG}, \overline{EH}$,
$\overline{IF}$ 16.a)$\triangle WIE$ b)WXYZ, BKTP c)BKTP d)DEFGHI
e)$\triangle ABC$, $\triangle QSM$, $\triangle QSD$, f)$\triangle GUM$ g)BRSK, WIEX

## 8.3 Exercise, page 302
2.a)$p° = 9°$, $q° = 69°$ (CAT) b)$p° = 50°$, $q° = 30°$ (SAT)
c)$p° = 50°$ (SAT), $q° = 50°$ (SAT) 5.a)$\angle 1 = \angle 3$,
$\angle 2 = \angle 4$, $\angle 5 = \angle 7$, $\angle 6 = \angle 8$ b)$\angle 4 = \angle 7$, $\angle 5 = \angle 8$,
$\angle 1 = \angle 2 = \angle 3 = \angle 6 = \angle 9 = \angle 10 = 90°$ 7.a)$x° = 10°$,
$y° = 152°$ b)$x° = 30°$, $y° = 90°$ c)$x° = 22.5°$, $y° = 90°$
d)$x° = 114°$, $y° = 20°$ e)$x° = 43.3°$, $y° = 79.3°$

## 8.4 Exercise, page 308
**1.a)**AB = PQ, AC = PR, BC = QR, $\angle$A = $\angle$P, $\angle$B = $\angle$Q, $\angle$C = $\angle$R **b)**EF = RS, EG = RT, FG = ST, $\angle$E = $\angle$R, $\angle$F = $\angle$S, $\angle$G = $\angle$T **c)**XY = ST, XZ = SU, YZ = TU, $\angle$X = $\angle$S, $\angle$Y = $\angle$T, $\angle$Z = $\angle$U **d)**BC = QR, BD = QS, CD = RS, $\angle$B = $\angle$Q, $\angle$C = $\angle$R, $\angle$D = $\angle$S **2.** (a), (c), (d), (e), (f), (h) **3.a)**$\triangle$ABC $\cong$ $\triangle$DEF **b)**$\triangle$PQS $\cong$ $\triangle$PRS **c)**$\triangle$SUT $\cong$ $\triangle$RMK **d)**$\triangle$WLY $\cong$ $\triangle$XLY **e)**$\triangle$PST $\cong$ $\triangle$QSV **f)**$\triangle$TUR $\cong$ $\triangle$OUP **4.** (a), (c), (d), (f) **5.** $\triangle$PRQ $\cong$ $\triangle$EGF, $\triangle$QPR $\cong$ $\triangle$FEG, $\triangle$QRP $\cong$ $\triangle$FGE, $\triangle$RQP $\cong$ $\triangle$GFE, $\triangle$RPQ $\cong$ $\triangle$GEF **6.** MN = QR, MP = QS, NP = RS, $\angle$M = $\angle$Q, $\angle$N = $\angle$R, $\angle$P = $\angle$S **7.b)**$\triangle$ABC $\cong$ $\triangle$TUS, $\triangle$DEF $\cong$ $\triangle$ETN, $\triangle$FGH $\cong$ $\triangle$PMN, $\triangle$JKL $\cong$ $\triangle$UTW, $\triangle$UVW $\cong$ $\triangle$XZY **8.a)**$\triangle$ABC $\cong$ $\triangle$PRQ, $\triangle$DEF $\cong$ $\triangle$NMO **9.b)**AB = DE, BC = DF, AC = EF **c)**$\angle$A = $\angle$E, $\angle$B = $\angle$D, $\angle$C = $\angle$F **d)**$\triangle$ABC $\cong$ $\triangle$EDF **10.b)**$\triangle$ABC $\cong$ $\triangle$NML, $\triangle$DEF $\cong$ $\triangle$PQR, $\triangle$GHI $\cong$ $\triangle$UST

## 8.5 Exercise, page 311
**1.a)**SSS **b)**$\triangle$MNO $\cong$ $\triangle$RST **2.b)**$\triangle$ABC $\cong$ $\triangle$JLK, $\triangle$MNP $\cong$ $\triangle$FCA, $\triangle$KLR $\cong$ $\triangle$YPS, $\triangle$GHI $\cong$ $\triangle$UTV **3.a)**20.0 cm **b)**40° **c)**28.0 cm **d)**80° **e)**23.0 cm **f)**60° **5.a)**JL = TR **b)**MP = WT **12.** 89 **13.** S(−2, 1)

## 8.6 Exercise, page 315
**1.a)**SAS **b)**$\triangle$PQR $\cong$ $\triangle$STU **c)**PQ = ST, $\angle$P = $\angle$S, $\angle$Q = $\angle$T **2.b)**$\triangle$ABC $\cong$ $\triangle$SUT, $\triangle$GHI $\cong$ $\triangle$MLN, $\triangle$DEF $\cong$ $\triangle$QRP **3.a)**40° **b)**42.0 cm **c)**25° **d)**30.0 cm **e)**20.0 cm **f)**115° **4.** $\triangle$ABC $\cong$ $\triangle$MSP (SAS), $\triangle$DEF $\cong$ $\triangle$QTA (SSS), $\triangle$SUT $\cong$ $\triangle$JIK (SSS), $\triangle$AVL $\cong$ $\triangle$JGH (SAS), $\triangle$MNO $\cong$ $\triangle$PRQ (SAS) **5.a)**BC = PR or $\angle$A = $\angle$Q **b)**SU = TV or $\angle$SWU = $\angle$TWV **c)**AB = PQ or $\angle$AOB = $\angle$POQ

## 8.7 Exercise, page 320
**1.a)**ASA **b)**$\triangle$DEF $\cong$ $\triangle$TUS **c)**DF = TS, DE = TU, $\angle$D = $\angle$T **2.a)**ASA **b)**$\triangle$DEF $\cong$ $\triangle$HTG **c)**DE = HT, DF = HG, $\angle$E = $\angle$I **3.b)**$\triangle$ABC $\cong$ $\triangle$DKE (ASA), $\triangle$JKL $\cong$ $\triangle$RTS (ASA), $\triangle$STU $\cong$ $\triangle$HIG (ASA), $\triangle$DEF $\cong$ $\triangle$VUY (ASA), $\triangle$MNO $\cong$ $\triangle$RPQ (ASA) **5.a)**AB = FL or $\angle$C = $\angle$E **b)**TU = DF or $\angle$S = $\angle$E **c)**DG = RP or $\angle$A = $\angle$Q **d)**HG = NM or $\angle$I = $\angle$B **e)**FS = FB or $\angle$P = $\angle$R **f)**$\angle$AOQ = $\angle$GOD or AQ = GD

**1.a)**HS **b)**$\triangle$ABC $\cong$ $\triangle$DFE **c)**AB = DF, $\angle$C = $\angle$E, $\angle$A = $\angle$D **2.b)**$\triangle$ABC $\cong$ $\triangle$OHC (HS), $\triangle$DEF $\cong$ $\triangle$FBL (SAS), $\triangle$AGK $\cong$ $\triangle$JEM (HS), $\triangle$GHI $\cong$ $\triangle$STU (SSS), $\triangle$JKL $\cong$ $\triangle$RPQ (ASA) **5.a)**$\angle$C = $\angle$P or AB = RQ or AC = RP **b)**DE = TU or EF = US **c)**AF = LK or $\angle$M = $\angle$N **d)**GH = NM or $\angle$I = $\angle$S

## CHAPTER 9

### 9.1 Exercise, page 333
**2.a)**(b), (c), (d), (e), (h) **b)**(a), (f), (g), (i), (j), (k)

### 9.2 Exercise, page 337
**2.a)**1, 5; 3, 7; 2, 6; 4, 8; 9, 13; 11, 15; 10, 14; 12, 16 **b)**3, 6; 4, 5; 11, 14; 12, 13 **c)**3, 5; 4, 6; 11, 13; 12, 14 **3.a)**1, 2; 2, 4; 3, 4; 1, 3; 5, 6; 6, 8; 7, 8; 5, 7; 9, 10; 10, 12;

11, 12; 9, 11; 13, 14; 14, 16; 15, 16; 13, 15 **b)**1, 4; 2, 3; 5, 8; 6, 7; 9, 12; 10, 11; 13, 16; 14, 15 **5.a)**alternate: $d$, $f$; $c$, $e$ corresponding: $a$, $e$; $d$, $h$; $b$, $f$; $c$, $g$ interior: $d$, $e$; $c$, $f$ **b)**alternate: $q$, $r$; $n$, $t$ corresponding: $p$, $t$; $q$, $v$; $m$, $r$; $n$, $s$ interior: $q$, $t$; $n$, $r$ **c)**alternate: $\angle$PQS, $\angle$QSR; $\angle$PSQ, $\angle$SQR interior: $\angle$QPS, $\angle$PSR; $\angle$PQR, $\angle$QRS **6.a)**1, 3; 2, 4; 5, 7; 6, 8; 3, 5; 2, 8; 1, 5; 2, 6; 4, 8; 3, 7; 1, 7; 4, 6 **b)**1, 2; 2, 3; 3, 4; 1, 4; 5, 6; 6, 7; 7, 8; 5, 8; 2, 5; 3, 8; 1, 6; 4, 7; 1, 8; 4, 5; 3, 6; 2, 7 **7.a)**$\angle$BAC, $\angle$ACD; $\angle$DAC, $\angle$ACB; $\angle$ABC, $\angle$ADC; $\angle$BAD, $\angle$BCD **b)**$\angle$BAD, $\angle$ADC; $\angle$ABC, $\angle$BCD; $\angle$DAB, $\angle$ABC; $\angle$ADC, $\angle$DCB

### 9.3 Exercise, page 339
**1.** 2, 5; 3, 4; 6, 9; 7, 8; 10, 13; 11, 12; 14, 17; 15, 16; 4, 7; 5, 6; 12, 15; 13, 14; 2, 6; 4, 8; 3, 7; 5, 9; 10, 14; 12, 16; 11, 15; 13, 17; 2, 9; 3, 8; 10, 17; 11, 16 **14.b)**60° **15.a)**$x + 60 = 3x + 40$ **b)**$\angle$EGH = 70°, $\angle$AGH = 110° **16.a)**40° **b)**140° **c)**40° **d)**140° **17.a)**$a° = b° = 57.5°$, $c° = 122.5°$ **b)**$a° = b° = 110°$, $c° = 40°$ **c)**$a° = 40°$, $b° = 60°$

### 9.4 Exercise, page 345
**2.b)**80° **3.b)**80° **4.a)**$x° = 96°$, $\angle$B = 96° **b)**$x° = 30°$, $\angle$D = 60°, $\angle$E = 90°, $\angle$F = 30° **c)**$x° = 30°$, $\angle$G = $\angle$I = 30° **d)**$x° = 60°$, $\angle$J = $\angle$L = 60° **e)**$x° = 19°$, $\angle$Q = 78°, $\angle$P = 64°, $\angle$R = 38° **5.a)**69° **6.a)**28° **b)**50° **7.a)**$a° = 150°$, $b° = 110°$ **b)**$b° = 60°$ **c)**$a° = 110°$, $b° = 110°$, $c° = 40°$ **d)**$a° = 57.5°$, $b° = 57.5°$, $c° = 122.5°$ **e)**$a° = 35°$, $b° = 45°$, $c° = 100°$ **f)**$b° = 100°$, $c° = 60°$ **8.a)**$\angle$P = 60°, $\angle$Q = 80°, $\angle$R = 40° **b)**$\angle$P = 54°, $\angle$Q = 18°, $\angle$R = 108° **14.** 444

### 9.5 Exercise, page 349
**11.a)**AI $\parallel$ BH, DC $\parallel$ JG **b)**ST $\parallel$ QP, QS $\parallel$ PT **c)**PQ $\parallel$ RS

### 9.7 Exercise, page 354
**4.a)**$\dfrac{1}{2}$ $ab$ **8.a)**10.3 **b)**12.7 **c)**11.3 **d)**12.3 **e)**13.7 **9.** 20.0 cm **10.b)**12.5 cm **11.** AB = BC = CD = AD = 8.6 cm **12.** 20.8 cm **13.a)**$\sqrt{26}$ units **b)**15 units **c)**$4\sqrt{2}$ units **d)**$\sqrt{53}$ units **15.** isosceles

### 9.8 Exercise, page 357 **1.** (a), (b), (f) **2.** (b), (c), (d)

## CHAPTER 10

### 10.1 Exercise, page 363
**1.b)**39.2 cm² **2.a)**1594 cm² **b)**159.7 m² **c)**77.8 cm² **3.a)**357.5 cm² **b)**2658.5 cm² **c)**68.3 m² **d)**271.5 cm² **4.b)**50.6 m² **5.a)**500 cm² **b)**169.7 cm² **c)**104.7 m² **6.b)**480.0 m² **7.a)**39.2 cm² **b)**161.6 m² **8.a)**939 cm² **b)**3.9 m² **c)**1719.9 cm² **9.a)**785 cm² **b)**150 cm² **c)**575 cm² **d)**65.3 cm² **e)**4584.8 cm² **(f)**51.5 m² **10.a)**8420 cm² **b)**$49.64 **11.** 320.3 cm² **12.a)**1649 cm² **b)**1217 cm² **13.** 11.5 m² **14.a)**2.8 m² **b)**10.3 L **15.b)**cube: 5 cm × 5 cm × 5 cm, cylinder: several possible dimensions

### 10.2 Exercise, page 367
**2.a)**201 cm² **b)**427 cm² **c)**628 cm² **3.a)**183 cm² **b)**1414 cm² **4.a)**182 cm² **b)**319 cm² **5.a)**600 cm² **b)**190 cm² **c)**725 cm² **6.a)**499 cm² **b)**840 m² **c)**67.0 cm² **7.** 140 cm² **8.a)**3.70 cm² **b)**8.72 cm² **9.a)**411 cm² **b)**57 cm² **10.a)**556 cm² **11.** 814 cm² **12.a)**100% increase **b)**lateral surface doubles, base area quadruples **c)**curved surface doubles, base area quadruples **d)**400%

## 10.3 Exercise, page 370
**1.a)**38.2 cm² **b)**160.4 cm³ **2.a)**89.9 cm³ **b)**28.3 m³
**c)**56.3 m³ **3.a)**20.1 cm² **b)**106.3 cm³ **4.a)**32.2 m²
**b)**209.0 m³ **5.a)**756 cm³ **b)**11 953.0 cm³ **c)**1080
**d)**8.7 m³ **e)**6159.4 cm³ **f)**776.5 cm³ **6.a)**1800 m³
**b)**25.8 m³ **c)**614.5 cm³ **d)**36.6 m³ **e)**1221.9 m³ **7.a)**20.1 m³
**b)**$3418.07 **8.a)**1800 cm³ **b)**2 **9.** 1750 cm³ **10.b)**2850 cm³,
360 cm³, 2700 cm³ **11.** $V = \pi h(R^2 - r^2)$, 16.0 m³
**12.a)**28.9 L **b)**23.3 L **c)**25.6 L **d)**27 kg
**13.** 37.0 m³ **14.a)**140 boxes **b)**9.0 m³

## 10.4 Exercise, page 373
**1.** 151 cm³, 393 cm³ **2.** 4.8 cm³, 12.6 cm³ **4.a)**$V = \dfrac{1}{3}\pi r^2 h$

**5.** $V = \dfrac{1}{3}s^2 h$, where $s$ is the length of the side of the square base

## 10.5 Exercise, page 375
**1.b)**14 100 cm³ **2.a)**65 400 cm³ **b)**170 cm³ **c)**1.38 km³
**3.a)**4190 cm³ **b)**180 000 cm³ **c)**3700 cm³ **d)**432 m³
**4.a)**11 500 cm³ **b)**555 m³ **c)**1050 mm³ **d)**306 m³
**5.a)**1100 cm³ **b)**1100 cm³ **6.b)**95 cm³ **7.a)**3080 cm³
**b)**180 cm³ **c)**430 cm³ **8.a)**20.5 cm³ **b)**20.5 cm³
**9.a)**200 cm³ **b)**160 cm² **10.a)**21 cm, 160 cm³ **b)**23 cm,
210 cm³ **c)**hardball, 6.7 cm² **11.a)**45 cm³ **b)**310 g
**12.** 1500 g **13.** 32% **14.** 2 times **15.** 2540 m³
**16.a)**46 **17.** $2.1 \times 10^6$ m³ **18.** 930 cm³

## 10.6 Exercise, page 379
**3.a)**820 cm³ **b)** 1000 m³ **c)**2000 cm³ **4.a)**145 m² **b)**287 cm²
**c)** 10 000 mm³ **5.b)**E, A, C, D, B **6.a)**17 cm³ **b)**170 m³
**7.a)**123 m³ **b)**$477.51 **8.a)**2.4 m³ **b)**25 000 **9.a)**435 L **b)**3630 kg
**10.a)**volume is halved **b)**volume is halved
**11.** 8 × $1, 1 × $10, 2 × $5 **12.a)**17.3 cm × 17.3 cm × 17.3 cm
**b)**2700 cm² **c)**1.05 times

## 10.7 Exercise, page 381
**5.b)**9 m³ **6.b)**88 m³

# CHAPTER 11

## 11.1 Exercise, page 387
**4.a)**census **b)**sample **c)**sample **d)**census **e)**sample
**f)**sample **g)**sample **h)**census **i)**sample **j)**census
**k)**sample **6.a)**10 **b)**yes **7.** B **8.a)**no **b)**$S_2$ **10.a)**C
**b)**A: 70%, B: 64%, C: 64.9%

## 11.2 Exercise, page 391
**1.a)**destructive **2.a)**clustered **3.a)**40 **b)**20 **c)**stratified
**4.a)**226 **b)**stratified **c)**clustered **5.a)**ND **b)**ND **c)**D
**d)**ND **e)**D **f)**ND **g)**D **6.a)**B **b)**G **c)**G **d)**B
**7.a)**should not **b)**should not **c)**should not **d)**should **e)**should

## 11.3 Exercise, page 395
**1.a)**1, 2, 3, 4, 5, 6 **b)**40–50, 50–60, 60–70, 70–80, 80–90,
90–100 **2.a)**2, 9 **b)**$\dfrac{13}{9}$, $\dfrac{13}{9}$ **3.a)**4 **b)**1, 2, 6 **7.b)**50–55, 55–60,
60–65, 65–70, 70–75, 75–80, 80–85, 85–90, 90–95,
95–100 **8.a)**75–80 **b)**none **9.** 9.09% **10.a)**205 **13.b)**30.1 cm,
16.3 cm **16.a)**10.3% **b)**31.0% **20.a)**(i)2 (ii)1 (iii)3
(iv)0 **b)**(i)15 (ii)2 (iii)4 (iv)25 **21.b)**30% **c)**28% **d)**72%

## 11.4 Exercise, page 400
**1.a)**10; 9; 8, 9 **b)**63.2; 63; no mode **c)**6; 6; 6 **d)**10.6; 11.7;
11.5 **2.a)**not necessarily **b)**yes **c)**not necessarily **3.** 8
**4.b)**12.9 **5.b)**9.3 **6.a)**72 kg; 73.8 kg; 72 kg **b)**less than
**c)**less than **7.a)**26.4 cm; 26.9 cm; 22.3 cm, **8.a)**$7.02;
$5.48; $5.15 **9.** mode **10.a)**M: 54.1, 18; N: 62.2, 94
**12.a)**45; 55.5; 0 **13.a)**$32 077; $32 000; $32 000
**16.a)**42.4¢ **b)**42.7¢ **17.** 8.2% **18.a)**$4.17 **b)**$3.77

## 11.5 Exercise, page 405
**1.a)**25.7 **b)**25.6 **2.b)**24.8, 22.5 **3.a)**31.2, 35
**b)**13.6, 13.8 **4.(ii)a)**46.0, 45 **b)**7.9, 9 **5.c)**29.3 years
**6.b)**4.3 min, 4.2 min, 3.8 min

## 11.6 Exercise, page 409
**1.a)**20, 14 **b)**24, 21 **c)**34.5, 18.4 **d)**7.5, 5.0 **2.a)**64.2%
**b)**40% **c)**12.8% **3.a)**5.4 cm, 5.6 cm, no mode
**b)**5.3 cm **c)**1.3 cm **4.a)**(i)58.0 (ii)19.0 **b)**(i)149.3
(ii)17.04 **5.a)**1.4 g **6.a)**14 h **b)**11 h **c)**4.1 h **d)**yes **7.a)**Kevin: 24.6
8.7; Paul: 24.5, 5.5 **b)**Paul **8.a)**11.1 **9.a)**17.0 **10.** 2-3C

## 11.7 Exercise, page 412
**1.a)**43 **b)**70 **c)**(i)$\geq 43$ and $\leq 70$ (ii)$<43$ and $>70$
**3.b)**between 54 and 83 **c)**84 to 100 **d)**27 to 53
**4.c)**2.9 **d)**1.5 to 4.0 **e)**1.0 to 1.4, 4.1 to 8.3 **5.a)**dry
concrete **b)**A: 9 m, B: 17 m **c)**A: 37 m, B: 43 m **d)**6 m

## 11.8 Exercise, page 416
**3.a)**5352 **b)**18 **c)**372 **d)**12 **5.a)**−$458 **6.b)**$2.80 **8.a)**11 992

## 11.9 Exercise, page 418
**1.a)**118 **b)**160 **c)**56 **2.a)**$71.16; $70; $61, $73, $77 **d)**A: 80%,
B: 27% **3.** C **4.b)**36% **c)**24.2 cm **d)**28% **5.b)**21.4 cm **c)**72%

## 11.10 Exercise, page 423
**1.a)** $\dfrac{1}{1000}$ or 0.001 **b)** $\dfrac{1}{50}$ or 0.02 **2.a)** $\dfrac{1}{2}$ or 0.5 **b)** $\dfrac{3}{10}$ or 0.3
**3.a)** $\dfrac{1}{6}$ or 0.17 **b)** $\dfrac{1}{2}$ or 0.5 **c)** $\dfrac{5}{6}$ or 0.83 **d)** $\dfrac{1}{2}$ or 0.5 **e)**0
**4.a)** $\dfrac{1}{26}$ **b)** $\dfrac{3}{26}$ **c)** $\dfrac{5}{26}$ **d)** $\dfrac{4}{13}$ **5.** $\dfrac{7}{13}$ **6.a)** $\dfrac{2}{3}$ **b)** $\dfrac{1}{3}$ **7.a)**50 **b)**0.96
**8.a)**0.49 **b)**0.51 **9.a)**0.48 **b)**0.52 **10.a)**0.5, 0.5 **11.a)**14.3%, 62.3%
**c)**64.6% **12.b)**113 **c)**229 **13.a)**0.67 **b)**0.33 **14.a)**0.83 **b)**0.67
**15.a)**0.41 **b)**0.59 **16.a)**0.36 **b)**0.64 **c)**0.60 **d)**0.24 **17.** 0.54 **18.b)**0.997

## 11.11 Exercise, page 427
**1.a)** $\dfrac{1}{8}$ **b)** $\dfrac{7}{8}$ **c)** $\dfrac{3}{8}$ **d)** $\dfrac{5}{8}$ **2.a)** $\dfrac{3}{8}$ **b)** $\dfrac{1}{4}$ **c)** $\dfrac{3}{4}$ **d)** $\dfrac{5}{8}$ **e)** $\dfrac{1}{8}$
**3.b)** $\dfrac{1}{8}$ **4.a)** $\dfrac{1}{16}$ **b)** $\dfrac{3}{8}$ **c)** $\dfrac{5}{8}$ **d)** $\dfrac{3}{4}$ **6.a)** $\dfrac{1}{18}$ **b)** $\dfrac{5}{36}$ **c)** $\dfrac{1}{36}$
**d)** $\dfrac{1}{18}$ **e)**2, 12; 3, 11; 4, 10; 5, 9; 6, 8 **7.a)**7 **b)**8
**c)**6 **d)**11 **8.a)** $\dfrac{35}{36}$ **b)** $\dfrac{5}{6}$ **c)** $\dfrac{1}{2}$ **d)** $\dfrac{1}{2}$ **9.a)** $\dfrac{5}{18}$ **b)** $\dfrac{1}{12}$ **10.b)** $\dfrac{25}{216}$

## 11.12 Exercise, page 430
**1.a)** $\dfrac{11}{117}$ or 0.094 **b)** $\dfrac{11}{117}$ or 0.094 **2.a)**G, J
**b)** $\dfrac{17}{39}$ or 0.44 **c)** $\dfrac{106}{117}$ or 0.91 **3.c)**14.4 cm **d)**38.3% **4.a)**0.20 **b)**0.58
**c)**0.23 **d)**0.55 **5.a)**14 cm **b)**66.7% **c)**0.50 **6.a)**0.05 **b)**0.55

**1.a)**A: $\frac{1}{2}$, B: $\frac{1}{6}$, C: $\frac{1}{12}$ **b)**A: $\frac{1}{2}$, B: $\frac{1}{6}$, C: $\frac{1}{12}$ **c)**A: $\frac{1}{2}$, B: $\frac{1}{2}$, C: $\frac{1}{4}$
**d)**C = A × B **2.b)**$\frac{1}{24}$ **3.a)**$\frac{1}{24}$ **b)**$\frac{1}{24}$ **c)**$\frac{1}{8}$ **4.b)**16 **c)**$\frac{1}{4}$ **5.a)**$\frac{1}{16}$ **b)**$\frac{1}{16}$
**c)**$\frac{3}{8}$ **d)**$\frac{1}{4}$ **6.a)**$\frac{1}{4}$ **b)**$\frac{1}{4}$ **7.a)**$\frac{1}{8}$ **b)**$\frac{1}{8}$ **c)**$\frac{1}{8}$ **8.a)**$\frac{1}{48}$ **b)**$\frac{1}{16}$ **9.a)**$\frac{1}{2704}$ **b)**$\frac{1}{169}$
**c)**$\frac{1}{169}$ **d)**$\frac{12}{169}$ **e)**$\frac{1}{4}$ **10.a)**$\frac{1}{81}$ **b)**1.23% **11.a)**0.16% **b)**$\frac{1}{25}$ **12.** $\frac{1}{59\,049}$

---

# CHAPTER 12

## 12.1 Exercise, page 439
**1.a)**△ABC ~ △DEF **b)**△MNO ~ △PQR **c)**△PQT ~ △PRS
**d)**△IJK ~ △IGH **e)**△MNU ~ △MST **f)**△OSV ~ △OKL
**g)**△NPM ~ △NKL **h)**△GHI ~ △GFE **2.a)**(i)AB (ii)BC
(iii)CA **b)**(i)∠S (ii)∠T (iii)∠U **3.a)**$\frac{ST}{AB} = \frac{SU}{AC} = \frac{TU}{BC}$;
∠S = ∠A, ∠T = ∠B, ∠U = ∠C **b)**$\frac{PQ}{VX} = \frac{PR}{VW} = \frac{QR}{XW}$;
∠P = ∠V, ∠Q = ∠X, ∠R = ∠W **4.a)**AC = 96 **b)**PM = 100
**5.a)**AB = 7.5 **b)**BC = 12.5 **6.a)**△PST ~ △PQR **b)**TR = $\frac{4}{7}$
**7.a)**△RQS ~ △RPT **b)**p = 60 **8.a)**△PRV ~ △PQS **b)**S = 15
**9.a)**△RTS ~ △RYA **10.a)**5 **b)**m = 3.3, n = 4.5
**c)**c = 35.0, d = 5.0 **d)**p = 40.0, q = 50.0 **e)**10.0
**f)**x = 4.7, y = 6.0 **11.** 9.8 **12.a)**25.6 cm **b)**35.8 m

## 12.2 Exercise, page 444
**1.a)**△HGK ~ △HDE **b)**$\frac{h}{2.5} = \frac{45.0}{5.0}$ **c)**22.5 m
**2.a)**△MNW ~ △MKE **b)**$\frac{40.0 + d}{40.0} = \frac{36.0}{8.0}$
**c)**140.0 m **3.a)**△CDE ~ △CBA **b)**$\frac{w}{13.8} = \frac{28.6}{4.6}$
**c)**85.8 m **4.b)**42.0 cm **5.** 645.0 m **6.** 435.2 m **7.** 2.8 m
**8.** 236.3 m **9.a)**36.4 m **b)**58.9 m **c)**14.4 m
**10.a)**△CDE ~ △CAB **b)**16.7 m **11.** 130 m **12.a)**107.8 m

## 12.3 Exercise, page 446
**1.a)**△PRT ~ △QRS **d)**△QRS: 0.58, 0.50, 0.87;
△PRT: 0.58, 0.50, 0.87 **2.a)**0.58 **b)**0.50 **c)**0.87
**3.b)**△DEF: 0.58, 0.50, 0.87; △PQR: 0.58, 0.50,
0.87 **4.a)**0.58 **b)**0.50 **c)**0.87 **5.** For △PQR, △ABC,
△DKL: t = 1.00, s = 0.71, c = 0.71
**6.** For △OPA, △OQB,
△ORC: t = 1.00, s = 0.71, c = 0.71

## 12.4 Exercise, page 449
**1.a)**0.84 = $\frac{h}{23.8}$ **b)**20.0 m **2.** 7.9 m **3.a)**13.0 m **b)**48.1 m
**c)**221.4 m **4.** 14.9 m **5.** 1305.5 m **6.** 267.5 m **7.** 10.9 m **8.** 0.5 m
**9.** 3.1 m **10.a)**97 **b)**14 goats, 16 chickens **11.** 278.4 m

## 12.5 Exercise, page 452
**1.a)**$\frac{2}{3}$ **b)**$\frac{2}{3}$ **c)**$\frac{2}{3}$ **2.a)**2√13, 4√13, 5√13 **b)**$\frac{3\sqrt{13}}{13}, \frac{3\sqrt{13}}{13}, \frac{3\sqrt{13}}{13}$
**3.a)**sin M = $\frac{15}{17}$, cos M = $\frac{8}{17}$, tan M = $\frac{15}{8}$ **b)**sin M = $\frac{\sqrt{2}}{2}$,

cos M = $\frac{\sqrt{2}}{2}$, tan M = 1 **c)**sin M = $\frac{3}{13}$, cos M = $\frac{4\sqrt{10}}{13}$,
tan M = $\frac{3\sqrt{10}}{40}$ **d)**sin M = $\frac{12}{13}$, cos M = $\frac{5}{13}$, tan M = $\frac{12}{5}$
**4.a)**$\frac{4}{3}$ **b)**$\frac{2\sqrt{5}}{5}$ **c)**√3 **5.b)**cos Q = $\frac{8\sqrt{73}}{73}$, sin R = $\frac{8\sqrt{73}}{73}$ **6.a)**$\frac{5}{13}$
**b)**$\frac{\sqrt{3}}{2}$ **c)**$\frac{4}{3}$ **d)**$\frac{\sqrt{51}}{10}$ **7.a)**0.64 **b)**0.77 **c)**1.20 **8.a)**0.42 **b)**2.14
**c)**0.47 **9.b)**116.48 **c)**116.5 m **10.b)**11.8 **c)**11.8 m **11.a)**32.4 m
**b)**12.5 m **c)**26.2 **13.a)**$\frac{\sqrt{2}}{2}$ **b)**$\frac{\sqrt{2}}{2}$ **c)**1 **14.b)**√3 units **15.a)**$\frac{\sqrt{3}}{2}$ **b)**$\frac{1}{2}$
**c)**√3 **d)**$\frac{1}{2}$ **e)**$\frac{\sqrt{3}}{2}$ **f)**$\frac{\sqrt{3}}{3}$ **16.a)**√2 **b)**$\frac{1}{4}$ **c)**$\frac{\sqrt{6}}{6}$ **d)**$\frac{1}{2}$ **e)**$-\frac{1}{4}$ **f)**1

## 12.6 Exercise, page 456
**1.a)**0.7431 **b)**0.5878 **c)**0.9135 **d)**4.0108 **e)**0.8480 **f)**0.7265
**g)**0.2079 **h)**0.6691 **i)**0.3249 **j)**1.6003 **2.a)**cos 36° **b)**sin 72°
**c)**tan 86° **3.b)**0.2588, 0.3420, 0.6018, 0.6691, 0.9455,
0.9976 **4.b)**0.9877, 0.9781, 0.8910, 0.7771, 0.7071,
0.4540, 0.3090 **5.a)**0.2924, 0.4540, 0.5878, 0.7071,
0.7986, 0.9336 **6.a)**0.9659, 0.9397, 0.8192, 0.7071,
0.5000, 0.3090 **7.a)**0.1405, 0.4245, 0.7002, 1.1504, 1.8040,
4.0108 **8.a)**46° **b)**59° **c)**36° **d)**36° **e)**53° **f)**71° **9.a)**∠P = 36°,
∠Q = 54° **b)**∠P = 34°, ∠Q = 56° **c)**∠P = 49°,
∠Q = 41° **10.a)**7.4 m **b)**31.7 m **c)**16.7 m **d)**13.8 m **e)**4.0 m
**f)**20.1 m **11.** 1.4 km **12.** 42.4 m **13.** 9.3 m **14.** 4155.8 m²

## 12.7 Exercise, page 460
**1.a)**0.9659 **b)**1.0355 **c)**0.4695 **d)**0.7265 **e)**0.2079
**f)**7.1154 **2.a)**0.2588 **b)**0.5000 **c)**0.7071 **d)**0.8660
**e)**0.9659 **f)**1.0000 **3.a)**0.9659 **b)**0.8660 **c)**0.7071
**d)**0.4226 **e)**0.2588 **f)**0.0000 **4.a)**66° **b)**29° **c)**84°
**5.a)**67° **b)**14° **c)**21° **6.a)**9.2 **b)**13.9 **c)**53° **7.a)**109.1
**b)**21.2 **c)**17.0 **8.a)**16° **b)**52° **c)**46° **d)**73° **e)**68° **f)**27°
**9.a)**9.1 m **b)**15.1 m **c)**240.0 m **d)**201.5 m **10.a)**39°
**b)**81° **11.** 31.6 m **12.** 15.9 m **13.** 34° **14.** 13° **15.** I, K **16.** 13.4 cm

## 12.8 Exercise, page 463
**1.a)**24.6 **b)**101.7 m **2.** 93.1 m **3.** 69.1 m **4.** 232.3 m
**5.** 2.0 km **6.** 17.4 m **7.** 187 m **8.a)**9.7 m **b)**91.5 m
**9.a)**99.2 m **b)**468.8 m **10.a)**77.9 m **11.** 69.8 m
**12.** 218.7 m **13.** 11.7 cm **14.a)**353.4 km **b)**48.7 km

---

# CHAPTER 13

## 13.1 Exercise, page 470
**1.a)**V **b)**S **c)**V **d)**S **e)**S **f)**S **3.a)**[8, −4] **b)**4√5 units
**c)**[−8, 4] **4.a)**[5, 4], √41 units **b)**[4, −6],
2√13 units **c)**[−6, 4], 2√13 units **d)**[−4, −6],
2√13 units **5.a)**3√5 units **b)**√29 units
**c)**√34 units **d)**2√10 units **e)**√89 units
**6.** $\overrightarrow{BA}$ = $\overrightarrow{HG}$, $\overrightarrow{MN}$ = $\overrightarrow{CD}$ **7.a)**m = 8, n = 4
**b)**m = 16, n = −4 **8.b)**$|\overrightarrow{AB}|$ = $|\overrightarrow{CD}|$ = 10 units
**c)**$\frac{4}{3}, \frac{4}{3}$ **9.** $\overrightarrow{AB}$ = [9, 2], $\overrightarrow{CD}$ = [3, −7], $\overrightarrow{EF}$ = [2, 7],
$\overrightarrow{GH}$ = [−5, 4] **12.a)**√65 units, N30°E
**b)**2√26 units, S79°E **13.** [−3, 4] **14.a)**12.1 km
**b)**N60°E **15.** [−6, −2] **16.a)**030° **b)**249° **c)**144°

**d)**317° **17.a)**S85°W **b)**N36°E **c)**N78°W **d)**S49°E
**20.a)**315 km/h, 120° **b)**342 km/h, 320° **c)**270 km/h, 210°

## 13.2 Exercise, page 475
**1.a)**$[-7, 4]$ **b)**$\sqrt{65}$ units **c)**$[7, -4]$ **2.** $\overrightarrow{AB}$: $[-6, -2]$,
$2\sqrt{10}$ units; $\overrightarrow{CD}$: $[-6, 4]$, $2\sqrt{13}$ units; $\overrightarrow{EF}$: $[4, 3]$, 5 units;
$\overrightarrow{GH}$: $[-9, 1]$, $\sqrt{82}$ units; $\overrightarrow{IJ}$: $[7, -4]$, $\sqrt{65}$ units;
$\overrightarrow{KL} = [0, 5]$, 5 units; $\overrightarrow{MN}$: $[-5, 0]$, 5 units **3.a)**$[6, 4]$,
$2\sqrt{13}$ units **b)**$[-6, -4]$, $2\sqrt{13}$ units **c)**$[-8, 5]$, $\sqrt{89}$ units
**d)**$[-7, 1]$, $5\sqrt{2}$ units **4.a)**$(11, -1)$ **b)**$(4, 3)$ **c)**$(-1, -1)$
**d)**$(-2, -8)$ **5.a)**$(0, 0)$ **b)**$(0, 8)$ **c)**$(-6, -2)$ **d)**$(-8, -1)$
**6.a)**$(-3, -1)$ **b)**$(0, 2)$ **c)**$(-9, 4)$ **d)**$(3, 0)$ **7.a)**$(-2, 6)$
**b)**$(0, 7)$ **8.** $(11, 9)$ **9.** $(1, -2)$ **10.b)**$[-6, -3]$ **c)**S63°W
**11.a)**$\overrightarrow{AB} = [4, 0]$, $\overrightarrow{DC} = [4, 0]$, $\overrightarrow{DA} = [0, 4]$, $\overrightarrow{CB} = [0, 4]$
**b)**$|\overrightarrow{AC}| = |\overrightarrow{DB}| = 4\sqrt{2}$ units **12.a)**$\overrightarrow{ST} = [4, 1]$, $\overrightarrow{QR} = [8, 2]$
**b)**$|\overrightarrow{ST}| = \sqrt{17}$ units, $|\overrightarrow{QR}| = 2\sqrt{17}$ units **c)**$\frac{1}{4}, \frac{1}{4}$

## 13.3 Exercise, page 478
**1.a)**$\vec{a} = [11, 3]$, $\vec{b} = [-3, 7]$ **b)**$[8, 10]$ **c)**$\overrightarrow{AC}$ **2.a)**$\vec{p} = [9, 3]$,
$\vec{q} = [2, 5]$ **b)**$[11, 8]$ **c)**$\overrightarrow{PS}$ **3.a)**$[3, 7]$ **c)**$\sqrt{58}$ units **4.b)**$[3, 10]$,
$\sqrt{109}$ units **5.a)**$[10, 8]$ **b)**$[5, 3]$ **c)**$[6, 4]$ **d)**$[-2, 2]$
**e)**$[-4, 3]$ **f)**$[0, 0]$ **6.a)**$\overrightarrow{AC}$, $\overrightarrow{AC}$ **7.a)**6.4 cm **b)**2.5 cm
**c)**3.0 cm **8.c)**$\vec{a} + \vec{b} = \vec{b} + \vec{a}$ **9.b)**A: $[0, 0]$, B: $[0, 0]$,
C: $[0, 0]$, D: $[0, 0]$ **10.a)**$a = -3$, $b = -2$ **b)**$a = 3$, $b = -6$
**c)**$a = 0$, $b = 3$ **d)**$a = -4$, $b = -5$ **11.c)**$\overrightarrow{AD}$ **12.a)**$[9, 7]$
**b)**$[0, 2]$ **13.a)**$[5, 5]$ **b)**$(5, 2)$ **14.b)**48 km, N83°E
**15.b)**306 km, N48°W **18.a)**$[-3, -2]$ **b)**$[-4, 3]$ **c)**$[5, -2]$
**d)**$[6, 8]$ **e)**$[2, 0]$ **f)**$[0, -5]$ **19.b)**$\sqrt{65}$ units **20.b)**$[7, -1]$

## 13.4 Exercise, page 483
**1.a)**$[3, -2]$ **b)**$[6, -4]$ **2.a)**$[-8, 4]$ **b)**$[8, -4]$ **c)**$[-16, 8]$
**d)**$[12, -6]$ **e)**$[-24, 12]$ **f)**$[-168, 84]$ **3.e)**$|\vec{a}| = \sqrt{13}$ units,
$|-\vec{a}| = \sqrt{13}$ units, $|3\vec{a}| = 3\sqrt{13}$ units, $|-2\vec{a}| = 2\sqrt{13}$ units
**4.a)**$[6, -18]$ **b)**$[-24, -30]$ **c)**$[-6, 0]$ **d)**$[0, -12]$ **5.a)**$4\vec{v}$
**b)**$3\vec{v}$ **c)**$-3\vec{v}$ **d)**$-2\vec{v}$ **e)**$4\vec{v}$ **f)**$-3\vec{v}$ **g)**$-\vec{v}$ **h)**$3\vec{v}$ **6.a)**$[11, 8]$
**b)**$[4, -2]$ **c)**$[-2, -4]$ **d)**$[-2, -13]$ **e)**$[21, -8]$
**f)**$[-21, 8]$ **g)**$[-24, -7]$ **7.b)**$2\vec{a} + \vec{b} = [10, 14]$,
$\vec{a} + 2\vec{b} = [2, 19]$ **c)**$2\sqrt{74}$ units, $\sqrt{365}$ units **8.a)**$[6, -16]$
**b)**$[9, -24]$ **c)**$[-6, 16]$ **d)**$[4, -8]$ **e)**$[-4, 8]$ **f)**$[-1, 2]$
**g)**$[5, -12]$ **h)**$[5, -14]$ **i)**$[13, -32]$ **9.a)**$m = 1$, $n = 8$
**b)**$m = 2$, $n = 6$ **10.a)**$x = 5$ **b)**$x = 3$, $y = -2$
**11.a)**A$(-5, 0)$, B$(2, 5)$, C$(6, -1)$, D$(-1, -6)$ **b)**$[7, 5]$,
$[4, -6]$, $[7, 5]$, $[4, -6]$ **c)**$\overrightarrow{AB} \parallel \overrightarrow{DC}$, $\overrightarrow{BC} \parallel \overrightarrow{AD}$

## 13.5 Exercise, page 486
**1.a)**N22°W **b)**11 km/h **2.a)**470 km **b)**770 km
**3.b)**560 km **4.a)**530 km **b)**none **5.a)**100 km
**b)**N27°W **7.** N47°E **8.a)**220 N **b)**37°

## 13.6 Exercise, page 487
**1.a)**$\overrightarrow{DB}$ **b)**$\overrightarrow{DB}$ **2.a)**$\overrightarrow{PR}$ **b)**$\overrightarrow{RP}$ **3.a)**$\overrightarrow{AC}$ **b)**$\overrightarrow{AC}$ **c)**$\overrightarrow{AS}$ **d)**$\overrightarrow{AS}$ **e)**$\overrightarrow{AF}$
**f)**$2\overrightarrow{AG}$ **4.a)**$\overrightarrow{AC}$ **b)**$\overrightarrow{DC}$ **c)**$\overrightarrow{DA}$ **d)**$\overrightarrow{DA}$ **5.a)**$\vec{a}$ **b)**$\vec{a}$ **c)**$\vec{b}$ **d)**$\vec{a} + \vec{b}$
**e)**$\vec{a} - \vec{b}$ **f)**$\vec{a} - \vec{b}$ **6.a)**$\overrightarrow{UP} + \overrightarrow{PT}$ **b)**$\overrightarrow{RS} + \overrightarrow{SQ}$ **c)**$\overrightarrow{RS} + \overrightarrow{ST} + \overrightarrow{TP}$
**d)**$\overrightarrow{TP} + \overrightarrow{PQ} + \overrightarrow{QS}$ **7.a)**$\overrightarrow{SR}$ **b)**$\overrightarrow{QR}$ **c)**$\overrightarrow{DA}$ **d)**$\overrightarrow{BC}$ **e)**$\overrightarrow{SQ}$
**9.a)**T **b)**F **c)**T **d)**T **e)**F **f)**T **g)**T **h)**F **11.a)**$-\vec{b}$ **b)**$-\vec{a}$ **c)**$\vec{a} - \vec{b}$
**d)**$\vec{b} - \vec{a}$ **e)**$\vec{a} + \vec{b}$ **f)**$\vec{a} + \vec{b}$ **g)**$2\vec{b}$ **12.a)**$2\overrightarrow{AJ} - \overrightarrow{AB}$ **b)**$2\overrightarrow{AJ} + 2\overrightarrow{AB}$

**c)**$2\overrightarrow{AB} + 3\overrightarrow{AJ}$ **d)**$2\overrightarrow{AJ} - 2\overrightarrow{AB}$ **e)**$-2\overrightarrow{AB} - 2\overrightarrow{AJ}$ **f)**$-2\overrightarrow{AB} + 2\overrightarrow{AJ}$
**15.a)**120 **b)**24

## 13.8 Exercise, page 493
**1.a)**$2 \times 3$ **b)**$2 \times 2$ **c)**$3 \times 4$ **d)**$3 \times 3$ **e)**$2 \times 4$ **f)**(b), (d)
**2.a)**3 rows, 1 column **b)**2 rows, 3 columns **c)**1 row,
2 columns **d)**2 rows, 2 columns **e)**5 rows, 2 columns
**f)**2 rows, 4 columns **3.a)**$4 \times 5$ **b)**16, 19, 2, 20, 18 **c)**3,
12, 20, 14 **d)**8 **e)**5 **4.a)**points scored at home by Jets in
January **b)**Jets away points in January **c)**Saints away
points in January **d)**Canucks away points in January
**5.**$\begin{pmatrix} 16 & 14 & 13 \\ 13 & 15 & 16 \end{pmatrix}$ **6.a)**home points scored by Canucks, Jets and Saints respectively
**b)**$(13 \quad 15 \quad 16)$, away points by Canucks, Jets
and Saints respectively **c)**home points and away points
scored by Saints **d)**Canucks: $\begin{pmatrix} 16 \\ 13 \end{pmatrix}$, Jets: $\begin{pmatrix} 14 \\ 15 \end{pmatrix}$
**7.a)**$\begin{pmatrix} 42 & 108 & 92 \\ 28 & 76 & 83 \end{pmatrix}$, **b)**$\begin{pmatrix} 38 & 92 & 82 \\ 36 & 72 & 79 \end{pmatrix}$ **c)**$\begin{pmatrix} 80 & 200 & 174 \\ 64 & 148 & 162 \end{pmatrix}$
$2 \times 3$

**8.a)**$(36 \quad 42 \quad 18)$, $1 \times 3$ **b)**$\begin{pmatrix} 36 & 42 & 18 \\ 31 & 36 & 12 \end{pmatrix}$, $2 \times 3$ **c)**$\begin{pmatrix} 36 & 42 & 18 \\ 31 & 36 & 12 \\ 18 & 24 & 6 \\ 12 & 30 & 25 \end{pmatrix}$, $4 \times 3$

**9.a)**$\begin{pmatrix} 6 & 2 \\ 7 & 3 \\ 5 & 1 \\ 8 & 2 \\ 6 & 3 \end{pmatrix}$, $5 \times 2$ **b)**$\begin{pmatrix} 6 & 2 & 4 \\ 7 & 3 & 3 \\ 5 & 1 & 5 \\ 8 & 2 & 2 \\ 6 & 3 & 2 \end{pmatrix}$, $5 \times 3$ **e)**$\begin{pmatrix} 6 & 2 & 4 \\ 7 & 3 & 3 \\ 5 & 1 & 5 \\ 8 & 2 & 2 \\ 6 & 3 & 2 \\ 7 & 2 & 4 \\ 8 & 1 & 3 \\ 9 & 2 & 1 \\ 7 & 3 & 2 \end{pmatrix}$, $9 \times 3$

**c)**$\begin{pmatrix} 7 & 2 \\ 8 & 1 \\ 9 & 2 \\ 7 & 3 \end{pmatrix}$, $4 \times 2$ **d)**$\begin{pmatrix} 7 & 2 & 4 \\ 8 & 1 & 3 \\ 9 & 2 & 1 \\ 7 & 3 & 2 \end{pmatrix}$, $4 \times 3$

**10.a)**① sends to ②, ② sends to ①, ③ sends
to ① and ② **b)**① sends to ② and ③, ② doesn't send,
③ sends to ① and ② **c)**① sends to ② and ③, ② sends
to ③, ③ sends to ① and ② **d)**3 stations in each
**11.a)**① sends to ② and ④ **b)**② receives from ① and ④
**c)**③ sends to ① and ④ **d)**④ receives from ①, ② and
③ **13.a)**4 **b)**①
sends to ② and
④; ② sends to   **14.a)**$\begin{pmatrix} 0 & 1 & 1 & 1 \\ 0 & 0 & 0 & 0 \\ 1 & 1 & 0 & 0 \\ 0 & 0 & 1 & 0 \end{pmatrix}$ **b)**$\begin{pmatrix} 0 & 1 & 0 & 0 \\ 1 & 0 & 1 & 1 \\ 1 & 0 & 0 & 1 \\ 1 & 1 & 1 & 0 \end{pmatrix}$
①; ③ sends to
①, ② and ④; ④
sends to ① and ③

**c)**$\begin{pmatrix} 0 & 1 & 1 & 1 \\ 0 & 0 & 1 & 1 \\ 1 & 0 & 0 & 0 \\ 1 & 0 & 1 & 0 \end{pmatrix}$ **15.b)**$\begin{pmatrix} 0 & 1 & 1 \\ 1 & 0 & 1 \\ 0 & 0 & 0 \end{pmatrix}$ **c)**$\begin{pmatrix} 0 & 1 & 1 & 1 \\ 1 & 0 & 1 & 0 \\ 0 & 0 & 0 & 0 \\ 1 & 0 & 0 & 0 \end{pmatrix}$

## 13.9 Exercise, page 498
**1.a)**$\begin{pmatrix} 7 & 0 & 3 \\ 3 & -2 & 1 \end{pmatrix}$ **b)**$\begin{pmatrix} 3 & 4 & -3 \\ 1 & -6 & 6 \\ -4 & 0 & -2 \end{pmatrix}$ **2.a)**$\begin{pmatrix} 8 & -15 \\ 10 & 4 \end{pmatrix}$
**b)**$\begin{pmatrix} -10 & -21 & -4 \\ -8 & -3 & -1 \end{pmatrix}$ **c)**$\begin{pmatrix} -3 & 0 & 5 \\ 27 & 0 & 5 \\ 8 & 7 & -12 \end{pmatrix}$ **3.a)**$\begin{pmatrix} 9 & 7 & 9 \\ 1 & -7 & 12 \end{pmatrix}$

b) $\begin{pmatrix} 1 & -2 & -3 \\ -8 & -19 & 0 \end{pmatrix}$ c) $\begin{pmatrix} 10 & 13 & 8 \\ -7 & 5 & 5 \\ 5 & 15 & 0 \end{pmatrix}$ d) $\begin{pmatrix} -4 & -9 & 6 \\ 5 & 10 & -4 \end{pmatrix}$

e) $\begin{pmatrix} 11 & 7 & 18 \\ 8 & 4 & 16 \end{pmatrix}$ f) $\begin{pmatrix} 8 & -5 & 2 \\ -5 & -3 & 17 \\ -1 & 1 & -14 \end{pmatrix}$ g) $\begin{pmatrix} 12 & -8 & 24 \\ -4 & -32 & 16 \end{pmatrix}$

h) $\begin{pmatrix} 2 & 18 & 6 \\ -2 & 8 & -12 \\ 6 & 14 & 14 \end{pmatrix}$ i) $\begin{pmatrix} 9 & 20 & 0 \\ 5 & 10 & 12 \end{pmatrix}$ j) $\begin{pmatrix} -26 & -3 & -12 \\ 17 & 1 & -39 \\ -3 & -17 & 28 \end{pmatrix}$

k) $\begin{pmatrix} 7 & -6 & 9 \\ -10 & -35 & 8 \end{pmatrix}$ l) $\begin{pmatrix} -15 & 19 & -1 \\ 9 & 10 & -40 \\ 5 & 5 & 35 \end{pmatrix}$ 4.a) $\begin{pmatrix} 12 & 19 \\ 16 & 17 \\ 18 & 21 \end{pmatrix}$, $\begin{pmatrix} 9 & 17 \\ 12 & 14 \\ 21 & 16 \end{pmatrix}$

b) $\begin{pmatrix} 21 & 36 \\ 28 & 31 \\ 39 & 37 \end{pmatrix}$ 5.a) $\begin{pmatrix} 42 & 46 & 36 \\ 36 & 50 & 32 \\ 40 & 48 & 34 \end{pmatrix}$, $\begin{pmatrix} 60 & 69 & 50 \\ 50 & 75 & 45 \\ 56 & 72 & 46 \end{pmatrix}$

b) $\begin{pmatrix} 18 & 23 & 14 \\ 14 & 25 & 13 \\ 16 & 24 & 12 \end{pmatrix}$ c) $\begin{pmatrix} 63 & 69 & 54 \\ 54 & 75 & 48 \\ 60 & 72 & 51 \end{pmatrix}$ d) $\begin{pmatrix} -3 & 0 & -4 \\ -4 & 0 & -3 \\ -4 & 0 & -5 \end{pmatrix}$

6.a)(12 90 100 8), (96 24 38 12), (46 48 36 16) b)(154 162 174 36)

7.a) $\begin{pmatrix} -1 & -5 \\ 4 & 2 \end{pmatrix}$ b) $\begin{pmatrix} 1 & 3 \\ -\dfrac{3}{2} & -\dfrac{1}{2} \end{pmatrix}$ c) $\begin{pmatrix} 1 & -3 \\ 0 & 7 \end{pmatrix}$

## 13.10 Exercise, page 501

1.a) $\begin{pmatrix} 3 \\ -4 \end{pmatrix}$ 2.a)(0) b) $\begin{pmatrix} 69 \\ -2 \end{pmatrix}$ c) $\begin{pmatrix} 21 & 18 \\ -18 & 0 \end{pmatrix}$ d) $\begin{pmatrix} 30 & 32 \\ 15 & -8 \end{pmatrix}$

3.a) $\begin{pmatrix} 57 & 105 \\ 66 & 50 \end{pmatrix}$ b) $\begin{pmatrix} -19 & 77 & -25 \\ -20 & 30 & -15 \\ 24 & -12 & 6 \end{pmatrix}$ 4.a) $\begin{pmatrix} 15 & 6 \\ 1 & 10 \end{pmatrix}$

b) $\begin{pmatrix} 4 & 0 \\ 0 & 9 \end{pmatrix}$ c) $\begin{pmatrix} -9 & 30 & 0 \\ -15 & -14 & 0 \\ 21 & -26 & 36 \end{pmatrix}$ 5.a) $\begin{pmatrix} 3 & -6 \\ -2 & 1 \end{pmatrix}$, $\begin{pmatrix} -2 & 3 \\ -4 & 5 \end{pmatrix}$

6.b)46 7.b)20 8.b) $\begin{pmatrix} 46 \\ 20 \end{pmatrix}$ 9.a) $\begin{pmatrix} 21 & 1 & 4 \\ 6 & 12 & 8 \\ 10 & 10 & 4 \end{pmatrix}\begin{pmatrix} 2 \\ 0 \\ 1 \end{pmatrix}$ b) $\begin{pmatrix} 46 \\ 20 \\ 24 \end{pmatrix}$

10. $\begin{pmatrix} 5 & 3 & 2 \\ 3 & 2 & 5 \\ 6 & 2 & 1 \end{pmatrix}$ 11. $\begin{pmatrix} 58 \\ 31 \\ 37 \end{pmatrix}$ 12. $\begin{pmatrix} 40 & 30 & 25 \\ 35 & 20 & 15 \end{pmatrix}$, $\begin{pmatrix} 90.35 & 102.80 \\ 193.25 & 201.90 \\ 292.60 & 302.65 \end{pmatrix}$

14.a)(35 20 15) $\begin{pmatrix} 90.35 \\ 193.25 \\ 292.60 \end{pmatrix}$ 15.a) $\begin{pmatrix} 40 & 30 & 25 \\ 35 & 20 & 15 \end{pmatrix}\begin{pmatrix} 90.35 \\ 193.25 \\ 292.60 \end{pmatrix}$

b)\$11 416.25   b)\$28 142.75

16.a) $\begin{pmatrix} 40 & 30 & 25 \\ 35 & 20 & 15 \end{pmatrix}\begin{pmatrix} 90.35 & 102.80 \\ 193.25 & 201.90 \\ 292.60 & 302.65 \end{pmatrix}$ 18.a) $\begin{pmatrix} -1 & 0 \\ 0 & -1 \end{pmatrix}$,

b)\$58 053.75

$\begin{pmatrix} 0 & 1 \\ -1 & 0 \end{pmatrix}$, $\begin{pmatrix} 1 & 0 \\ 0 & 1 \end{pmatrix}$ b) $\begin{pmatrix} 0 & -1 \\ 1 & 0 \end{pmatrix}$ c)n = 1, 5, 9, ..., $K^n = \begin{pmatrix} 0 & -1 \\ 1 & 0 \end{pmatrix}$;

n = 2, 6, 10, ..., $K^n = \begin{pmatrix} -1 & 0 \\ 0 & -1 \end{pmatrix}$; n = 3, 7, 11, ...,

$K^n = \begin{pmatrix} 0 & 1 \\ -1 & 0 \end{pmatrix}$; n = 4, 8, 12, ..., $K^n = \begin{pmatrix} 1 & 0 \\ 0 & 1 \end{pmatrix}$

## 13.11 Exercise, page 505

1.a)16 b)−31 c)15 d)−13 e)−2 f)0 g)−16 h)−7 2. (c)

3.a) $\begin{pmatrix} -1 & 1 \\ 2 & -1 \end{pmatrix}$ b) $\begin{pmatrix} 1 & -1 \\ -1 & 2 \end{pmatrix}$ c) $\begin{pmatrix} -1 & 2 \\ 1 & -1 \end{pmatrix}$ d) $\begin{pmatrix} 2 & -1 \\ -1 & 1 \end{pmatrix}$

4.a) $\begin{pmatrix} \dfrac{1}{6} & 0 \\ 0 & \dfrac{1}{3} \end{pmatrix}$ b) $\begin{pmatrix} 1 & 0 \\ 0 & 1 \end{pmatrix}, \begin{pmatrix} 1 & 0 \\ 0 & 1 \end{pmatrix}$ 5.a) $\begin{pmatrix} \dfrac{1}{3} & 0 \\ \dfrac{1}{6} & \dfrac{1}{4} \end{pmatrix}$ b) $\begin{pmatrix} 1 & 0 \\ 0 & 1 \end{pmatrix}$ c) $\begin{pmatrix} 1 & 0 \\ 0 & 1 \end{pmatrix}$

7.a) $\begin{pmatrix} \dfrac{2}{11} & -\dfrac{1}{11} \\ \dfrac{5}{33} & \dfrac{8}{33} \end{pmatrix}$ b) $\begin{pmatrix} 1 & 0 \\ 0 & 1 \end{pmatrix}, \begin{pmatrix} 1 & 0 \\ 0 & 1 \end{pmatrix}$ 8.a) $\begin{pmatrix} \dfrac{1}{6} & \dfrac{1}{3} \\ -\dfrac{1}{6} & \dfrac{2}{3} \end{pmatrix}$ b) $\begin{pmatrix} \dfrac{2}{5} & \dfrac{1}{5} \\ \dfrac{1}{5} & -\dfrac{2}{5} \end{pmatrix}$

c) $\begin{pmatrix} \dfrac{1}{11} & \dfrac{4}{11} \\ -\dfrac{2}{11} & \dfrac{3}{11} \end{pmatrix}$ d) $\begin{pmatrix} \dfrac{1}{6} & \dfrac{1}{3} \\ \dfrac{1}{18} & -\dfrac{2}{9} \end{pmatrix}$ e) $\begin{pmatrix} \dfrac{1}{34} & \dfrac{5}{34} \\ \dfrac{3}{17} & -\dfrac{2}{17} \end{pmatrix}$ f) $\begin{pmatrix} 0 & \dfrac{1}{2} \\ -\dfrac{1}{8} & \dfrac{3}{8} \end{pmatrix}$

g)no inverse 9.c)$cx_1 + dx_3 = 0, cx_2 + dx_4 = 1$

h) $\begin{pmatrix} -\dfrac{1}{3} & -\dfrac{1}{6} \\ \dfrac{4}{3} & -\dfrac{7}{6} \end{pmatrix}$

d)$x_1 = \dfrac{d}{ad - bc}$, $x_2 = \dfrac{-b}{ad - bc}$, $x_3 = \dfrac{-c}{ad - bc}$, $x_4 = \dfrac{a}{ad - bc}$ e) $\begin{pmatrix} \dfrac{d}{ad - bc} & \dfrac{-b}{ad - bc} \\ \dfrac{-c}{ad - bc} & \dfrac{a}{ad - bc} \end{pmatrix}$

10.a)(19 22) b)(15 11) c)(14 22); HELP ME
11.a)56 94 31 50 43 68 b)50 78 40 71 58 100 c)23 39 57 88 59 96 74 124 52 91 72 121 d)54 94 33 59 44 70 43 68
12. I NEVER KNEW THAT MATH WAS SO MUCH FUN

## 13.12 Exercise, page 509

1.a) $\begin{pmatrix} 1 & -1 \\ 3 & 4 \end{pmatrix}\begin{pmatrix} x \\ y \end{pmatrix} = \begin{pmatrix} 6 \\ 7 \end{pmatrix}$ b) $\begin{pmatrix} 2 & 1 \\ -3 & -1 \end{pmatrix}\begin{pmatrix} x \\ y \end{pmatrix} = \begin{pmatrix} -1 \\ 6 \end{pmatrix}$

c) $\begin{pmatrix} 7 & -4 \\ 2 & 1 \end{pmatrix}\begin{pmatrix} x \\ y \end{pmatrix} = \begin{pmatrix} -1 \\ 5 \end{pmatrix}$ d) $\begin{pmatrix} 1 & -4 \\ 2 & 1 \end{pmatrix}\begin{pmatrix} x \\ y \end{pmatrix} = \begin{pmatrix} -3 \\ 7 \end{pmatrix}$

2.a) $\begin{pmatrix} x \\ y \end{pmatrix} = \begin{pmatrix} \dfrac{51}{23} \\ -\dfrac{58}{23} \end{pmatrix}$ b) $\begin{pmatrix} x \\ y \end{pmatrix} = \begin{pmatrix} \dfrac{7}{4} \\ \dfrac{1}{5} \end{pmatrix}$ c) $\begin{pmatrix} x \\ y \end{pmatrix} = \begin{pmatrix} \dfrac{51}{24} \\ -\dfrac{15}{8} \end{pmatrix}$

3.a)x = 1, y = 0 b)x = 2, y = −1 c)x = −3, y = 0
d)x = 3, y = 0 e)x = 1, y = 4 f)$x = \dfrac{18}{11}, y = \dfrac{19}{11}$
g)$x = \dfrac{44}{17}, y = -\dfrac{19}{17}$ h)x = 2, y = −1

## CHAPTER 14

### 14.1 Exercise, page 513

1.a)(6, 4) b)(1, −1) c)(2, 2) d)(5, −5) 2.a)(1, 9)
b)(11, 8) c)(7, 1) d)(1, 3) 3.a)$(x, y) \to (x - 6, y - 5)$
b)$(x, y) \to (x + 11, y - 5)$ 4.a)A′(1, 5), B′(1, 2), C′(4, 2) b)undefined, undefined; same c)−1, −1; same d)0, 0; same 5.a)L′(2, −6), M′(6, −4),

N'(0, −2) **b)**$2\sqrt{5}$ units, $2\sqrt{5}$ units; same
**c)**$2\sqrt{10}$ units, $2\sqrt{10}$ units; same **d)**$2\sqrt{5}$ units,
$2\sqrt{5}$ units; same **6.a)**$\triangle ABC \cong \triangle A'B'C'$,
$\triangle LMN \cong \triangle L'M'N'$ **b)**$\triangle ABC = \triangle A'B'C' = 4.5$
square units, $\triangle LMN = \triangle L'M'N' = 10$ square
units **c)**same orientation **7.** all invariant

**14.2 Exercise, page 516**
**1.a)**A'(3, 6) **b)**B'(2, 2) **c)**C'(4, −5) **d)**D'(5, 2),
E'(6, 2), F'(2, 2) **2.a)**A'(−3, −2) **b)**B'(6, 4) **c)**C'(7, −6)
**d)**D'(−1, 3), E'(−4, −3), F'(−3, −5) **3.a)**(2, −3)
**b)**(−2, −3) **c)**(−2, 4) **d)**$(x, y) \to (x, -y)$
**4.a)**(−3, 4) **b)**(3, 4) **c)**(5, −2) **d)**$(x, y) \to (-x, y)$
**5.a)**P'(−3, 4) **b)**Q'(2, 5) **c)**R'(0, −1) **d)**G'(4, 3),
H'(5, −1), I'(−2, −4) **6.a)**X'(−3, −5) **b)**Y'(−7, 2)
**c)**Z'(4, −6) **d)**R'(−5, 0), S'(5, 3), T'(−4, 2)
**7.a)**(2, 3) **b)**(4, −6) **c)**(−8, 3) **d)**(−6, 2)

**8.b)**$-4, 4;\ -\dfrac{1}{4}, \dfrac{1}{4};\ 1, -1$ **c)**additive inverses

**9.b)**NP = N'P' = 8 units; PQ = P'Q' = $4\sqrt{5}$ units;
NQ = N'Q' = 4 units **c)**same **10.a)**$\triangle ABC \cong \triangle A'B'C'$,
$\triangle NPQ \cong \triangle N'P'Q'$
**b)**$\triangle ABC = \triangle A'B'C' = 7.5$ square units,
$\triangle NPQ = \triangle N'P'Q' = 16$ square units
**c)**orientation reversed **11.a)**invariant: lengths,
angles, areas; not invariant: slopes, orientation

**14.3 Exercise, page 519**
**1.a)**F'(3, 8), G'(−6, 3), H'(−6, 8) **b)**$(x, y) \to (y, -x)$
**2.a)**U'(0, −3), V'(−4, −7), W'(−6, 0) **b)**$(x, y) \to (y, -x)$
**c)**$-90°$ **3.a)**R'(−6, −7), S'(−2, −3), T'(2, −7)
**b)**$(x, y) \to (-x, -y)$ **4.a)**A'(−5, 2) **b)**B'(3, 4) **c)**C'(4, −1)
**d)**D'(−5, −2), E'(0, −6), F'(5, −3) **e)**$+90°$ **5.a)**G'(−5, 0)
**b)**H'(3, −7) **c)**I'(5, 3) **d)**J'(−3, −3), K'(−3, −8),
L'(2, −3) **e)**$+180°$ **6.a)**M'(7, −4) **b)**N'(−3, 6)
**c)**P'(−7, −2) **d)**Q'(3, 2), R'(3, 8), S'(−5, 2) **e)**$+270°$
**7.a)**(−4, −7) **b)**(−3, −5) **c)**(−3, −6) **d)**(−5, 4)
**8.b)**PQ = P'Q' = 5 units; QR = Q'R' = 7 units;
PR = P'R' = $\sqrt{74}$ units **c)**same **9.a)**X'(−3, 2), Y'(−8, 2),
Z'(−5, 6) **c)**undefined, 0; $-\dfrac{3}{4}, \dfrac{4}{3};\ \dfrac{1}{2}, -2$ **d)**negative
reciprocals **10.a)**image points: X'(3, −2), Y'(8, −2),
Z'(5, −6); slopes: undefined, 0; $-\dfrac{3}{4}, \dfrac{4}{3};\ \dfrac{1}{2}, -2$; negative
reciprocal slope **b)**image points: X'(−2, −3), Y'(−2, −8),
Z'(−6, −5); slopes: undefined, undefined; $-\dfrac{3}{4}, -\dfrac{3}{4};\ \dfrac{1}{2}, \dfrac{1}{2}$;
same slope **c)**same as $+180°$ **d)**same as $-90°$
**11.a)**$\triangle PQR \cong \triangle P'Q'R'$, $\triangle XYZ \cong \triangle X'Y'Z'$
**b)**$\triangle PQR = \triangle P'Q'R' = 17.5$ square units,
$\triangle XYZ = \triangle X'Y'Z' = 10$ square units
**c)**same orientation **12.** invariant: (a), (c), (d), (e)

**14.4 Exercise, page 522**
**1.a)**P'(2, 5), Q'(4, 1), R'(2, 1) **b)**$(x, y) \to \left(\dfrac{1}{2}x, \dfrac{1}{2}y\right)$

**2.a)**X'(−6, −6), Y'(−12, −4), Z'(−8, 8)
**c)**$(x, y) \to (-2x, -2y)$ **3.a)**P'(4, 4) **b)**Q'(−8, 8)
**c)**R'(12, −4) **d)**S'(−8, 12), T'(8, 16), U'(4, 20)

**4.a)**A'(−6, −3) **b)**B'(9, −3) **c)**C'(3, 9) **d)**D'(0, −6),
E'(−9, −6), F'(−3, 6) **5.b)**$-\dfrac{1}{4}, -\dfrac{1}{4};\ -1, -1;\ 2, 2$ **c)**same

**6.a)**slopes: $-\dfrac{1}{4}, -\dfrac{1}{4};\ -1, -1;\ 2, 2$ **b)**slopes: $-\dfrac{1}{4}, -\dfrac{1}{4};\ -1, -1;$
$2, 2$ **c)**slopes: $-\dfrac{1}{4}, -\dfrac{1}{4};\ -1, -1;\ 2, 2$ **7.a)**$\triangle FGH \cong \triangle F'G'H'$
**b)**$\triangle FGH = 4.5$ square units, $\triangle F'G'H' = 18$,
40.5, 1.125, 10.125 square units; $A = k^2 \times$ Area of
triangle, where k is the dilatation factor
**c)**same orientation **8.** invariant: (a), (c), (d)

**14.5 Exercise, page 524**
**1.a)**yes **b)**direct **c)**$(x, y) \to (x - 6, y + 4)$ **2.a)**yes
**b)**opposite **c)**$(x, y) \to (-x, y)$ **3.a)**yes **b)**direct
**c)**$(x, y) \to (-y, x)$ **4.a)**no **b)**neither
**c)**$(x, y) \to (3x, 3y)$ **5.** $1 \to 12$: y-axis reflection,
opposite; $2 \to 10$: y-axis reflection, opposite;
$3 \to 7$: $+180°$ rotation, direct; $4 \to 12$:
translation, direct; $5 \to 11$: y = x reflection,
opposite; $6 \to 5$: translation, direct; $8 \to 9$: x-axis reflection,
opposite **6.** translation: F, T, T, T, T, T, T, T; reflection: T, F,
T, T, F, T, F, T; rotation: F, T, T, T, T, T, F, T; dilatation:
F, F, F, F, T, T, T, F **7.a)**reflection **b)**translation **c)**rotation

**14.6 Exercise, page 528**
**1.a)**orientation reversed **b)**no **2.b)**$(x, y) \to (x + 3, y - 5)$
**c)**yes, direct **3.c)**glide-reflection **d)**yes, opposite
**4.c)**x-axis reflection **5.c)**$(x, y) \to (x - 6, y)$ **6.c)**$(x, y) \to (x, y - 2)$
**7.b)**a translation **9.b)**$+180°$ rotation **10.b)**$+180°$ rotation
**11.c)**$+90°$ rotation **12.b)**angle of rotation $= 2 \times$ (smaller
angle between two mirror lines) **13.b)**none **14.b)**a reflection

**14.9 Exercise, page 537**
**1.a)**$2x + y = -3$ **b)**$x + 3y = -2$ **2.a)**$x + 3y = 8$
**b)**$2x - 3y = 5$ **3.** $x + y = 1$ **4.** $2x + 3y = -6$
**5.a)**$3x - 2y = -6$ **b)**$2x + y = 4$
**6.** $3x - 5y = -10$ **7.** $Ax + By = Aa + Bb + C$

**14.10 Exercise, page 539**

**1.a)**$\begin{pmatrix} 4 \\ -5 \end{pmatrix}$ **b)**A'$\begin{pmatrix} 4 \\ -5 \end{pmatrix}$ **2.a)**$\begin{pmatrix} 4 \\ 0 \end{pmatrix}$ **b)**$\begin{pmatrix} 4 \\ 0 \end{pmatrix}$ **c)**$\begin{pmatrix} 4 \\ 0 \end{pmatrix}$
**c)**same **d)**reflection **d)**same **e)**rotation of $-90°$
in x-axis or $+270°$

**3.a)**$\begin{pmatrix} 0 \\ 8 \end{pmatrix}, \begin{pmatrix} 2 \\ 10 \end{pmatrix}, \begin{pmatrix} 0 \\ 12 \end{pmatrix}, \begin{pmatrix} -2 \\ 10 \end{pmatrix}$ **b)**$+90°$ rotation **c)**$-270°$ rotation

**4.a)**$\begin{pmatrix} 7 \\ 0 \end{pmatrix}, \begin{pmatrix} 9 \\ -4 \end{pmatrix}, \begin{pmatrix} 6 \\ -4 \end{pmatrix}$ **b)**$+180°$ rotation
**c)**$-180°$ rotation

**5.a)**$\begin{pmatrix} 0 \\ 0 \end{pmatrix}, \begin{pmatrix} 6 \\ 0 \end{pmatrix}, \begin{pmatrix} 6 \\ 6 \end{pmatrix}, \begin{pmatrix} 0 \\ 6 \end{pmatrix}$ **b)**dilatation
factor 2 **6.a)**$\begin{pmatrix} 2 \\ 3 \end{pmatrix}, \begin{pmatrix} 1 \\ 3 \end{pmatrix}, \begin{pmatrix} 2 \\ 5 \end{pmatrix}$
**b)**reflection in $y = x$ **7.a)**B **b)**E **c)**H **d)**F **e)**C **f)**D
**g)**G **h)**A **i)**A **8.a)**A'(3, −1), B'(5, −3), C'(7, 2),
D'(3, 5) **b)**P'(7, −3), Q'(4, −2), R'(5, 1), S'(8, 0)
**c)**M'(−5, 8), N'(−11, 8), Q'(−9, 4) **d)**E'(4, −5),
F'(3, 0), G'(8, 0), H'(9, −5) **e)**W'(1, 2), X'(3, 3),
Y'(4, 1), Z'(2, −1) **f)**J'(2, −7), K'(−5, 3), L'(6, 5)

# Index

abscissa, 126
additive identity, 55
additive inverse, 55, 481
adjacent, 445, 451
altitude, 299
angle, 297
    alternate, 336
    arms, 296
    bisector, 297
    complementary, 298
    corresponding, 336
    interior, 336
    supplementary, 294, 298
    vertex, 296
    vertically opposite, 292
array, 492
arrow diagram, 132, 167
ASTT, 343
associative property, 55
average, 46
axiom, 295

bar graph, 394
base, 10, 26
bearing, 473
biconditional statement, 333
box and whisker diagram, 411,
    412

Cartesian plane, 128
census, 386
classes, 393
class limits, 394, 395
clockwise, 514
closed half plane, 144
closure property, 54
clustered data, 407
commutative property, 55
collinear points, 161, 296
common factor, 76
conclusion, 301, 332
conditional statement, 332
congruence transformation, 524
congruent, 297, 306, 307, 438
congruent postulates
    angle-side-angle, (ASA), 318
    side-angle-side, (SAS), 314
    hypotenuse-side, (HS), 324
    side-side-side, (SSS), 310
conjecture, 343
consistent system, 212
contained, angle, side, 318

continuous data, 394
constant of variation, 266, 274
constraints, 258, 262
converse, 332
coplanar points, 296
cosine, 451

decomposition, 84
deductive thinking, 291, 301
defining equation, 190
definition, 295
dense, 24
dependent system of equations,
    120
depression, angle of, 462
Descartes, 126
descending order, 67
descriptive statistics, 393
determinant, 504
deviation, mean, 407, 408
diagonal, 299
difference of squares, 87
direct congruence, 524
directed line segment, 468
direct variation, 266, 270, 274
discrete data, 394
displacement, 474
distance, 147, 150
distributive property, 35, 55, 63,
    67, 72
domain, 11, 133

elevation, angle of 462
entire radical, 35
equation of line, 181, 182
    slope point form, 202
    slope $y$-intercept form, 181,
    191
    standard form, 191
equivalent equations, 210
event, 421
    certain, 422
    impossible, 422
    independent, 432
experimental probability, 422
exponents, 10
    laws of, 26
    negative, 30
    rational, 31, 34
    zero, 30
extrapolation, 267

family of lines, 197
FOIL, 72

frequency, 393, 394
    distribution, 393
function, 166
    linear, 393

glide-reflection, 528
graph, 126, 137

heading, 473
histogram, 395
horizontal component, 474
horizontal co-ordinate, 126
hypotenuse, 43, 445, 451

image, 512, 536
inconsistent, 212
indirect proof, 347
inductive thinking, 291
inequations, 10, 121, 144
    systems of, 254, 258
inferential statistics, 418
initial point, 474
intercepts, $x$, $y$, 171, 172
interpolation, 267
invariant, 513
isometry, 524

like factors, 26
like radicals, 35
like rationals, 35
like terms, 66
linear function, 171
linear programming, 262,
line of best fit, 414
line of reflection, 515
line of sight, 462
line segment, 296
literal coefficient, 58, 233

magnitude, 468, 469
mapping notation, 167
mapping rule, 512, 515, 518,
    522, 536
matrix, 492
    coefficient, 508
    column, 492, 538
    decoder, 507
    dimensions, 492
    encoder, 507
    identity, 504
    inverse, 504
    order, 492
    row, 492
    square, 492

mean, 399
    deviation, 408
    weighted, 403
measures of central tendency, 400
median, 299, 399
median averaging method, 415
midpoint, 153, 296
mirror line, 515
mixed radical, 35
mode, 400
multiplicative identity, 55
multiplicative inverse, 14, 55

negative reciprocal, 186
negative rotation, 518
net, 362, 363
network, 495
Newton's Method, 18, 19
numbers
    consecutive, 13
    even, $(E)$, 54
    integers, $(I)$, 10, 14, 22, 23
    irrational, $(\bar{Q})$, 22
    non-terminating, 22
    natural, $(N)$, 10
    odd, $(O)$, 54
    rational, $(Q)$, 14, 17, 22
    real, $(R)$, 22
    triangular, 18
    square, 18
    whole, $(W)$, 10

open half plane, 144
opposite congruence, 524
ordered pair, 126, 132, 167
order of operations, 11
ordinate, 126
orientation, 514, 524
outcome, 393, 421
    equally likely, 421
    favourable, 421
    possible, 421
    probable, 421

parallel lines, 336, 338, 339, 347
parallelogram, 352
parameter, 181, 258
partial graph, 137
partial variation, 283, 285
patterned thinking, 51, 290
period, 17
period length, 17
perpendicular bisector, 297
pi $(\pi)$, 22
PLT theorem, 339
polygons, 298

polynomial, 58
population, 386
positive rotation, 518
power, 10, 26
pre-image, 512
primary ratios of trigonometry, 451
prime factor, 18
principle cube root, 34
principal square root, 18, 34
principle $n$th root, 34
problem-solving plan, PSP,
    46–48, 51, 53, 236, 239, 242,
    245, 248, 250, 442, 459
projection, 381
Pythagorean Property, 43, 354, 357

quadrant, 128
quadratic equation, 93
quadrilateral, 352

radical, 18, 35
radicand, 18
range, 133, 393, 407
rationalizing the denominator, 40
rational numbers, $(Q)$, 14, 22, 25
    like, 35
    unlike, 35
ray, 296
reciprocal, 14
    negative, 186
rectangle, 352
relation, 132, 133
    linear, 137
    non-linear, 137
repeating decimal, 17
rhombus, 352
rise, 156
run, 156

sample, random, 386, 390
    clustered, 390
    destructive, 391
    space, 427
    stratified, 390
scalar, 468, 482, 497
scalar product, 482
scale factor, 522
scatter diagram, 414
sector, area of, 366
similar triangles, 438
sine, 451
slant height,
slope, 156, 160
    parallel lines, 185, 186
    perpendicular lines, 186
square, 352

square root, 18
stem-and-leaf plot, 398
subset, 23
surface area, 362–366

tangent of angle, 448, 449, 451
term, 58
terminal point, 474
terminating decimal, 17, 22
theoretical probability, 422
theorems, 295, 301
    CAT, 302
    SAT, 303
    VOAT, 305
transformation
    composition of, 527
    dilatation, 522
    matrix, 538, 539
    reflection, 515
    rotation, 518
    translation, 512
transversal, 336
trapezoid, 352
tree diagram, 427
triangle, 298
    acute, 299
    equiangular, 299
    equilateral, 299
    isosceles, 299
    obtuse, 299
    right, 299
    scalene, 299
trigonometric tables, 455
trinomial, 58

undefined terms, 295
unlike radical, 35
unlike terms, 66

variable, 11
vector, 468
    additive inverse, 481
    components, 469, 478
    displacement, 470
    equal, 469
    inverse, 481
    magnitude of, 468, 469
    non-parallel, 477
    opposite, 481
    parallel, 477, 482
    parallelogram law, 478
    resultant, 477, 478
    triangle law, 477
vertical co-ordinate, 126
vertical line test, 167
volume, 369–378